# Electricity With Chemical Applications

## SCI 102

*Author*

**Malone**

Printed in the United States of America 10 9 8 7 6 5 4 3 2

# List of Titles

*Basic Concepts of Chemistry, 9th edition*
by Leo J. Malone and Theodore O. Dolter
Copyright © 2013, ISBN: 978-0-470-93845-4

# Table of Contents

# BASIC CONCEPTS
# OF CHEMISTRY

**NINTH EDITION**

## Leo J. Malone

*Saint Louis University*

## Theodore O. Dolter

*Southwestern Illinois College*

### In Collaboration With
## Steven Gentemann

*Southwestern Illinois College*

John Wiley & Sons, Inc.

| | |
|---|---|
| VICE PRESIDENT AND EXECUTIVE PUBLISHER | Kaye Pace |
| ASSOCIATE PUBLISHER | Petra Recter |
| ACQUISITIONS EDITOR | Nick Ferrari |
| PROJECT EDITOR | Jennifer Yee |
| MARKETING MANAGER | Kristine Ruff |
| PRODUCT DESIGNER | Geraldine Osnato |
| MEDIA SPECIALIST | Evelyn Brigandi |
| CREATIVE DIRECTOR | Harry Nolan |
| SENIOR DESIGNER | James O'Shea |
| SENIOR PHOTO EDITOR | Lisa Gee |
| EDITORIAL ASSISTANT | Lauren Stauber |
| PRODUCTION SERVICES | Ingrao Associates |
| COVER IMAGE | © Sylvain Grandadam/age fotostock |

This volume contains selected illustrations from the following texts, reprinted by permission from John Wiley and Sons, Inc.
- Brady, James E.; Senese, Fred, *Chemistry: Matter and Its Changes, Fourth Edition,* ©2004.
- Brady, James E.; Senese, Fred, *Chemistry: Matter and Its Changes, Fifth Edition,* ©2009.
- Hein, Morris; Arena, Susan, *Foundations of College Chemistry, Twelfth Edition,* ©2007.
- Murck, Barbara; Skinner, Brian, MacKenzie, *Visualizing Geology, First Edition,* ©2008.
- Olmsted III, John; Williams, Gregory M., *Chemistry, Fourth Edition,* ©2006.
- Pratt, Charlotte W.; Cornely, Kathleen, *Essential Biochemistry, First Edition,* ©2004.
- Raymond, Kenneth, *General, Organic, and Biological Chemistry: An Integrated Approach, Second Edition,* ©2008.

This book was set in ITC New Baskervile 10/12 by Preparé, and printed and bound by Courier/Kendallville. The cover was printed by Courier/Kendallville.

This book is printed on acid-free paper.

Founded in 1807, John Wiley & Sons, Inc. has been a valued source of knowledge and understanding for more than 200 years, helping people around the world meet their needs and fulfill their aspirations. Our company is built on a foundation of principles that include responsibility to the communities we serve and where we live and work. In 2008, we launched a Corporate Citizenship Initiative, a global effort to address the environmental, social, economic, and ethical challenges we face in our business. Among the issues we are addressing are carbon impact, paper specifications and procurement, ethical conduct within our business and among our vendors, and community and charitable support. For more information, please visit our website: *www.wiley.com/go/citizenship*.

Evaluation copies are provided to qualified academics and professionals for review purposes only, for use in their courses during the next academic year. These copies are licensed and may not be sold or transferred to a third party. Upon completion of the review period, please return the evaluation copy to Wiley. Return instructions and a free-of-charge return shipping label are available at www.wiley.com/go/returnlabel. If you have chosen to adopt this textbook for use in your course, please accept this book as your complimentary desk copy. Outside of the United States, please contact your local representative.

*Library of Congress Cataloging-in-Publication Data*

Malone, Leo J., 1938-

Basic concepts of chemistry / Leo J. Malone, Theodore O. Dolter, Steve Gentemann. – 9th ed.

p. cm.

Includes index.

ISBN 978-0-470-93845-4 (hardback)

1. Chemistry.   I. Dolter, Theodore O., 1965-   II. Gentemann, Steve.   III. Title.
QD31.3.M344 2012
540–dc23

2011019567

ISBN 978-0-470-93845-4

Printed in the United States of America

10 9 8 7 6 5 4 3 2 1

## ► LEO J. MALONE

Leo Malone is a native of Kansas where he received his B.S. in Chemistry from Wichita State University in 1960 and M.S. in Chemistry in 1962. At WSU he worked under the direction of Dr. Robert Christian. He moved on to the University of Michigan where he received his Ph.D. in 1964 under the direction of Dr. Robert Parry. Dr. Malone began his teaching career at Saint Louis University in 1965 where he remained until his retirement as Professor Emeritus in 2005. Although his early research at SLU involved boron hydride chemistry, he eventually concentrated his efforts on the teaching of basic chemistry and in the field of chemical education.

## ► THEODORE (TED) O. DOLTER

Ted Dolter received his B.S. in Chemistry from St. Louis University in 1987, where he was a student of Dr. Malone's. He went on to the University of Illinois where he received a Masters of Chemical Education in 1990. He concurrently earned a secondary teaching certificate, and it was there that he received most of his training in modern educational theory. After six years of teaching high school chemistry and evening courses at Southwestern Illinois College, he joined the faculty at SWIC full time. He served as department chair of the Physical Science Department from 2004 to 2010, during which time he was in charge of the department's outcomes assessment activities.

Professor Dolter's background in educational training and his knowledge of the needs of the growing numbers of community college students compliment Dr. Malone's years of traditional university educational experience. Together, they have produced a text that remains flexible and applicable to the rapidly changing face of today's post-secondary student population.

# Preface

## Why we wrote this book

*Basic Concepts of Chemistry* was written over thirty years ago to address the needs of general chemistry students with little or no background in chemistry. Over time, the text evolved beyond purposes solely aimed at a preparatory chemistry course. For some preparatory chemistry students, a main sequence in general chemistry may follow, but for others, a semester of organic and biochemistry may follow. Other students enroll to simply satisfy a basic science or chemistry requirement. The text was written with a level and functionality designed to accommodate the needs of each of these varied groups of students. *Basic Concepts of Chemistry* was designed with a flexibility that allowed instructors to emphasize or omit certain clearly delineated sections. Over the next eight editions, the mission of the text has evolved in response to the increased diversity of students and the emphasis on outcomes assessment. Leo Malone, Professor Emeritus in the Chemistry Department of St. Louis University, was the sole author of the first seven editions of *Basic Concepts of Chemistry*. Ted Dolter, Professor of Chemistry at SWIC (Southwestern Illinois Community College) joined with Leo Malone for the eighth edition. Ted brought a rich talent in Chemical Education with expertise in outcomes assessment as an integral part of the eighth, and now ninth, edition. Professor Steve Gentemann, a colleague of Ted's at SWIC, has collaborated with the team for the ninth edition. Steve, a St. Louis native, received his B.S. in 1987 and M.S. in 1989, both from the Department of Chemistry of St. Louis University. In 1994, Steve received his Ph.D. from Washington University where he studied the ultrafast photophysical behavior of porphyrins and authored several publications. Steve joined the faculty at Southwestern Illinois College in 1998 and has taught introductory, general, and organic chemistry.

## Basic Concepts of Chemistry Today

Today, more students are entering post-secondary education with a diversity of learning styles and varied stages of preparedness to further their studies. Recent data on student populations indicate that many of them are visual and kinesthetic learners. It is critical therefore, that textbook authors both recognize and integrate this pedagogy into their books and overall learning solution. Achievement of this goal has been of paramount importance to us. Furthermore, the students that enroll in preparatory chemistry have diverse mathematical backgrounds and so we have provided essential resources to assist students struggling with the mathematics encountered in studying chemistry. To accommodate visual and kinesthetic learners, and to support students with weaker math backgrounds, we continue to emphasize outcomes assessment, which provides timely feedback. This emphasis on learning outcomes is evident both within the text and in our online teaching and learning solution, *WileyPLUS*.

## The Role of Outcomes Assessment in the Ninth Edition

Surveys of programs across the country show that chemistry is being taught in numerous ways. From packed lecture halls to intimate classrooms, from Ph.D.s to adjunct instructors, to teaching assistants, chemistry education is being delivered

**xv**

in multiple formats, often within the same institution. Outcomes Assessment is an attempt to insure consistency in evaluating student achievement across these multiple formats. By delineating the expected outcomes or objectives for each chapter, and then devising assessment tools, such as homework and exam questions, lab experiments, group work, and the like, that are designed to target those specific objectives, schools can insure that all students in all sections are being served. By incorporating outcomes assessment into the curriculum, students can receive the same topical instruction and be evaluated against the same standard.

Implementing and justifying an outcomes assessment program can be time consuming. To that end, the authors, having already been through an outcomes assessment program, have designed an overarching solution with objectives and assessments already in place, along with the required information needed to show how all of it ties together.

## Learning Objectives

In the Ninth Edition, each chapter section includes a list of the relevant objectives for that chapter.

These are measurable outcomes that the student should master by the completion of that part of the chapter. Assessments of varying complexity follow each section so that the student, upon completion, can evaluate to what degree the material has been internalized. These assessments are also available within *WileyPLUS* so that students can engage in the material and get immediate answer feedback, along with some question assistance. *Level 1* tests basic definitions and concepts. *Level 2* requires application of section concepts and *Level 3* requires a more thorough understanding and may require extension to more advanced concepts, or incorporation of previously learned material.

---

▶ **ASSESSING THE OBJECTIVE FOR SECTION 3-1**

**EXERCISE 3-1(a) LEVEL 1:** Identify the following as an example of a physical or chemical change:
| | | |
|---|---|---|
| **(a)** boiling | **(c)** evaporating | **(e)** rotting |
| **(b)** burning | **(d)** rusting | **(f)** dissolving |

**EXERCISE 3-1(b) LEVEL 2:** Calcium, an element, is a dull, gray solid that melts at 839°C. When it is placed in water, bubbles form, as the solid calcium slowly disappears in the water. When the water is evaporated, a white powder remains, but elemental calcium is not recovered. Which are the physical properties of calcium? Which is a chemical property?

**EXERCISE 3-1(c) LEVEL 2:** A beaker of an unknown clear and colorless liquid has a volume of 100.0 mL and a mass of 78.9 g. Initially, its temperature is 25°C. When heated, it boils at 78.5°C. If ignited, it burns completely with a blue flame, leaving no residue behind. Which of these pieces of information will be helpful in identifying the liquid?

**EXERCISE 3-1(d) LEVEL 3:** In lab you are handed a metallic object and charged with determining its identity. What types of things can you do to determine what the object is made from?

*For additional practice, work chapter problems 3-4, 3-6, and 3-10.*

---

Each chapter concludes with an objectives grid which correlates the objectives to examples within the sections, assessment exercises at the end of each section, and relevant chapter problems at the end of each chapter. This correlation is emulated within the *WileyPLUS* course. The organization of our content around objectives holds utility for both the student and instructor, allowing them to easily locate tools within the text and in our *WileyPLUS* course to help address a specific student need.

**OBJECTIVES**

| SECTION | YOU SHOULD BE ABLE TO... | EXAMPLES | EXERCISES | CHAPTER PROBLEMS |
|---------|--------------------------|----------|-----------|------------------|
| 3-1 | List several properties of matter and distinguish them as physical or chemical. | | 1a, 1b, 1c | 4, 5, 6, 9, 11 |
| 3-2 | Perform calculations involving the density of liquids and solids. | 3-1, 3-2, 3-3, 3-4 | 2a, 2b, 2c | 12, 14, 16, 20, 22, 24 28, 29 |
| 3-3 | Perform calculations involving the percent of a pure substance in a mixture. | 3-5, 3-6 | 3a, 3b, 3c, 3d, 3e, 3f, 3g | 41, 42, 48, 49, 50, 52, 53, 55 |
| 3-4 | Define terms associated with energy exchanges in physical and chemical processes. | | 4a, 4b, 4c | 56, 57, 59, 60 |
| 3-5 | Perform calculations involving the specific heat of a substance. | 3-7, 3-8, 3-9, 3-10 | 5a, 5b, 5c, 5d, 5e, 5f | 63, 64, 67, 68, 69, 71, 79, 81 |

## Additional Math Support For Students

- **Math Check** - The chemical concepts mentioned in Chapter 1 are again presented in Chapters 2 and 3 but with more discussion and detail. When a math concept is to be required in an example problem in these two chapters a new feature called **Math Check** is presented, which allows a student to quickly assess the needed basic skill. If the student is not mathematically ready for the problem, he or she is referred back to Chapter 1 or the math appendices for further review before tackling the problem. With this new feature, it is now a viable option for instructors who wish to avoid the heavy early emphasis on mathematics to begin the text with Chapter 2 and use the Math Checks to alert the student to skills as needed, along with the references to the relevant discussions.

 **MATH CHECK:**

### Math Operations and Significant Figures

In the example problem that follows, you will be asked to divide two numbers expressed in different degrees of precision. Correctly expressing the results of mathematical operations using numbers with different numbers of decimal places or significant figures is a necessary skill in chemistry. Unfortunately, the calculator can't help us here. We have to know the rules. The following questions test your understanding of these principles.

    **a.** What is the sum of 11.841 mL, 0.009 mL, and 5.1 mL?

    **b.** What is the result and unit of the following calculation: 98.020 $cm^3$ divided by 32.0 cm?

**Answers: a.** 17.0 mL   **b.** 3.06 $cm^2$

Refer to Section 1-2.1 for help with significant figures related to addition and subtraction.
Refer to Section 1-2.2 for help with significant figures related to multiplication and division.

## Facilitating Problem Solving

- **Chapter Synthesis Problem** - At the end of each chapter we have included a multi-faceted problem that brings the key concepts of the chapter into one encompassing problem. It is a challenging but entirely workable problem that tests the overall understanding of what may seem like diverse concepts. The worked-out solutions to the problem immediately follow. We then present a mirror problem for the student entitled **Your Turn** with only the answers provided at the end of the chapter.

---

**CHAPTER 3 SYNTHESIS PROBLEM**

In this chapter, we learned that density and specific heat are intensive physical properties that can be used to identify pure substances. These properties can also be used to convert among a number of measurements. Density can be used to convert between volume and mass and specific heat can be used to convert among heat, mass, and temperature change. Solutions are homogeneous mixtures where the concentration can be expressed as percent by mass, which allows us to convert among mass of solute, mass of solvent, and mass of solution. At a specified concentration, solutions also have a certain density and specific heat. Consider the following solution of ethanol (ethyl alcohol) in water.

| PROBLEM | SOLUTION |
|---|---|
| **a.** The density of water at 25.0°C is 0.9971 g/mL. What is the mass of 1255 mL of water? | **a.** $1255 \text{ mL} \times \dfrac{0.9971 \text{ g}}{\text{mL}} = \underline{1251 \text{ g water}}$ |
| **b.** What mass of ethanol must be mixed with this amount of water to form a 5.45% by mass ethanol solution? | **b.** For a 5.45% solution, in 100 g solution, there are 5.45 g ethanol and $100.00 - 5.45 = 94.55$ g water $1251 \text{ g water} \times \dfrac{5.45 \text{ g ethanol}}{94.55 \text{ g water}} = \underline{72.1 \text{ g ethanol}}$ |
| **c.** What volume of ethanol is needed for this solution? (See Table 3-1.) | **c.** $72.1 \text{ g ethanol} \times \dfrac{1 \text{ mL}}{0.790 \text{ g ethanol}} = \underline{91.3 \text{ mL}}$ |
| **d.** What is the total mass of the solution? | **d.** $72.1 \text{ g ethanol} + 1251 \text{ g water} = \underline{1323 \text{ g (solution)}}$ |
| **e.** Determine the amount of heat (in kJ) needed to warm the solution from 25.0°C to 35.0°C. The specific heat of the solution is 3.97 J/g·°C | **e.** specific heat $= \dfrac{\text{joules}}{\text{g} \cdot {}^\circ\text{C}}$ joules = specific heat $\times$ g $\times$ °C $= \dfrac{3.97 \text{ J}}{\text{g} \cdot {}^\circ\text{C}} \times 10.0\,{}^\circ\text{C} \times 1323 \text{ g}$ $= 52500 \text{ J} \times \dfrac{1 \text{ kJ}}{10^3 \text{ J}} = \underline{52.5 \text{ kJ}}$ |

**YOUR TURN**

Windshield-washing solvent is a solution of methanol and water (and a small amount of detergent which we will neglect in this problem).

    **a.** Determine the volume of water (density = 0.9971 g/mL) that must be combined with 375 mL of methanol (density = 0.7914 g/mL) to make a 45.0% by mass methanol solution.

    **b.** Determine the total mass of the solution.

    **c.** Determine the amount of heat (in kJ) that is required to warm the solution from 25.0°C to 55.0°C. The specific heat of the solution is 3.52 J/g·°C

Answers on p. 111.

---

# Organization

The **Prologue** is a unique feature which introduces the origin of science in general and chemistry in particular. There are no quizzes, exercises, or problems; rather, it is meant to be a relaxing, historical glimpse at the origin of this fascinating subject and how it now affects our lives. Our intent is build interest and engage the student in further study. Also included in the prologue is a discussion of the scientific method and tips on studying chemistry and effectively using this textbook.

We recognize the changing needs of students and balance that with the requirements to successfully study chemistry. As such, we continue to provide the necessary support for students continuing on in the study of chemistry. **Chapter 1, Measurements in Chemistry,** provides the necessary math tools in a non-threatening way. This chapter now includes brief introductions to several fundamental chemical concepts such as elements, compounds, atoms, molecules and atomic weight. The intention is to bring relevance to the math concepts used in chemistry, which are introduced in the first chapter. Based upon feedback from reviewers, the authors agreed that a math introduction would be more meaningful if the student first understood why the skills are necessary.

In **Chapter 2, Elements and Compounds,** the elements are introduced starting from what we see and sense about us (the macroscopic) to the atoms of which they are composed, and finally into the structure within the atom (the microscopic and submicroscopic.) We do the same for compounds in the second part of this chapter. **Chapter 3, The Properties of Energy and Matter,** continues the discussion of matter and its properties. Some additional yet relevant math concepts such as density, percent composition, and specific heat are introduced in this chapter as properties of matter. **Chapter 4, The Periodic Table and Chemical Nomenclature,** allows us to draw in one of the primary tools of the chemist, the periodic table. We see its functionality and organization, and begin using it in a thorough discussion of how to name most common chemicals, whose structure was discussed in Chapter 2.

In this edition, **Quantities in Chemistry** (now **Chapter 5**) has been switched with **Chemical Reactions** (now **Chapter 6**). It seems that more instructors prefer this order although the two chapters can still be switched without any disadvantage. **Chapter 7** continues with **Quantitative Relationships in Chemical Reactions**. **Chapter 8, Modern Atomic Theory** and **Chapter 9, The Chemical Bond** follow. Still, the two latter chapters can be moved ahead of Chapter 5 without prejudice, depending on the preferences of the instructor, and the ease with which the material can be incorporated into the overall curriculum. Many still prefer to cover the more abstract concepts of the atom before the quantitative aspects. **Chapter 10, The Gaseous State,** begins a three chapter in-depth study of the states of matter by examining the unique and predictable behaviors of gases. This is followed by similar discussions of the condensed states of matter in **Chapter 11, The Liquid and Solid States,** which includes a thorough but understandable discussion of intermolecular forces and how those affect the properties of matter. This discussion continues in **Chapter 12, Aqueous Solutions,** where we discuss both the qualitative and quantitative aspects of solute-solvent interactions. This chapter serves as a wrap-up of the quantitative relationships introduced in Chapters 5 and 7.

**Chapter 13, Acids, Bases, and Salts,** provides an in-depth discussion of how these important classes of compounds interact with water and each other. A second class of reaction is explored in depth in **Chapter 14, Oxidation-Reduction Reactions.** The relationship of these types of reactions to the creation of batteries and electrical currents is explained.

The remaining chapters offer a survey of topics that are of general chemical interest, and are appropriate for those looking to expose their students to a broad set of topics. **Chapter 15, Reaction Rate and Equilibrium,** introduces the concepts of Kinetics and Equilibrium and gives a taste of the sophisticated mathematical treatment these topics receive. **Chapter 16, Nuclear Chemistry,** explores how radioactivity is a phenomenon associated with certain elements and isotopes. **Chapter 17, Organic Chemistry,** gives the briefest introduction to organic functional groups, structure, and bonding. **Chapter 18, Biochemistry,** gives a similar treatment to common biochemical structures like carbohydrates, proteins, lipids, and nucleic acids. The latter two chapters are available on the Web.

## Hallmark Features of the Ninth Edition

- Every concept in the text is clearly illustrated with one or more **step by step examples**. Most examples, in addition to a *Procedure* and *Solution* step, are followed by two steps: *Analysis* and *Synthesis*. The *Analysis* step discusses the problem in light of the reasonableness of the answer, or perhaps suggests an alternate way to solve the problem involving different learning modes. The concluding *Synthesis* step gives the student the opportunity to delve deeper, asking the student to extend their knowledge. These added steps promote critical thinking and facilitate deeper conceptual understanding.
- **Making it Real** essays have been updated to present timely and engaging real-world applications, emphasizing to the student the relevance of the material they are learning. For example, in the high-interest field of forensics, we describe how glass shards from crime scenes can be identified by their density in Chapter 3, and then in Chapter 7, explore how the refractive index of glass is also used as important evidence in solving crimes. In Chapter 7, we take a look at the chemical reactions involved in the breathalyzer and in Chapter 13, how salts are used to analyze fingerprints. Other essays emphasize useful types of energy.
- This edition continues the end of chapter **Student Workshop** activities. These are intended to cater to the many different student learning styles and to engage students in the practical aspect of the material discussed in the chapter. Each "Student Workshop" includes a statement of purpose and an estimated time for completion. These activities work well as dry labs, and for those students involved in recitation sessions and small group work.

## Teaching and Learning Resources

*WileyPLUS* is an online teaching and learning environment that integrates the **entire digital textbook** with the most effective instructor and student resources to fit every learning style. It contains a variety of rich repositories of assessment, much of which are algorithmic. The diverse problem types are designed to enable and support problem-solving skills development and conceptual understanding. *WileyPLUS* offers three unique repositories of questions which provide breadth, depth and flexibility in instructional and assessment content.

- **End of chapter questions** are available, featuring immediate answer feedback. A subset of these end of chapter questions are linked to **Guided Online Tutorials** which are stepped out problem-solving tutorials that walk the student through the problem, offering individualized feedback at each step. The **testbank** is also offered as assignable questions for homework. In addition to the test bank and end of chapter questions, *WileyPLUS* offers an assignment type called **CATALYST**, which are **prebuilt concept mastery assignments**, organized by topic and concept, allowing for iterative drill and skill practice. For more information on CATALYST, visit: **www.wiley.com/college/catalyst**.

**For Students** *WileyPLUS* addresses different learning styles, different levels of proficiency, and different levels of preparation—each of your students is unique. *WileyPLUS* empowers them to take advantage of their individual strengths:

- Students receive timely access to resources that address their demonstrated needs, and get immediate feedback and remediation when needed.
- Integrated, multimedia resources—including audio and visual exhibits, demonstration problems, and much more—provide multiple study-paths to fit each student's learning preferences and encourage more active learning.
- *WileyPLUS* includes many opportunities for self-assessment linked to the relevant portions of the text. Students can take control of their own learning and practice until they master the material.

**For Instructors** *WileyPLUS* empowers you with the tools and resources you need to make your teaching even more effective:

- You can customize your classroom presentation with a wealth of resources and functionality from PowerPoint slides to a database of rich visuals. You can even add your own materials to your *WileyPLUS* course.
- With *WileyPLUS* you can identify those students who are falling behind and intervene accordingly, without having to wait for them to come to office hours.
- *WileyPLUS* simplifies and automates such tasks as student performance assessment, marking assignments, scoring student work, keeping grades, and more.

*WileyPLUS* can be used in conjunction with your textbook or it can replace the printed text altogether, as a complete eBook comes standard.

### How Do I Access *WileyPLUS*?

To access *WileyPLUS*, students need a *WileyPLUS* registration code. This can be purchased stand alone, or the code can be bundled with a textbook. For more information and/or to request a WileyPLUS demonstration, contact your local Wiley sales representative or visit **www.wileyplus.com**.

## Additional Instructor Resources

All of these resources can be accessed within WileyPLUS or by contacting your local Wiley sales representative.

*Instructor's Manual and Test Bank* by Leo J. Malone, St Louis University; Ted Dolter and Steve Gentemann, Southwestern Illinois College; and Kyle Beran, University of Texas-Permian Basin. The Instructor's Manual consists of two parts; the first part includes an overview and comments for each chapter by Ted Dolter, followed by daily lesson plans by Steve Gentemann. The second part of the manual contains answers and worked-out solutions to all chapter-end problems in the text by Leo Malone. The test bank, by Kyle Beran, consists of multiple choice, short answer, and fill in the blank questions. PC and Macintosh compatible versions of the entire test bank are available with full editing features to help the instructor to customize tests.

*Instructor's Manual for Experiments in Basic Chemistry,* written by Steven Murov and Brian Stedjee, Modesto Junior College, contains answers to post-lab questions, lists of chemicals needed, suggestions for other experiments, as well as suggestions for experimental set-ups.

*Power Point Lecture Slides,* created by Wyatt Murphy, of Seton Hall University, contain key topics from each chapter of the text, along with supporting artwork and figures from the text. The slides also contain assessment questions that can be used to facilitate discussions during lecture.

*PowerPoint Art Slides*, PPT slides containing images, tables, and figures from the text.

*Digital Image Archive.* The text web site includes downloadable files of text images in JPEG format.

## Additional Student Resources

*Study Guide/Solutions Manual by Leo J. Malone* is available to accompany this text. In the Study Guide/Solutions Manual, the same topics in a specific section are also grouped in the same manner for review, discussion, and testing. In this manner, the Study Guide/Solutions Manual can be put to use before the chapter is completed. The Study Guide/Solutions Manual contains answers and worked-out solutions to all problems in green lettering in the text. [ISBN: 978-1-118-15643-8]

*Experiments in Basic Chemistry, Seventh Edition by Steven Murov and Brian Stedjee,* Modesto Junior College. Taking an exploratory approach to chemistry, this hands-on lab manual for preparatory chemistry encourages critical thinking and allows students to make discoveries as they experiment. The manual contains 26 experiments that parallel text organization and provides learning objectives, discussion sections outlining each experiment, easy-to-follow procedures, post-lab questions, and additional exercises.   [ISBN: 978-0-470-42373-8]

# Acknowledgments

A revision of this magnitude involves efforts spanning several years and requiring the input of many people. In particular, Dr. Malone thanks his colleagues at Saint Louis University for their helpful comments in previous editions of this text. He's grateful to his wife Meg, who demonstrated patience and put up with occasional crabbiness during the new text's preparation. Dr. Malone also appreciates the support of his children and their spouses: Lisa and Chris, Mary and Brian, Katie and Rob, and Bill. They and their eleven children were both a source of great inspiration and a large amount of noise.

Professor Dolter continues to thank his general chemistry instructor, who provided a sound understanding of the basic principles needed in forming his craft. Although his professor (LJM) was a taskmaster, the end result was worth it. He'd also like to thank his colleagues at SWIC, who happily allowed him to bounce ideas off of them, and delighted in giving their advice. Professor Dolter is thankful for his wife Peggy, who endured the single-parent lifestyle many weekends during the writing of this text. A nod also goes to, Isabel and Zachary, who wondered if their Dad was ever going to finish this book; they're owed some Dad-time.

The authors also wish to thank the many people at John Wiley who helped and encouraged this project, including Nick Ferrari, our editor, for his support of this revision; Jennifer Yee, our Project Editor; Lauren Stauber, Editorial Assistant; Elizabeth Swain, Production Editor; Lisa Gee, Photo Editor; James O'Shea, Designer, Janet Foxman, Production Editor, and Suzanne Ingrao of Ingrao Associates, who kept an eye on every production detail, and kindly made sure we kept on schedule. Thank you all for remaining wonderfully patient in the face of missed deadlines and family conflicts.

Finally, the following people offered many useful comments and suggestions for the development of the Ninth Edition:

Dale Arrington *North Idaho College*
Satinder Bains *Paradise Valley Community College*
Ruth Birch *Saint Louis University*
Joseph Caddell *Modesto Junior College*
Jeff Cavalier *SUNY Dutchess*
Bertrand Chiasson *College of Southern Nevada*
Claire Cohen *The University of Toledo*
Michael Cross *Northern Essex Community College*
Paul Edwards *Edinboro University of Pennsylvania*
Eugenio Jaramillo *Texas A&M International University*
James Falender *Central Michigan University*
Rick Fletcher *University of Idaho*
Nancy Foote *Chandler Gilbert Community College*
Joy Frazier-Earhart *James Madison University*
Darlene Gandolfi *Manhattanville College*
Gregory Hanson *Otterbein University*
Theresa Hill *Rochester Community & Technical College*

Rebecca Hoenigman *Community College of Aurora*
Byron Howell *Tyler Junior College*
Jason Jadin *Rochester Community & Technical College*
Jodi Kreiling *University of Nebraska at Omaha*
Carla Kegley-Owen *University of Nebraska at Kearney*
Michael Lewis *Saint Louis University*
Richard Lomneth *University of Nebraska at Omaha*
Hussein Samha *Southern Utah University*
John Seeley *Oakland University*
Kris Slowinski *California State University, Long Branch*
Duane Smith *Nicholls State University*
Mackay Steffensen *Southern Utah University*

**Leo J. Malone**
*Saint Louis University*
**Theodore O. Dolter**
*Southwestern Illinois College*

# BASIC CONCEPTS
# OF CHEMISTRY

# Science and the Magnificent Human Mind

A campfire on a chilly night provides not only warmth but also serenity. Fire is an awesome force of nature which our ancient ancestors tamed and put to use.

# SETTING THE STAGE

Among the animal kingdom, only humans have the ability to take their minds beyond simple survival. We also analyze, ponder, and predict the future based on observations. This has led us to a remarkable understanding of all that we see and otherwise sense about us. So this prologue is dedicated to how the wonderful workings of our minds have allowed us to establish the realm of modern science. In Section A, we present an abbreviated history that begins with the first chemical process that occurred billions of years ago and proceed to how the human race eventually put these processes to work starting with the taming of fire. In Section B, we take note of how science in general and chemistry in particular has progressed from random discoveries and serendipity to the complex technical world in which we exist today. This section emphasizes what we call the "scientific method." Finally, in Section C, we discuss how an individual can come to understand and appreciate this wonderful branch of science we know as "chemistry." After proceeding through the prologue, we will build this science from the most basic substances of the universe to the complex world of chemistry that serves us in so many ways today.

# A Brief History of Chemistry

The history of chemistry can be developed on three levels. First, what was the first chemical process and when did it occur? Second, when and how did the human race put chemical processes to practical use? And finally, when did we arrive at reasonable explanations of these chemical processes?

## A-1 The First Chemical Process

Chemistry has been happening for a very long time, indeed. Billions of years ago, when the universe was still very young, matter was composed of very minuscule, individual particles called *atoms*. Most of these were the simple atoms of the most fundamental element that we know as *hydrogen* (symbol H). At the time the cosmos was extremely hot, which meant that the atoms moved so fast that when atoms collided, they simply bounced off of each other. But as time went on, the cosmos cooled and then something very significant happened. When two atoms of hydrogen, now moving somewhat slower, collided they stuck or bonded to each other to form a *molecule* (symbol $H_2$). (See Figure P-1.) If two atoms were not more stable bonded together rather than apart, we could not be here. The trillions of trillions of atoms that make up the complex molecules of our bodies (and everything else) would simply exist as individual atoms scattered throughout space. So chemical processes began in the early universe when atoms came together to form chemical bonds. In fact, current astronomers have discovered hundreds of more complex molecules that have formed in outer space.

## A-2 The Application of Chemical Processes

Chemistry has been going on since almost the beginning of time, but when did chemical processes become useful to the human race? Our second aspect of the history of chemistry lies with fire. This phenomenon first made its appearance on Earth about 400 million years ago when carbon in the form of vegetation, oxygen in the atmosphere, and lightning all came together. Fire is a chemical process where chemical bonds are changing and heat and light energy are being given off. So fire certainly falls into the realm of chemistry.

It is difficult to imagine how our ancient ancestors could have managed without fire. Humans do not have sharp night vision like the raccoon, but fire brought light to the long, dark night. We have no protective fur like the deer, but fire lessened the chill of winter. We do not have sharp teeth or powerful jaws like the lion, but fire rendered meat tender. Humans are not as strong or as powerful as the other large animals, but fire repels even the most ferocious of beasts. It seems reasonable to suggest that the taming of fire was one of the most monumental events in the history of the human race. The use of fire made our species dominant over all others.

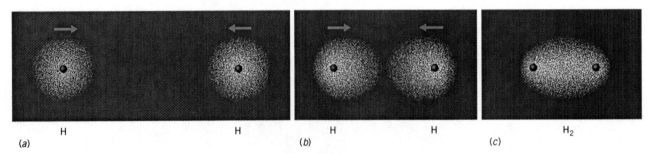

(a) H    H    (b) H    H    (c) $H_2$

**FIGURE P-1  A Hydrogen Molecule** Chemistry first occurred when two hydrogen atoms bonded together to form a hydrogen molecule.

Let's fast-forward in time to near the end of the Stone Age, about 10,000 years ago, when fire was purposely applied to effect a unique chemical process. In the Stone Age, weapons and utensils were fashioned from rocks and a few chunks of copper metal (an element) that were found in nature. Copper was superior to stone because pounding could easily shape it into fine points and sharp blades. Unfortunately, native copper was quite rare. But about 7000 years ago this changed. Some anthropologists speculate that some resident of ancient Persia found copper metal in the ashes remaining from a hot charcoal fire. The free copper had not been there before, so it must have come from a green stone called *malachite* (see Figure P-2), which probably lined the fire pit. Imagine the commotion that this discovery must have caused. Hot coals could transform a particular but plentiful stone into a valuable metal. Fire was the key that launched the human population into the age of metals. The recovery of metals from their ores is now a branch of chemical science called *metallurgy*. The ancient persians must have considered this discovery a dramatic example of the magic of fire.

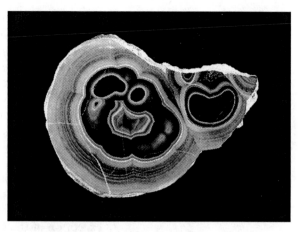

**FIGURE P-2 Malachite**
Malachite is a copper ore. When heated with charcoal, it forms metallic copper.

Other civilizations used chemistry in various ways. About 3000 B.C., the Egyptians learned how to dye cloth and embalm their dead through the use of certain chemicals found in nature. They were very good at what they did. In fact, we can still determine from ancient mummies the cause of death and even diseases the person may have had. The Egyptians were good chemists, but they had no idea why any of these procedures worked. Every chemical process they used was discovered by accident.

The early centuries of the Middle Ages (A.D. 500–1600) in Europe are sometimes referred to as the Dark Ages because of the lack of art and literature and the decline of central governments. The civilizations that Egypt, Greece, and Rome had previously built began to decline. Chemistry, however, began to grow during this period, especially in the area of experimentation. Chemistry was then considered a combination of magic and art rather than a science. Many of those who practiced chemistry in Europe were known as *alchemists*. Some of these alchemists were simply con artists who tried to convince greedy kings that they could transform cheaper metals such as lead and zinc into gold. Gold was thought to be the perfect metal. Such a task was impossible, of course; so many of these alchemists met a drastic fate for their lack of success. However, all was not lost. Many important laboratory procedures such as distillation and crystallization were developed. Alchemists also discovered or prepared many previously unknown chemicals that we now know as elements and compounds.

## A-3 The Understanding of Chemistry

Now we step back a little in time where we find the first theoretical explanations of chemical phenomena. Around 400 B.C., while some Greeks were speculating about their various gods, other Greek philosophers were trying to understand and describe nature. These great thinkers argued about why things occurred in the world around them, but they were not inclined (or able) to check out their ideas by experimentation or to put them to practical use. At the time, however, people believed that there were four basic elements of nature—earth, air, water, and fire. Everything else was simply a specific combination of these basic elements. Of the original four elements, fire was obviously the most mysterious. It was the transforming element; that is, it had the capacity to change one substance into another (e.g., certain rocks into metals). We now call such transformations "chemistry." Fire itself consists of the hot, glowing gases associated with certain chemical changes. If fire is a result of an ongoing chemical transformation, then it is reasonable to suggest that chemistry and many significant advances in the human race are very much related.

Modern chemistry has its foundation in the late 1700s when the use of the *analytical balance* became widespread. Chemistry then became a quantitative science in which theories had to be correlated with the results of direct laboratory experimentation. From these experiments and observations came the *modern atomic theory*, first proposed by John Dalton around 1803. This theory, in a slightly modified form, is still the basis of our understanding of nature today. Dalton's theory gave chemistry the solid base from which it could serve humanity on an impressive scale. Actually, most of our understanding of chemistry has evolved in the past 130 years. In a way, this makes chemistry a very young science. However, if we mark the beginning of the use of chemistry with fire, it is also the oldest science.

From the Persians of five millennia ago, to the ancient Egyptians, to the alchemists of the Middle Ages, various cultures have stumbled on assorted chemical procedures. In many cases, these were used to improve the quality of life. With the exception of the Greek philosophers, there was little attention given to why a certain process worked. The *why* is very important. In fact, the tremendous explosion of scientific knowledge and applications in the past 200 years can be attributed to how science is now approached. This is called the "scientific method," which we will discuss next.

# B The Scientific Method

## B-1 The Development of the Scientific Method

In ancient times, scientific advances were discovered by accident. This still occurs to some extent, but we have made great strides in how we approach science such that most modern advances occur by design. Later we will discuss how our modern approach to science produces so many new and wonderful things such as drugs that cure certain cancers or other illnesses. The modern approach is known as the *scientific method.*

The first step in the scientific method is a long way from producing a useful drug. It simply involves *making observations and gathering data.* As an example, imagine that we are the first to make a simple observation about nature: "The sun rises in the East and sets in the West." This never seems to vary and, as far as we can tell from history, it has always been so. In other words, our scientific observation is strictly *reproducible.* So now we ask, "Why?" We are ready for a hypothesis. A **hypothesis** *is a tentative explanation of observations.* The first plausible hypothesis to explain our observations was advanced by Claudius Ptolemy, a Greek philosopher, in A.D. 150. He suggested that the sun, as well as the rest of the universe, revolves around the Earth from east to west. That made sense. It certainly explained the observation. In fact, this concept became an article of religious faith in much of the Western world. However, Ptolemy's hypothesis did not explain other observations known at the time, which included the movement of the planets across the sky and the phases of the moon.

Sometimes new or contradictory evidence means a hypothesis, just like a broken-down old car, must either receive a major overhaul or be discarded entirely. In 1543, a new hypothesis was proposed. Nicolaus Copernicus explained all of the observations about the sun, moon, and planets by suggesting that Earth and the other planets orbit around the sun instead of vice versa. Even though this hypothesis explained the mysteries of the heavenly bodies, it was considered extremely radical and even heretical at the time. (It was believed that God made Earth the center of the universe.) In 1609, a Venetian scientist by the name of Galileo Galilei built a telescope, which had just been invented, to view ships still far out at sea. When he turned the telescope up to the sky, he eventually produced almost unquestionable proof that Copernicus was correct. Galileo is sometimes credited with the beginning of the modern scientific method because he provided direct experimental data in support of a concept. The hypothesis had withstood the challenge of experiments and thus could be considered a theory. A **theory** *is a well-established hypothesis*. A theory should not only explain known phenomena, but also predict the results of future experiments or observations. A scientific theory must explain or incorporate all the known relevant facts. It cannot be selective.

The next part of this story comes in 1684, when an English scientist named Sir Isaac Newton stated a law that governs the motion of planets around the sun. A **law** *is a concise scientific statement of fact to which no exceptions are known*. Newton's law of universal gravitation states that planets are held by gravity in stationary orbits around the sun. (See Figure P-3.)

In summary, these were the steps that led to a law of nature:

**FIGURE P-3 The Solar System** The Copernican theory became the basis of a natural law of the universe.

1. Reproducible observations (e.g., the sun rises in the East)
2. A hypothesis advanced by Ptolemy and then a better one by Copernicus
3. Experimental data gathered by Galileo in support of the Copernican hypothesis and eventual acceptance of the hypothesis as a theory
4. The statement by Newton of a universal law based on the theory

Variations on the scientific method serve us well today as we pursue an urgent search for cures of diseases. An example follows.

## B-2 The Scientific Method in Action

The healing power of plants and plant extracts has been known for thousands of years. For example, ancient Sumerians and Egyptians used willow leaves to relieve the pain of arthritis. We now know that extracts of the common willow contain a drug very closely related to aspirin. This is the observation that starts us on our journey to new drugs. An obvious hypothesis comes from this observation, namely, that there are many other useful drugs among the plants and soils of the world. We should be able to find them. There are several modern discoveries that support this hypothesis. For example, the rosy periwinkle is a common tropical plant not too different from thousands of other tropical plants except that this one saves lives. The innocent-looking plant contains a powerful chemical called *vincristine*, which can cure childhood leukemia. Another relatively new drug called Taxol has been extracted from the pacific yew tree. (See Figure P-4.) Taxol was originally used exclusively in treating ovarian cancer but is now used to treat breast cancer. Others include *cyclosporine*, isolated from a fungus in 1957, which made organ transplants possible, and *digoxin*, isolated from the foxglove plant, used for treatment of heart failure. In fact, many of the best-selling medicines in the United States originated from plants and other natural sources. Besides those mentioned, other drugs treat conditions such as high blood pressure, cancer, glaucoma, and malaria. The search for effective drugs from natural sources and newly synthesized compounds is very active today. These chemicals are screened for potential anticancer, antiarthritic, and anti-AIDS activity. Since the greatest variety of plants, molds, and fungi are found in tropical forests, these species are receiving considerable attention. Lately,

**FIGURE P-4 The Pacific Yew**
The bark of this tree is a source of an anticancer drug known as Taxol.

scientists are focusing on plants and algae in the ocean for possible drugs. The introduction of a new medicine from a natural source involves the following steps.

1. *Collection of materials.* "Chemical prospectors" scour the backwoods of the United States and the tropical forests such as those in Costa Rica, collecting and labeling samples of leaves, barks, and roots. Soil samples containing fungi and molds are also collected and carefully labeled.

2. *Testing of activity.* Scientists at several large chemical and pharmaceutical companies make extracts of the sample in the laboratory. These extracts are run through a series of chemical tests to determine whether there is any antidisease activity among the chemicals in the extract. New methods such as high-throughput-screening (HTS) allow certain chemical companies to screen thousands of chemicals in a single day. If there is antidisease activity, it is considered a "hit" and the extract is taken to the next step.

3. *Isolation and identification of the active ingredient.* The next painstaking task is to separate the one chemical that has the desired activity from among the soup of chemicals present. Once that's done, the particular structure of the active chemical must be determined. A hypothesis is then advanced about what part of the structure is important and how the chemical works. The hypothesis is tested by attempting to make other more effective drugs (or ones with fewer side effects) based on the chemical's structure. It is then determined whether the chemical or a modified version of it is worth further testing.

4. *Testing on animals.* If the chemical is considered promising, it is now ready to be tested on animals. This is usually done in government and university labs under strictly controlled conditions. Scientists study toxicity, side effects, and the chemical's activity against the particular disease for which it is being tested. If, after careful study, the chemical is considered both effective and safe, it is ready for the next step.

5. *Testing on humans.* Perhaps the most important step regards clinical trials. This involves careful testing on humans, which is carefully monitored by agencies such as the FDA. Effectiveness, dosage, and long-term side effects are carefully recorded and evaluated. All told, it currently takes from 10 to 15 years for a new drug to make it all the way from research and development to market. Sometimes the process is speeded up if the drug is especially effective or treats a rare disease.

When chemicals with the desired activity are randomly discovered, only about 1 in 1000 may actually find its way into general use. Still, the process works. Many chemicals active against cancer and even AIDS are now in the pipeline for testing. There is some urgency in all of this. Not only are we anxious to cure specific diseases, but the tropical forests that contain the most diverse plants are disappearing at an alarming rate. In any case, nature is certainly our most important chemical laboratory.

At this time, most of the drugs that originated from synthetic or natural sources are considered cases of "serendipity." We are now moving more toward the concept of "rational drug design." Here, the goal is to identify the active sites on the molecules of diseases such as viruses, tumors, or bacteria. The next step is to deliberately synthesize a drug that attaches to that active site and either destroys or otherwise alters the disease molecules. This sounds easy, but it is not. It requires that we know more about the structure and geometry of these disease molecules. We can then advance hypotheses as to how designed molecules would interact. This is the direction in which pharmaceutical chemists are heading, however.

## C The Study of Chemistry and Using This Textbook

Chemistry is the *fundamental natural science*. This is not just an idle boast. Chemistry is concerned with the basic structure and properties of all matter, be it a huge star or a microscopic virus. Biology, physics, and geology, as well as all branches of engineering and medicine, are based on an understanding of the chemical substances of which nature is composed. Chemistry is the beginning point in the course of studies that eventually produce all scientists, engineers, and physicians. But it is also important for all responsible citizens. Our environment is very fragile—more fragile than we realized just a few years ago. Many of the chemicals that make life easier also affect our surroundings. Control of air, water, and land pollution needs as much attention from citizens and scientists as the invention of new materials did in the twentieth century. (See Figure P-5.) We all have a big stake in the future, so it is reasonable that chemistry is a prerequisite not only for courses of study but also for life, especially in these complex times. What follows is a brief look at academic self-disciplines and skills needed in the study of chemistry.

**FIGURE P-5 Our Environment Is a Fragile System** Pollution of ocean waters is a serious problem as seen from the Gulf oil spill in 2010.

## C-1 Time Management and Study Skills

**Establish a Schedule** Chemistry is not unlike basketball or piano—it requires lots of practice. It is not only a question of putting in the time but *how* and *when* you put in the time. One does not wait until the night before the big game to first practice jump shots or the night before the recital to first practice the sonata. A master schedule should be prepared, with chemistry (as well as all other subjects) receiving a regularly scheduled study time. The study period should follow as soon as possible after the lecture. In setting up your schedule, it is wise to select short but frequent study periods. Two separate one-hour sessions are more effective than one two-hour period. After a length of time, the mind tends to wander into areas not directly related to chemistry (e.g., baseball—what else?).

**Organize Problems and Exercises** Now that we have a good study schedule, we need to plan an efficient approach to the tasks at hand. Many of the problems that are required in chemistry require a step-by-step approach. It is a lot like planning an extended trip. Usually, we don't just get in the car and drive. We plan our journey so that we can take the shortest or the easiest route. We may also plan ahead on what we want to accomplish and when we want to do it. The secret is advance planning. This is certainly true with chemistry problems. We don't just start doing a calculation—we should take some time to plan the journey through the problem from beginning to end. This requires that we first write down the steps that we will take.

**Take Good Notes** The most useful approach takes some work but is *extremely* effective. As soon as you can after a lecture, recopy your class notes. As you do this, imagine that you are explaining the material to someone else (out loud, if you can). If you do this, you will become aware of concepts that are still hazy to you. Also, the logical progression of problems may now seem more obvious. As you recopy your notes, leave about one-third of the paper as a blank margin so that you can add thoughts, emphasis, or questions for later review. All this assumes that one is going to the lectures. No electronic presentation can substitute for being present at a lecture.

**Be Able to Memorize** Most of us wish that we could just grasp a concept and, with little effort, have it permanently imprinted in our brains. Unfortunately, it rarely works that way. In many cases, we need to memorize a definition or rule so as to be able to categorize facts as fitting the concept or not. We certainly could not begin to play a sport such as soccer without first knowing the object of the game and some basic rules. Likewise, in chemistry we wouldn't be able to write a molecular structure until we first know the steps involved. Even in this age, the use of $3 \times 5$ note cards can help especially if you are expected to know the formulas and names of ions. An old tried-and-true method of memorizing still is the most effective.

**Read Ahead**   This one is hard to do but it does help. Recall that even in high school, football and basketball opponents are scouted before the game. Every team likes to know what they are up against and what lies ahead. In studying science, the equivalent to scouting is reading ahead. Even if you do not grasp the concepts, reading ahead will give you a feeling for some of the material that you will be discussing in the next lecture or two. If you know something is coming that seems confusing, you will be more alert when the concept is discussed. Reading ahead is also a time saver. When you know that certain definitions or tables are in the book, you can save note-taking time.

**Attendance and Participation**   Despite all of the support media from various web sites, almost all instructors still give face-to-face lectures in front of real people. The importance of regular class attendance cannot be overemphasized. You really need to be there. This text is a great ally, but what material your instructor covers and in what depth can be discovered only in class. Nor can you sense your instructor's emphasis or benefit from his or her problem-solving hints by reading someone else's notes. The key to what will be on the exams is found in the lecture. You need to be there.

If you hesitate to ask questions in class or the class is too big, take advantage of help sessions or your instructor's office hours. In many cases, instructors are a significantly underutilized resource during their office hours. Most teachers would still rather talk to you in person rather than answer an e-mail or text message. You may discover that, in the office, the instructor is really a very nice person and very helpful. The bottom line is that you owe yourself answers and understanding. Do what you have to do. Somebody is paying big bucks for you to take this course.

**Perseverance**   Everyone hopes to start off with an A on the first test or quiz. However, few do that, including many who are subsequently very successful in the study of chemistry. If you are disappointed with an exam grade, reanalyze your study habits, make adjustments, and try again. Don't expect better results by doing the same thing. Remember to use your instructor as your primary resource for advice in this matter. Perhaps your problem is not the material but test anxiety. This is a very real phenomenon and has to be acknowledged. Most colleges have a counseling center that can help you overcome this problem. Sometimes your instructor can give you helpful hints on taking chemistry tests so that you won't have the fear of freezing up. If you are ultimately not successful in the study of chemistry, at least you can say that you gave it your best try.

## C-2 Using This Textbook

Finally, make good use of this textbook. Most textbooks have many study aids within the chapters. This text is no exception and, in fact, has many unique features that can help you understand the concepts as well as assess and evaluate your progress. The following are special aids and features to help you through this course.

**Setting a Goal and Section Objectives**   Each chapter is divided into at least two distinct parts. At the beginning of the chapter, the parts are listed along with the topics within each part. A brief discussion titled *Setting the Stage* gives an introduction to the purpose of the chapter. *Part A* then begins with a statement titled *Setting a Goal* and a list of *Objectives* that relate to this overall goal.

**Continuity Between Sections**   Each section begins with a short paragraph entitled *Looking Ahead.* The intention is to give an overview of what the section will cover and perhaps how it relates to the previous topic.

**Topics and Subtopics**   This text helps you appreciate the fact that chemistry builds slowly, one concept at a time. The sections are divided into bite-sized subheadings, each covering a separate concept. For example, consider the following heading with three subheadings:

### 2-3   The Composition of the Atom
#### 2-3.1   The Electron and Electrostatic Forces

### 2-3.2   The Nuclear Model of the Atom
### 2-3.3   The Particles in the Nucleus

The authors have put together what they feel is a logical sequence of topics for the introduction of chemistry. There are other logical ways to introduce this science, however. The text has been written with this in mind, so it is quite flexible in order to accommodate alternative sequences.

**Example Problems**   This text has many in-chapter practice problems. These are worked through in a step-by-step manner. Most of the example problems start with a *Procedure* that analyzes the problem and establishes a path to the answer. The *Solution* follows, which works through the problem. The *Analysis* has us look at whether the answer is reasonable and may suggest alternative ways to solve the problem using different learning modes. Finally, the *Synthesis* takes the discussion a little deeper and may project how this problem relates to future concepts. The analysis and synthesis steps, which are unique to this text, promote critical thinking and a deeper understanding.

**Assessing Progress**   At the end of each section is a collection of exercises titled *Assessing the Objectives*. This provides you with a chance to evaluate your understanding and mastery of the objectives for that section. The problems are presented in three levels: *Level 1*, *Level 2*, and *Level 3*. Each level is progressively more sophisticated. It is expected that the student should be able to answer the Level 1 and Level 2 questions correctly. The Level 1 exercises would assure basic understanding, Level 2 tests a slightly higher level of understanding, and Level 3 indicates mastery of the topic with possible applications to related concepts. The answers to these exercises are at the end of the chapter.

**Summarizing Concepts**   At the end of each part you will find a list of *Key Terms* introduced in the relevant sections. The key term is shown in bold and is part of a definition. Also at the end of each part is at least one *Summary Chart* that can help you visualize a key concept. At the end of the chapter there is a *Chapter Summary*, which is an easy way to quickly check or review your understanding of the key concepts of the chapter. There is also an *Objectives Grid*, which can help you refer to the Examples, Exercises, and Chapter Problems relevant to each objective.

**Chapter Synthesis Problem**   This problem is unique to this text and is presented at the end of the chapter. It is a multiconcept problem that requires the application of several different topics presented in the chapter. It contains a brief discussion and two problems. The first problem is immediately followed by worked-out solutions. The second problem, titled "Your Turn," presents the students with a similar comprehensive problem to work on their own. The answers to the second problem are included at the end of the chapter.

**End-of-Chapter Problems**   A large number of *Chapter Problems* are provided to establish and practice your skills for each topic listed. There are a wide variety of problems, some quite basic, some that test your knowledge at a higher level, and some that are quite challenging. The latter are shown with an asterisk (*). The problems with numbers shown in color have answers at the end of the text.

**Making it Real**   Finally, we have included at least two *Making It Real* essays in each chapter. We hope you find these short discussions fun to read and can then see the connections between the chapter topics being discussed and the real world.

Good luck in the study of chemistry. The authors and the publisher hope you enjoy the course and find this textbook a very real aid in your understanding and appreciation of this science.

### KEY TERMS

B-1   A **hypothesis** is a tentative explanation of observations.  p. 6

B-1   A **theory** is a well-established hypothesis.  p. 7

B-1   A **law** is a concise scientific statement of fact to which no exceptions are known.  p. 7

# 2 Elements and Compounds

This small robot explorer found convincing evidence that our neighbor planet once had water. This common compound on Earth is essential for life, at least as we know it.

# SETTING THE STAGE

In early 2004, two small rovers named *Spirit* and *Opportunity* began their historic exploration on opposite sides of the dry, harsh surface of the planet Mars. Their primary mission was to explore this barren landscape for signs of the familiar substance, *water*. Apparently their mission was successful; photos and analysis of nearby rock formations did indeed indicate that water had at one time been present in the form of a lake or shallow ocean. In fact, spacecraft sent to Mars decades ago relayed photos showing channels that must have been formed from a flowing liquid. Since then, we have wondered whether, at one time, conditions on Mars may have allowed liquid water to exist on its surface much like it does on Earth today. If so, then there is a reasonable chance that some elementary form of life may have existed on Mars and perhaps still does below the surface. Scientists are convinced that water is a necessary component for the formation of living creatures. It is the medium in which other substances can rearrange and combine into the most basic forms of living creatures. In 2010, substantial water in the form of ice was also discovered in the polar region of our moon. This is an important discovery although scientists do not suggest the possibility that life does or ever existed on the moon.

Water is just one example of matter. Mars, the moon, and all of the flickering stars in the night sky are all composed of the same kinds of matter that we find on Earth. The forms of matter that we see on Earth are often changing. Plants grow, die, and decay; rocks weather, crumble, and become part of the fertile soil of the plains or deposits in the oceans. These changes are also the domain of chemistry.

We will first describe the fundamental composition of matter of which there are two types—elements and compounds. In Part A in this chapter we will discuss elements, which are the most basic form of visible matter. In Part B we will explore the more complex form of matter, compounds. In both parts we begin our discussion with the matter that we can see in front of us (the macroscopic) and then delve into the unseen world within the matter (the microscopic).

## Part A

## The Elements and their Composition

**SETTING A GOAL**

■ You will become familiar with the basic components of matter and the properties that make each type of matter unique.

**OBJECTIVES**

2-1  List the names and symbols of common elements.

2-2  List the postulates of the atomic theory.

2-3  List the components of an atom and their relative masses, charges, and location in the atom.

2-4  From the percent abundance of specific isotopes of an element, determine the atomic mass of the element and the number of protons, neutrons and electrons in each isotope.

▶ **OBJECTIVE FOR SECTION 2-1**
List the names and symbols of common elements.

# 2-1   The Elements

**LOOKING AHEAD!** Many of the most basic forms of matter—the elements—are familiar to us, but some are not. The names and symbolic representation of the elements are the first topics that we will discuss. ■

At first glance, the world around us seems so complex. However, we can simplify our understanding by organizing it into general classifications. Many sciences group their disciplines into categories. For example, biology is divided into the study of plants (the flora) and animals (the fauna.) Geology divides its study into the continents and the oceans. The matter we study in chemistry can also be placed into one of two categories.

*Chemistry is defined as the study of matter and the changes it undergoes.* Matter has mass and occupies space. All of the matter that we see around us from the contents of your room to the farthest stars in space is essentially composed of fewer than 90 unique substances called *elements. Because it cannot be broken down into simpler substances, an* **element** *is the most basic form of matter that exists under ordinary conditions.* The more complex forms of matter are known as compounds. *A* **compound** *is a unique substance that is composed of two or more elements that are chemically combined.* When we say chemically combined we do not mean merely a mixture of elements. Rather, the elements are intimately joined together into a unique form of matter that is distinct from the elements that compose the compound. We will return to a discussion of compounds in Part B.

## 2-1.1 Free Elements in Nature

Only a few elements are found around us in their free state; that is, they are not combined with any other element. The shiny gold in a ring, the life-supporting oxygen in air, and the carbon in a sparkling diamond are examples of free elements. (See Figure 2-1.)

Other free elements that we have put to use include the aluminum in a can and the iron in a bridge support. These elements were not originally found in the free state in nature but in compounds containing other elements. (A small amount of iron is found in the free state in certain meteorites.) In most cases, elements are extracted from their compounds by rigorous chemical processes.

## 2-1.2 The Names of Elements

The names of elements come from many sources. Some are derived from Greek, Latin, or German words for colors—for example, bismuth (white mass), iridium (rainbow), rubidium (deep red), and chlorine (greenish-yellow). Some relate to

**FIGURE 2-1 Some Elements Found in Nature** Three elements found in their free state are copper (left), sulfur, and gold.

the locality where the element was discovered (e.g., germanium, francium, and californium). Four elements (yttrium, erbium, terbium, and ytterbium) are all named after a town in Sweden (Ytterby) near where they were discovered. Other elements honor noted scientists (e.g., seaborgium, einsteinium, fermium, and curium) or mythological figures (e.g., plutonium, uranium, titanium, and mercury.) Many of the oldest known elements have names with obscure origins.

### 2-1.3 The Distribution of the Elements

In the earliest stage of the universe, about 14 billion years ago, only three elements existed: hydrogen (90%), helium (10%), and just a trace of lithium. Since that time, all the other elements have been produced from the original hydrogen in the cores of billions of stars and from the supernova explosions at the end of the stars' lives. Still, since the beginning of time, the abundances of the elements have changed little. In fact, all of this solar activity has converted only about 0.25% of the mass of the universe into elements heavier than helium. Fortunately, that was enough to form the solid earth on which we exist.

Earth and the other planets in our system were formed 4.5 billion years ago from the original elements and the debris of earlier stars. There is comparatively little hydrogen and helium on Earth, although these elements are predominant in the universe as a whole. Figure 2-2a shows the relative abundances of the elements present in Earth's crust in percent by weight. The crust is the outer few miles of the solid surface plus the oceans and atmosphere. Since the core of this planet is mostly iron and nickel, these two elements are more plentiful for Earth as a whole. However, the crust is the region from which we can most easily acquire all our natural resources. It is therefore more meaningful to us to evaluate the distribution of elements found there. Notice that of all the elements, just the top 10 constitute 99% of the mass of the crust. Similarly, consider the human body. Over 96% of the mass of our bodies is composed of only four elements: oxygen, carbon, nitrogen, and hydrogen. This is shown in Figure 2-2b.

### 2-1.4 The Symbols of the Elements

An element can be conveniently identified by a symbol. *A **symbol** is usually the first one or two letters of the element's English or Latin name.* When an element has a two-letter symbol, the first is capitalized but the second is not. The table on the inside cover of the text includes a complete list of elements along with their symbols. Some common elements and their symbols are listed in Table 2-1. The symbols of some common elements are derived from their original Latin names (or, in the case of tungsten, its German name—Wolfram). The symbols of these elements are listed in Table 2-2.

**TABLE 2-1**

**Some Common Elements**

| ELEMENT | SYMBOL |
| --- | --- |
| Aluminum | Al |
| Bromine | Br |
| Calcium | Ca |
| Carbon | C |
| Chlorine | Cl |
| Chromium | Cr |
| Fluorine | F |
| Helium | He |
| Hydrogen | H |
| Iodine | I |
| Magnesium | Mg |
| Nickel | Ni |
| Nitrogen | N |
| Oxygen | O |
| Phosphorus | P |
| Silicon | Si |
| Sulfur | S |
| Zinc | Zn |

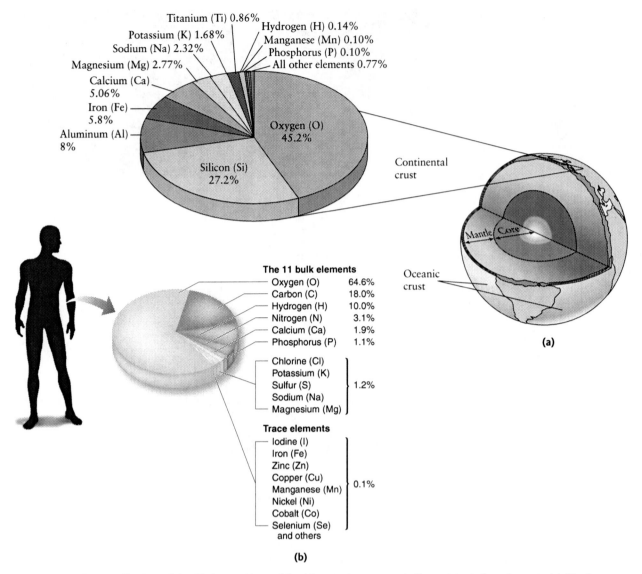

**FIGURE 2-2 The Distribution of the Elements** Most of Earth's crust is composed of surprisingly few elements (a). The human body is composed mostly of just three elements (b).

TABLE 2-2

### Elements with Symbols from Earlier or Alternative Names

| ELEMENT | SYMBOL | FORMER LATIN NAME |
|---------|--------|-------------------|
| Antimony | Sb | Stibium |
| Copper | Cu | Cuprum |
| Gold | Au | Aurum |
| Iron | Fe | Ferrum |
| Lead | Pb | Plumbum |
| Mercury | Hg | Hydragyrum |
| Potassium | K | Kalium |
| Silver | Ag | Argentum |
| Sodium | Na | Natrium |
| Tin | Sn | Stannum |
| Tungsten | W | Wolfram |

## MAKING IT REAL

# Iridium, the Missing Dinosaurs, and the Scientific Method

The dinosaurs, such as the T-Rex, probably had a catastrophic end.

"It's elementary, my dear Watson." If Sherlock Holmes had been on the case of the missing dinosaurs, that statement would have been brilliant. The first major clue was indeed "elementary" or, more specifically, "elemental." Iridium is a very rare element found on Earth's surface. Four billion years ago the Earth was molten, and most iridium (which is very dense) sank deep into the interior. However, matter from space including meteors, asteroids, and comets also contain comparatively high amounts of this element. The following application of the scientific method, as discussed in the Prologue, provides us with a theory of how the element iridium is connected to the extinction of the dinosaurs.

In 1979, American scientists discovered a thin layer of sediment in various locations around the world that was deposited about 65 million years ago, coincidentally the same timeframe in which the dinosaurs became extinct. Indeed, there were dinosaur fossils below that layer but none above. Interestingly, that layer contained comparatively high amounts of iridium. Scientists proposed that this layer contained the dust and debris from a collision of a huge asteroid or comet (about 6 miles in diameter) with Earth. They concluded that a large cloud of dust must have formed, encircling Earth and completely shutting out the sunlight. A bitter cold wave followed, and most animals and plants quickly died. A *hypothesis* (a tentative explanation of facts) was proposed that the dinosaurs must have been among the casualties. After many months the dust settled, forming a thin layer of sediment. Scientists further proposed that small mammals and some reptiles had survived and inherited the planet.

More information has since been discovered to support the original hypothesis. Perhaps most important was the discovery in 1991 of a huge impact crater near the Yucatan Peninsula in Mexico. The crater, 110 miles wide, is buried miles under the ocean surface and was formed about 65 million years ago, evidence that surely a huge asteroid or comet had collided with Earth. Since it landed in the ocean, huge tidal waves must have formed. Evidence of waves over 1 mile high has been found in North and Central America.

Based on all the evidence, most scientists have now embraced the originally proposed hypothesis as a plausible *theory* (a well-established hypothesis). Despite its acceptance, there are still unanswered questions regarding the death of the dinosaurs. So, the issue may not be completely closed. However, it looks likely that the end many of the dinosaurs was sudden and dramatic. Now, instead of worrying about a nasty Tyrannosaurus Rex lurking in the forest, we can instead worry about collisions with asteroids!

▶ **ASSESSING THE OBJECTIVE FOR SECTION 2-1**

**EXERCISE 2-1(a) LEVEL 1:** The following chemicals are either elements or compounds. Which are elements and which are compounds?

(a) tin    (b) baking soda    (c) water    (d) quartz    (e) mercury

**EXERCISE 2-1(b) LEVEL 1:** Provide the symbols for the following elements.

(a) copper    (b) sulfur    (c) calcium

**EXERCISE 2-1(c) LEVEL 1:** Provide the name of the element from its symbol.
(a) Pb    (b) P    (c) Na

**EXERCISE 2-1(d) LEVEL 3:** There are nearly 120 different elements. Would you expect the number of compounds to be roughly the same, slightly more, or significantly more than that?

EXERCISE 2-1(e) LEVEL 3: What might you assume about the possibility of finding elements in their free state based on the name being of Latin origin?

EXERCISE 2-1(f) LEVEL 3: How could you tell if an unknown substance was an element or a compound?

*For additional practice, work chapter problems 2-1, 2-5, 2-7, and 2-32.*

▶ OBJECTIVE
FOR SECTION 2-2
List the postulates of the atomic theory.

# 2-2 The Composition of Elements: Atomic Theory

**LOOKING AHEAD!** We are now ready to look deeper into the composition of the elements. We will see that they are composed of basic particles called atoms. ■

Our modern understanding of the particulate nature of matter actually had its beginning over 2000 years ago. A Greek philosopher named Democritus suggested that all matter is like grains of sand on a beach. In other words, he proposed that matter is composed of tiny indivisible particles that he called *atoms*. However, as recently as two centuries ago, the idea of matter being composed of atoms was not accepted. Most knowledgeable scientists thought that a sample of an element such as copper could be divided (theoretically) into infinitely smaller pieces without changing its nature. In other words, they believed that matter was continuous.

## 2-2.1 The Atomic Theory

In 1803, an English scientist named John Dalton (1766–1844) proposed a theory of matter based on the original thoughts of Democritus. His ideas are now known as **atomic theory**. The major conclusions of atomic theory are as follows:

- Matter is composed of small, indivisible particles called atoms.
- Atoms of the same element are identical and have the same properties.
- Chemical compounds are composed of atoms of different elements combined in small whole-number ratios.
- Chemical reactions are merely the rearrangement of atoms into different combinations.

The atomic theory is now universally accepted as our current view of matter. Thus, we may define an **atom** *as the smallest fundamental particle of an element that has the properties of that element.*

Democritus' proposal 2000 years ago was simply the product of his own rational thought. Dalton's theory was a brilliant and logical explanation of many experimental observations and laws that were known at the time but had not been explained. One of these laws, the law of conservation of mass, will be discussed in the next chapter.

Why are we so sure that Dalton was right? Besides the overwhelming amount of indirect experimental evidence, we now have direct proof. In recent years, a highly sophisticated instrument called the scanning tunneling microscope (STM) has produced images of atoms of several elements. Although these images are somewhat fuzzy, they indicate that an element such as gold is composed of spherical atoms packed closely together, just as you would find in a container of marbles all of the same size. (See Figure 2-3.)

**FIGURE 2-3 STM of the Atoms of an Element** The atoms are shown in an orderly pattern.

## 2-2.2 The Size of an Atom

When we look at a small piece of copper wire, it is hard to imagine that it is not continuous. This is because it is so difficult to comprehend the small size of the atom. Since the diameter of a typical atom is on the order of 0.00000001 cm ($1 \times 10^{-8}$ cm), it would take about 10 quadrillion atoms to appear as a tiny speck. The piece of copper wire is like a brick wall: from a distance it looks completely featureless, but up close we notice that it is actually composed of closely packed basic units.

## MATH CHECK:

### Exponential Notation and the Metric System

The atom is extremely small. Exponential notation (i.e., $1 \times 10^{-8}$) can be used to conveniently represent its diameter. Notice also that the unit of diameter is expressed in the metric system of centimeters (cm). The following questions are meant to check your understanding in these two areas.

1. **Exponential and Scientific Notation**

    a. Convert the number 89,260,000 into scientific notation.

    b. Express the number $0.00825 \times 10^8$ in scientific notation.

2. **The Metric System**

    c. What are the principal units and the symbols in the metric system for mass, volume, and length?

    d. Give the weight in grams of 0.078 kg. Give the volume in L of 345 mL. Give the length in meters of 45.6 cm.

Answers: **1. a.** $8.926 \times 10^7$  **b.** $8.25 \times 10^5$  **2. c.** mass−grams (g), volume−liters (L) length−meters (m) **d.** 78 g, 0.345 L, 0.456 m

Refer to Sections 1-3.1, 1.3.2, and Appendix C for help with scientific notation.

Refer to Sections 1-4.1 and 1-4.2 for help with the metric system.

▶ **ASSESSING THE OBJECTIVE FOR SECTION 2-2**

**EXERCISE 2-2(a) LEVEL 1:** Fill in the blanks.

An _____ is composed of small, indivisible particles called _____.

Atoms of the same _____ are identical and have the same _____.

Chemical _____ are composed of atoms of different elements combined in small _____ ratios. Chemical _____ are rearrangements of _____ into different combinations.

**EXERCISE 2-2(b) LEVEL 2:** Are each of the following statements supported by any of Dalton's postulates?

**(a)** Any chemical experiment on an element should always yield the same result.

**(b)** Any two elements will always form the same compound.

**(c)** There is a limit to how far a substance can be divided.

**(d)** All atoms involved before a chemical reaction are there after the chemical reaction.

**EXERCISE 2-2(c) LEVEL 3:** The ideas of Democritus and Dalton are very similar. Why, then, is Dalton considered the father of modern chemistry? Why is Dalton's statement of his ideas superior to that of Democritus?

*For additional practice, work chapter problem 2-8.*

---

▶ OBJECTIVE
FOR SECTION 2-3

List the components of an atom and their relative masses, charges, and location in the atom.

# 2-3 Composition of the Atom

**LOOKING AHEAD!** We now look even deeper into the nature of matter—the structure of the atom itself. In this section, we will describe the contents of the atom as if we could peer into its tiny confines. ■

Just over 130 years ago, scientists perceived the atom to be a hard, featureless sphere. However, beginning in the late 1880s and continuing today, the mysteries and complexities of the atom have been slowly discovered and understood. Ingenious experiments of brilliant scientists such as Thomson, Rutherford, Becquerel, Curie, and Roentgen, among others, contributed to the current model of the atom.

## 2-3.1 The Electron and Electrostatic Forces

If we had a magical microscope that would allow us to see inside the atom, we would find that the atom itself is composed of basic particles. The first particle that we would notice is relatively small (compared to the other particles in the atom) and is called an **electron**. The electron was the first subatomic particle to be identified. In 1897, J. J. Thomson characterized the electron by proving that it has a negative electrical charge (assigned a value of −1) and is common to the atoms of all elements. The identification of electrons indicated that matter is electrical in nature and that electrostatic forces are at work within the confines of the atom. **Electrostatic forces** *consist of forces of attraction between unlike charges and forces of repulsion between like charges.* (See Figure 2-4.) Atoms themselves have no net electrical charge, so they must contain positive charges that counterbalance the negative charge of the electrons.

The first model of the atom based on this information was proposed by Thomson and was known as the *plum pudding* model of the atom (plum pudding was a popular English dessert). It was suggested that the positive charge would be diffuse and evenly distributed throughout the volume of the atom (analogous to pudding). This is logical—the like positive charges would tend to spread out as much as possible because of their mutual repulsion. The negative particles (electrons) would be embedded throughout the atom like raisins in the pudding. There would be enough electrons to balance the positive charge. Since few of us are familiar with plum pudding, a better analogy would be to picture the atom as a ball of cotton with tiny seeds (representing electrons) distributed throughout the cotton. (See Figure 2-5.)

## 2-3.2 The Nuclear Model of the Atom

The next major development in understanding the atom occurred in 1911. Ernest Rutherford in England conducted experiments that he fully expected would support the accepted model of Thomson. His results, however, suggested a radically different model. Radioactivity had recently been discovered, one form of which is called *alpha* radiation. It is composed of positively charged helium atoms that are spontaneously ejected at high velocities from certain heavy elements. When students in his laboratories bombarded a thin foil of gold with the small, fast-moving alpha particles, they expected that the alpha particles would pass right through the large atoms of gold with very little effect. The small, hard alpha particles should easily

Metal spheres with opposite charges are attracted to each other.

Metal spheres with like charges are repelled from each other.

**FIGURE 2-4 Electrostatic Forces** Opposite charges attract; like charges repel.

**FIGURE 2-5 The Plum Pudding Model** Electrons were thought to be like tiny particles distributed in a positively charged medium.

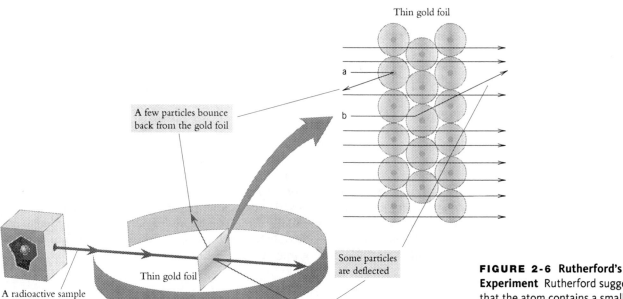

Thin gold foil

a

b

A few particles bounce back from the gold foil

Some particles are deflected

Thin gold foil

A radioactive sample emits a beam of alpha particles

Detector screen

**FIGURE 2-6 Rutherford's Experiment** Rutherford suggested that the atom contains a small nucleus, since a few alpha particles were deflected or reflected back.

push the tiny electrons within the gold atoms aside and pass unaffected through the diffuse positive charge, similar to bullets through a bale of cotton. Instead, a small number of the alpha particles were deflected significantly from their path; a few even came straight back. Imagine shooting a volley of bullets into a thin bale of cotton and finding one or two bullets being ricocheted at a large angle. The conclusion would have to be that something hard, like a rock, was embedded in the soft cotton. Likewise, Rutherford was forced to conclude that the gold atoms had a small, hard core containing most of the mass of the atom and all of the positive charge.

Rutherford's new model was needed to explain the experimental results. The close encounters between the alpha particles and core, or **nucleus**, would cause the alpha particles to be deflected because of the repulsion of like positive charges. Occasional "direct hits" onto the nucleus would reflect the alpha particle back toward the source. (See Figure 2-6.) The alpha particles that were unaffected indicated that most of the volume of the atom is actually empty space containing the very small electrons. At first scientists were skeptical because they wondered why the electrons would not be pulled into the positive nucleus. However, an explanation of this puzzle would eventually be advanced through modern theories. To get an idea about proportions of the atom, imagine a nucleus expanded to the size of a softball. In this case, the radius of the atom would extend for about 1 mile.

### 2-3.3 The Particles in the Nucleus

Later experiments showed that the nucleus is composed of particles called **nucleons**. There are two types of nucleons: **protons**, which have a positive charge (assigned a value of $+1$, equal and opposite to that of an electron), and **neutrons**, which do not carry a charge. (See Figure 2-7.) Data on these three particles in the atom are summarized in Table 2-3. The proton and neutron have roughly the same mass, which is about "1 amu" $(1.67 \times 10^{-24}\,\text{g})$. The amu (atomic mass unit) is a convenient unit for the masses of individual atoms and subatomic particles. This unit will be defined more precisely in the next section.

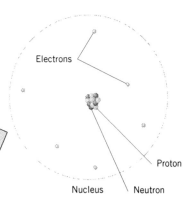

Electrons

Nucleus

Proton

Neutron

Diamond

A carbon atom

**FIGURE 2-7 The Composition of the Atom** A diamond is composed of carbon atoms. The carbon atoms are composed of electrons, protons, and neutrons.

TABLE 2-3

**Atomic Particles**

| NAME | SYMBOL | ELECTRICAL CHARGE | MASS (amu) | MASS (g) |
|------|--------|-------------------|------------|----------|
| Electron | $e$ | −1 | 0.000549 | $9.110 \times 10^{-28}$ |
| Proton | $p$ | +1 | 1.00728 | $1.673 \times 10^{-24}$ |
| Neutron | $n$ | 0 | 1.00867 | $1.675 \times 10^{-24}$ |

For some time, it was thought that the atom was composed of just these three particles. As experimental procedures became more elaborate and sophisticated, however, this model became outdated. It now appears that the proton and the neutron are themselves composed of various combinations of even more fundamental particles called *quarks*. Fortunately for us, the original three-particle model of the atom still meets the needs of the chemist.

## MATH CHECK:

### Significant Figures

Consider the measurements shown in Table 2-3. The masses are expressed in various degrees of precision such as 0.000549 and 1.00728. This relates to how we express measurements. Questions a and b check your knowledge of significant figures.

**a.** How many significant figures are in the numbers 9.110 and 1.00728? Which is the more precise?

**b.** Round off the following number to three significant figures: 7.8956

**c.** What is the degree of uncertainty in the number 9.110?

Answers: **a.** 9.110—four, 1.00728—six.  1.00728 is more precise.  **b.** 7.90  **c.** ±0.001

Refer to Sections 1-1.1 and 1-1.2 for help with significant figures.

▶ **ASSESSING THE OBJECTIVE FOR SECTION 2-3**

**EXERCISE 2-3(a) LEVEL 1:** Identify the specific subatomic particle(s).
(a) smallest of the three
(b) found in the nucleus
(c) most massive
(d) positive in charge

**EXERCISE 2-3(b) LEVEL 1:** Complete the following table.

| PARTICLE | MASS (amu) | CHARGE | LOCATION |
|----------|-----------|--------|----------|
| Proton | | | |
| | | Neutral | |
| | | | Outside of nucleus |

**EXERCISE 2-3(c) LEVEL 2:** Answer the following questions.
(a) Where is virtually all of the mass of an atom located?
(b) What takes up most of the volume of an atom?
(c) Historically, which was the first particle to be identified?

**EXERCISE 2-3(d) LEVEL 3:** It has been proposed that neutrons are simply particles formed when protons and electrons are combined into one particle. What facts about neutrons suggest this might be the case?

*For additional practice, work chapter problems 2-9 and 2-10.*

# 2-4 Atomic Number, Mass Number, and Atomic Mass

**LOOKING AHEAD!** We are now ready to look into how protons, neutrons, and electrons define the atoms of a particular element. We will see in this section why not all atoms of an element are exactly the same and how the atoms of one element differ from another. ■

▶ **OBJECTIVE FOR SECTION 2-4**
From the percent abundance of specific isotopes of an element, determine the atomic mass of the element and the number of protons, neutrons and electrons in each isotope.

## 2-4.1 Atomic Number, Mass Number, and Isotopes

In Dalton's original atomic theory, he suggested that all atoms of an element are identical. But if we look at a number of atoms of most elements, we find that this statement is not exactly true. For example, consider the atoms of the element copper. Most atoms are composed of a nucleus containing a total of 63 nucleons, of which 29 are protons and 34 are neutrons. The atom also contains 29 electrons that exactly balance the positive charge of the protons, resulting in a neutral atom. *The number of protons in the nucleus (which is equal to the total positive charge) is referred to as the atom's* **atomic number**. *The total number of nucleons (protons and neutrons) is called the* **mass number**. Therefore, this particular copper atom has an atomic number of 29 and a mass number of 63. There are other copper atoms that are not exactly the same, however. These atoms of copper have a mass number of 65 rather than 63. This means that these atoms have 36 neutrons as well as 29 protons. *An atom of a specific element with a specific mass number is known as an* **isotope**. Isotopes of an element have the same atomic number but different mass numbers.

Most elements that are present in nature exist as a mixture of isotopes. *It is the atomic number, however, that distinguishes one element from another.* Any atom with an atomic number of 29, regardless of any other consideration, is an atom of copper. If the atomic number is 28, the element is nickel; if it is 30, the element is zinc.

Specific isotopes are written in a form known as *isotopic notation.* In isotopic notation, the mass number is written as a superscript to the left of the element. Sometimes, the atomic number is written as a subscript, also on the left. The indication of the atomic number is strictly a convenience. Since the atomic number determines the identity of the element, it can therefore be determined from the symbol. The isotopic notations for the two isotopes of copper are written as follows.

Mass number (number of nucleons)
(29 protons and 34 neutrons)

(29 protons and 36 neutrons)

$$^{63}_{29}Cu \quad ^{65}_{29}Cu$$

Atomic number (number of protons)
(29 protons)

The convention for verbally naming specific isotopes is to use the element's name followed by its mass number. For example, $^{63}$Cu is called copper-63, and $^{65}$Cu is called copper-65. From either the written isotopic notation or the isotope name, we can determine the number of each type of particle in an isotope, as we will see in Example 2-1.

---

### EXAMPLE 2-1    Calculating the Number of Particles in an Isotope

How many protons, neutrons, and electrons are present in $^{90}_{38}$Sr?

#### PROCEDURE

The subscript (and symbol) provide us information on protons. Since this is a neutral atom, the number of protons and electrons is the same. The superscript gives us the total number of protons and neutrons. The number of neutrons alone is the difference.

#### SOLUTION

$$\text{number of protons} = \text{atomic number} = \underline{38}$$

$$\text{number of neutrons} = \text{mass number} - \text{number of protons } 90 - 38 = \underline{52}$$

$$\text{number of electrons} = \text{number of protons} = \underline{38}$$

#### ANALYSIS

If you knew only the name of an element, which, if any, of the fundamental particles could you determine? Protons and electrons can be determined directly from the identity of the element, but the number of neutrons must be determined from the mass number. Knowing the specific isotope of an element allows you to determine the exact numbers of protons, neutrons, and electrons.

#### SYNTHESIS

What would happen in an atom if the number of protons and electrons were not exactly balanced? What if there was an extra electron? Or one too few? Would the positive and negative charges cancel out? Clearly not. If there was an extra electron, the atom would have an overall negative charge. If there was one too few, there would be an overall positive charge. This situation occurs and is explored later in this chapter.

---

In Chapter 5, we'll consider how the mass of one element compares to another. The mass of the electrons is extremely small compared to the masses of the protons and neutrons, so it is not included in the mass of an isotope. Thus, the mass number of an isotope is a convenient but rather imprecise measure of its mass. It is imprecise because electrons are not included and protons and neutrons do not have exactly the same mass.

### 2-4.2 Isotopic Mass and Atomic Mass

A more precise measure of the mass of one isotope relative to another is known as the isotopic mass. **Isotopic mass** *is determined by comparison to a standard,* $^{12}C$, *which is defined as having a mass of exactly 12 atomic mass units. Therefore, one* **atomic mass unit** *(amu) is a mass of exactly 1/12 of the mass of* $^{12}C$. For example, precise measurements show that the mass of $^{10}$B is 0.83442 times the mass of $^{12}C$, which means it has an isotopic mass of 10.013 amu. From similar calculations, we find that the atomic mass of $^{11}$B is 11.009 amu. Since boron, as well as most other naturally occurring elements, is found in nature as a mixture of isotopes, the atomic mass of the element reflects this mixture. *The* **atomic mass** *of an element is obtained from the weighted average of the atomic masses of all isotopes present in nature.* A weighted average relates the isotopic mass of each isotope present to its percent abundance. It can be considered as the isotopic mass of an "average atom," although an average atom does not itself exist. Example 2-2 illustrates how atomic mass relates to the distribution of isotopes.

## Isotopes and the History of Earth's Weather

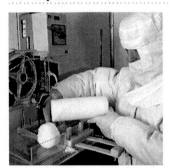
Greenland.

Lately it seems like we are always hearing of some great storm or heat record. Is something strange going on, or are the media just doing a better job of reporting these events? Actually, we are all anxious to know whether the climate is permanently changing and, if so, whether it is going to get worse. The key to predicting the future, however, may lie in understanding the past. An ingenious key to past climates is found with the naturally occurring isotopes of oxygen and hydrogen. We will consider here how the isotopes of oxygen are put to use.

Oxygen is composed of 99.76% $^{16}O$, 0.04% $^{17}O$, and 0.20% $^{18}O$, which produces a weighted average of 15.9994. This means that only 24 out of 10,000 oxygen atoms are "heavy" oxygen atoms (i.e., $^{17}O$ or $^{18}O$). When $^{17}O$ or $^{18}O$ is part of a water molecule, the properties are very slightly different from normal water ($H_2$ $^{16}O$). For example, the heavier water evaporates just a little more slowly than normal water. The colder the temperature of the oceans, the less heavy oxygen ends up in the clouds. This means that the amount of water with the heavier oxygen is slightly less in fresh water (which comes from precipitation of the evaporated water) than in the ocean. But even this can vary ever so slightly. When the climate is colder than normal, less water evaporates from the ocean and so the amount of heavy water in precipitation is less than normal.

Greenland and Antarctica are our natural weather-history laboratories. Greenland has been covered with ice for more than 100,000 years and Antarctica for almost 1 million years. In some areas of Greenland, the ice is now 2 miles deep. Year by year, the snow has been accumulating and has been pressed down into layers that resemble tree rings. Scientists have bored through the ice and analyzed the layers for their content of dust, trapped gases, and the ratio of oxygen isotopes. Results of isotope studies indicate that the Northern Hemisphere was a whopping 20°C (or 36°F) colder during the last ice age (about 30,000 years ago) than it is now. More important, variations in the weather from then to now have also been determined. These studies will help us understand and perhaps predict what's going to happen to our weather in the future. Is our current warming a natural occurrence or a new phenomenon? Most evidence indicates that humans have a hand in the warming weather.

## MATH CHECK:

### Percent and Decimal Fractions

In the following example, you will be asked to convert percent to a decimal fraction. To check your ability with percent, answer the following two questions.

**a.** A crowd of spectators is composed of 42 women and 74 men. What is the decimal fraction of men and what is the percent of women present? Express both answers to two significant figures.

**b.** Another crowd of 611 people had the same percent of women and men. Using the results from **a** above, calculate how many women were in this crowd?

**Answers: a.** 0.64 men, 36% women   **b.** 220 women

Refer to Appendix A-6 for help with percent and decimal fractions.

## EXAMPLE 2-2 Calculating the Atomic Mass of an Element from Percent Distribution of Isotopes

In nature, the element boron occurs as 19.9% $^{10}B$ and 80.1% $^{11}B$. If the isotopic mass of $^{10}B$ is 10.013 and that of $^{11}B$ is 11.009 amu, what is the atomic mass of boron?

### PROCEDURE
Find the contribution of each isotope toward the atomic mass by multiplying the percent in decimal form by the isotopic mass. Recall that percent can be expressed as a normal fraction or a decimal fraction (e.g., 25% = 1/4 = 0.25).

### SOLUTION

$$^{10}B \quad 0.199 \times 10.013 = \underline{1.99 \text{ amu}}$$
$$^{11}B \quad 0.801 \times 11.009 = \underline{8.82 \text{ amu}}$$
$$\text{atomic mass of boron} = \underline{10.81}$$

### ANALYSIS
Based on the percentages of boron-10 and boron-11, does this answer seem reasonable? Since the atomic mass is a weighted average of the two isotopes, and they have mass numbers of 10 and 11, the answer should be between those values. It should be closer to the isotope with the higher percent abundance. The answer of 10.81 is between the two numbers and closer to the isotope of 80.1% abundance.

### SYNTHESIS
The atomic mass of boron is approximately 80% of the way between the mass numbers of boron-10 and boron-11. What can you conclude about the percentages of various isotopes of an element whose atomic mass is very close to an integer? Consider carbon as an example. Its atomic mass is 12.011, just a little higher than 12 exactly. We would most likely conclude that the isotope with mass 12 is by far the most common (actually, more than 99%).

▶ ASSESSING THE OBJECTIVE FOR SECTION 2-4

**EXERCISE 2-4(a) LEVEL 1:** Identify the following as atomic number, mass number, or isotopic mass.

(a) always an integer value

(b) the superscript in isotopic notation

(c) the total mass of the atom

(d) the number of protons

(e) determines the number of protons and neutrons combined.

**EXERCISE 2-4(b) LEVEL 2:** Determine the number of protons, neutrons, and electrons in the following isotopes.

(a) $^{13}_{6}C$      (b) $^{1}_{1}H$      (c) $^{238}_{92}U$

**EXERCISE 2-4(c) LEVEL 2:** Write the isotopic notation for the following three species.

(a) protons = 9, neutrons = 10, electrons = 9

(b) protons = 35, neutrons = 44, electrons = 35

(c) protons = 20, neutrons = 20, electrons = 20

**EXERCISE 2-4(d) LEVEL 2:** Antimony (Sb) has two naturally occurring isotopes: $^{121}Sb$, with a mass of 120.903 amu and a 57.3% abundance, and $^{123}Sb$, with a mass of 122.904 amu and a 42.7% abundance. Determine antimony's atomic mass.

**EXERCISE 2-4(e) LEVEL 2:** Lithium has two naturally occurring isotopes: $^6$Li has a mass of 6.015 and is 7.42% abundant; $^7$Li has a mass of 7.016 and is 92.58% abundant. Calculate the atomic mass of lithium.

**EXERCISE 2-4(f) LEVEL 3:** All through the Middle Ages, alchemists searched for ways to turn base metals, such as lead, into gold. Why was this a chemically fruitless endeavor?

**EXERCISE 2-4(g) LEVEL 3:** Bromine has two naturally occurring isotopes, $^{79}$Br and $^{81}$Br. From its atomic weight, estimate the percentage abundances of the two isotopes.

*For additional practice, work chapter problems 2-11, 2-13, 2-15, 2-26, and 2-28.*

PART A **SUMMARY**

## KEY TERMS

| | |
|---|---|
| 2-1 | All substances can be classified as either **elements** or **compounds**. p. 54 |
| 2-1.4 | Each element is designated by a unique **symbol**. p. 55 |
| 2-2.1 | According to **atomic theory**, the basic particle of an element is an **atom**. p. 58 |
| 2-3.1 | The discovery of the **electron** proved the presence of **electrostatic forces** in the atom. p. 60 |
| 2-3.2 | Experiments indicated that the atom contained a central positively charged core called a **nucleus**. p. 61 |
| 2-3.3 | The nucleus consists of particles called **nucleons**, which are either **neutrons** or **protons**. p. 61 |
| 2-4.1 | The number of protons in a nucleus is known as its **atomic number**, and the number of nucleons is known as its **mass number**. p. 63 |
| 2-4.1 | Naturally occurring elements are composed of one or more **isotopes**. p. 63 |
| 2-4.2 | The standard of mass is $^{12}$C, which is defined as exactly 12 **atomic mass units** (amu). The **isotopic mass** of an isotope is determined experimentally by comparison to this standard. p. 64 |
| 2-4.2 | The **atomic mass** of an element is determined by its naturally occurring isotopes and their percent abundance. p. 64 |

## SUMMARY CHART

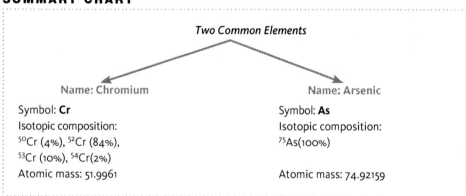

*Two Common Elements*

Name: Chromium

Symbol: **Cr**
Isotopic composition:
$^{50}$Cr (4%), $^{52}$Cr (84%),
$^{53}$Cr (10%), $^{54}$Cr(2%)
Atomic mass: 51.9961

Name: Arsenic

Symbol: **As**
Isotopic composition:
$^{75}$As(100%)

Atomic mass: 74.92159

Part B

# Compounds and Their Composition

### SETTING A GOAL

✳ You will learn to distinguish between ionic and molecular compounds based on their chemical structure and general properties.

### OBJECTIVES

2-5 List the characteristics of compounds composed of molecules.

2-6 Write the formulas of simple ionic compounds given the charges on the ions.

► OBJECTIVE
FOR SECTION 2.5
List the characteristics of compounds composed of molecules.

# 2-5 Molecular Compounds

**LOOKING AHEAD!** The atoms of elements are usually joined together with other atoms of the same element or other elements into a more complex form of particulate matter. In this section, we will examine one of the two principal forms of matter formed by the combined atoms. ∎

Every element and compound has a unique set of properties. Properties *describe the particular characteristics or traits of a substance.* We will have more to say about specific properties in the next chapter. Elements and compounds can be referred to as pure substances. **Pure substances** *have definite compositions and definite, unchanging properties.* (See Figure 2-8.)

## 2-5.1 Recognizing the Names of Compounds

The names of the simplest compounds are usually based on the elements from which they are composed, and most contain two words. Carbon dioxide, sodium sulfite, and silver nitrate all refer to specific compounds. Notice that the second word ends in *-ide, -ite,* or *-ate.* A few compounds have three words, such as sodium hydrogen carbonate. A number of compounds have common names of one word, such as water, ammonia, lye, and methane. We will talk in more detail about how we determine the names of compounds in Chapter 4.

## 2-5.2 Molecules, Molecular Compounds, and Covalent Bonds

About three centuries ago, water was thought to be an element. When scientists were able to decompose water into hydrogen and oxygen, it became apparent that water is a compound. Just as the basic particles of most elements are atoms, the basic particles of a particular type of compound are known as molecules. *A* **molecule** *is formed by the chemical combination of two or more atoms. Molecules composed of different atoms are the basic particles of* **molecular compounds**. *The atoms in a molecule are joined and held together by a force called the* **covalent bond**. (The nature of the covalent bond will be examined in more detail in Chapter 9.) If it were possible to magnify a droplet of water and visualize its basic particles, we would see that it is an example of a molecular compound. Each molecule of water is composed of two atoms of hydrogen joined by covalent bonds to one atom of oxygen. (See Figure 2-9.) Molecules can contain as few as two atoms or, in the case of the

**FIGURE 2-8 Some Familiar Compounds** These products all contain one compound. Notice their common names do not indicate the elements in the compounds.

complex molecules on which life is based, millions of atoms. We will concentrate on molecular compounds in the remainder of this section. In the next section we will discuss a second category of compounds known as ionic compounds.

Hydrogen atom    Oxygen atom

(a)

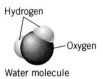
Hydrogen

Oxygen

Water molecule

(b)

### 2-5.3 The Formulas of Molecular Compounds

*A compound is represented by the symbols of the elements of which it is composed. This is called the* **formula** *of the compound.* The familiar formula for water is therefore $H_2O$. Note that the 2 is written as a subscript, indicating that the molecule has two hydrogen atoms. When there is only one atom of a given element present (e.g., oxygen), a subscript of "1" is assumed but not shown.

What makes one molecular compound different from another? The answer is that each chemical compound has a unique formula or arrangement of atoms in its molecules. For example, there is another compound composed of just hydrogen and oxygen, but it has the formula $H_2O_2$. Its name is hydrogen peroxide, and its properties are distinctly different from those of water ($H_2O$). Figure 2-10 illustrates how the *atoms* of hydrogen and oxygen combine to form the *molecules* of two different compounds. The formulas of other well-known compounds are $C_{12}H_{22}O_{11}$ (sucrose, which we know as table sugar), $C_9H_8O_4$ (aspirin), $NH_3$ (ammonia), and $CH_4$ (methane).

Sometimes two or more compounds may share the same chemical formula. What, then, makes them unique? In this case, their difference stems from the sequence of the atoms within the molecule. For example, ethyl alcohol and dimethyl ether are two distinct compounds, but both have the formula $C_2H_6O$. The difference in the two compounds lies in the order of the bonded atoms.

Notice that in ethyl alcohol the order of bonds is $C - C - O$ and in ether the order is $C - O - C$. (The dashes between atoms represent covalent chemical bonds, which hold the atoms together.) The difference in the arrangement has a profound effect on the properties of these two compounds. Ingestion of alcohol causes intoxication, while a similar amount of ether may cause death. *Formulas that show the order and arrangement of specific atoms are known as* **structural formulas**.

(c)

**FIGURE 2-9 Molecules of Water** A molecule of water is composed of one atom of oxygen and two atoms of hydrogen.

ethyl alcohol

```
    H   H
    |   |
H—C—C—O—H
    |   |
    H   H
```

dimethyl ether

```
    H       H
    |       |
H—C—O—C—H
    |       |
    H       H
```

### 2-5.4 Molecular Elements

Each breath of fresh air that we inhale is primarily composed of just three elements—nitrogen (78%), oxygen (21%), and argon (less than 1%), although there are traces of other gases as well. What would we see if we could magnify a sample of air so that the atoms of these three elements could become visible? The most noticeable difference among these elements is that argon exists as solitary atoms, but atoms of nitrogen and oxygen are joined together in pairs to form molecules. (See Figure 2-11.)

Hydrogen, fluorine, chlorine, bromine, and iodine in their elemental form also exist as diatomic (two-atom) molecules under normal temperature conditions. A form of elemental phosphorus consists of molecules composed of four atoms, and a form of sulfur consists of molecules composed of eight atoms. There is also a

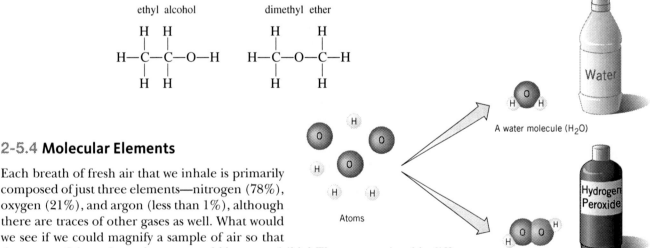

Atoms

A water molecule ($H_2O$)

A hydrogen peroxide molecule ($H_2O_2$)

**FIGURE 2-10 Atoms and Molecules** Atoms of hydrogen and atoms of oxygen can combine to form molecules of two different compounds.

**FIGURE 2-11 The Composition of the Atmosphere** Our atmosphere is composed mostly of nitrogen and oxygen molecules with a small amount of argon atoms.

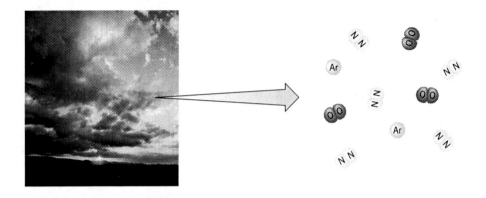

**FIGURE 2-11 The Composition of the Atmosphere** Our atmosphere is composed mostly of nitrogen and oxygen molecules with a small amount of argon atoms.

second form of elemental oxygen, known as ozone, which is composed of three atoms of oxygen. Molecules composed of two or more atoms of the same element are also referred to by formulas such as $I_2$ (iodine), $O_2$ (oxygen), $O_3$ (ozone), $P_4$ (phosphorus), and $S_8$ (sulfur).

▶ **OBJECTIVE FOR SECTION 2.6**
Write the formulas of simple ionic compounds given the charges on the ions.

# 2-6 Ionic Compounds

**LOOKING AHEAD!** There is a second classification of compounds known as ionic compounds. You may have noticed that molecular compounds are often found as gases or liquids. Ionic compounds are always solids at normal temperatures. We will discuss ionic compounds next. ■

## 2-6.1 Cations and Anions

When you scrape your stocking feet along a carpet in a dry room, you often pick up a charge of static electricity that discharges when you touch something metallic, resulting in an unpleasant shock. Atoms can also achieve an electrostatic charge. *When atoms have an electrostatic charge, they are known as* **ions.** *Positively charged ions are known as* **cations,** *and negatively charged ions are called* **anions.** Ordinary table salt is a compound named sodium chloride. In sodium chloride, the sodium exists as a cation with a single positive charge and the chlorine exists as an anion with a single negative charge. This is illustrated with a + or − as a superscript to the right of the symbol of the element as follows.

$$Na^+ \text{ and } Cl^-$$

## 2-6.2 The Origin of the Charge on Ions

To understand why the $Na^+$ cation has a positive charge, we must look at its basic particles and how an atom of Na differs from a $Na^+$ cation. A cation contains fewer electrons than the number of protons found in a neutral atom. An anion contains more electrons than there are protons in a neutral atom. *In both cases, it is the electrons that are out of balance, not the protons.* A +1 charge on a cation indicates that it has one *less* electron than its number of protons (its atomic number), and a +2 charge indicates that the cation has two *fewer* electrons than its atomic number. For example, the $Na^+$ cation has 11 protons (the atomic number of Na) and 10 electrons. The +1 charge arises from this imbalance [i.e., $(11p \times +1) + (10e \times -1) = +1$]. An anion with a −1 charge has one *more* electron than the atomic number of the element, and a −2 charge indicates two *more* electrons than its atomic number. For example, the $S^{2-}$ ion has 16 protons in its nucleus and 18 electrons. The $-2$ charge arises from the two extra electrons [i.e., $(16p \times +1) + (18e \times -1) = -2$].

Why does Na specifically form a $+1$ charge and Cl a $-1$ charge and not vice versa or some other charge? In fact, there are valid reasons for this, which we will discuss in detail in a later chapter. For now, however, we can make some simple observations that provide us with some solid clues. It concerns a group of elements, sometimes called a *family*, known as the *noble gases*. These elements exist in nature as free atoms forming neither cations nor anions. The number of electrons that these elements possess lends them particular stability so they have little or (in most cases) no tendency to lose or gain electrons. As a result they all exist in nature as gaseous, monatomic elements (e.g., Ar in the air). The noble gases are the elements helium, neon, argon, krypton, and xenon. A neutral helium atom (He) has 2 electrons, neon (Ne) has 10, argon (Ar) has 18, krypton (Kr) has 36, and Xenon (Xe) has 54. Elements with atomic numbers that are near these elements tend to add or lose electrons so as to have the same number of electrons as their neighboring noble gas. For example, chlorine has 17 electrons. By adding 1 electron it has 18 (like argon) but now has a $-1$ charge. Sodium has 11 electrons. By losing 1 electron it has 10 (like neon) but acquires a $+1$ charge. In general, elements with 1 to 3 extra electrons beyond those of a noble gas lose electrons to form cations, while elements with 1 to 3 fewer electrons than a noble gas gain electrons to form anions. These generalizations do not work for all elements, however. Determining the charge on many of these ions will be made much simpler when we employ the *periodic table*, which we will do in Chapter 4. In Chapter 8, we will take up the topic again to present the theoretical bases of ion formation.

### 2-6.3 The Formulas of Ionic Compounds

Since the sodium cations and the chlorine anions are oppositely charged, the ions are held together by electrostatic forces of attraction. In Figure 2-12 the ions in sodium chloride are shown as they would appear if sufficient magnification were possible. Note that each cation (one of the smaller spheres) is attached to more than one anion. In fact, each ion is surrounded by six oppositely charged ions. The reason that cations are usually small compared to anions will be discussed in Chapter 8. Bonding in these compounds is much different from that of the previously discussed molecular compounds, in which atoms bond together to form discrete entities (molecules.)

*Compounds consisting of ions are known as* **ionic compounds**. *The electrostatic forces holding the ions together are known as* **ionic bonds**. The ions in ionic compounds are locked tightly in their positions by the strong electrostatic attractions. This results in solid compounds that are almost all hard and rigid. They are the material of most rocks and minerals.

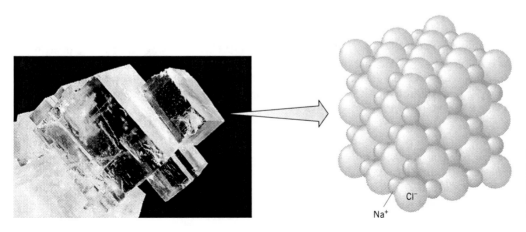

**FIGURE 2-12 The Ions in Sodium Chloride** A solid ionic compound such as sodium chloride exists as an arrangement of ions.

The formula of sodium chloride is

$$1 \;\; Na^+ \;\; + \;\; 1 \;\; Cl^- \;\; = NaCl$$
$$+1 \;\; + \;\; -1 \;\; = 0$$

This represents the simplest ratio of cations to anions present (in this case, one-to-one). This ratio reflects the fact that the two ions have equal and opposite charges and that *in any ionic compound, the anions and cations exist together in a ratio such that the negative charge balances the positive charge* [e.g., $+1 + (-1) = 0$]. Notice that the charges are not displayed in the formula. *The simplest whole-number ratio of ions in an ionic compound is referred to as a* **formula unit.**

Ions may also have charges greater than 1. In these cases, the ratio of ions in the formula may not be simply one-to-one.

Calcium chloride is a compound composed of $Ca^{2+}$ cations and $Cl^-$ anions. Two chlorine anions are needed to balance the +2 charge on the calcium [$+2 + (2 \times -1) = 0$]. Thus the formula is

$$Ca^{2+} \;\; +\; Cl^- \atop +\; Cl^- \;\; = CaCl_2$$
$$+2 \;\; + \;\; (2 \times -1) \;\; = 0$$

---

### EXAMPLE 2-3   Determining the Formula of an Ionic Compound

What is the formula unit of an ionic compound formed from the $Al^{3+}$ cation and the $S^{2-}$ anion?

#### PROCEDURE
In an ionic compound, the total positive charge of all cations and the total negative charge of all anions must be the same absolute value. We need to determine how many +3's will cancel with how many −2's. Look for the least common multiple of the charges.

#### SOLUTION
The least common multiple of 2 and 3 is 6:

$$2 \times (+3) = +6$$
$$3 \times (-2) = -6$$

$(+6) + (-6) = 0$, a neutral compound. It will take **2** $Al^{3+}$ and **3** $S^{2-}$ to form an ionic compound. The formula is written **$Al_2S_3$**.

#### ANALYSIS
Do you notice a pattern between the charges on the ions and the subscripts? The absolute value of the charge on the sulfur, 2, becomes the subscript for the aluminum. Similarly, the charge on the aluminum, 3, becomes the subscript for the sulfur. This works in most cases, but don't lose sight of the fact that we do this to *balance the charge*. Do not write $Mg_2S_2$, even though the charges on the ions are +2 and −2 respectively. It is sufficient to have one of each to balance the charge: MgS.

#### SYNTHESIS
A positive charge means a loss of electrons. What happened to these electrons? A negative charge means a gain of electrons. Where did they come from? It becomes clear that the electrons lost by one atom in a compound were gained by the other. It now makes all the more sense that charges have to balance. As electrons shift from one atom to another, there must always be the same number of electrons lost as gained.

### 2-6.4 The Formulas of Compounds Containing Polyatomic Ions

*Groups of atoms that are covalently bonded to each other may as a whole also be cations or anions. They are known as* **polyatomic ions**. Examples include the nitrate anion ($NO_3^-$), the perchlorate anion ($ClO_4^-$), and the ammonium cation ($NH_4^+$). While properly classified as ionic, compounds containing polyatomic ions can be viewed as a combination of the two types of substances we've discussed in this chapter. The elements involved in the polyatomic ion are joined by covalent bonds, the same as in neutral molecular compounds. Then, when the cation is added, the entirety is ionic. When more than one polyatomic ion is in a formula unit, parentheses are placed around the polyatomic ion and a subscript used. When there is only one polyatomic ion, no parentheses are used. Barium perchlorate (a compound containing one $Ba^{2+}$ ion and two $ClO_4^-$ ions) is represented in the margin in (a), and calcium carbonate (a compound containing one $Ca^{2+}$ ion and one $CO_3^{2-}$ ion) is represented in (b).

$$Ba^{2+} \quad + \quad ClO_4^- \quad + \quad ClO_4^- \qquad = Ba(ClO_4)_2$$
$$+2 \quad + \quad (2 \times -1) \qquad = 0$$
**(a)**

$$Ca^{2+} \quad + \quad CO_3^{2-} \qquad = CaCO_3$$
$$(+2) \quad + \quad (-2) \qquad = 0$$
**(b)**

Sometimes the formulas of molecular compounds are confused with those of ions. (See Figure 2-13.) For example, $NO_2$ is the formula of a molecular compound known as nitrogen dioxide. The $NO_2$ molecules are neutral entities. This compound is a brownish gas responsible for some air pollution. Notice that no charge is shown by the formula. The $NO_2^-$ species (known as the nitrite ion) contains a negative charge, which means that it is a polyatomic ion. It exists only with a cation as part of an ionic compound (e.g., $NaNO_2$, sodium nitrite). This compound is a solid. Remember that cations and anions do not normally exist alone but only as the two oppositely charged parts of an ionic compound. We will spend more time writing and naming ionic compounds in Chapter 4.

The charge on polyatomic ions also arises from an imbalance of electrons. For example, the $CO_3^{2-}$ ion has a total of 30 protons in the four nuclei [i.e., $6(C) + (3 \times 8)(O) = 30$]. The presence of a $-2$ charge indicates that 32 negatively charged electrons are present in the ion.

In the next chapter we will see how the properties of molecular and ionic compounds differ.

**FIGURE 2-13 Molecules and Ions** $NO_2$ is a gaseous compound composed of discrete neutral molecules, whereas the $NO_2^-$ (nitrite) ion is part of a solid, ionic compound.

**EXAMPLE 2-4  Determining the Formula of an Ionic Compound Containing a Polyatomic Ion**

What is the formula unit of an ionic compound formed from the $Fe^{3+}$ cation and the $NO_3^-$ anion?

**PROCEDURE**

Again, the total positive charge of all cations and the total negative charge of all anions must be the same absolute value. Determine the least common multiple of the two charges, and then use the necessary numbers as subscripts to get a neutral entity.

**SOLUTION**

The least common multiple of 3 and 1 is 3:

$$1 \times (+3) = +3$$
$$3 \times (-1) = -3$$

$(+3) + (-3) = 0$, a neutral compound. It will take **1** $Fe^{3+}$ and **3** $NO_3^-$ to form an ionic compound with no net charge (neutral). Remember to include parentheses around the $NO_3^-$ ion with "3" as a subscript to indicate three $NO_3^-$ ions along with the one $Fe^{3+}$ ion: **$Fe(NO_3)_3$**.

**ANALYSIS**

How many atoms of each type—Fe, N, and O—are present in one formula unit of $Fe(NO_3)_3$? When the subscript is "1," as in the case of iron, it is understood to be present. Subscripts apply only to what they immediately follow. The interior "3," next to oxygen, applies only to the oxygen. The exterior "3," by the parenthesis, applies to everything within the parenthesis. The formula unit therefore consists of one Fe atom, three N atoms, and nine O atoms.

**SYNTHESIS**

Is it possible to form an ionic compound composed of only two anions or of only two cations? If we again think of charges as resulting from the gain or loss of electrons, we realize that a theoretical substance made from two anions would have a total number of electrons greater than the number of protons. The substance would not be neutral and therefore not stable. The same argument applies to theoretical substances made entirely of cations. You must always match a cation with an anion to generate a neutral compound.

▶ **ASSESSING THE OBJECTIVES FOR SECTIONS 2-5 and 2-6**

**EXERCISE 2-6(a) LEVEL 1:** Determine whether the following statements apply to molecular compounds, ionic compounds, or both.

**(a)** composed of charged particles

**(b)** have properties different from their constituent elements

**(c)** consist of individual molecules

**(d)** have an overall neutral charge

**(e)** formula written as the smallest whole-number ratio of elements

**(f)** held together by a covalent bond

**EXERCISE 2-6(b) LEVEL 2:** What is the formula of the ionic compounds formed by combining the following?

**(a)** $Mg^{2+}$ and $I^-$ **(b)** $Li^+$ and $SO_4^{2-}$ **(c)** $Al^{3+}$ and $Se^{2-}$ **(d)** $Na^+$ and $HCO_3^-$

**EXERCISE 2-6(c) LEVEL 2:** Complete the table by writing the chemical formula for ionic compounds formed from the corresponding cations and anions:

| | $Cs^+$ | $Zn^{2+}$ | $Fe^{3+}$ |
|---|---|---|---|
| $ClO_3^-$ | | | |
| $O^{2-}$ | | | |
| $PO_4^{3-}$ | | | |

**EXERCISE 2-6(d) LEVEL 3:** If you saw that the formula of a compound was $C_6H_{12}O_6$ and were asked whether the compound was ionic or molecular, which would you answer, and what evidence would you cite?

**EXERCISE 2-6(e) LEVEL 3:** You are a research scientist analyzing athletes' blood for a particular illegal chemical whose formula is $C_8H_{12}O_2N$. You found a chemical with that exact formula in one of the athelete's blood samples. Is that enough evidence to indict the athlete?

*For additional practice, work chapter problems 2-36, 2-42, 2-45, 2-46, and 2-56.*

---

**MAKING IT REAL**

## Ionic Compounds and Essential Elements

As our bodies age, it becomes more important that we include adequate amounts of trace elements in our diets. Some of these elements include boron, calcium, chromium, copper, iodine, iron, magnesium, phosphorus, potassium, and zinc. This is not an all-inclusive list—there are several others. In fact, we are learning more all the time about the role of other trace elements in our body chemistry. As a result, the list will only grow. Deficiencies of any of these elements can cause serious health effects. For example, one of the most widespread maladies is *anemia*. Anemia is caused by a shortage of red blood cells, which are involved in the transport of oxygen from the lungs to the tissues. Iron plays a key role in the action of the hemoglobin in red blood cells. If there is too little iron in the body, anemia results; on the other hand, too much iron in the body can also cause serious problems. Genetic problems can cause some individuals to accumulate excess iron in certain organs, resulting in a condition known as *hemochromatosis*. The victims of such "iron overload" can be very sick, indeed. This condition is usually treated by periodically removing blood from the individual. However, iron deficiency is the more common malady.

Of course, we all hear on television of the need for older individuals to take plenty of calcium supplements. As we age, bones may become brittle, especially among women. This condition is known as *osteoporosis*. It is important to take calcium supplements so as to slow or even stop this degenerative process.

The best way to make sure our bodies get all the necessary elements is to eat a balanced diet. This

### Supplement Facts

Serving Size 2 tablets
Servings Per Container 180

| Amount Per Serving | | % Daily Value |
|---|---|---|
| Vitamin A (as beta carotene) | 5,000IU | 100% |
| Vitamin C (as ascorbic acid) | 200mg | 333% |
| Vitamin D3 (as cholecalciferol) | 400IU | 100% |
| Vitamin E (as d-alpha tocopheryl succinate) | 100IU | 333% |
| Thiamine (as thiamine hydrochloride) | 30mg | 2000% |
| Riboflavin | 30mg | 1765% |
| Niacin (as niacinamide) | 100mg | 500% |
| Vitamin B6 (as pyridoxine hydrochloride) | 30mg | 1500% |
| Folic Acid | 400mcg | 100% |
| Vitamin B12 (as cyanocobalamin) | 100mcg | 1667% |
| Biotin (as d-biotin) | 25mcg | 8% |
| Pantothenic Acid (as calcium pantothenate) | 30mg | 300% |
| Calcium (as calcium carbonate and dicalcium phosphate) | 200mg | 20% |
| Iron (as ferrous fumarate) | 18mg | 100% |
| Phosphorous (as dicalcium phosphate) | 60mg | 6% |
| Iodine (from kelp) | 150mcg | 100% |
| Magnesium (as magnesium oxide) | 20mg | 5% |
| Zinc (as zinc oxide) | 5mg | 33% |
| Copper (as copper gluconate) | 2mg | 100% |
| Manganese (as manganese carbonate) | 7mg | 350% |

| Proprietary Blend | 148mg | * |
|---|---|---|
| Citrus Bioflavonoids, Inositol, Choline Bitartrate, Rutin, Alfalfa Leaf Powder, Lecithin (Soy), Parsley Leaf Powder, Watercress Powder. | | |

\* Daily Value not established

includes green leafy vegetables as well as the usual meats, vegetables, dairy products, and carbohydrates. If that isn't enough, we may include a multivitamin on a daily basis. A typical multivitamin includes (besides vitamins) all of the trace elements, usually referred to as minerals, that we need. Actually, the minerals are not present as free elements but rather as components of a compound. For example, the most common calcium supplement is actually calcium carbonate ($CaCO_3$). In nature, $CaCO_3$ is known as limestone, chalk, or marble.

The essential element, the name of the compound containing the element, and its formula are shown in the accompanying table. Except for boric acid, all of the compounds shown are ionic. All are solid compounds that can be included in a solid pill.

| ELEMENT | NAME OF COMPOUND | FORMULA OF COMPOUND |
|---|---|---|
| Boron (B) | boric acid | $H_3BO_3$ |
| Calcium (Ca) | calcium carbonate | $CaCO_3$ |
| | calcium citrate | $Ca_3(C_6H_5O_7)_2$ |
| Chromium (Cr) | chromic chloride | $CrCl_3$ |
| Copper (Cu) | cupric sulfate | $CuSO_4$ |
| | cupric gluconate | $Cu(C_6H_{11}O_7)_2$ |
| Iodine (I) | sodium iodide | $NaI$ |
| Iron (Fe) | ferrous sulfate | $FeSO_4$ |
| | ferrous fumarate | $FeC_4H_2O_4$ |
| | ferrous gluconate | $Fe(C_6H_{11}O_7)_2$ |
| Magnesium (Mg) | magnesium oxide | $MgO$ |
| Phosphorus (P) | calcium phosphate | $Ca_3(PO_4)_2$ |

Refer to the Student Workshop at the end of the chapter.

## PART B   SUMMARY

### KEY TERMS

| | |
|---|---|
| 2-5 | A sample of a particular element or compound is known as a **pure substance**. p. 68 |
| 2-5.2 | **Molecular compounds** are composed of discrete **molecules**. p. 68 |
| 2-5.2 | The atoms in molecules are held together by **covalent bonds**. p. 68 |
| 2-5.3 | The **formula** of a molecular compound indicates the number of atoms of each element in one molecule. p. 69 |
| 2-5.3 | The **structural formula** of a compound shows the position of the atoms relative to each other. p. 69 |
| 2-6.1 | **Ions** are charged species that are either **cations** (positive) or **anions** (negative). p. 70 |
| 2-6.3 | **Ionic compounds** are held together by **ionic bonds**, which are electrostatic interactions between positive and negative ions. p. 71 |
| 2-6.3 | A **formula unit** of an ionic compound contains the simplest whole-number ratio of ions that balances the positive and negative charge. p. 72 |
| 2-6.4 | Ionic compounds may contain **polyatomic ions**, which are groups of atoms that are held together by covalent bonds but that have a positive or negative charge. p. 73 |

### SUMMARY CHART

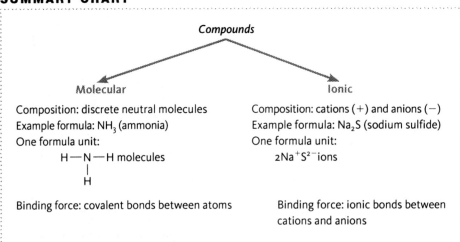

*Compounds*

**Molecular**

Composition: discrete neutral molecules
Example formula: $NH_3$ (ammonia)
One formula unit:

$$H—N—H \text{ molecules}$$
$$|$$
$$H$$

Binding force: covalent bonds between atoms

**Ionic**

Composition: cations (+) and anions (−)
Example formula: $Na_2S$ (sodium sulfide)
One formula unit:

$2Na^+ S^{2-}$ ions

Binding force: ionic bonds between cations and anions

---

### CHAPTER 2 SYNTHESIS PROBLEM

This chapter presents a wealth of information about the basic forms of matter—elements and compounds—and their composition. The purpose of this problem is to apply the information from Chapter 2 in some detective work to eventually establish the formula of an ionic compound and some additional information about the cation. Here are the facts. An ion of an element has 12 protons and 10 electrons. This cation forms a compound with a polyatomic anion that has a −3 charge and a total of 68 electrons. The anion is composed of four oxygen atoms and one atom of another element. An isotope of the cation has a mass of $4.34 \times 10^{-23}$ g and has an 11.01% abundance in nature.

| PROBLEM | SOLUTION |
|---|---|
| **a.** Write the symbol of the cation and its charge. | **a.** The cation has 12 protons, which is its atomic number. From inside the front cover (or the periodic table), we find that this is the element magnesium (symbol Mg). Since it has two fewer electrons than protons, it has a +2 charge. The ion is $Mg^{2+}$. |
| **b.** Write the formula of the anion including its charge. | **b.** (See Section 2-6.4.) Four neutral oxygen atoms have a total of $4 \times 8 = 32$ electrons. If the ion has a −3 charge, it has three additional electrons plus those of the neutral oxygen atoms (i.e., $32 + 3$). The other element thus has $68 - 35 = 33$ electrons. This is the element arsenic (As). The anion is $AsO_4^{3-}$. |

| **c.** What is the formula of the compound formed from these two ions? | **c.** Three cations $(3 \times +2 = +6)$ are needed to balance two anions $(2 \times -3 = -6)$. Parentheses are needed for the polyatomic anion. The formula of the compound is $$Mg_3(AsO_4)_2$$ |
| --- | --- |
| **d.** How many neutrons are in the isotope of the cation described above? (Refer to Table 2-3.) | **d.** From Table 2-3, notice that neutrons and protons each weigh about $1.67 \times 10^{-24}$ g/am. Therefore, the mass of the isotope in amu is about $$4.34 \times 10^{-23} \text{ g}/1.67 \times 10^{-24} \text{ g/amu} = 26.0 \text{ amu}.$$ The total of neutrons and protons is therefore 26. There are $26 - 12 = \underline{14 \text{ neutrons}}$. |
| **e.** What is the approximate mass in amu that the isotope described above contributes to the atomic mass of the element? | **e.** The mass contribution in amu to three significant figures is this mass times its abundance in decimal fraction form. $$26.0 \text{ amu} \times 0.1101 = \underline{2.86 \text{ amu}}$$ |

**YOUR TURN**

A common element forms a monatomic cation with a charge of +3. This cation has a total of 23 electrons. It forms a compound with a polyatomic anion that is composed of one chromium atom and four oxygen atoms with a total of 58 electrons. The cation has an isotope with a mass of $9.35 \times 10^{-23}$ g and has an abundance of 91.8% in nature.

    **a.** What is the symbol of the cation and its charge?

    **b.** Write the formula of the anion and its charge.

    **c.** What is the formula of the compound formed from these two ions?

    **d.** How many neutrons are in the isotope of the cation described above?

    **e.** What is the approximate mass in amu that the isotope described above contributes to the atomic mass of the element?

Answers are on p. 79.

# CHAPTER SUMMARY

All of the various forms of nature around us, from the simple elements in the air to the complex **compounds** of living systems, are composed of only a few basic forms of matter called **elements**. Each element has a name and a unique one- or two-letter **symbol**.

A little more than 200 years ago, John Dalton's **atomic theory** introduced the concept that elements are composed of fundamental particles called **atoms**. It has been about 30 years since we have been able to produce images of these atoms with a special microscope.

The atom is the smallest unique particle that characterizes an element. It is composed of more basic particles called **electrons** and **nucleons**. There are two types of nucleons, **protons** and **neutrons**. The relative charges and masses of these three particles are summarized in Table 2-3. The proton and electron are attracted to each other by **electrostatic forces**.

Rather than being a hard sphere, an atom is mostly empty space containing the negatively charged electrons. The protons and neutrons are located in a small dense core called the **nucleus**. The number of protons in an atom is known as its **atomic number**, which distinguishes the atoms of one element from those of another. The total number of nucleons in an atom is known as its **mass number**. Atoms of the same element may have different mass numbers and are known as **isotopes** of that element. An atom is neutral because it has the same number of electrons as protons.

Since protons and neutrons do not have exactly the same mass, the mass number is not an exact measure of the comparative masses of isotopes. A more precise measure of mass is the **isotopic mass**. This is obtained by comparing the mass of the particular isotope with the mass of $^{12}C$, which is defined as having a mass of exactly 12 **atomic mass units** (amu). The **atomic mass** of an element is the weighted average of all of the naturally occurring isotopes found in nature.

Most elements are present in nature as aggregates of individual atoms. In some elements, however, two or more atoms are combined by **covalent bonds** to produce basic units called **molecules. Molecular compounds** are also composed of molecules, although, in this case, the atoms of at least two different elements are involved. The **formula** of a molecular compound represents the actual number of atoms of each element contained in a molecular unit. Each compound has a unique arrangement of atoms in the molecular unit. These are sometimes conveniently represented by **structural formulas.**

There is another type of compound, however. Atoms can become electrically charged to form **ions.** An atom can have a net positive charge if there are fewer electrons than protons in the nucleus or a net negative charge when there are more electrons than protons. Groups of atoms that are covalently bonded together can also have a net charge and are known as **polyatomic ions.** An **ionic compound** is composed of **cations** (positive ions) and **anions** (negative ions). The interactions of cations and anions are known as **ionic bonds.** The formula of an ionic compound shows the type and number of ions

in a **formula unit.** A formula unit represents the smallest whole-number ratio of cations and anions, which reflects the fact that the positive charge is balanced by the negative charge. The four most common ways that we find atoms in nature are summarized as follows:

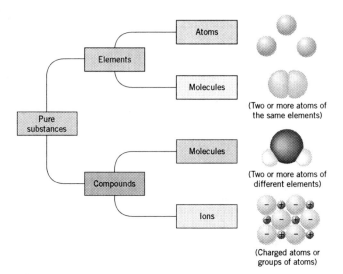

(Two or more atoms of the same elements)

(Two or more atoms of different elements)

(Charged atoms or groups of atoms)

## OBJECTIVES

| SECTION | YOU SHOULD BE ABLE TO... | EXAMPLES | EXERCISES | CHAPTER PROBLEMS |
|---------|--------------------------|----------|-----------|------------------|
| 2-1 | List the names and symbols of common elements. | | 1a, 1b, 1c, 1d, 1e, 1f, 1g | 1, 5, 6, 7, 31, 32, 34 |
| 2-2 | List the postulates of the atomic theory. | | 2a, 2b, 2c | 8 |
| 2-3 | List the components of an atom and their relative masses, charges, and location in the atom. | | 3a, 3b, 3c, 3d | 9, 10 |
| 2-4 | From the percent abundance of specific isotopes of an element, determine the atomic mass of the element and the number of protons, neutrons and electrons in each isotope. | 2-1, 2-2 | 4a, 4b, 4c, 4d, 4e, 4f, 4g | 11, 13, 14, 18, 19, 22, 26, 27, 28 |
| 2-5 | List the characteristics of compounds composed of molecules. | | | 44, 45, 56, 63 |
| 2-6 | Write the formulas of simple ionic compounds given the charges on the ions. | 2-3, 2-4 | 6a, 6d, 6e | 39, 41, 43, 46, 50 |

## ▶ ANSWERS TO ASSESSING THE OBJECTIVES

### Part A
**EXERCISES**

**2-1 {a}** Look at the table of elements inside the front cover. If the substance is present, it is an element. **(a)** element **(b)** compound (made from Na, C, H, and O) **(c)** compound (made from H and O) **(d)** compound (made from Si and O) **(e)** element

**2-1 {b} (a)** Cu **(b)** S **(c)** Ca

**2-1 {c} (a)** lead **(b)** phosphorus **(c)** sodium

**2-1 {d}** Compounds are combinations of elements. How many different ways can 120 objects be combined? Theoretically, there are an infinite number of combinations. The actual number is in the tens of millions, with new ones created every day.

**2-1 {e}** The elements with Latin roots for their names and symbols were likely discovered in ancient times (like gold). Since technology was not as advanced back then, it stands to reason that those elements must be the most stable and the most easily found in their free state.

**2-1 {f}** You would have to run some sort of chemical test on it to see if it could be broken down any further. If test after test failed to break the substance down any further, you might begin to assume that the unknown substance was an element.

**2-2 {a}** *An element* is composed of small, indivisible particles called *atoms*. Atoms of the same *element* are identical and have the same *properties*. Chemical *compounds* are composed of atoms of different elements combined in small *whole-number* ratios. Chemical *reactions* are rearrangements of *atoms* into different combinations.

**2-2 {b}** **(a)** True. If all atoms of an element are identical, then an experiment should always yield the same result. **(b)** False. Even though compounds have specific whole number ratios of atoms, nothing prohibits them from combining in different numbers to form a different compound. **(c)** True. Indivisible means indivisible, at least as far as chemical properties are concerned. **(d)** True. The rearrangement that occurs in a chemical reaction ensures that no atoms disappear, nor are any atoms formed, in the reaction.

**2-2 {c}** Democritus, the philosopher, based his ideas on nothing more than rational thought. Dalton used experimental evidence to support his conclusions. These conclusions have stood up to 200 years of scrutiny.

**2-3 {a}** **(a)** electron **(b)** proton and neutron **(c)** neutron (just barely) **(d)** proton

**2-3 {b}**

| PARTICLE | MASS (AMU) | CHARGE | LOCATION |
|----------|-----------|--------|----------|
| Proton | 1 | +1 | Nucleus |
| Neutron | 1 | Neutral | Nucleus |
| Electron | 0 | −1 | Outside nucleus |

**2-3 {c}** **(a)** Virtually all of the mass is in the nucleus with the protons and neutrons. **(b)** The electrons take up most of the volume. **(c)** The electron was first to be identified by Thompson in 1897. Its existence implied the proton. The neutron was the last identified.

**2-3 {d}** Neutrons are neutrally charged, which is what would happen if a positive proton and negative electron combined into one particle. Also, the mass of the neutron is just a little more than the combined mass of the proton and the electron.

**2-4 {a}** **(a)** atomic number and mass number **(b)** mass number **(c)** isotopic mass **(d)** atomic number **(e)** mass number

**2-4 {b}** The protons are determined by matching an elemental symbol to its atomic number. The numbers of electrons in these neutral species are the same. The number of neutrons is equal to the difference between the atomic number and the mass number. **(a)** protons = 6, neutrons = 7, electrons = 6 **(b)** protons = 1, neutrons = 0, electrons = 1 **(c)** protons = 92, neutrons = 146, electrons = 92

**2-4 {c}** **(a)** $^{19}F$ **(b)** $^{79}Br$ **(c)** $^{40}Ca$

**2-4 {d}** $(120.903 \times 0.573) + (122.904 \times 0.427) = 122$

**2-4 {e}** $(6.015 \times 0.0742) + (7.016 \times 0.9258) = 6.94$. Compare this answer to lithium's atomic mass on the periodic table. It's a match.

**2-4 {f}** Lead and gold are both elements with their own sets of protons, neutrons, and electrons. To convert one element to another, these three particles, and specifically the number of protons, would have to change. There is no chemical way to add or subtract protons from the nucleus of an atom.

**2-4 {g}** The weighted average (atomic mass) of the two isotopes is 79.9, or almost 80. This is halfway between the two isotopes. It stands to reason that each isotope contributes roughly evenly to the mass number. Therefore, the percentage abundance of each is nearly 50%.

Part B

**EXERCISES**

**2-6 {a}** **(a)** ionic **(b)** both **(c)** molecular **(d)** both **(e)** ionic **(f)** molecular

**2-6 {b}** **(a)** $MgI_2$ **(b)** $Li_2SO_4$ **(c)** $Al_2Se_3$ **(d)** $NaHCO_3$

**2-6 {c}**

|  | $Cs^+$ | $Zn^{2+}$ | $Fe^{3+}$ |
|---|--------|-----------|-----------|
| $ClO_3^-$ | $CsClO_3$ | $Zn(ClO_3)_2$ | $Fe(ClO_3)_3$ |
| $O^{2-}$ | $Cs_2O$ | $ZnO$ | $Fe_2O_3$ |
| $PO_4^{3-}$ | $Cs_3PO_4$ | $Zn_3(PO_4)_2$ | $FePO_4$ |

**2-6 {d}** In ionic compounds, atoms are present in the smallest whole-number ratio. If this were an ionic compound, the formula would be $CH_2O$. Since the formula is six times bigger, it must be molecular.

**2-6 {e}** No, not nearly. Two or more compounds can share the same formula, but the order of their bonds might be quite different. Further tests would be required to establish the identity of the substance beyond a reasonable doubt.

**ANSWERS TO CHAPTER SYNTHESIS PROBLEM**

**a.** $Fe^{3+}$  **b.** $CrO_4^{2-}$  **c.** $Fe_2(CrO_4)_3$  **d.** 30 neutrons  **e.** 51.4 amu

## CHAPTER PROBLEMS

*Throughout the text, answers to all exercises in color are given in Appendix E. The more difficult exercises are marked with an asterisk.*

### Names and Symbols of the Elements (SECTION 2-1)

**2-1.** Write the symbols of the following elements. Try to do this without referring to a table of elements.

(a) bromine    (c) lead    (e) sodium

(b) oxygen    (d) tin    (f) sulfur

**2-2.** The following elements all have symbols that begin with the letter C: cadmium, calcium, californium, carbon, cerium, cesium, chlorine, chromium, cobalt, copper, and curium. The symbols are C, Ca, Cd, Ce, Cf, Cl, Cm, Co, Cr, Cs, and Cu. Match each symbol with an element and then check with the table of elements inside the front cover.

**2-3.** The names of seven elements begin with the letter B. What are their names and symbols?

**2-4.** The names of nine elements begin with the letter S. What are their names and symbols?

**2-5.** Using the table inside the front cover, write the symbols for the following elements.

(a) barium    (c) cesium    (e) manganese

(b) neon    (d) platinum    (f) tungsten

**2-6.** Name the elements corresponding to the following symbols. Try to do this without reference to a table of the elements.

(a) S    (c) Fe    (e) Mg

(b) K    (d) N    (f) Al

**2-7.** Using the table, name the elements corresponding to the following symbols.

(a) B    (c) Ge    (e) Co    (g) Be

(b) Bi    (d) U    (f) Hg    (h) As

### Composition of the Atom (SECTIONS 2-2 AND 2-3)

**2-8.** Which of the following were not part of Dalton's atomic theory?

(a) Atoms are the basic building blocks of nature.

(b) Atoms are composed of electrons, neutrons, and protons.

(c) Atoms are reshuffled in chemical reactions.

(d) The atoms of an element are identical.

(e) Different isotopes can exist for the same element.

**2-9.** Which of the following describes a neutron?

(a) +1 charge, mass 1 amu    (c) 0 charge, mass 1 amu

(b) +1 charge, mass 0 amu    (d) −1 charge, mass 0 amu

**2-10.** Which of the following describes an electron?

(a) +1 charge, mass 1 amu    (c) −1 charge, mass 1 amu

(b) +1 charge, mass 0 amu    (d) −1 charge, mass 0 amu

**2-11.** Give the mass numbers and atomic numbers of the following isotopes. Refer to the table of the elements inside the front cover.

(a) $^{193}$Au    (b) $^{132}$Te    (c) $^{118}$I    (d) $^{39}$CI

**2-12.** Give the numbers of protons, neutrons, and electrons in each of the following isotopes. Refer to the table of the elements inside the front cover.

(a) $^{45}$Sc    (b) $^{232}$Th    (c) $^{223}$Fr    (d) $^{90}$Sr

**2-13.** Three isotopes of uranium are $^{234}$U, $^{235}$U, and $^{238}$U. How many protons, neutrons, and electrons are in each isotope?

**2-14.** Using the table of elements inside the front cover, complete the following table for neutral isotopes.

| Isotope | Isotopic Notation | Atomic Number | Mass Number | Subatomic Particles Protons | Neutrons | Electrons |
|---|---|---|---|---|---|---|
| molybdenum-96 | $^{96}_{42}$Mo | 42 | 96 | 42 | 54 | 42 |
| (a) | $^{?}_{?}$Ag | | | | 61 | |
| (b) | | 14 | | | 14 | |
| (c) | | | 39 | | 20 | |
| (d) cerium-140 | | | | | | |
| (e) | | | | | 26 | 30 |
| (f) | | 50 | 110 | | | |
| (g) | $^{118}_{?}$I | | | | | |
| (h) mercury-? | | | | | 116 | |

**2-15.** Using the table of elements inside the front cover, complete the following table for neutral isotopes.

| Isotope | Isotopic Notation | Atomic Number | Mass Number | Subatomic Particles Protons | Neutrons | Electrons |
|---|---|---|---|---|---|---|
| (a) tungsten-? | | | 184 | | | |
| (b) | | | | | 12 | 11 |
| (c) | $^{200}_{?}$Au | | | | | |
| (d) | $^{?}_{?}$Pm | | | | 87 | |
| (e) | | | 109 | 46 | | |
| (f) | | | 48 | | | 23 |
| (g) | | 21 | | | 29 | |

**2-16.** Write the isotopic notation for an isotope of cobalt that has the same number of neutrons as $^{60}$Ni.

**2-17.** Write the isotopic notation for an isotope of uranium that has the same number of neutrons as $^{240}$Pu.

### Atomic Number and Mass (SECTION 2-4)

**2-18.** How do the following concepts relate and differ?

(a) element and atomic number

(b) atomic mass and atomic number

(c) mass number and atomic mass

(d) isotopes and number of protons

(e) isotopes and number of neutrons

2-19. Determine the atomic number and the atomic mass of each of the following elements. Use the table inside the front cover.

(a) Re      (b) Co      (c) Br      (d) Si

2-20. About 75% of a U.S. "nickel" is an element with an atomic mass of 63.546 amu. What is the element?

**2-21.** White gold is a mixture of gold containing an element with an atomic mass of 106.4 amu. What is the element?

2-22. The elements O, N, Si, and Ca are among several that are composed *primarily* of one isotope. Using the table inside the front cover, write the atomic number and mass number of the principal isotope of each of these elements.

**2-23.** The atomic mass of hydrogen is given inside the front cover as 1.00794. The three isotopes of hydrogen are $^1H$, $^2H$, and $^3H$. What does the atomic mass tell us about the relative abundances of the three isotopes?

2-24. A given element has a mass 5.81 times that of $^{12}C$. What is the atomic mass of the element? What is the element?

**2-25.** The atomic mass of a given element is about 3.33 times that of $^{12}C$. Give the atomic mass, the name, and the symbol of the element.

2-26. Bromine is composed of 50.5% $^{79}Br$ and 49.5% $^{81}Br$. The isotopic mass of $^{79}Br$ is 78.92 amu and that of $^{81}Br$ is 80.92 amu. What is the atomic mass of the element?

2-27. Silicon occurs in nature as a mixture of three isotopes: $^{28}Si$ (27.98 amu), $^{29}Si$ (28.98 amu), and $^{30}Si$ (29.97 amu). The mixture is 92.21% $^{28}Si$, 4.70% $^{29}Si$, and 3.09% $^{30}Si$. Calculate the atomic mass of naturally occurring silicon.

**2-28.** Naturally occurring Cu is 69.09% $^{63}Cu$ (62.96 amu). The only other isotope is $^{65}Cu$ (64.96 amu). What is the atomic mass of copper?

*2-29. Chlorine occurs in nature as a mixture of $^{35}Cl$ and $^{37}Cl$. If the isotopic mass of $^{35}Cl$ is approximately 35.0 amu and that of $^{37}Cl$ is 37.0 amu, and the atomic mass of the mixture as it occurs in nature is 35.5 amu, what is the proportion of the two isotopes?

*2-30. The atomic mass of the element gallium is 69.72 amu. If it is composed of two isotopes, $^{69}Ga$ (68.926 amu) and $^{71}Ga$ (70.925 amu), what is the percent of $^{69}Ga$?

## Molecular Compounds and Formulas (SECTION 2-5)

2-31. How do the following concepts relate and differ?

(a) a molecule and an atom

(b) a molecule and a compound

(c) an element and a compound

(d) a molecular element and a monatomic element

2-32. Which of the following are formulas of elements rather than compounds?

(a) $P_4O_{10}$      (c) $F_2O$      (e) $MgO$

(b) $Br_2$      (d) $S_8$      (f) $P_4$

2-33. Name all of the elements shown in the previous problem.

2-34. What is the difference between Hf and HF?

**2-35.** What is the difference between NO and No?

2-36. Which of the following is the formula of a diatomic element? Which is the formula of a diatomic compound?

(a) $NO_2$      (c) $K_2O$      (e) $N_2$

(b) $CO$      (d) $(NH_4)_2S$      (f) $CO_2$

**2-37.** Give the name and number of atoms of each element in the formulas of the following compounds.

(a) $H_2SeO_3$      (c) $NI_3$      (e) $Ba(BrO_3)_2$

(b) $Na_4SiO_4$      (d) $NiI_2$      (f) $B_3N_3(CH_3)_6$

**2-38.** What is the total number of atoms in each formula unit for the compounds in problem 2-37?

2-39. Determine the number of atoms of each element in the formulas of the following compounds.

(a) $C_6H_4Cl_2$

(b) $C_2H_5OH$ (ethyl alcohol)

(c) $CuSO_4 \cdot 9H_2O$ ($H_2O$'s are part of a single formula unit)

(d) $C_9H_8O_4$ (aspirin)

(e) $Al_2(SO_4)_3$

(f) $(NH_4)_2CO_3$

2-40. What is the total number of atoms in each molecule or formula unit for the compounds listed in problem 2-39?

2-41. How many carbon atoms are in each molecule or formula unit of the following compounds?

(a) $C_8H_{18}$ (octane in gasoline)      (c) $Fe(C_2O_4)_2$

(b) $NaC_7H_4O_3NS$ (saccharin)      (d) $Al_2(CO_3)_3$

2-42. Write the formulas of the following molecular compounds.

(a) sulfur dioxide (one sulfur and two oxygen atoms)

(b) carbon dioxide (one carbon and two oxygen atoms)

(c) sulfuric acid (two hydrogens, one sulfur, and four oxygen atoms)

(d) acetylene (two carbons and two hydrogens)

**2-43.** Write the formulas of the following molecular compounds.

(a) phosphorus trichloride (one phosphorus and three chlorines)

(b) naphthalene (ten carbons and eight hydrogens)

(c) dibromine trioxide (two bromines and three oxygens)

## Ions and Ionic Compounds (SECTION 2-6)

**2-44.** How do the following concepts relate and differ?

**(a)** an atom and an ion

**(b)** a molecule and a polyatomic ion

**(c)** a cation and an anion

**(d)** a molecular and an ionic compound

**(e)** a molecular unit and an ionic formula unit

**2-45.** The gaseous compound HF contains covalent bonds, and the compound KF contains ionic bonds. Sketch how the basic particles of these two compounds appear.

**2-46.** Write the formulas of the following ionic compounds.

**(a)** calcium perchlorate (one $Ca^{2+}$ and two $ClO_4^-$ ions)

**(b)** ammonium phosphate (three $NH_4^+$ ions and one $PO_4^{3-}$ ion)

**(c)** iron(II) sulfate (one $Fe^{2+}$ and one $SO_4^{2-}$ ion)

**2-47.** What is the number of atoms of each element present in the compounds in problem 2-46?

**2-48.** Write the formulas of the following ionic compounds.

**(a)** calcium hypochlorite (one $Ca^{2+}$ ion and two $ClO^-$ ions)

**(b)** magnesium phosphate (three $Mg^{2+}$ ions and two $PO_4^{3-}$ ions)

**(c)** chromium(III) oxalate (two $Cr^{3+}$ ions and three $C_2O_4^{2-}$ ions)

**2-49.** What is the number of atoms of each element present in the compounds in problem 2-48?

**2-50.** The formula of an ionic compound indicates one $Fe^{2+}$ ion combined with one anion. Which of the following could be the other ion?

**(a)** $F^-$ **(b)** $Ca^{2+}$ **(c)** $S^{2-}$ **(d)** $N^{3-}$

**2-51.** An ionic compound is composed of two $ClO_4^-$ ions and one cation. Which of the following could be the other ion?

**(a)** $SO_4^{2-}$ **(b)** $Ni^{2+}$ **(c)** $Al^{3+}$ **(d)** $Na^+$

**2-52.** An ionic compound is composed of one $SO_3^{2-}$ and two cations. Which of the following could be the cations?

**(a)** $I^-$ **(b)** $Ba^{2+}$ **(c)** $Fe^{3+}$ **(d)** $Li^+$

**2-53.** An ionic compound is composed of two $Al^{3+}$ ions and three anions. Which of the following could be the anions?

**(a)** $S^{2-}$ **(b)** $Cl^-$ **(c)** $Sr^{2+}$ **(d)** $N^{3-}$

**2-54.** Write the formulas of the compounds in problems 2-50 and 2-52.

**2-55.** Write the formulas of the compounds in problems 2-51 and 2-53.

**2-56.** Explain the difference between $SO_3$ and $SO_3^{2-}$. Which one would be a gas?

**2-57.** What are the total number of protons and the total number of electrons in each of the following ions?

**(a)** $K^+$ **(c)** $S^{2-}$ **(e)** $Al^{3+}$

**(b)** $Br^-$ **(d)** $NO_2^-$ **(f)** $NH_4^+$

**2-58.** What are the total number of protons and the total number of electrons in each of the following ions?

**(a)** $Sr^{2+}$ **(c)** $V^{3+}$ **(e)** $SO_3^{2-}$

**(b)** $P^{3-}$ **(d)** $NO^+$

**2-59.** Write the element symbol or symbols and the charge for the following ions.

**(a)** 20 protons and 18 electrons

**(b)** 52 protons and 54 electrons

**(c)** one phosphorus and three oxygens with a total of 42 electrons

**(d)** one nitrogen and two oxygens with a total of 22 electrons

**2-60.** Write the element symbol or symbols and the charge for the following ions.

**(a)** 50 protons and 48 electrons

**(b)** 53 protons and 54 electrons

**(c)** one aluminum and two oxygens with a total of 30 electrons

**(d)** one chlorine and three fluorines with a total of 43 electrons

**2-61.** A monatomic bromine species has 36 electrons. Does it exist independently?

**2-62.** A species is composed of one chlorine atom chemically bonded to two oxygen atoms. It has a total of 33 electrons. Is this species most likely a gaseous molecular compound or part of an ionic compound?

## General Problems

**2-63.** Describe the difference between a molecular and an ionic compound. Of the two types of compounds discussed, is a stone more likely to be a molecular or an ionic compound? Is a liquid more likely to be a molecular or an ionic compound?

**2-64.** Write the symbol, mass number, atomic number, and electrical charge of the element given the following information. Refer to the table of the elements.

**(a)** An ion of Sr contains 36 electrons and 52 neutrons.

**(b)** An ion contains 24 protons, 28 neutrons, and 21 electrons.

**(c)** An ion contains 36 electrons and 45 neutrons and has a −2 charge.

**(d)** An ion of nitrogen contains 7 neutrons and 10 electrons.

**(e)** An ion contains 54 electrons and 139 nucleons and has a +3 charge.

**2-65.** Write the symbol, mass number, atomic number, and electrical charge of the element given the following information. Refer to the table of the elements.

**(a)** An ion of Sn contains 68 neutrons and 48 electrons.

**(b)** An ion contains 204 nucleons and 78 electrons and has a +3 charge.

**(c)** An ion contains 45 neutrons and 36 electrons and has a −1 charge.

**(d)** An ion of aluminum has 14 neutrons and a +3 charge.

2-66. Give the number of protons, electrons, and neutrons represented by the following species. These elements are composed almost entirely of one isotope, which is implied by the atomic mass.

**(a)** Na and $Na^+$  **(c)** F and $F^-$

**(b)** Ca and $Ca^{2+}$  **(d)** Sc and $Sc^{3+}$

**2-67.** Give the number of protons, electrons, and neutrons represented by the following species. These elements are composed almost entirely of one isotope, which is implied by the atomic mass.

**(a)** Cr and $Cr^{2+}$  **(c)** I and $I^-$

**(b)** Au and $Au^{3+}$  **(d)** P and $P^{3-}$

*2-68. An isotope of iodine has a mass number that is 10 amu less than two-thirds the mass number of an isotope of thallium. The total mass number of the two isotopes is 340 amu. What is the mass number of each isotope? (*Hint:* There are two equations and two unknowns.)

*2-69. An isotope of gallium has a mass number that is 22 amu more than one-fourth the mass number of an isotope of osmium. The osmium isotope is 122 amu heavier than the gallium isotope. What is the mass number of each isotope? (*Hint:* There are two equations and two unknowns.)

*2-70. A given element is composed of 57.5% of an isotope with an isotopic mass of 120.90 amu. The remaining percentage of isotope has an isotopic mass of 122.90 amu. What

is the atomic mass of the element? What is the element? How many electrons are in a cation of this element if it has a charge of 3? How many neutrons are in each of the two isotopes of this element? What percent of the isotopic mass of each isotope is due to neutrons?

2-71. A given isotope has a mass number of 196, and 60.2% of the nucleons are neutrons. How many electrons are in a cation of this element if it has a charge of 2?

**2-72.** A given isotope has a mass number of 206. The isotope has 51.2% more neutrons than protons. What is the element?

2-73. A given molecular compound is composed of one atom of nitrogen and one atom of another element. The mass of nitrogen accounts for 46.7% of the mass of one molecule. What is the other element? What is the formula of the compound? This molecule can lose one electron to form a polyatomic ion. How many electrons are in this ion?

**2-74.** A given molecular compound is composed of one atom of carbon and two atoms of another element. The mass of carbon accounts for 15.8% of the mass of one molecule. What is the other element? What is the formula of the compound?

2-75. If the isotopic mass of $^{12}C$ were defined as exactly 8 instead of 12, what would be the atomic mass of the following elements to three significant figures? Assume that the elements have the same masses relative to each other as before: that is, hydrogen still has a mass of one-twelfth that of carbon.

**(a)** H  **(b)** N  **(c)** Na  **(d)** Ca

2-76. Assume that the isotopic mass of $^{12}C$ is defined as exactly 10 and that the atomic mass of an element is 43.3 amu on this basis. What is the element?

**2-77.** Assume that the isotopic mass of $^{12}C$ is defined as exactly 20 instead of 12 and that the atomic mass of an element is 212.7 amu on this basis. What is the element?

STUDENT WORKSHOP ──────────────

### Chemical Formulas

**Purpose: To evaluate chemical compounds for their composition, and to create new compounds from their constituent parts. (Work in groups of three or four. Estimated time: 25 min.)**

Divide up the compounds listed in Making It Real, "Ionic Compounds and Essential Elements," so that each person has three or four. Using a periodic table, do the following:

- Name the elements found in each compound.
- Determine how many atoms of each element are contained within each compound.

- Calculate the total number of protons in each compound.
- Do the same for the number of neutrons. (You should assume that the isotope present is the one with the closest integer value to the mass number found on the periodic table.)
- Determine whether the compound contains a polyatomic ion.

Now, using the following ions (all found in the compounds above), construct three or four new compounds each, with the necessary numbers to make their formulas neutral.

Cations:  $H^+$  $Cr^{2+}$  $Cu^{2+}$  $Na^+$  $Fe^{2+}$  $Mg^{2+}$  $Ca^{2+}$

Anions:  $BO_3^{3-}$  $CO_3^{2-}$  $I^-$  $SO_4^{2-}$  $O^{2-}$  $PO_4^{3-}$

# The Periodic Table and Chemical Nomenclature

The periodic table allows the chemist to systematize and categorize the elements. It is also used for the naming of compounds formed by the elements. The vast amount of information presented in this table and its use in naming compounds are the subjects of this chapter.

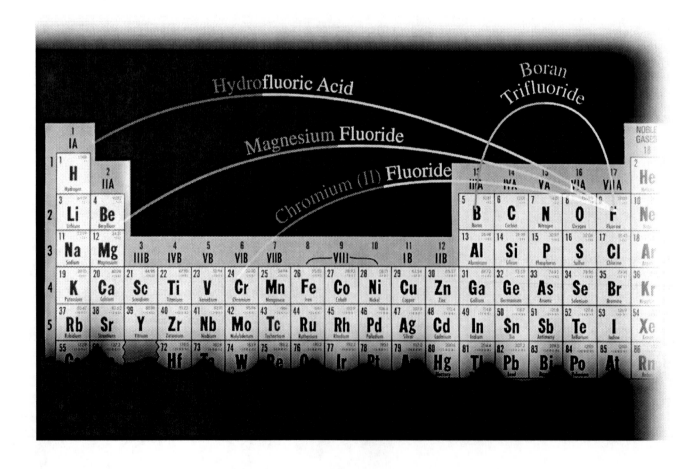

# SETTING THE STAGE

In any geography course we would certainly find a globe of the earth. Let's consider the location of two cities on the globe that are in the United States: Duluth, Minnesota, and Miami, Florida. We can make some fairly good observations just from their respective locations. On one hand, we would predict that in December, Duluth would have short days and a ton of snow. On the other hand, Miami is located far to the south and so we would predict it to have longer days and maybe warm, beach-like weather at this time of the year. Is there anything for chemistry students that would be as useful as a globe is to geography students? Indeed there is. It is known as the *Periodic Table of the Elements*. By locating an element on the table, we can predict many of its physical and chemical properties. It brings much order to the huge number of facts inherent to this science. It is no wonder that we find this magnificent table in almost any chemistry lab or lecture hall.

Along with the periodic table, chemists are also known for their own language and vocabulary for the over 10 million known compounds. The vocabulary of chemistry is known as *chemical nomenclature*. Like any other language, learning chemical nomenclature requires organization and, of course, some memorization.

These two topics, the periodic table and chemical nomenclature, may at first seem unrelated. In fact, to properly name many compounds we need access to some information displayed by a periodic table.

In Part A of this chapter we will present the periodic table and much of the information it displays. We will put the periodic table to use in Part B by writing formulas and naming compounds.

## Part A

## Relationships Among the Elements and the Periodic Table

**SETTING A GOAL**

■ You will be able to explain the significance of the periodic table, its origins, and how different properties of an element can be predicted by its location on the table.

**OBJECTIVES**

4-1 Describe the origins of the periodic table and locate the metals and nonmetals.

4-2 Using the periodic table, identify a specific element with its group number and name, period, and physical state.

▶ **OBJECTIVE FOR SECTION 4-1**
Describe the origins of the periodic table and locate the metals and nonmetals.

# 4-1 The Origin of the Periodic Table

**LOOKING AHEAD!** It had been known for centuries that there were chemical similarities among certain elements. How these similarities led to a chart called the periodic table is the subject of this section. ■

### 4-1.1 Construction of the Periodic Table

Ever since ancient times, it has been known that the properties of the elements were not all completely random. There were strong similarities among certain elements so that they could be grouped into several *families*. For example, one family of elements is composed of copper, silver, and gold. These were known as the *noble metals* and were found in the free state in nature. They are chemically unreactive so they have been used in coins and jewelry for thousands of years. (See Figure 4-1.) Three other elements—lithium, sodium, and potassium — were members of a different family and are known as the *active metals*. Their properties were very distinct from the noble metals. They are chemically reactive and as a result are found only as parts of compounds in nature.

In the middle of the 19th century, two scientists realized that elements in families were related in a periodic fashion that could be systematized by a table. The earliest version of this table was introduced in 1869 by Dmitri Mendeleev of Russia. Lothar Meyer of Germany independently presented a similar table in 1870. When these two scientists arranged the elements in order of increasing atomic masses (atomic numbers were still unknown), they observed that elements in families appeared at regular (periodic) intervals. The **periodic table** was constructed so that elements in the same families (e.g., Li, Na, and K) fell into vertical columns.

At first this did not always happen. Sometimes the next-heaviest element did not seem to chemically fit in a certain family. For example, the next-heaviest known element after zinc (Zn) was arsenic (As). Arsenic seemed to belong under phosphorus (P), not aluminum (Al). Mendeleev solved this problem by leaving two blank spaces. For example, a space was left under silicon (Si) and above tin (Sn) for what Mendeleev suggested was a yet-undiscovered element. Mendeleev called the missing element "ekasilicon" (meaning one place away from silicon). Later, an element was discovered that had properties intermediate between silicon and tin, as predicted by the location of the blank space. The element was later named germanium (Ge). Gallium (Ga) was eventually discovered and fit comfortably under aluminum.

A second problem involved some misfits when the elements were ordered according to atomic mass. For example, notice that tellurium (number 52, Te) is heavier than iodine (number 53, I). But Mendeleev realized that iodine clearly belonged under bromine and tellurium under selenium, not vice versa. Mendeleev simply reversed the order, suggesting that perhaps the atomic masses reported were in error. (That was known to happen sometimes.) We now know that this problem does not occur when the elements are listed in order of increasing atomic number

**FIGURE 4-1 Silver and Gold** With a little polish, these gold and silver coins regained their original luster after three centuries at the bottom of the ocean.

## The Modern Periodic Table of the Elements

| | | Atomic number | metal | metalloid | nonmetal | | Noble gases |
|---|---|---|---|---|---|---|---|

*(Legend: Atomic number, Atomic mass, metal, metalloid, nonmetal, Noble gases)*

| | IA (1) | IIA (2) | | | | | | | | | | | IIIA (13) | IVA (14) | VA (15) | VIA (16) | VIIA (17) | VIIIA (18) |
|---|---|---|---|---|---|---|---|---|---|---|---|---|---|---|---|---|---|---|
| 1 | 1 H 1.00794 | | | | | | | | | | | | | | | | | 2 He 4.00260 |
| 2 | 3 Li 6.941 | 4 Be 9.01218 | | | | | | | | | | | 5 B 10.811 | 6 C 12.011 | 7 N 14.00674 | 8 O 15.9994 | 9 F 18.99840 | 10 Ne 20.1797 |
| 3 | 11 Na 22.98977 | 12 Mg 24.3050 | IIIB (3) | IVB (4) | VB (5) | VIB (6) | VIIB (7) | (8) | (9) | (10) | IB (11) | IIB (12) | 13 Al 26.98154 | 14 Si 28.0855 | 15 P 30.97376 | 16 S 32.066 | 17 Cl 35.4527 | 18 Ar 39.948 |
| 4 | 19 K 39.0983 | 20 Ca 40.078 | 21 Sc 44.95591 | 22 Ti 47.88 | 23 V 50.9415 | 24 Cr 51.9961 | 25 Mn 54.9380 | 26 Fe 55.847 | 27 Co 58.93320 | 28 Ni 58.69 | 29 Cu 63.546 | 30 Zn 65.39 | 31 Ga 69.723 | 32 Ge 72.61 | 33 As 74.92159 | 34 Se 78.96 | 35 Br 79.904 | 36 Kr 83.80 |
| 5 | 37 Rb 85.4678 | 38 Sr 87.62 | 39 Y 88.90585 | 40 Zr 91.224 | 41 Nb 92.90638 | 42 Mo 95.94 | 43 Tc 98.9072 | 44 Ru 101.07 | 45 Rh 102.90550 | 46 Pd 106.42 | 47 Ag 107.8682 | 48 Cd 112.411 | 49 In 114.82 | 50 Sn 118.710 | 51 Sb 121.75 | 52 Te 127.60 | 53 I 126.90447 | 54 Xe 131.29 |
| 6 | 55 Cs 132.90543 | 56 Ba 137.327 | 57 *La 138.9055 | 72 Hf 178.49 | 73 Ta 180.9479 | 74 W 183.85 | 75 Re 186.207 | 76 Os 190.2 | 77 Ir 192.22 | 78 Pt 195.08 | 79 Au 196.96654 | 80 Hg 200.59 | 81 Tl 204.3833 | 82 Pb 207.2 | 83 Bi 208.98037 | 84 Po 208.9824 | 85 At 209.9871 | 86 Rn 222.0176 |
| 7 | 87 Fr 223.0197 | 88 Ra 226.0254 | 89 †Ac (227) | 104 Rf (267) | 105 Db (268) | 106 Sg (271) | 107 Bh (272) | 108 Hs (270) | 109 Mt (276) | 110 Ds (281) | 111 Rg (280) | 112 Cn (285) | 113 Uut (284) | 114 Uuq (289) | 115 Uup (288) | 116 Uuh (293) | 117 Uus (294) | 118 Uuo (294) |

| * | 58 Ce 140.115 | 59 Pr 140.90765 | 60 Nd 144.24 | 61 Pm 144.9127 | 62 Sm 150.36 | 63 Eu 151.965 | 64 Gd 157.25 | 65 Tb 158.92534 | 66 Dy 162.50 | 67 Ho 164.93032 | 68 Er 167.26 | 69 Tm 168.93421 | 70 Yb 173.04 | 71 Lu 174.967 |
|---|---|---|---|---|---|---|---|---|---|---|---|---|---|---|
| † | 90 Th 232.0381 | 91 Pa 231.0359 | 92 U 238.0289 | 93 Np 237.0482 | 94 Pu 244.0642 | 95 Am 243.0614 | 96 Cm 247.0703 | 97 Bk 247.0703 | 98 Cf 242.0587 | 99 Es 252.083 | 100 Fm 257.0951 | 101 Md 258.10 | 102 No 259.1009 | 103 Lr 260.105 |

**FIGURE 4-2 The Periodic Table**

instead of atomic mass. This method of ordering conveniently displays the **periodic law**, which states that *the properties of elements are periodic functions of their atomic numbers.*

The modern periodic table is shown in Figure 4-2 and inside the back cover. Before we put it to use, we should be aware of the vast amount of information presented in this table. In a later chapter, we will examine the theoretical foundation for the ordering of the elements in the table.

### 4-1.2 Metals and Nonmetals

It seems like many sciences divide their subject into two categories. Biology studies flora (plants) and fauna (animals). Geology studies the continents and the oceans. Before going forward, we will use the periodic table to locate the two main categories of elements, which are *metals* and *nonmetals*. But first, we will discuss the difference between these two categories. **Metals** *are generally hard, lustrous elements that are malleable* (can be pounded into thin sheets) *and ductile* (can be drawn into wires). (See Figure 4-3.) We also know they readily conduct electricity and heat. Many metals such as iron, copper, and aluminum form the strong framework on which our modern society is built. Recall from the Prologue of this text that the discovery and use of metals over 5000 years ago moved civilization beyond the Stone Age.

The second type of element is noted by its *lack* of metallic properties. These are the nonmetals. **Nonmetals** *are generally gases or soft solids that do not conduct electricity.* (See Figure 4-4.) Notice that the lightest element, hydrogen, is a nonmetal.

There are notable exceptions to the general properties of metals and nonmetals. Still, almost everyone has a general idea of what a metal is like. In addition to these physical properties, there are some very important chemical differences between metals and nonmetals, which we will explore in Chapter 9. The division between metallic

**FIGURE 4-3 Two Properties of Metals** (a) Metals can be pressed into thin sheets (malleable) or (b) drawn into wires (ductile).

and nonmetallic properties is not distinct. Some elements have intermediate properties and are sometimes classified as a separate group called *metalloids*. In most of the discussions in this text, however, we will stick to the two main categories.

The metals and nonmetals are separated by the heavy stair-step line in Figure 4-2. The metals are to the left (about 80% of the elements) and are shown in blue. The nonmetals lie to the right and are shown in pink. The metalloids, on either side of the stair-step line, are shown in orange.

▶ **ASSESSING THE OBJECTIVE FOR SECTION 4-1**

**EXERCISE 4-1(a) LEVEL 1:** Fill in the blanks.
The periodic table was first displayed by _____ in the year _____. Elements are grouped vertically into _____ that share the same _____. _____ are lustrous and malleable. _____ are dull and brittle.

**EXERCISE 4-1(b) LEVEL 2:** Metals conduct electricity. Nonmetals serve as insulators. What electronic properties would metalloids have?

**EXERCISE 4-1(c) LEVEL 3:** Many individuals attempted to create arrangements of atoms that illustrated their repetitive properties. Why did Mendeleev succeed where others had failed?

*For additional practice, work chapter problems 4-1 and 4-2.*

▶ **OBJECTIVE FOR SECTION 4-2**
Using the periodic table, identify a specific element with its group number and name, period, and physical state.

# 4-2 Using the Periodic Table

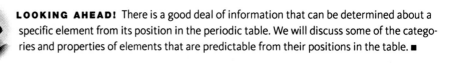

**LOOKING AHEAD!** There is a good deal of information that can be determined about a specific element from its position in the periodic table. We will discuss some of the categories and properties of elements that are predictable from their positions in the table. ■

## 4-2.1 Periods

The periodic table allows us to locate families of elements in vertical columns. In fact, there are common characteristics in the horizontal rows as well. *Horizontal rows of elements in the table are called* **periods**. Each period ends with a member of the family of elements called the *noble gases*. The first period contains only 2 elements, hydrogen and helium. The second and third contain 8 each (Figure 4-4); the fourth and fifth contain 18 each; the sixth and seventh contain 32. The last element synthesized is at the end of the seventh period. Should another element be synthesized in the future it would be in the eighth period.

## 4-2.2 Groups

*Families of elements fall into vertical columns called* **groups**. Each group is designated by a number at the top of the group. The most commonly used label employs Roman numerals followed by an A or a B. Another method, which is becoming more common, numbers the groups 1 through 18. The periodic tables used in the text display both numbering systems. For instructional reasons, however, we will use the traditional method involving Roman numerals along with the letters A and B.

The groups of elements can be classified even further into four main categories of elements.

1. **The Main Group or Representative Elements (Groups IA–VIIA)** Most of the familiar elements that we will discuss and use as examples in this text are **main group** or **representative elements**. These are the elements labeled A in the periodic table. For example, the four main elements of life—carbon, oxygen, nitrogen,

**FIGURE 4-4 Nonmetals** The bottle on the left contains liquid bromine and its vapor. The flask in the back contains pale-green chlorine gas. Solid iodine is in the flask on the right. Powdered red phosphorus is in the dish in the middle, and black powdered graphite (carbon) in the watch glass in front. Lumps of yellow sulfur are shown in the front.

and hydrogen—are in this category. One group of the representative elements includes the highly reactive metals that we discussed earlier. Notice that lithium, sodium, and potassium are found in Group IA. This family of elements (not including hydrogen) is known as the **alkali metals**. Another set of metals that are also somewhat chemically reactive is found in Group IIA and is known as the **alkaline earth metals**. Group VIIA elements are all nonmetals and are known as the **halogens**. The other representative element groups (IIIA, IVA, VA, and VIA) are not generally referred to by a family name but are instead identified by the element at the top of the column. Hence, any element in column VA is part of the nitrogen family. In Chapter 9, we will discuss in more detail some of the physical and chemical properties of the representative elements.

2. **The Noble or Inert Gases (Group VIIIA)** These elements form few chemical compounds. In fact, helium, neon, and argon do not form any compounds. The **noble gases** all exist as individual atoms in nature.

3. **The Transition Metals (Group B Elements)** Transition metals include many of the familiar structural metals, such as iron and chromium, as well as the noble metals—copper, silver, and gold (Group IB)—which we discussed earlier.

4. **The Inner Transition Metals** The 14 **inner transition metals** between lanthanum (number 57) and hafnium (number 72) are known as the **lanthanides**. These metals are also known as the **rare earths** and several of them are essential for uses in sophisticated electronic equipment. Deposits are found mainly in China. The 14 metals between actinium (number 89) and rutherfordium (number 104) are known as the **actinides**. All of the elements are radioactive.

### 4-2.3 Physical States and the Periodic Table

Next we will consider what the periodic table can tell us about the physical state of an element. We must be cautious, however, as to the temperature conditions we define. If the temperature is low enough, all elements exist as solids (except helium); if it is high enough, all elements are in the gaseous state. On Triton, a moon of the planet Neptune, the temperature is −236°C (37 K). The atmosphere is very thin because most substances that are gases under Earth conditions are solids or liquids under Triton conditions. At the outer part of the sun, however, the temperature is 50,000°C, so only gases exist. Thus, we must come to some agreement as to a reference temperature to define the physical state of an element. **Room temperature**, which is defined as exactly *25°C, is the standard reference temperature* used to describe physical state. At this temperature, all three physical states are found among the elements on the periodic table. Fortunately, except for hydrogen, the gaseous elements are all found at the extreme right top of the table (nitrogen, oxygen, fluorine, and chlorine) and in the right-hand vertical column (the noble gases). There are only two liquids: a metal, mercury, and a nonmetal, bromine. All other elements are solids. (See Figure 4-5.) (Two solid metals, gallium and cesium, melt to become liquids at approximately 29°C, slightly above the reference temperature. Since body temperature is 37°C, both of these elements would melt in your hand.)

Many of the nonmetals exist as diatomic molecules rather than individual atoms. The periodic table can help us locate these elements. All the gaseous elements except for the noble gases, which exist as individual atoms, are composed of diatomic molecules (e.g., $N_2$, $O_2$, and $H_2$). Or one might notice that all the naturally occurring halogens (Group VIIA) are diatomic. Not all molecular nonmetals are diatomic, however. The formula for the most common form of phosphorus is $P_4$, which indicates the presence of molecules composed of four atoms. The most common form of sulfur is $S_8$, indicating eight-atom molecules. The forms of carbon will be discussed in Chapter 11.

**FIGURE 4-5 The Physical States of the Elements** The elements are found in all three physical states at room temperature.

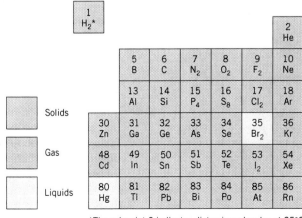

*The subscript 2 indicates diatomic molecules at 25°C

67

## MAKING IT REAL

# The Discovery of a Group VIIA Element, Iodine

It was a cold day in a small seaside town on the Atlantic coast of France in 1811. A few dozen seamen were extracting potassium salts with acid from the sludge of seaweed. Bernard Courtois, the employer of these seamen, was a chemist by training and a graduate of the Polytechnical Institute in Paris. His factory prepared saltpeter (potassium nitrate) to be used in ammunition for Napoleon's armies. Today, however, the workers' efforts turned fruitless. One of the workers decided to use a more concentrated form of acid. At that point, a huge volume of violet fumes rose from the tanks and dark crystals started depositing on every cold surface that was nearby. Their observations would lead to the discovery of a very important element.

Courtois collected those unique crystals for examination and found out they would combine with hydrogen and phosphorus, but not with oxygen. He also discovered they would form an explosive compound with ammonia. He later gave samples to two of his Paris Polytechnical Institute friends, C. Desormes and N. Clement, who published the discoveries two years later. Soon thereafter, Frenchman Joseph Louis Gay-Lussac and Englishman Sir Humphry Davy announced the discovery of a new element, which was first named *iode* (from the Greek word for "violet") by Gay-Lussac and finally *iodine*, to give it the same ending as *chlorine*, an element with similar properties. (Because of its chemical properties, iodine would later be classified as a *halogen* along with chlorine and bromine in Group VIIA.)

What happened on that day in 1811? Seaweed concentrates several ionic compounds other than sodium chloride (table salt), but no one had attached very much importance to them. That day, however, the iodine compounds must have become considerably concentrated after the extraction of the sodium chloride. The concentrated acid converted the iodine compounds to elemental iodine. The iodine vaporized (sublimed) but quickly condensed on the cool surfaces.

The practical applications of the new element had an immediate impact on patients with goiter, the enlargement of the thyroid gland. In 1820, Jean Francois Coinder associated the lack of goiter among seamen with the presence of iodine compounds in their working environment. The thyroid gland, he concluded, needs iodine to function properly and this could be achieved by adding small amounts of sodium iodide to table salt (i.e., iodized salt).

▶ **ASSESSING THE OBJECTIVE FOR SECTION 4-2**

*(Answer these questions using a periodic table.)*

**EXERCISE 4-2(a) LEVEL 1:** Provide the term being defined.

i. _____ A horizontal column on the periodic table.

ii. _____ Any element found in a B column.

iii. _____ Any entire row of the periodic table.

iv. _____ The nonreactive elements in the VIIIA column.

v. _____ Any element in an A column.

**EXERCISE 4-2(b) LEVEL 1:** Fill in the blanks.

Of the two general classifications of elements, nickel is a \_\_\_\_\_ and sulfur is a \_\_\_\_\_. Some borderline elements such as germanium are sometimes referred to as \_\_\_\_\_. In the periodic table, elements are ordered according to increasing \_\_\_\_\_ so that \_\_\_\_\_ of elements fall into vertical columns. Of the four general categories of elements, calcium is a \_\_\_\_\_ element, nickel is a \_\_\_\_\_, and xenon is a \_\_\_\_\_. An element in Group IIA, such as calcium, is also known as an \_\_\_\_\_ metal. A solid nonmetal that is composed of diatomic molecules is in the group known as the \_\_\_\_\_. Metals are all solids except for \_\_\_\_\_.

**EXERCISE 4-2(c) LEVEL 2:** Assign each of the following elements to one of the four major categories, give its symbol and physical state, tell whether it's a metal or nonmetal, and give its period and group number.

**(a)** copper          **(b)** argon          **(c)** barium          **(d)** bromine          **(e)** uranium

**EXERCISE 4-2(d) LEVEL 2:** Identify the element that fits each description.

**(a)** the fourth-period alkaline earth metal

**(b)** the liquid halogen

**(c)** the IIIA nonmetal

**(d)** the last transition metal of the fifth period

**(e)** the gaseous element in Group VA.

**EXERCISE 4-2(e) LEVEL 3:** A few elements that have been created in recent years have never existed outside of a laboratory. Yet we can still use the periodic table to predict what these elements would be like if we could somehow isolate a measurable quantity. Evaluate element 118 and the hypothetical 119 for category, physical state, period, group number, and whether they are metals or nonmetals.

*For additional practice, work chapter problems 4-4, 4-10, 4-12, and 4-14.*

## PART A SUMMARY

### KEY TERMS

4-1.1   The **periodic table** is a chart that displays the relationships among the elements. p. 118

4-1.1   The **periodic law** describes the ordering of the elements based on atomic numbers. p. 119

4-1.2   **Metals** are generally hard, lustrous elements that are malleable and ductile. p. 119
**Nonmetals** are generally gases or soft solids that do not conduct electricity. p. 119

4-2.1   All elements can be assigned to a specific **period**. p. 120

4-2.2   The main classifications of **groups** of elements are the **main groups** or **representative elements**, the **noble gases**, the **transition metals**, and the **inner transition metals**. pp. 120–121

4-2.2   The named groups of representative elements are the **alkali metals**, the **alkaline earth metals**, and the **halogens**. p. 121

4-2.2   The inner transition elements are known as either the **lanthanides (rare earths)** or **actinides**. p. 121

4-2.3   The physical state of an element at **room temperature** can be determined from the periodic table. p. 121

### SUMMARY CHART

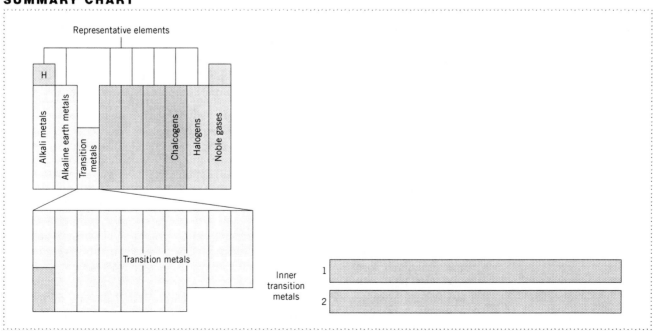

## The Formulas and Names of Compounds

**SETTING A GOAL**

■ You will learn how to systematically name various types of molecular and ionic compounds and determine the formulas of compounds from the names.

**OBJECTIVES**

**4-3** Write the names and formulas of ionic compounds between metals and nonmetals using the IUPAC conventions.

**4-4** Write the name and formulas of compounds containing polyatomic ions.

**4-5** Name binary molecular (nonmetal–nonmetal) compounds using proper Greek prefixes or common names.

**4-6** Write the names and formulas of acids.

▶ **OBJECTIVE FOR SECTION 4-3**
Write the names and formulas of ionic compounds between metals and non-metals using the IUPAC conventions.

# 4-3 Naming and Writing Formulas of Metal–Nonmetal Binary Compounds

**LOOKING AHEAD!** There are now over 10 million recorded compounds. With such a number, systematic methods of naming the compounds must be employed. We will need a periodic table, since we need to know whether an element is a metal or nonmetal and the charge on its monatomic ion. Our first task is to look at binary (i.e., two-element) compounds made from a metal and a nonmetal. For the most part, these are ionic compounds, which is one of the two major classes of compounds described in Chapter 2. ■

Chemical compounds can be roughly divided into two groups: organic and inorganic. Organic compounds are composed principally of carbon, hydrogen, and oxygen. These are the compounds of life. All other compounds are called inorganic compounds, and we will focus on these. As mentioned, many inorganic compounds were given common names, and some of these names have survived the years. For example, $H_2O$ is certainly known as *water* rather than the more exact systematic name of *hydrogen oxide*. Ammonia ($NH_3$) and methane ($CH_4$) are two other compounds that are known exclusively by their common names. Other compounds have ancient common names but are best described by their more modern systematic names, which we will use here.

One of the most important chemical properties of a metal is its tendency to form positive ions (cations). Most nonmetals, on the other hand, can form negative ions (anions). (The noble gases form neither cations nor anions.) Inorganic compounds composed of just two elements—metal cations and nonmetal anions—will be referred to as *metal–nonmetal binary compounds*. Metals fall into two categories. Some metals form cations with only one charge (e.g., $Ca^{2+}$). Others form cations with two or more charges (e.g., $Fe^{2+}$ and $Fe^{3+}$). The rules for the latter compounds are somewhat different from those for the first. So we initially consider metals with ions of only one charge.

### 4-3.1 Metals with Ions of Only One Charge

In Chapter 2, we noticed a pattern for the charges on many of the ions involving the noble gases. As mentioned at that time, noble gases have little or no tendency to lose or gain electrons and so exist as solitary gaseous atoms in nature. We can now relate this to the periodic table. Representative element groups on either side of the noble gases gain or lose electrons so as to have the same number of electrons as a noble gas. For this reason, we see that metals form positive ions when they lose electrons and nonmetals form negative ions when they gain electrons. These are important chemical characteristics of metals and nonmetals. Thus Group IA metals (which does not include hydrogen) lose one electron to form +1 ions, which gives them the same number of electrons as the previous noble gas. Group IIA metals lose two to form +2 ions, and Group IIIA *metals* lose three to form +3 ions for the same reason. Except for Al, the other Group IIIA metals also form a +1 ion. (Since formation of positive ions is a metal characteristic, boron is excluded.) On the other side of the periodic table, notice Groups VIIA nonmetals (and hydrogen) form −1 ions by gaining one electron to have the same number as the next noble gas. Group VIA gain two to form −2 ions, and Group VA nonmetals, N and P, gain three to form −3 ions. (See Figure 4-6.) The noble gas stability does not explain all of the representative ions or the transition metal ions. We will explore the reasons for formation of these ions in Chapter 8.

| | IA | IIA | IIIA | IVA | VA | VIA | VIIA |
|---|---|---|---|---|---|---|---|
| | Hydride $H^-$ | | | | | | |
| | Lithium $Li^+$ | Beryllium $Be^{2+}$ | | | Nitride $N^{3-}$ | Oxide $O^{2-}$ | Fluoride $F^-$ |
| | Sodium $Na^+$ | Magnesium $Mg^{2+}$ | Aluminum $Al^{3+}$ | | Phosphide $P^{3-}$ | Sulfide $S^{2-}$ | Chloride $Cl^-$ |
| | Potassium $K^+$ | Calcium $Ca^{2+}$ | | | | Selenide $Se^{2-}$ | Bromide $Br^-$ |
| | Rubidium $Rb^+$ | Strontium $Sr^{2+}$ | | | | Telluride $Te^{2-}$ | Iodide $I^-$ |
| | Cesium $Cs^+$ | Barium $Ba^{2+}$ | | | | | |

**FIGURE 4-6 Monatomic Ions of the Representative Elements** Metals form specific cations, and nonmetals form specific anions.

Note that metal and nonmetal ions are distinctly different from their neutral atoms. When we monitor our dietary intake of sodium or calcium we are in fact referring to the intake of sodium or calcium ions. The metal ions are parts of ionic compounds such as sodium chloride or calcium carbonate. We would not wish to ingest the neutral atoms of the metal, which would be in the form of a solid metal. (See Making It Real in this chapter.)

*Note also that positive and negative ions do not exist separately. They are always found together in ordinary matter.* In both naming and writing the formula for a binary ionic compound, the metal comes first and the nonmetal second. The unchanged English name of the metal is used. (If a metal cation is named alone, the word *ion* is also included to distinguish it from the free metal.) The name of the anion includes only the English root plus -*ide*. For example, *chlorine* as an anion is named *chloride* and *oxygen* as an anion is named *oxide*. So the names for NaCl and CaO are sodium chloride and calcium oxide.

Some other examples of writing names from formulas are shown in Example 4-1. Writing formulas from names can be a somewhat more challenging task, since we must determine the number of each element present in the formula. In Chapter 2, we practiced writing formulas given specific ions with specific charges. In this chapter, we are now able to determine the charge on the ion by reference to the periodic table. Recall also from Chapter 2 that the formulas represent neutral compounds where the positive and negative charges add to zero. In other words, the total positive charge is canceled by the total negative charge. Thus, NaCl is neutral because one $Na^+$ is balanced by one $Cl^-$ [i.e., $+1 + (-1) = 0$] and CaO is neutral because one $Ca^{2+}$ is balanced by one $O^{2-}$ [i.e., $+2 + (-2) = 0$]. The formula for magnesium chloride, however, requires two $Cl^-$ ions to balance the one $Mg^{2+}$ ion, so it is written as $MgCl_2$ [i.e., $+2 + (2 \times -1) = 0$]. We will practice writing formulas from names in Example 4-2.

## EXAMPLE 4-1    Naming Binary Ionic Compounds

Name the following binary ionic compounds: KI, $Li_2S$, and $Mg_3N_2$.

PROCEDURE

A quick glance at the periodic table reveals that the first element in each compound is a representative metal and the second is a representative nonmetal. Use the metal name unchanged, and change the ending of the nonmetals to -*ide*.

**SOLUTION**

| FORMULA | METAL | NONMETAL | COMPOUND NAME |
|---------|-------|----------|---------------|
| KI | potassium | iodine | potassium iodide |
| $Li_2S$ | lithium | sulfur | lithium sulfide |
| $Mg_3N_2$ | magnesium | nitrogen | magnesium nitride |

## EXAMPLE 4-2   Writing the formulas of binary ionic compounds

Write the formulas for the following binary metal–nonmetal compounds: **(a)** aluminum fluoride and **(b)** calcium selenide.

**PROCEDURE**

From the names, recognize that these compounds are representative elements. Identify their charges based on their column on the periodic table. Determine how many of each element are necessary to produce a neutral compound. Use these as subscripts in the formula.

**SOLUTION**

**(a)** Aluminum is in Group IIIA, so it forms a cation with a +3 charge exclusively. Fluorine is in Group VIIA, so it forms an anion with a −1 charge. Since the positive charge must be balanced by the negative charge, we need three $F^{1-}$ anions to balance one $Al^{3+}$ ion [e.g., $+3 + (3 \times -1) = 0$]. Therefore, the formula is written as

$$Al^{3+} + 3(F^-) = \underline{AlF_3}$$

**(b)** Calcium is in Group IIA, so it forms a +2 cation. Selenium is in Group VIA, so it forms a −2 anion. Together the charges add to zero, so one of each atom is sufficient in the formula:

$$Ca^{2+} + Se^{2-} = \underline{CaSe}$$

**ANALYSIS**

Another convenient way to establish the formula is to write the ions with their appropriate charges side by side. The numerical value of the charge on the cation becomes the subscript on the anion, and vice versa. The number 1 is understood instead of written as a subscript. This is known as the cross-charge method. Notice that, in (b), by exchanging values of the charge, we first indicate a formula of $Ca_2Se_2$. This is not a correct representation, however. Ionic compounds should be expressed with the simplest whole numbers for subscripts. Therefore, the proper formula is written as CaSe.

**SYNTHESIS**

What is the formula of a compound made from a metal (M) with a +3 charge and a nonmetal (X) with a −2 charge? Using the cross-charge method, we get a formula of $M_2X_3$. Charges are rarely higher than +3 or −3, so this is typically as complicated as balancing the charges in ionic compounds ever gets.

$$M^{3+} \quad X^{2-} = M_2X_3$$

### 4-3.2 Metals with Ions of More than One Charge

Except for Groups IA, IIA, and aluminum, other representative metals and most transition metals can form more than one cation. Therefore, a name such as iron chloride would be ambiguous since there are two iron chlorides, $FeCl_2$ and $FeCl_3$. An even more dramatic case is that of the oxides of manganese—there are five different compounds ($MnO$, $Mn_3O_4$, $Mn_2O_3$, $MnO_2$, and $Mn_2O_7$). To distinguish among these compounds, we use the Stock method. *In the* **Stock method,** *the charge on the metal ion follows the name of the metal in Roman numerals and in parentheses.* By this convention, the two chlorides of iron are named iron(II) chloride ($FeCl_2$) and iron(III) chloride ($FeCl_3$).

In order to use the Stock method, it is sometimes necessary to determine the charge on the metal cation by working backward from the known charge on the anion. For example, in a compound with the formula FeS, we can establish from Figure 4-6 that the charge on the S is $-2$. Therefore, the charge on the one Fe must be $+2$. The compound is named *iron(II) sulfide.* In the following examples, we will use a simple algebra equation that will help us determine the charge on the metal and thus the proper Roman numeral to use for more complex compounds. The equation is

$$\text{(number of metal cations)} \times \text{(+ charge on metal)} +$$
$$\text{(number of nonmetal anions)} \times \text{(− charge on nonmetal)} = 0$$

### 4-3.3 The Classical Method for Metals with More than One Charge (Optional)

Another method of naming compounds is known as the **classical method.** Though no longer widely used in chemistry, it is still found in many pharmaceuticals and drug labels. In this system, *the name of the metal ion that has the lower charge ends in -ous and the higher ends in -ic.*

If the symbol of the element is derived from a Latin word, the Latin root is generally used rather than an English root. Thus the two chlorides of iron are named ferrous chloride ($FeCl_2$) and ferric chloride ($FeCl_3$). The disadvantage of this method is that you have to remember the possible charges of a specific metal, whereas the Stock method tells you explicitly. The classical method will not be included in examples or problems in this text. However, for reference purposes, several common examples of names of ions of metals that form more than one cation are shown in Table 4-1.

**TABLE 4-1**

**Metals that Form More than One Ion**

| ION | STOCK NAME | CLASSICAL NAME |
|---|---|---|
| $Cr^{2+}$ | chromium(II) | chromous |
| $Cr^{3+}$ | chromium(III) | chromic |
| $Fe^{2+}$ | iron(II) | ferrous |
| $Fe^{3+}$ | iron(III) | ferric |
| $Pb^{2+}$ | lead(II) | plumbous |
| $Pb^{4+}$ | lead(IV) | plumbic |
| $Au^{+}$ | gold(I) | aurous |
| $Au^{3+}$ | gold(III) | auric |
| $Cu^{+}$ | copper(I) | cuprous |
| $Cu^{2+}$ | copper(II) | cupric |
| $Mn^{2+}$ | manganese(II) | manganous |
| $Mn^{3+}$ | manganese(III) | manganic |
| $Sn^{2+}$ | tin(II) | stannous |
| $Sn^{4+}$ | tin(IV) | stannic |
| $Co^{2+}$ | cobalt(II) | cobaltous |
| $Co^{3+}$ | cobalt(III) | cobaltic |

**EXAMPLE 4-3 Naming Binary Compounds with Metals with More than One Charge**

Name the following compounds: $SnO_2$ and $Co_2S_3$.

PROCEDURE

To determine the charge on the metal cation, we can work backward from the known charge on the anion. Recall that Group VIA nonmetals form a $-2$ charge in binary compounds. We can use the general algebra equation introduced in the preceding discussion to determine the proper Roman numeral to use for the metal.

SOLUTION

The equation applied to the given compound is

$$[1 \times (\text{Sn charge})] + [2 \times (\text{O charge})] = 0$$

Substitute the known charge on the oxygen and solve for the charge on the tin.

$$Sn + (2 \times -2) = 0$$
$$Sn - 4 = 0$$
$$Sn = +4(IV)$$

The name of the compound is, therefore, tin (IV) oxide.

For $Co_2S_3$, we can construct the following equation.

$$[2 \times (\text{Co charge})] + [3 \times (\text{S charge})] = 0$$

The charge on a Group VIA nonmetal such as S is −2.

$$2Co + (3 \times -2) = 0$$
$$2Co = +6$$
$$Co = +3(III)$$

The name of the compound is <u>cobalt(III) sulfide</u>.

## EXAMPLE 4-4   Writing the Formulas of Compounds with Metals that Form More than One Charge

Write the formulas for lead(IV) oxide, nickel(II) bromide, and chromium(III) sulfide.

### PROCEDURE

These types of compounds are actually easier than those with normal representative elements. The charge on the metal is already stated explicitly for you. Determine the charge on the nonmetal, balance the charges, and write the formula.

### SOLUTION

Lead(IV) oxide: If lead has a +4 charge, two $O^{2-}$ ions are needed to form a neutral compound [i.e., $(1 \times +4) - (2 \times -2) = 0$].

$$\underline{PbO_2}$$

Nickel(II) bromide: Two bromines are needed to balance the +2 nickel [i.e., $(\mathbf{1} \times +2) - (2 \times -1) = 0$].

$$\underline{NiBr_2}$$

Chromium(III) sulfide: Two $Cr^{3+}$ ions are needed to balance three $S^{2-}$ ions [i.e., $(2 \times +3) - (3 \times -2) = 0$].

$$\underline{Cr_2S_3}$$

### ANALYSIS

The key to successful nomenclature is recognizing the type of compound you are dealing with, and then naming it according to the rules set down for that type of compound. A periodic table is indispensable in this regard. With it, you can determine whether the metal in question is in column I or II (or Al) and therefore does not require a charge in the name, or whether it is any of the other metals available to us and therefore does.

### SYNTHESIS

Students often become confused over the meaning of the number in parenthesis. Remember that it is the *charge* on the metal, not the number of metal atoms in the compound. So what are the formulas of copper(I) sulfide and copper(II) sulfide? $Cu_2S$ and $CuS$, respectively. Notice that copper(I) requires two ions of copper and copper(II) requires one ion of copper. Can you see from the charges why this is so?

## ▶ ASSESSING THE OBJECTIVE FOR SECTION 4-3

**EXERCISE 4-3{a} LEVEL 1:** For which of the following metals must a charge be placed in parenthesis when naming one of its compounds? Co, Li, Sn, Al, Ba

**EXERCISE 4-3{b} LEVEL 2:** Name the following compounds.
**(a)** $Li_2O$      **(b)** $CrI_3$      **(c)** PbS      **(d)** $Mg_3N_2$      **(e)** $Ni_3P_2$

**EXERCISE 4-3{c} LEVEL 3:** Provide the formula for the following compounds.
**(a)** aluminum iodide      **(c)** tin(IV) bromide      **(e)** sodium sulfide
**(b)** iron(III) oxide      **(d)** calcium nitride      **(f)** copper(I) phosphide

**EXERCISE 4-3{d} LEVEL 3:** Using an M to represent the metal and an X to represent the nonmetal, write theoretical formulas for all possible combinations of M and X with charges of +1, +2, +3 and -1, -2, and -3.

*For additional practice, work chapter problems 4-18, 4-20, 4-22, and 4-24.*

# 4-4 Naming and Writing Formulas of Compounds with Polyatomic ions

► OBJECTIVE
FOR SECTION 4-4
Write the names and formulas of compounds containing polyatomic ions.

**LOOKING AHEAD!** Two or more atoms that are chemically combined with covalent bonds may have an imbalance of electrons and protons just like monatomic cations and anions. This results in a charged species called a polyatomic ion. How compounds containing these ions are named is our next topic. Again, you should recognize these as ionic compounds, so we find them as solids under normal conditions. ■

We use bicarbonates and carbonates for indigestion, as well as sulfites and nitrites to preserve foods. So we are probably familiar with some of these names, which are commonly used. A list of some common polyatomic ions is given in Table 4-2. Notice that all but one ($NH_4^+$ ammonium) are anions.

## 4-4.1 Oxyanions

There is some systematization possible that will help in understanding Table 4-2. In most cases, *the anions are composed of oxygen and one other element.* Thus these anions are called **oxyanions**. When there are two oxyanions of the same element (e.g., $SO_3^{2-}$ and $SO_4^{2-}$), they, of course, have different names. The anion with the smaller number of oxygens uses the root of the element plus *-ite*. The one with the higher number uses the root plus *-ate*.

$$SO_3^{2-} \text{ sulf} ite \qquad SO_4^{2-} \text{ sulf} ate$$

There are four oxyanions containing Cl. The middle two are named as before (i.e., with *-ite* and *-ate*). The one with one less oxygen than the chlorite has a prefix of *hypo-*, which means "under." (as in *hypo*glycemic, meaning "low blood sugar"). The one with one more oxygen than chlorate has a prefix of *per-*, which in this usage means "highest" (a shortening of *hyper*, as in hy*per*active, meaning "overactive").

$$ClO^- \text{ hypochlorite} \qquad ClO_3^- \text{ chlorate}$$
$$ClO_2^- \text{ chlorite} \qquad ClO_4^- \text{ perchlorate}$$

Certain anions are composed of more than one atom but behave similarly to monatomic anions in many of their chemical reactions. Two such examples in Table 4-2 are the $CN^-$ ion and the $OH^-$ ion. Both of these have *-ide* endings similar to the monatomic anions. Thus, the $CN^-$ anion is known as the cyanide ion and the $OH^-$ as the hydroxide ion, just as the $Cl^-$ ion is named the chloride ion.

Most of the ionic compounds that we have just named are also referred to as salts. *A **salt** is an ionic compound formed by the combination of a cation with an anion.* (Cations combined with hydroxide or oxide form a class of compounds that are not considered salts and are discussed in the next chapter.) For example, potassium nitrate is a salt composed of $K^+$ and $NO_3^-$ ions, and calcium sulfate is a salt composed of $Ca^{2+}$ and $SO_4^{2-}$ ions. Ordinary table salt is NaCl, composed of $Na^+$ and $Cl^-$ ions.

## 4-4.2 Naming and Writing the Formulas of Salts with Polyatomic Ions

In naming and writing the formulas of compounds with polyatomic ions, as in Example 4-5, we follow the same procedures as with metal–nonmetal compounds. The metal is written first with its charge (if it is not Al or in Group IA or IIA) followed by the name of the polyatomic ion. To calculate the charge on the cation, if necessary, we

**TABLE 4-2**

**Polyatomic Ions**

| ION | NAME |
|-----|------|
| $C_2H_3O_2^-$ | acetate |
| $NH_4^+$ | ammonium |
| $CO_3^{2-}$ | carbonate |
| $ClO_3^-$ | chlorate |
| $ClO_2^-$ | chlorite |
| $CrO_4^{2-}$ | chromate |
| $CN^-$ | cyanide |
| $Cr_2O_7^{2-}$ | dichromate |
| $H_2PO_4^-$ | dihydrogen phosphate |
| $HCO_3^-$ | hydrogen carbonate or bicarbonate |
| $HPO_4^{2-}$ | hydrogen phosphate |
| $HSO_4^-$ | hydrogen sulfate or bisulfate |
| $HSO_3^-$ | hydrogen sulfite or bisulfite |
| $OH^-$ | hydroxide |
| $ClO^-$ | hypochlorite |
| $NO_3^-$ | nitrate |
| $NO_2^-$ | nitrite |
| $C_2O_4^{2-}$ | oxalate |
| $ClO_4^-$ | perchlorate |
| $MnO_4^-$ | permanganate |
| $PO_4^{3-}$ | phosphate |
| $SO_4^{2-}$ | sulfate |
| $SO_3^{2-}$ | sulfite |

can use the same simple algebra equation as before. For example, consider $Cr_2(SO_4)_3$. Since the sulfate ion has a -2 charge, the charge on the chromium is

$$(2 \times Cr) + (3 \times -2) = 0$$
$$2\,Cr = +6$$
$$Cr = +3$$

The name of the compound is *chromium(III) sulfate*.

When writing formulas from names, as in Example 4-6, we recall from Chapter 2 that when more than one polyatomic ion is present in the compound, parentheses enclose the polyatomic ion. If only one polyatomic ion is present, parentheses are not used (e.g., $CaCO_3$).

---

**EXAMPLE 4-5    Naming Compounds Containing Polyatomic Ions**

Name the following compounds: $K_2CO_3$ and $Fe_2(SO_4)_3$.

**PROCEDURE**
Evaluate the metal as in Section 4-3. Recognize that after the metal in each compound is a grouping of atoms that form polyatomic ions. Name the anion with the appropriate ending: *-ate*, *-ite*, or *-ide*.

**SOLUTION**
$K_2CO_3$: The cation is $K^+$ (Group IA). The charge is not included in the name because it forms a +1 ion only. The anion is $CO_3^{2-}$ (the carbonate ion).

<u>potassium carbonate</u>

$Fe_2(SO_4)_3$: The charge on the Fe cation can be determined from the charge on the $SO_4^{2-}$ (sulfate) ion.

$$2Fe + 3SO_4^{2-} = 0$$
$$2Fe + 3(-2) = 0$$
$$2Fe = +6$$
$$Fe = +3$$

<u>Iron (III) sulfate</u>

---

**EXAMPLE 4-6    Writing the Formulas for Ionic Compounds Containing Polyatomic Ions**

Give the formulas for barium acetate, ammonium sulfate, and manganese(II) phosphate.

**PROCEDURE**
Write the formulas for the metal ion and the polyatomic ion, including their charges. Determine how many of each are needed to balance the charges. Write the formulas with those appropriate subscripts.

**SOLUTION**
Barium acetate: Barium is in Group IIA, so it has a +2 charge. Acetate is the $C_2H_3O_2^-$ ion. Two acetates are required to balance one $Ba^{2+}$ ion. The formula is

<u>$Ba(C_2H_3O_2)_2$</u>

Ammonium sulfate: From Table 4-2, ammonium = $NH_4^+$, sulfate = $SO_4^{2-}$. Two ammoniums are needed to balance one sulfate. The formula is

<u>$(NH_4)_2SO_4$</u>

Manganese(II) phosphate: The stated charge on manganese is +2. Phosphate is the $PO_4^{3-}$ ion. Using the cross-charge method (Example 4-2b), we will need three manganese ions to balance two phosphate ions. Since there is more than one polyatomic ion, the whole ion is placed in parentheses.

<u>$Mn_3(PO_4)_2$</u>

ANALYSIS

While it is not a major mistake to use parentheses when there is only one polyatomic ion, as in $Mg(SO_3)$, parentheses do have an important purpose. Subscripts affect only what they immediately follow. In order to demonstrate two or three of the group of atoms that make up the polyatomic ion, parentheses are placed around the entire group so that the subscript refers to all. What is the formula of calcium hydroxide? It is $Ca(OH)_2$. Some students may write $CaOH_2$, assuming that because hydroxide has no subscript itself, no parentheses are necessary. However, notice the difference in the two formulas. The first shows one calcium, two oxygens, and two hydrogens. The second incorrectly shows one calcium, one oxygen, and two hydrogens. The parentheses are necessary to indicate the correct number of elements.

SYNTHESIS

There are clear patterns in the names of the polyatomic ions that can be used to decipher the names of compounds with ions that are not in Table 4-2. What would we name $NaBrO_4$ and $Cu(IO)_2$? When Mendeleev organized the periodic table, he placed elements with similar properties in the same column. Notice that Br and I are in the same column as Cl. It is not unreasonable, then, to assume that the ions $BrO_4^-$ and $IO^-$ might be named similarly to $ClO_4^-$ and $ClO^-$. Perchlorate, then, becomes the model for perbromate and hypochlorite suggests hypoiodite. The charges, too, should remain constant. $NaBrO_4$ then becomes sodium perbromate. $Cu(IO)_2$ requires two −1's to balance the single Cu ion. Copper in this compound, then, must be +2, and the compound is named copper(II) hypoiodite.

## MAKING IT REAL

## Ionic Compounds in the Treatment of Disease

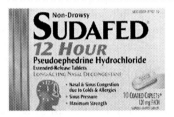

Since antiquity, it has been believed that drinking mineral waters from certain spas can have a soothing effect on the mood as well as the body. Some of these magical minerals may have been compounds containing the lithium ion. Lithium (in the form of the $Li^+$ ion) is found in certain rocks, in seawater, and in some freshwater springs. It is not known for sure that lithium was present in these waters, but it may have been an ancient treatment for manic-depressive disorder, which is now known more commonly as *bipolar disorder*. This is a debilitating disease that affects about 2.5 million Americans alone. Its symptoms include exaggerated mood swings from exhilarating highs to extremely depressive lows. In the manic mood, a person has boundless energy but acts impulsively and makes poor judgments. In the depressive state, the same person goes in the other direction and the world feels hopelessly glum. If untreated, about one in five commit suicide when in the depressive stage. The disease is known to be hereditary, with a neurological basis in certain chromosomes. It is certainly not due to weakness or any character flaw.

In 1949, John Cade, an Australian physician, found that lithium compounds had a calming effect on small animals. He then tested the toxicity of the compound on himself. Since he seemed okay and suffered no adverse effects, he began treating manic patients with lithium. Unfortunately, it was not known at the time that lithium can build up to toxic levels in the blood. In other uses, such as for cardiac patients, lithium caused several deaths, so its use in treating bipolar disorder did not gain much ground at that time in the United States. In the 1960s, however, it was reintroduced along with careful monitoring of the levels of lithium in the patient's blood. Under controlled conditions, studies quickly found that lithium was extremely effective. It was approved by the Food and Drug Administration (FDA) in 1970 to treat mania. In 1974, it was approved for use as a preventive (i.e., prophylactic) treatment for bipolar disease.

Treatment for bipolar disorder is most effective when lithium is combined with "talk therapy" with a trained professional. It is taken in the form of lithium carbonate ($Li_2CO_3$) or lithium citrate ($Li_3C_6H_5O_7$). In any case, many of those that suffer from this illness can now lead normal, productive lives.

There are many other ionic compounds that we ingest for their curative value. Magnesium hydroxide [$Mg(OH)_2$] and calcium carbonate ($CaCO_3$) treat indigestion or "heartburn." Many antihistamines and decongestants are also ionic compounds. If the drug name ends in "hydrochloride" or "HCl," it is an ionic compound. For example, pseudoephedrine hydrochloride ($C_{10}H_{14}NOH_2^+Cl^-$) is an ionic compound used as a nasal decongestant in products such as Sudafed. Like other ionic compounds, it is a solid and can be taken in pill form.

▶ **ASSESSING THE OBJECTIVE FOR SECTION 4-4**

**EXERCISE 4-4(a) LEVEL 1:** What are the names of the following ions?
**(a)** $NO_2^-$        **(b)** $OH^-$        **(c)** $C_2H_3O_2^-$        **(d)** $PO_4^{3-}$        **(e)** $HSO_4^-$

**EXERCISE 4-4(b) LEVEL 2:** What are the formulas for the following compounds?
**(a)** nickel(II) cyanide        **(c)** magnesium bicarbonate        **(e)** ammonium phosphate
**(b)** aluminum sulfite          **(d)** iron(III) perchlorate          **(f)** sodium dichromate

**EXERCISE 4-4(c) LEVEL 3:** What are the names of the following compounds?
**(a)** $Ba(OH)_2$        **(b)** $LiH_2PO_4$        **(c)** $AgClO$        **(d)** $K_2CrO_4$        **(e)** $Co_2(CO_3)_3$

**EXERCISE 4-4(d) LEVEL 3:** The prefix *thio-* means to replace one of the oxygen atoms with a sulfur atom. If $OCN^-$ is cyanate, what is iron(III) thiocyanate? What is sodium thiosulfate?

*For additional practice, work chapter problems 4-29, 4-32, 4-34, and 4-35.*

---

▶ **OBJECTIVE FOR SECTION 4-5**
Name binary molecular (nonmetal–nonmetal) compounds using proper Greek prefixes or common names.

Chemical names are familiar to us in many common drugs and cleansers.

# 4-5 Naming Nonmetal-Nonmetal Binary Compounds

**LOOKING AHEAD!** The compounds that we have named so far are generally ionic compounds. They constitute much of the hard, solid part of nature. When nonmetals bond to other nonmetals, however, molecular compounds are formed. These are very likely to be gases or liquids. How we name molecular compounds is the topic of this section. ■

## 4-5.1 Writing the Formulas of Binary Molecular Compounds

When a metal is combined with a nonmetal, it is simple to decide which element to name and write first. But which do we write first if neither is a metal? In these cases, we generally write the one closer to being a metal first—that is, the nonmetal closer to the metal–nonmetal border in the periodic table (farther down or farther to the left). Thus, we write $CO_2$ rather than $O_2C$ but $OF_2$ rather than $F_2O$. In cases where both elements are equidistant from the border, Cl is written before O (e.g., $Cl_2O$) and the others in the order S, N, then Br (e.g., $S_4N_4$ and $NBr_3$). When hydrogen is one of the nonmetals and is combined with nonmetals in Groups VIA and VIIA (e.g., $H_2O$ and HF), hydrogen is written first. When combined with other nonmetals (Groups IIIA, IVA, and VA) and metals, however, it is written second (e.g., $NH_3$ and $CH_4$).*

## 4-5.2 Naming Binary Molecular Compounds

The nonmetal closer to the metal borderline is also named first, using its English name. The less metallic is named second, using its English root plus *-ide*, as discussed before. These are not ionic compounds, so there are no charges that require balancing. However, this also means that more than one combination of the two elements is possible. Because more than one compound of the same two nonmetals could exist, *the number of atoms of each element present in the compound is indicated by the use of* **Greek prefixes**. (See Table 4-3.) Table 4-4 illustrates the nomenclature of nonmetal–nonmetal compounds with the six oxides of nitrogen. Notice that if there is only one atom of the nonmetal written first, *mono-* is not used. However, if there is only one of the second nonmetal, *mono-* is used. (Notice that the second *o* in *mono* is dropped in *monoxide* for ease in pronunciation.) The Stock method is

---

**TABLE 4-3**

**Greek Prefixes**

| NUMBER | PREFIX |
| --- | --- |
| 1 | mono- |
| 2 | di- |
| 3 | tri- |
| 4 | tetra- |
| 5 | penta- |
| 6 | hexa- |
| 7 | hepta- |
| 8 | octa- |
| 9 | nona- |
| 10 | deca- |

---

*With few exceptions, in organic compounds containing C, H, and other elements, the C is written first followed by H and then other elements that are present.

TABLE 4-4

**The Oxides of Nitrogen**

| FORMULA | NAME |
|---|---|
| $N_2O$ | dinitrogen monoxide (sometimes referred to as nitrous oxide) |
| $NO$ | nitrogen monoxide (sometimes referred to as nitric oxide) |
| $N_2O_3$ | dinitrogen trioxide |
| $NO_2$ | nitrogen dioxide |
| $N_2O_4$ | dinitrogen tetroxide[a] |
| $N_2O_5$ | dinitrogen pentoxide[a] |

*[a]The a is often omitted from* tetra *and* penta *with oxides for ease in pronunciation.*

Nitrogen dioxide contributes to the brownish haze in polluted air.

rarely applied to the naming of nonmetal–nonmetal compounds because it can be ambiguous in some cases. For example, both $NO_2$ and $N_2O_4$ could be named nitrogen(IV) oxide.

Several of these compounds are known only by their common names, such as water ($H_2O$), methane ($CH_4$) and related carbon–hydrogen compounds, and ammonia ($NH_3$).

According to the rules, compounds such as $TiO_2$ and $UF_6$ should be named by the Stock method—for example, titanium(IV) oxide and uranium(VI) fluoride, respectively. Sometimes, however, we hear them named in the same manner as nonmetal–nonmetal binary compounds (i.e., titanium dioxide and uranium hexa-fluoride). The rationale for the latter names is that when the charge on the metal exceeds +3, the compound has properties more typical of a molecular nonmetal–nonmetal binary compound than an ionic one. For example, $UF_6$ is a liquid at room temperature, whereas true ionic compounds are all solids under these conditions. In any case, in this text we will identify all metal–nonmetal binary compounds by the Stock method regardless of their properties and confine the use of Greek prefixes to the nonmetal–nonmetal compounds.

## EXAMPLE 4-7   Naming Binary Molecular Compounds

What are the names of **(a)** $SeBr_4$ and **(b)** $B_2O_3$? What are the formulas of **(c)** dichlorine trioxide and **(d)** sulfur hexafluoride?

### PROCEDURE

Check in the periodic table for the location of all the elements involved. Note that they are all nonmetals, mean-ing that these are examples of binary molecular compounds. Use the Greek prefixes and the ending -*ide* in the names.

### SOLUTION

**(a)** selenium tetrabromide       **(b)** diboron trioxide       **(c)** $Cl_2O_3$       **(d)** $SF_6$

### ANALYSIS

These are some of the easiest types of compounds to deal with. The prefixes essentially do all the work for you. The real chore comes in identifying these as binary molecular compounds in the first place.

### SYNTHESIS

Sometimes formulas can be very confusing. In Chapter 2 (Figure 2-13) we discussed the difference between $NO_2$ (nitrogen dioxide) and $NO_2^-$ (the nitrite ion). Another case involves $SO_3$ and $SO_3^{2-}$. How would you expect these two to differ from each other? $SO_3$ is a binary molecular compound named sulfur trioxide. It is a molecular compound made from one sulfur and three oxygen atoms. It is a gas at room temperature. $SO_3^{2-}$ is the sulfite anion. It is not a compound in and of itself. It cannot stand alone; instead, it needs to be combined with a charge-balancing cation, such as $Na^+$. It would then form the solid ionic compound, sodium sulfite ($Na_2SO_3$).

**TABLE 4-5**

**The Straight-Chained Alkanes**

| FORMULA | NAME |
|---------|------|
| $CH_4$ | methane |
| $C_2H_6$ | ethane |
| $C_3H_8$ | propane |
| $C_4H_{10}$ | butane |
| $C_5H_{12}$ | pentane |
| $C_6H_{14}$ | hexane |
| $C_7H_{16}$ | heptane |
| $C_8H_{18}$ | octane |
| $C_9H_{20}$ | nonane |
| $C_{10}H_{22}$ | decane |

### 4-5.3 Naming Alkanes

There is a special class of binary molecular compounds generally referred to as **hydrocarbons**, *which contain only carbon and hydrogen.* These compounds are of immense importance in our society. They serve as the fuels that power our cars, heat our homes, and cook our food. One specific class of hydrocarbons is distinguished by its relative number of carbons to hydrogens. **Alkanes** have the general formula $C_nH_{2n+2}$. In other words, for the number of carbon atoms in the molecule, there are double that number of hydrogen atoms plus two. Alkanes make up some of the best-known fuels that we use. Methane is natural gas used in furnaces and gas stoves. Propane is used as a portable fuel because it remains as a liquid under moderate pressure. Butane is found in lighters because it is a liquid under normal atmospheric pressures. It also serves as a propellant in aerosol cans. Other hydrocarbons will be dealt with in Chapter 17. But for now, it will be helpful to know the names of the first 10 alkanes based on the number of carbon atoms. (See Table 4-5.) After the first four on the list, the names are derived from the prefix for the number of carbons, and the ending *-ane*, indicating the carbon-to-hydrogen relationship.

▶ **ASSESSING THE OBJECTIVE FOR SECTION 4-5**

**EXERCISE 4-5(a) LEVEL 1:** What are the Greek prefixes for the following numbers?
**(a)** one     **(b)** four     **(c)** six     **(d)** ten

**EXERCISE 4-5(b) LEVEL 2:** What are the formulas of the following compounds?
**(a)** carbon tetrachloride
**(b)** phosphorus pentabromide
**(c)** sulfur dioxide
**(d)** carbon monoxide
**(e)** pentane
**(f)** octane

**EXERCISE 4-5(c) LEVEL 3:** What are the names of the following compounds?
**(a)** $SiS_2$     **(b)** $P_2O_5$     **(c)** $BF_3$     **(d)** $AsH_3$

*For additional practice, work chapter problems 4-43, 4-44, 4-45, and 4-46.*

▶ **OBJECTIVE FOR SECTION 4-6**
Write the names and formulas of acids.

# 4-6 Naming Acids

**LOOKING AHEAD!** We have one last category of compounds. These involve most of the anions listed in Figure 4-6 and Table 4-2 when combined with hydrogen. Since hydrogen is not a metal, these are molecular compounds in the pure state. However, many of these compounds have an important property when present in water. This special property allows us to give them special names, and we will do so in this section. ■

When hydrogen is combined with an anion such as $Cl^-$, the formula of the resulting compound is HCl. The fact that HCl is a gas, not a hard solid, at room temperature indicates that HCl is molecular rather than ionic. When dissolved in water, however, the HCl is ionized by the water molecules to form $H^+$ ions and $Cl^-$ ions. This ionization is illustrated as

$$HCl \xrightarrow{H_2O} H^+ + Cl^-$$

Most of the hydrogen compounds formed from the anions in Figure 4-6 and Table 4-2 behave in a similar manner, at least to some extent. *This common property of forming $H^+$ in aqueous solution is a property of a class of compounds called* **acids**. Acids are important enough to earn their own nomenclature. The chemical nature of acids is discussed in more detail in Chapters 6 and 13.

### 4-6.1 Binary Acids

The acids formed from the anions listed in Figure 4-6 *are composed of hydrogen plus one other element, so they are called* **binary acids**. These compounds can be named in two ways. In the pure state, the hydrogen is named like a metal with only one charge (+1). That is, HCl is named *hydrogen chloride*, and $H_2S$ is named *hydrogen sulfide*. When dissolved in water, however, these compounds are generally referred to by their acid names. The acid name is obtained by dropping the word *hydrogen*, adding the prefix *hydro-* to the anion root, and changing the *-ide* ending to *-ic* followed by the word *acid*. Both types of names are illustrated in Table 4-6. Polyatomic anions that have an *-ide* ending are also named in the same manner as the binary acids. For example, the acid formed by the cyanide ion ($CN^-$) has the formula HCN and is named hydrocyanic acid.

The following hydrogen compounds of anions listed in Figure 4-6 are not generally considered to be binary acids: $H_2O$, $NH_3$, $CH_4$, and $PH_3$.

### 4-6.2 Oxyacids

*The acids formed by combination of hydrogen with most of the polyatomic anions in Table 4-2 are known as* **oxyacids** *because they are formed from oxyanions.* To name an oxyacid, we use the root of the anion to form the name of the acid. If the name of the oxyanion ends in *-ate*, it is changed to *-ic* followed by the word *-acid*. If the name of the anion ends in *-ite*, it is changed to *-ous* plus the word *-acid*. Most hydrogen compounds of oxyanions do not exist in the pure state as do the binary acids. Generally, only the acid name is used in the naming of these compounds. For example, $HNO_3$ is called nitric acid, not hydrogen nitrate. Development of the acid name from the anion name is shown for some anions in Table 4-7.

In summary, acids -are named as follows:

| ENDING ON ANION | CHANGE | ANION EXAMPLE | ACID NAME |
|---|---|---|---|
| -ide | add *hydro-* and change ending to *-ic* | brom-*ide* | *hydro-*brom*ic* acid |
| -ite | change ending to *-ous* | hypochlor*ite* | hypochlor*ous* acid |
| -ate | change ending to *-ic* | perchlor*ate* | perchlor*ic* acid |

TABLE 4-6

**Binary Acids**

| ANION | FORMULA OF ACID | COMPOUND NAME | ACID NAME |
|---|---|---|---|
| $Cl^-$ | HCl | hydrogen chloride | hydrochloric acid |
| $F^-$ | HF | hydrogen fluoride | hydrofluoric acid |
| $I^-$ | HI | hydrogen iodide | hydroiodic acid |
| $S^{2-}$ | $H_2S$ | hydrogen sulfide | hydrosulfuric acid |

TABLE 4-7

### Oxyacids

| ANION | NAME OF ANION | FORMULA OF ACID | NAME OF ACID |
|---|---|---|---|
| $C_2H_3O_2^-$ | acetate | $HC_2H_3O_2$ | acetic acid |
| $CO_3^{2-}$ | carbonate | $H_2CO_3$ | carbonic acid |
| $NO_3^-$ | nitrate | $HNO_3$ | nitric acid |
| $PO_4^{3-}$ | phosphate | $H_3PO_4$ | phosphoric acid |
| $ClO_2^-$ | chlorite | $HClO_2$ | chlorous acid |
| $ClO_4^-$ | perchlorate | $HClO_4$ | perchloric acid |
| $SO_3^{2-}$ | sulfite | $H_2SO_3$ | sulfurous acid |
| $SO_4^{2-}$ | sulfate | $H_2SO_4$ | sulfuric acid |

## EXAMPLE 4-8 Naming Acids

Name the following acids: $H_2Se$, $H_2C_2O_4$, and $HClO$.

### PROCEDURE

Identify the type of acid and the typical ending of the anion (-*ide*, -*ate*, or -*ite*). Change the ending as appropriate and add the word *acid* to the name.

### SOLUTION

| ACID | ANION | ANION NAME | ACID NAME |
|---|---|---|---|
| $H_2Se$ | $Se^{2-}$ | selenide | hydroselenic acid |
| $H_2C_2O_4$ | $C_2O_4^{2-}$ | oxalate | oxalic acid |
| $HClO$ | $ClO^-$ | hypochlorite | hypochlorous acid |

## EXAMPLE 4-9 Writing Formulas of Acids

Give formulas for the following: permanganic acid, dichromic acid, and acetic acid.

### PROCEDURE

Pay attention to the ending for each acid. Decide from what anion the acid is derived. Add enough hydrogens to that anion to balance the charge.

### SOLUTION

| ACID NAME | ANION NAME | ANION | ACID |
|---|---|---|---|
| permanganic acid | permanganate | $MnO_4^-$ | $HMnO_4$ |
| dichromic acid | dichromate | $Cr_2O_7^{2-}$ | $H_2Cr_2O_7$ |
| acetic acid | acetate | $C_2H_3O_2^-$ | $HC_2H_3O_2$ |

### ANALYSIS

It helps to have a few models on which to base the naming patterns. Many people are aware that HCl is hydrochloric acid and that $H_2SO_4$ is sulfuric acid. These are among the most common of all acids. Use the principles of similarity to name other acids that resemble these in much the same fashion. HBr then becomes hydrobromic acid and $HBrO_3$ becomes bromic acid.

### SYNTHESIS

The hydrogen in a pure acid is not present as a positive ion. It forms a covalent bond to the anion. Since hydrogen is nearer the metal–nonmetal borderline, it is more metallic and is written first. When acids are present in aqueous (water) solutions, however, they do form positive hydrogen ions. This is what makes them distinctive compounds. Hydrogen can be present in compounds as a negative ion, however. What is it called when the hydrogen is negatively charged? A hydride (just as $Cl^-$ would be called a chloride). In a molecule like acetic acid, $HC_2H_3O_2$, hydrogen is written in two separate locations. The first hydrogen is an acidic one. The next three are neutral, part of the covalent polyatomic anion. Consider the following three compounds: NaH, HI, and $CH_4$. These represent three different situations for hydrogen. NaH is a typical ionic compound where the hydrogen exists as a −1 anion. HI is an acid that forms $H^+$ and $I^-$ ions in aqueous solution. $CH_4$ is a typical molecular compound where the hydrogen is covalently bonded to the carbon. The hydrogens do not ionize in water, nor are they present as anions. We will learn more about this in Chapter 9.

▶ **ASSESSING THE OBJECTIVE FOR SECTION 4-6**

**EXERCISE 4-6(a) LEVEL 1:** What changes are made to the name of an acidic compound whose anion would normally end in the following?
**(a)** -ide  **(b)** -ite  **(c)** -ate

**EXERCISE 4-6(b) LEVEL 2:** What are the formulas of the following compounds?
**(a)** acetic acid  **(c)** hydroiodic acid  **(e)** hydrofluoric acid
**(b)** nitrous acid  **(d)** perchloric acid

**EXERCISE 4-6(c) LEVEL 2:** What are the names of the following compounds?
**(a)** $H_3PO_4$  **(b)** HClO  **(c)** HCN  **(d)** $HClO_3$  **(e)** $H_2SO_3$

**EXERCISE 4-6(d) LEVEL 3:** Classify each compound as being an acid, a binary molecular compound, a binary ionic compound with either a representative or a variable cation, or an ionic compound with a polyatomic ion.
**(a)** $SeBr_4$  **(c)** $HNO_3$  **(e)** $CS_2$  **(g)** $K_3N$
**(b)** PbO  **(d)** $Mg(OH)_2$  **(f)** $AgNO_3$  **(h)** HF

**EXERCISE 4-6(e) LEVEL 3:** Water is a unique chemical that can be viewed as fitting in many of the classes of compounds we've outlined. How would you scientifically name water according to the rules of:
**(a)** binary molecular compounds
**(b)** acids
**(c)** ionic compounds with a polyatomic anion ($OH^-$)
**(d)** ionic compound of representative elements

*For additional practice, work chapter problems 4-47 and 4-48.*

**PART B SUMMARY**

### KEY TERMS

| | | |
|---|---|---|
| 4-3.2 | Metals that have more than one charge are named by the **Stock method**. p. 127 | |
| 4-3.3 | Metals that have more than one charge can also be named by the **classical method**. p. 127 | |
| 4-4.1 | Most polyatomic anions are **oxyanions**. A **salt** is an ionic compound. p. 129 | |
| 4-5.2 | Binary molecular compounds are named with the use of **Greek prefixes**. p. 132 | |
| 4-5.3 | **Alkanes** have the general formula $C_nH_{2n+2}$. p. 134 | |
| 4-6 | **Acids** are compounds that produce in ion in aqueous solution. p. 135 | |
| 4-6.1 | **Binary acids** contain hydrogen combined with a monatomic anion. p. 135 | |
| 4-6.2 | **Oxyacids** contain hydrogen combined with an oxyanion. p. 135 | |

**SUMMARY CHART**

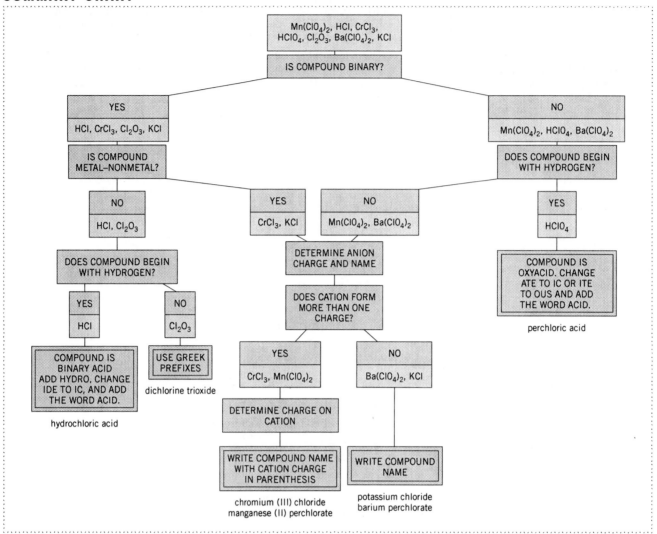

---

**CHAPTER 4 SYNTHESIS PROBLEM**

The periodic table is as essential to a chemist as a road map is to a traveler (at least for those who do not totally trust a GPS system). Consider the element fluorine. It is the most reactive element, forming compounds with all other elements except He, Ne, and Ar. Answer the following questions about fluorine and some of the compounds it forms. The last question is a more challenging problem.

| PROBLEM | SOLUTION |
|---|---|
| **a.** By its location on the periodic table, give as much information about the element as possible including its group number, group name, physical state, charge on its ions, and its formula. | **a.** Locate fluorine in the upper-right side of the periodic table. Fluorine is a nonmetal and a member of group VIIA known as the halogens. It is a gas with the formula $F_2$. In binary compounds with metals it forms a −1 ion. |

| PROBLEM | SOLUTION |
|---|---|
| **b.** Give names for the following fluorine compounds.<br>**i.** $BF_3$  **ii.** $AlF_3$  **iii.** $IF_3$  **iv.** $TlF_3$  **v.** $IrF_3$  **vi.** HF | **b. i.** Boron is a nonmetal in group IIIA, so this is a nonmetal–nonmetal binary compound. Use Greek prefixes. The name is <u>boron trifluoride</u>. **ii.** Aluminum is a metal in group IIIA that forms only one charge of +3. Its name is <u>aluminum fluoride</u>. **iii.** Iodine is a halogen in group VIIA. This is also a nonmetal–nonmetal compound. Its name is <u>iodine trifluoride</u>. **iv.** This is a metal–nonmetal binary compound where the metal has more than one charge. Since the fluorine has a −1 charge the thallium must have a +3 charge. The name is <u>thallium(III) fluoride</u>. **v.** Iridium is a transition metal and would also have a +3 charge. Its name is <u>iridium(III) fluoride</u>. **vi.** This is a binary acid with two names. The pure compound is named <u>hydrogen fluoride</u>. As an acid it is named <u>hydrofluoric acid</u>. |
| **c.** Give the formulas of the following compounds formed by fluorine:<br>**i.** xenon tetrafluoride  **ii.** chromium(III) fluoride<br>**iii.** barium fluoride  **iv.** ammonium fluoride | **c. i.** $XeF_4$  **ii.** $CrF_3$  **iii.** $BaF_2$  **iv.** $NH_4F$ |
| **d.** Classify each of the compounds in **b** and **c** above as molecular or ionic compounds. | **d. b.** $BF_3$, $IF_3$, and HF are molecular compounds. $AlF_3$, $TlF_3$, and $IrF_3$ are ionic compounds. **c.** xenon tetrafluoride is a molecular compound. The other three are all ionic compounds. |
| **e.** Give the name and formula of the anion and the name and formula of the compound from the following information. The metal is in the sixth period and in group VIB. The anion is composed of one sulfur and several oxygens and has a total of 50 electrons. Two of the anions and one cation are in the formula of the compound. | **e.** The metal is tungsten (W). If the anion has 50 electrons and 16 are from the sulfur, that leaves 34 electrons. Four oxygens would provide 32 electrons. Two are left over from one sulfur and four oxygens, forming a −2 charge. This is the sulfate ion, $SO_4^{2-}$. The formula is $W(SO_4)_2$ and the name is tungsten(IV) sulfate. |

**YOUR TURN**

Oxygen is the second-most-reactive element. It also forms compounds with almost all other elements. Answer the following questions concerning oxygen.

   **a.** Locate oxygen in the periodic table and give as much information as you can from its location.

   **b.** Give names for the following compounds; **i.** SrO  **ii.** $SeO_2$  **iii.** $H_2O$  **iv.** $OF_2$  **v.** $Ti_2O_3$  **vi.** $Cs_2O$

   **c.** Write formulas for **i.** aluminum oxide **ii.** dichlorine monoxide **iii.** tin(iv) oxide

   **d.** Describe the compounds in part b and c as either ionic or molecular.

   **e.** Give the name and formula of the anion and the name and formula of the compound from the following information. The metal is in the fifth period and is in group IIIA. The anion has one silicon and four oxygens and has a total of 48 electrons. Three anions are present for two cations.

Answers are on p. 141.

# CHAPTER SUMMARY

There is no more important time-saving device for the chemist than the **periodic table**, which demonstrates in table form the **periodic law** for the elements. One important function of the periodic table is that it shows a clear boundary between elements that are classified as **metals** and **nonmetals**. Some metals and nonmetals have intermediate characteristics and may be referred to as **metalloids**.

Horizontal rows are known as **periods**, and vertical columns are known as **groups**. Although there are four categories of elements in the table, the category that we will emphasize in the text is the **main group** or **representative elements**. This category includes some named groups such as the **alkali metals**, the **alkaline earth metals**, and the **halogens**. The other three categories are the **noble gases**, the **transition metals**, and the **inner transition metals**. The last category includes the **lanthanides** and the **actinides**.

All three physical states are found among the elements at the reference temperature of 25°C, or **room temperature**. Some of the nonmetals also exist as molecules rather than individual atoms at the reference temperature.

Our first important use of the periodic table is to aid us in **chemical nomenclature** by determining the type of chemical compound we are attempting to name. For example, binary compounds containing a metal and a nonmetal are named differently from those composed of two nonmetals. Also, all metals form cations, but some form only one charge and others form more than one. In using the **Stock method** of nomenclature, we need the periodic table to tell us which metals are in the latter group. The **classical method** is still used in the medical field. In addition to the binary compounds, we discussed the naming of **salts** containing **oxyanions**. Binary molecular compounds are named using **Greek prefixes** rather than the Stock method. A category of carbon-hydrogen compounds, known as **alkanes**, are identified by common names. Finally, a class of hydrogen compounds called **acids** (both **binary** and **oxyacids**) was discussed as a special group of molecular compounds.

## OBJECTIVES

| SECTION | YOU SHOULD BE ABLE TO ... | EXAMPLES | EXERCISES | CHAPTER PROBLEMS |
|---------|---------------------------|----------|-----------|------------------|
| 4-1 | Describe the origins of the periodic table and identify the locations of the metals and nonmetals. | | 1a, 1b | |
| 4-2 | Using the periodic table, identify a specific element with its group number and name, period, and physical state. | | 2a, 2b, 2c, 2d | 3, 4, 6, 7, 9, 11, 14, 15 |
| 4-3 | Write the names and formulas of ionic compounds between metals and nonmetals using the IUPAC conventions. | 4-1, 4-2, 4-3, 4-4 | 3a, 3b, 3c, 3d | 18, 19, 20, 21, 22, 23, 24, 25 |
| 4-4 | Write the names and formulas of containing polyatomic ions. | 4-5, 4-6 | 4a, 4b, 4c | 32, 33, 34, 35, 36, 38, 40 |
| 4-5 | Name binary molecular (nonmetal-nonmetal) compounds using proper Greek prefixes, or common names. | 4-7 | 5a, 5b, 5c | 41, 43, 44, 45, 46 |
| 4-6 | Write the names and formulas of acids. | 4-8, 4-9 | 6a, 6b, 6c, 6d | 47, 48, 49, 50 |

## ▶ ANSWERS TO ASSESSING THE OBJECTIVE

### Part A

#### EXERCISES

**4-1(a)** The periodic table was first displayed by <u>Dimitri Mendeleev</u> in the year <u>1869</u>. Elements are grouped vertically into <u>families</u> that share the same <u>chemical properties</u>. <u>Metals</u> are lustrous and malleable. <u>Nonmetals</u> are dull and brittle.

**4-1(b)** Metalloids have properties halfway between metals and nonmetals. They conduct electricity to a small extent. They are *semiconductors*.

**4-1(c)** Mendeleev chose to focus on chemical properties rather than physical properties, and he was not afraid to shift things around when those properties didn't line up. He also correctly assumed that not all elements had been discovered at that time, so he left spaces in his table to be filled in later.

**4-2(a)** i. group or family   ii. transition metal   iii. period   iv. noble gas   v. representative or main group element

**4-2(b)** Of the two general classifications of elements, nickel is a <u>metal</u> and sulfur is a <u>nonmetal</u>. Some borderline elements such as germanium are sometimes referred to as <u>metalloids</u>. In the periodic table, elements are ordered according to increasing <u>atomic number</u> so that <u>families</u> of elements fall into vertical columns. Of the four general categories of elements, calcium is a <u>representative</u> element, nickel is a <u>transition metal</u>, and xenon is a <u>noble gas</u>. An element in Group IIA, such as calcium, is also known as an <u>alkaline earth</u> metal. A solid nonmetal that is composed of diatomic molecules is in the group known as the <u>halogens</u>. Metals are all solids except for <u>mercury</u>.

**4-2(c)** (a) transition metal, Cu, solid, metal, fourth period, Group IB (b) noble gas, Ar, gas, nonmetal, third period, Group VIIIA (c) representative element, Ba, solid, metal, sixth period, Group IIA (d) representative element, Br, liquid, nonmetal, fourth period, Group VIIA (e) inner transition metal, U, solid, metal, seventh period, no group number

**4-2(d)** (a) calcium (b) bromine (c) boron (d) cadmium (e) oxygen

**4-2(e)** 118: noble gas, gas, seventh period, VIIIA, nonmetal 119: representative element, solid, eighth period, IA, metal

## Part B
### EXERCISES

**4-3(a)** Co and Sn

**4-3(b)** (a) lithium oxide (b) chromium(III) iodide (c) lead(II) sulfide (d) magnesium nitride (e) nickel(II) phosphide

**4-3(c)** (a) $AlI_3$ (b) $Fe_2O_3$ (c) $SnBr_4$ (d) $Ca_3N_2$ (e) $Na_2S$ (f) $Cu_3P$

**4-3(d)** $MX$, $MX_2$, $MX_3$, $M_2X$, $M_2X_3$, $M_3X$, $M_3X_2$

**4-4(a)** (a) nitrite (b) hydroxide (c) acetate (d) phosphate (e) bisulfate

**4-4(b)** (a) $Ni(CN)_2$ (b) $Al_2(SO_3)_3$ (c) $Mg(HCO_3)_2$ (d) $Fe(ClO_4)_3$ (e) $(NH_4)_3PO_4$ (f) $Na_2Cr_2O_7$

**4-4(c)** (a) barium hydroxide (b) lithium dihydrogen phosphate (c) silver(I) hypochlorite (d) potassium chromate (e) cobalt(III) carbonate

**4-4(d)** $Fe(SCN)_3$; $Na_2S_2O_3$

**4-5(a)** (a) mono (b) tetra (c) hexa (d) deca

**4-5(b)** (a) $CCl_4$ (b) $PBr_5$ (c) $SO_2$ (d) $CO$ (e) $C_5H_{12}$ (f) $C_8H_{18}$

**4-5(c)** (a) silicon disulfide (b) diphosphorus pentoxide (c) boron trifluoride (d) arsenic trihydride (e) ethane (f) decane

**4-6(a)** (a) -ide → hydro- -ic acid (b) -ite → -ous acid (c) -ate → -ic acid

**4-6(b)** (a) $HC_2H_3O_2$ (b) $HNO_2$ (c) $HI$ (d) $HClO_4$ (e) $HF$

**4-6(c)** (a) phosphoric acid (b) hypochlorous acid (c) hydrocyanic acid (d) chloric acid (e) sulfurous acid

**4-6(d)** (a) binary molecular compound (b) ionic compound with a variable cation (c) acid (with an oxyanion) (d) ionic compound with a representative cation and a polyatomic anion (e) binary molecular compound (f) ionic compound with a variable cation and a polyatomic anion (g) ionic compound with a representative cation (h) acid (binary)

**4-6(e)** (a) dihydrogen monoxide (b) hydroxic acid (c) hydrogen hydroxide (d) hydrogen oxide

---

### ANSWERS TO CHAPTER SYNTHESIS PROBLEM

**a.** Oxygen is a nonmetal in group VIA. It is a gas that forms diatomic molecules ($O_2$) and, under special circumstances, triatomic molecules, ($O_3$) known as ozone. It forms a −2 ion with metals in binary compounds.

**b. i.** strontium oxide **ii.** selenium dioxide **iii.** water **iv.** oxygen difluoride **v.** titanium(III) oxide **vi.** cesium oxide

**c. i.** $Al_2O_3$ **ii.** $Cl_2O$ **iii.** $SnO_2$

**d.** $SeO_2$, $H_2O$, $OF_2$, and $Cl_2O$ are molecular compounds. $SrO$, $Ti_2O_3$, $Cs_2O$, $Al_2O_3$, and $SnO_2$ are ionic. ($SnO_2$ is actually on the border.)

**e.** The metal is indium (In). The anion is $SiO_3^{2-}$ known as the silicate ion. (The $CO_3^{2-}$ ion in the period above is the carbonate ion.) The formula of the compound is $In_2(SiO_4)_3$ and its name is indium(III) silicate.

---

## CHAPTER PROBLEMS

*Throughout the text, answers to all exercises in color are given in Appendix E. The more difficult exercises are marked with an asterisk.*

### The Periodic Table (SECTION 4-2)

**4-1.** How is an active metal different from a noble metal?

**4-2.** How many elements are in the recently completed seventh period?

**4-3.** Which of the following elements are halogens?

(a) $O_2$    (c) $I_2$    (e) Li    (g) $Br_2$
(b) $P_4$    (d) $N_2$    (f) $H_2$

**4-4.** Which of the following elements are alkaline earth metals?

(a) Sr    (c) B    (e) Na
(b) C    (d) Be    (f) K

**4-5.** Classify the following elements into one of the four main categories of elements.

(a) Fe    (c) Pm    (e) Xe    (g) In
(b) Te    (d) La    (f) H

**4-6.** Classify the following elements into one of the four main categories of elements.

(a) Se    (c) Ni    (e) Zn    (g) Er

(b) Ti    (d) Sr    (f) I

**4-7.** Which of the following elements are transition metals?

(a) In    (c) Ca    (e) Pd    (g) Ag

(b) Ti    (d) Xe    (f) Tl

## Physical States of the Elements (SECTION 4-2)

**4-8.** What is the most common physical state of the elements at room temperature? Which are more common, metals or nonmetals?

**4-9.** Which metals, if any, are gases at room temperature? Which metals, if any, are liquids? Which nonmetals, if any, are liquids at room temperature?

**4-10.** Referring to Figure 4-5, tell which of the following are gases at room temperature.

(a) Ne    (c) B    (e) Br    (g) Na

(b) S    (d) Cl    (f) N

**4-11.** Referring to Figure 4-5, tell which of the following elements exist as diatomic molecules under normal conditions.

(a) N    (c) Ar    (e) H    (g) Xe

(b) C    (d) F    (f) B    (h) Hg

**4-12.** Referring to Figure 4-4, tell which of the following elements are metals.

(a) Ru    (c) Hf    (e) Ar    (g) Se

(b) Sn    (d) Te    (f) B    (h) W

**4-13.** Which, if any, of the elements in problem 4-12 can be classified as a metalloid?

**4-14.** Identify the following elements using the information in Figures 4-4 and 4-5.

(a) a nonmetal, monatomic gas in the third period

(b) a transition metal that is a liquid

(c) a diatomic gas in Group VA

(d) the second metal in the second period

**4-15.** Identify the following elements using the information in Figures 4-4 and 4-5.

(a) a nonmetal, diatomic liquid

(b) the last element in the third period

(c) a nonmetal, diatomic solid

(d) the only member of a group that is a nonmetal

**4-16.** What properties would you expect for element 118 if enough atoms were produced to actually study? (Assume that the border between metals and nonmetals continues as before.)

**4-17.** What is the atomic number of the alkaline earth metal that would appear after element 118?

## Metal-Nonmetal Binary Compounds (SECTION 4-3)

**4-18.** Name the following compounds.

(a) LiF    (c) $Sr_3N_2$    (e) $AlCl_3$

(b) BaTe    (d) $BaH_2$

**4-19.** Name the following compounds.

(a) $CaI_2$    (c) BeSe    (e) RaS

(b) FrF    (d) $Mg_3P_2$

**4-20.** Give formulas for the following compounds.

(a) rubidium selenide    (d) aluminum telluride

(b) strontium hydride    (e) beryllium fluoride

(c) radium oxide

**4-21.** Give formulas for the following compounds.

(a) potassium hydride    (c) potassium phosphide

(b) cesium sulfide    (d) barium telluride

**4-22.** Name the following compounds using the Stock method.

(a) $Bi_2O_5$    (c) $SnS_2$    (e) $TiO_2$

(b) SnS    (d) $Cu_2Te$

**4-23.** Name the following compounds using the Stock method.

(a) $CrI_3$    (c) $IrO_4$    (e) $NiCl_2$

(b) $TiCl_4$    (d) $MnH_2$

**4-24.** Give formulas for the following compounds.

(a) copper(I) sulfide    (d) nickel(II) phosphide

(b) vanadium(III) oxide    (e) chromium(VI) oxide

(c) gold(I) bromide

**4-25.** Give formulas for the following compounds.

(a) yttrium(III) hydride    (c) bismuth(V) fluoride

(b) lead(IV) chloride    (d) palladium(II) selenide

**4-26.** From the magnitude of the charges on the metals, predict which of the compounds in problems 4-22 and 4-24 may be molecular compounds.

**4-27.** From the magnitude of the charges on the metals, predict which of the compounds in problems 4-23 and 4-25 may be molecular compounds.

## Compounds with Polyatomic Ions (SECTION 4-4)

**4-28.** Which of the following is the chlorate ion?

(a) $ClO_2^-$    (c) $ClO_3^-$    (e) $ClO_3^+$

(b) $ClO_4^-$    (d) $Cl_3O^-$

**4-29.** Which of the following ions have a $-2$ charge?

(a) sulfate    (c) chlorite    (e) sulfite

(b) nitrite    (d) carbonate    (f) phosphate

**4-30.** What are the name and formula of the most common polyatomic cation?

4-31. Which of the following oxyanions contain four oxygen atoms?

(a) nitrate      (d) sulfite      (g) carbonate

(b) permanganate      (e) phosphate

(c) perchlorate      (f) oxalate

4-32. Name the following compounds. Use the Stock method where appropriate.

(a) $CrSO_4$      (d) $RbHCO_3$      (g) $Bi(OH)_3$

(b) $Al_2(SO_3)_3$      (e) $(NH_4)_2CO_3$

(c) $Fe(CN)_2$      (f) $NH_4NO_3$

**4-33.** Name the following compounds. Use the Stock method where appropriate.

(a) $Na_2C_2O_4$      (c) $Fe_2(CO_3)_3$

(b) $CaCrO_4$      (d) $Cu(OH)_2$

4-34. Give formulas for the following compounds.

(a) magnesium permanganate

(b) cobalt(II) cyanide

(c) strontium hydroxide

(d) thallium(I) sulfite

(e) iron(III) oxalate

(f) ammonium dichromate

(g) mercury(I) acetate [The mercury(I) ion exists as $Hg_2^{2+}$.]

**4-35.** Give formulas for the following compounds.

(a) zirconium(IV) phosphate

(b) sodium cyanide

(c) thallium(I) nitrite

(d) nickel(II) hydroxide

(e) radium hydrogen sulfate

(f) beryllium phosphate

(g) chromium(III) hypochlorite

4-36. Complete the following table. Write the appropriate anion at the top and the appropriate cation to the left. Write the formulas and names in other blanks as is done in the upper-left-hand box.

| Cation/Anion | $HSO_3^-$ | ___ | ___ |
|---|---|---|---|
| $NH_4^+$ | $NH_4HSO_3$ Ammonium bisulfite | ___ | ___ |
| ___ | ___ | CoTe ___ (name) | ___ |
| ___ | ___ | ___ | ___ (formula) aluminum phosphate |

**4-37.** Complete the following table. Write the appropriate anion at the top and the appropriate cation to the left. Write the formulas and names in other blanks as is done in the upper-left-hand box.

| Cation/Anion | ___ | $C_2O_4^{2-}$ | ___ |
|---|---|---|---|
| ___ | ___ (formula) thallium (I) hydroxide | ___ | ___ |
| $Sr^{2+}$ | ___ | ___ | ___ |
| ___ | ___ | ___ | TiN (name) |

4-38. Give the systematic name for each of the following.

| | Common Name | Formula |
|---|---|---|
| (a) | table salt | NaCl |
| (b) | baking soda | $NaHCO_3$ |
| (c) | marble or limestone | $CaCO_3$ |
| (d) | lye | NaOH |
| (e) | Chile saltpeter | $NaNO_3$ |
| (f) | sal ammoniac | $NH4Cl$ |
| (g) | alumina | $Al_2O_3$ |
| (h) | slaked lime | $Ca(OH)_2$ |
| (i) | caustic potash | KOH |

4-39. The perxenate ion has the formula $XeO_6^{4-}$. Write formulas of compounds of perxenate with the following.

(a) calcium      (b) potassium      (c) aluminum

*4-40. Name the following compounds. In these compounds, an ion is involved that is not in Table 4-2. However, the name can be determined by reference to other ions of the central element or from ions in Table 4-2 in which the central atom is in the same group.

(a) $PH_4F$      (c) $Co(IO_3)_3$      (e) $AlPO_3$

(b) KBrO      (d) $CaSiO_3$      (f) $CrMoO_4$

## Nonmetal-Nonmetal Binary Compounds (SECTION 4-5)

4-41. The following pairs of elements combine to form binary compounds. Which element should be written and named first?

(a) Si and S      (c) H and Se      (e) H and F

(b) F and I      (d) Kr and F      (f) H and As

**4-42.** The following pairs of elements combine to make binary compounds. Which element should be written and named first?

(a) S and P      (c) O and Br

(b) O and S      (d) As and Cl

4-43. Name the following.

(a) $CS_2$      (c) $P_4O_{10}$      (e) $CH_4$      (g) $PCl_5$

(b) $BF_3$      (d) $Br_2O_3$      (f) $Cl_2O$      (h) $SF_6$

**4-44.** Name the following.

(a) $PF_3$      (c) $ClO_2$      (e) $SeCl_4$

(b) $I_2O_3$      (d) $AsF_5$      (f) $SiH_4$

**4-45.** Write the formulas for the following.

**(a)** tetraphosphorus hexoxide     **(d)** hexane

**(b)** carbon tetrachloride     **(e)** sulfur hexafluoride

**(c)** iodine trifluoride     **(f)** xenon dioxide

**4-46.** Write formulas for the following.

**(a)** xenon trioxide

**(b)** sulfur dichloride

**(c)** dibromine monoxide

**(d)** pentane

**(e)** diboron hexahydride (also known as diborane)

## Naming Acids (SECTION 4-6)

**4-47.** Name the following acids.

**(a)** HCl     **(c)** HClO     **(e)** $HIO_4$

**(b)** $HNO_3$     **(d)** $HMnO_4$     **(f)** HBr

**4-48.** Write formulas for the following acids.

**(a)** hydrocyanic acid     **(d)** carbonic acid

**(b)** hydroselenic acid     **(e)** hydroiodic acid

**(c)** chlorous acid     **(f)** acetic acid

**4-49.** Write formulas for the following acids.

**(a)** oxalic acid     **(c)** dichromic acid

**(b)** nitrous acid     **(d)** phosphoric acid

*__4-50.__ Refer to the ions in problems 4-39 and 4-40. Write the acid names for the following.

**(a)** HBrO     **(c)** $H_3PO_3$     **(e)** $H_4XeO_6$

**(b)** $HIO_3$     **(d)** $HMoO_4$

*__4-51.__ Write the formulas and the names of the acids formed from the arsenite ($AsO_3^{3-}$) ion and the arsenate ($AsO_4^{3-}$) ion.

## General Problems

**4-52.** A gaseous compound is composed of two oxygens and one chlorine. It has been used to kill anthrax spores in contaminated buildings. Write the formula of the compound and give its name.

**4-53.** The halogen ($A_2$) with the lowest atomic number forms a compound with another halogen ($X_2$) that is a liquid at room temperature. The compound has the formula $A_5X$ or $XA_5$. Write the correct formula with the actual elemental symbols and the name.

**4-54.** A metal that has only a +2 ion and is the third member of the group forms a compound with a nonmetal that has a −2 ion and is in the same period. What are the formula and name of the compound?

**4-55.** The only gas in a certain group forms a compound with a metal that has only a +3 ion. The compound contains one ion of each element. What are the formula and name of the compound? What are the formula and name of the compound the gas forms with a $Ti^{2+}$ ion?

**4-56.** An alkali metal in the fourth period forms a compound with the phosphide ion. What are the formula and name of the compound?

**4-57.** A transition metal ion with a charge of +2 has 25 electrons. It forms a compound with a nonmetal that has only a −1 ion. The anion has 36 electrons. What are the formula and name of the compound?

**4-58.** The lightest element forms a compound with a certain metal in the third period that has a +2 ion and with a nonmetal in the same period that has a −2 ion. What are the formulas and names of the two compounds?

**4-59.** The thiosulfate ion has the formula. $S_2O_3^{2-}$. What are the formula and name of the compound formed between the thiosulfate ion and an Rb ion; an Al ion; an $Ni^{2+}$ ion; and a $Ti^{4+}$ ion? What are the formula and name of the acid formed from the thiosulfate ion?

**4-60.** Name the following compounds: $NiI_2$, $H_3PO_4$, $Sr(ClO_3)_2$, $H_2Te$, $As_2O_3$, $Sb_2O_3$, and $SnC_2O_4$.

**4-61.** Name the following compounds: $SiO_2$, $SnO_2$, MgO, $Pb_3(PO_4)_2$, $HClO_2$, $BaSO_4$, and HI.

**4-62.** Give formulas for the following compounds: tin(II) hypochlorite, chromic acid, xenon hexafluoride, barium nitride, hydrofluoric acid, iron(III) telluride and lithium phosphate.

**4-63.** Which of the following is composed of a metal that can have one charge and a polyatomic ion?

**(a)** $H_2CO_3$     **(c)** $B_2O_3$     **(e)** $Rb_2C_2O_4$

**(b)** $CaH_2$     **(d)** $V(NO_3)_3$

**4-64.** Which of the following is composed of a metal that can have more than one charge and a monatomic anion?

**(a)** $Ti(ClO_4)_2$     **(c)** $Cu_2Se$     **(e)** $MgCrO_4$

**(b)** $Mg_2S$     **(d)** $H_2Se$

**4-65.** The peroxide ion has the formula $O_2^{2-}$. What are the formulas of compounds formed with Rb, Mg, Al, and $Ti^{4+}$? What is the formula of the acid for this anion? What is the name of this compound as a pure compound and as an acid?

**4-66.** The cyanamide ion has the formula $CN_2^{2-}$ What are the formulas of compounds formed with Li, Ba, $Sc^{3+}$, and $Sn^{4+}$? What is its formula as an acid? What is the name of this compound as a pure compound and as an acid?

**4-67.** Give the formulas of the following common compounds.

**(a)** sodium carbonate     **(d)** aluminum nitrate

**(b)** calcium chloride     **(e)** calcium hydroxide

**(c)** potassium perchlorate     **(f)** ammonium chloride

**4-68.** Give the names of the following common compounds.

**(a)** $TiCl_4$     **(d)** $Mg(OH)_2$     **(g)** $NaClO_4$

**(b)** $NH_4NO_3$     **(e)** $HNO_3$

**(c)** LiH     **(f)** $H_2SO_4$

**4-69.** Nitrogen is found in five ions mentioned in this chapter. Write the formulas and names of these ions.

**4-70.** Carbon is found in five ions mentioned in this chapter. Write the formulas and names of these ions.

**4-71.** Which of the following is the correct name for $Cr_2(CO_3)_3$?

**(a)** dichromium tricarbonate

**(b)** chromium carbonate

**(c)** chromium(II) carbonate

**(d)** chromium(III) tricarbonate

**(e)** chromium(III) carbonate

**4-72.** Which of the following is the correct name for $SiCl_4$?

**(a)** sulfur tetrachloride

**(b)** silicon tetrachloride

**(c)** silicon(IV) chloride

**(d)** sulfur chloride

**(e)** silicon chloride

**4-73.** Which of the following is the correct name for $Ba(ClO_2)_2$?

**(a)** barium dichlorite

**(b)** barium(II) chlorite

**(c)** barium chlorite

**(d)** barium chlorite(II)

**(e)** barium chlorate

**4-74.** Which of the following is the correct name for $H_2CrO_4$?

**(a)** hydrogen(I) chromate

**(b)** hydrogen chromate

**(c)** chromic acid

**(d)** dichromic acid

**(e)** dihydrogen chromate

**(f)** chromous acid

## STUDENT WORKSHOP

### A New Periodic Table

**Purpose:** To create a table that illustrates the relationships in properties between elements. (Work in groups of three or four. Estimated time: 40 min.)

1. Cut heavy cardstock into 18 equal-sized squares, approximately 2 in. per side. Onto each of them, transfer the data from one line in the following table.

2. Arrange the cards into rows and columns using whatever information seems relevant. Try to use at least one property for your rows and one for your columns to establish a pattern.

3. Be prepared to discuss your arrangement and give justifications for it. Have any other patterns emerged other than the two that you used to establish rows and columns?

| MELTING POINT | BOILING POINT | DENSITY | MASS | FORMULA WITH Cl | FORMULA WITH O |
|---|---|---|---|---|---|
| −272 | −269 | 0.18 | 4 | NONE | NONE |
| −259 | −253 | 0.09 | 1 | XCL | $X_2O$ |
| −249 | −246 | 0.90 | 20 | NONE | NONE |
| −220 | −188 | 1.70 | 19 | NONE | $X_2O$ |
| −218 | −183 | 1.43 | 16 | NONE | NONE |
| −210 | −196 | 1.25 | 14 | $XCL_3$ | MULTIPLE |
| −189 | −186 | 1.78 | 40 | NONE | NONE |
| −101 | −35 | 3.21 | 36 | NONE | MULTIPLE |
| 44 | 280 | 1.82 | 31 | $XCL_3$ | MULTIPLE |
| 98 | 553 | 0.97 | 23 | XCL | $X_2O$ |
| 113 | 445 | 2.07 | 32 | MULTIPLE | MULTIPLE |
| 180 | 1347 | 0.53 | 7 | XCL | $X_2O$ |
| 650 | 1107 | 1.74 | 24 | $XCL_2$ | XO |
| 660 | 2467 | 2.70 | 27 | $XCL_3$ | $X_2O_3$ |
| 1278 | 2970 | 1.85 | 9 | $XCL_2$ | XO |
| 1410 | 2355 | 2.33 | 28 | $XCL_4$ | $XO_2$ |
| 2300 | 2550 | 2.34 | 11 | $XCL_3$ | $X_2O_3$ |
| 3500 | 4827 | 2.62 | 12 | $XCL_4$ | $XO, XO_2$ |

# 6 Chemical Reactions

In the rain forest a cycle of life occurs. Green leaves, powered by sunlight, maintain life. The decay of dead trees returns the ingredients for life to the air and Earth.

# SETTING THE STAGE

The weather seems to be crazy lately. More violent storms, record floods, melting at the poles, and even severe droughts seem to be happening regularly. Indeed, the past 20 years or so have been the warmest on record. In fact, 2010 tied the record for the highest average global temperature. All of this may be related to what we call global warming. Most scientists agree that the surface of the planet is warming, and at least part of that is due to the increase in carbon dioxide in the atmosphere.

Carbon dioxide is naturally removed from the atmosphere by the oceans and ocean life and also by trees and other vegetation. In a complex series of chemical reactions called *photosynthesis*, green leaves use energy from the sun, carbon dioxide, and water to produce carbohydrates (carbon, hydrogen, and oxygen compounds) along with elemental oxygen. These compounds can then undergo a type of chemical reaction called *combustion*. In this reaction, the carbon compounds from trees or fossil fuels (coal, oil, and natural gas) combine with oxygen in the air to re-form carbon dioxide and water and release the heat energy that originated from the sun. This fascinating cycle of chemical reactions maintains life on this beautiful planet.

The problem is that things have gotten out of balance in the past 160 years since the Industrial Revolution. There is considerably more combustion going on in our world than photosynthesis, so the level of carbon dioxide in the atmosphere is definitely increasing. Carbon dioxide is a gas that traps heat in the atmosphere much as heat is trapped inside a closed automobile on a sunny day. This is referred to as the *greenhouse effect*. The existence of nearly 7 billion people on our globe, all burning fuel and needing space at the expense of forests, assures that the balance will remain in favor of combustion.

Photosynthesis and combustion are only two types of chemical changes. In fact, the atoms of the elements combine, separate, and recombine in millions of ways, all indicating unique chemical changes. The rusting of iron, the decay of a fallen tree in the forest, the formation of muscle in our bodies, the cooking of food—all of these everyday, common occurrences are chemical changes.

Many of the more important chemical reactions on this planet occur in a water (aqueous) medium. Water has a unique ability to hold ionic and polar compounds in solution. Much of the chemistry that occurs in our bodies is a result of the interaction of these compounds circulating in our bloodstream. So it seems appropriate to take a deeper look at the particular chemistry that occurs in aqueous solution.

In Part A, we will introduce the chemical equation, how it is balanced, and three simple types of reactions. Types of reactions are extended in Part B to include the many important reactions that occur in water.

Part A

## The Representation of Chemical Changes and Three Types of Changes

**SETTING A GOAL**

■ You will begin to use the symbolic language of chemistry by writing balanced chemical equations for several identifiable reaction types.

**OBJECTIVES**

6-1 Write balanced chemical equations for simple reactions from inspection.

6-2 Classify certain chemical reactions as being combustion, combination, or decomposition reactions.

▶ **OBJECTIVE FOR SECTION 6-1**

Write balanced chemical equations for simple reactions from inspection.

# 6-1 Chemical Equations

 **LOOKING AHEAD!** The main rocket thruster of the space shuttle uses a simple but powerful chemical reaction. Hydrogen combines with oxygen to form water and a lot of heat energy. The way chemical reactions such as this are symbolized is the topic of this section. ■

### 6-1.1 Constructing an Equation

A chemical change can be illustrated symbolically by a chemical equation. *A **chemical equation** is the representation of a chemical reaction using the symbols of elements and the formulas of compounds.* In the following discussion, we will focus on the matter that undergoes a change in the reaction. In Chapter 7, we will include the heat energy involved.

Let's start with a simple and fundamental reaction. We will build the chemical equation one step at a time that represents the reaction between hydrogen and oxygen to form water. This reaction powers the space shuttle. First, let's represent with symbols the reaction of hydrogen combining with oxygen to form water.

$$H + O \longrightarrow H_2O$$

In a chemical equation, *the original reacting species are shown to the left of the arrow and are called the **reactants**. The species formed as a result of the reaction are to the right of the arrow and are called the **products**.* In this format, note that the phrase *combines with* (or *reacts with*) is represented by a plus sign (+). When there is more than one reactant or product, the symbols or formulas on each side of the equation are separated by a +. The word *produces* (or *yields*) may be represented by an arrow ($\longrightarrow$). Note in Table 6-1 that there are other representations for the yield sign, depending on the situation.

The chemical equation shown above tells us only about the elements involved. However, we know more information than just the elements involved. First, if an element exists as molecules under normal conditions, then the formula of the molecule is shown. Recall from Chapter 4 that both hydrogen and oxygen exist as diatomic molecules under normal conditions. Including this information, the equation is

$$\underset{\text{reactants}}{H_2 + O_2} \longrightarrow \underset{\text{products}}{H_2O}$$

An important duty of a chemical equation is to demonstrate faithfully the law of conservation of mass, which states that *mass can be neither created nor destroyed.* In Dalton's atomic theory, this law was explained for chemical reactions. He suggested that reactions are simply rearrangements of the same number of atoms. A close look at the equation above shows that there are two oxygen atoms on the left but only one on the right. To conform to the law of conservation of mass, an equation

TABLE 6-1

**Symbols in the Chemical Equation**

| SYMBOL | USE |
|---|---|
| + | Between the symbols and/or formulas of reactants or products |
| $\longrightarrow$ | Means "yields" or "produces"; separates reactants from products |
| = | Same as arrow |
| $\rightleftharpoons$ | Used for reversible reactions in place of a single arrow (see Chapter 14) |
| $(g)$ | Indicates a gaseous reactant or product |
| $\uparrow$ | Sometimes used to indicate a gaseous product |
| $(s)$ | Indicates formation of a solid reactant or product |
| $\downarrow$ | Sometimes used to indicate formation of a solid product |
| $(l)$ | Indicates a liquid reactant or product |
| $(aq)$ | Indicates that the reactant or product is in aqueous solution (dissolved in water) |
| $\xrightarrow{\Delta}$ | Indicates that heat must be supplied to reactants before a reaction occurs |
| $\xrightarrow{MnO_2}$ | An element or compound written above the arrow is a *catalyst; a catalyst speeds up a reaction but is not consumed in the reaction.* It may also indicate the solvent, such as water. |

must be balanced. *A* **balanced equation** *has the same number and type of atoms on both sides of the equation. An equation is balanced by introducing* **coefficients**. Coefficients are whole numbers in front of the symbols or formulas. The equation in question is balanced in two steps. If we introduce a 2 in front of the $H_2O$, we have equal numbers of oxygen atoms, but the number of hydrogen atoms is now unbalanced.

$$H_2 + O_2 \longrightarrow 2H_2O$$

This problem can be solved rather easily. Simply return to the left and place a coefficient of 2 in front of the $H_2$. The equation is now completely balanced.

$$2H_2 + O_2 \longrightarrow 2H_2O$$

*Note that equations cannot be balanced by changing or adjusting the subscripts of the elements or compounds.* For example, the original equation could seem to be balanced in one step if the $H_2O$ were changed to $H_2O_2$. However, $H_2O_2$ is a compound known as hydrogen peroxide. This is a popular antiseptic but definitely not water.

Finally, the physical states of the reactants and products under the reaction conditions are sometimes added in parentheses after the formula for each substance. Hydrogen and oxygen are gases, and water is a liquid at room temperature. Using the proper letters shown in Table 6-1, we have the balanced chemical equation in proper form.

$$\mathbf{2H_2(g) + O_2(g) \longrightarrow 2H_2O(l)}$$

Note that if we describe this reaction in words, we have quite a bit to say. "Two molecules of gaseous hydrogen react with one molecule of gaseous oxygen to produce two molecules of liquid water."

A powerful chemical reaction blasts the space shuttle into Earth orbit.

## 6-1.2 Rules for Balancing Equations

Properly balanced equations are a necessity when we consider the quantitative aspects of reactants and products, as we will do in Chapter 7. Before we consider some guidelines in balancing equations, there are three points to keep in mind concerning balanced equations.

1. The subscripts of a compound are fixed; they cannot be changed to balance an equation.
2. The coefficients used should be the smallest whole numbers possible.
3. The coefficient multiplies all of the number of atoms in the formula. For example, $2K_2SO_3$ indicates the presence of four atoms of K, two atoms of S, and six atoms of O.

In this chapter, equations will be balanced by *inspection*. Certainly, many complex equations are extremely tedious to balance by this method, but such equations will be discussed in Chapter 14, where more systematic methods can be employed. The following rules are helpful in balancing simple equations by inspection.

1. In general, it is easiest to consider balancing elements other than hydrogen or oxygen first. Look to the compound on either side of the equation that contains the greatest number of atoms of an element other than oxygen or hydrogen. Balance the element in question on the other side of the equation.
2. If polyatomic ions appear unchanged on both sides of the equation, consider them as single units.
3. Balance all other elements except hydrogen and oxygen, except those that appear as free elements (not as part of a compound).
4. Balance hydrogen or oxygen next. Choose the one that is present in the fewer number of compounds first. (Usually, that is hydrogen.)
5. Finally, balance any free element.
6. Check to see that the atoms of all elements are balanced. The final balanced equation should have the smallest whole-number ratio of coefficients.

Sometimes fractional coefficients (e.g., 3/2) are used initially, especially with regard to balancing $O_2$. In this case, multiply the whole equation through by the denominator (usually 2) to clear the fraction and produce only whole numbers. (This is illustrated in Example 6-3.)

---

### EXAMPLE 6-1 Balancing a Simple Equation

Ammonia is an important industrial commodity that is used mainly as a fertilizer. It is manufactured from its constituent elements. Write a balanced chemical equation from the following word equation: "Nitrogen gas reacts with hydrogen gas to produce ammonia gas."

**PROCEDURE**

Refer to Table 6-1 for the proper symbols. Apply the rules above as needed.

**SOLUTION**

The unbalanced chemical equation using the proper formulas of the elements and compound is

$$N_2(g) + H_2(g) \longrightarrow NH_3(g)$$

First consider the $N_2$ molecule, since it has the most atoms of an element other than hydrogen or oxygen. Balance the N's on the other side by adding a coefficient of **2** in front of the $NH_3$.

$$N_2(g) + H_2(g) \longrightarrow 2NH_3(g)$$

Now consider hydrogen atoms. We have "locked in" six hydrogen atoms on the right, so we will need six on the left. By adding a coefficient of 3 in front of the $H_2$, we have completed the balancing of the equation. (See Figure 6-1.)

$$\underline{N_2(g) + 3H_2(g) \longrightarrow 2NH_3(g)}$$

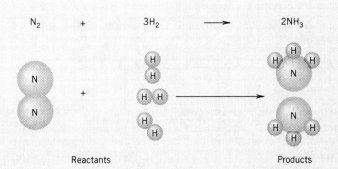

**FIGURE 6-1 Nitrogen Plus Hydrogen Yields Ammonia** In a chemical reaction, the atoms are simply rearranged into different molecules.

$N_2$    +    $3H_2$    ⟶    $2NH_3$

Reactants                          Products

### ANALYSIS

Many students new to this topic prefer to keep what is called an atom inventory during the course of balancing. In this way, they can see what coefficients are needed and how the addition of one coefficient changes the number of atoms of other elements. In each of the three equations in the solution, write underneath it the number of N atoms and the number of H atoms present on both the reactant side of the equation and the product side.

| $N_2(g) + H_2(g) \longrightarrow NH_3(g)$ | | $N_2(g) + H_2(g) \longrightarrow 2NH_3(g)$ | | $N_2(g) + 3H_2(g) \longrightarrow 2NH_3(g)$ | |
|---|---|---|---|---|---|
| N 2 | N 1 | N 2 | N 2 | N 2 | N 2 |
| H 2 | H 3 | H 2 | H 6 | H 6 | H 6 |

Notice that in the final solution, the number of atoms on both the reactant and the product side must be identical. This technique can be abandoned once you become proficient in balancing reactions.

### SYNTHESIS

Deciding on the proper order in which to balance the elements is the difference between smoothly solving a problem and having to attempt the same problem several times before success is achieved. In what order should the atoms in the following equation be checked and balanced?

$$PbO_2 + HCl \longrightarrow PbCl_2 + Cl_2 + H_2O$$

Balance lead first, then oxygen, hydrogen, and finally chlorine. The chlorine is last, because it is in its free state, $Cl_2$. The lead is first, since it is not hydrogen or oxygen. Now, why choose the oxygen second and the hydrogen third? Because the oxygen is bonded to the lead in $PbO_2$. Once we know the correct number of reactant lead atoms, we also know the correct number of reactant oxygen atoms and can predict the coefficient needed on the product side.

---

## EXAMPLE 6-2    Balancing an Equation

Boron hydrogen compounds are being examined as a possible way to produce hydrogen for automobiles that will run on fuel cells. Although $B_2H_6$ is not the compound that will be used (i.e., it ignites spontaneously in air), the following equation illustrates how boron–hydrogen compounds react with water to produce hydrogen. Balance the following equation.

$$B_2H_6(g) + H_2O(l) \longrightarrow H_3BO_3(aq) + H_2(g)$$

### PROCEDURE

Decide in what order the atoms should be balanced. Change coefficients in front of one molecule at a time and notice the effect on the other atoms in that molecule.

### SOLUTION

First consider the $B_2H_6$ molecule, since it has the most atoms of an element other than hydrogen or oxygen. Balance the B by adding a coefficient of **2** in front of the $H_3BO_3$ on the right.

$$B_2H_6(g) + H_2O(l) \longrightarrow 2H_3BO_3(aq) + H_2(g)$$

Next, we notice that oxygen is in the fewer number of compounds, so we balance it next. Since there are 6 oxygen atoms in **2**$H_3BO_3$, place a **6** before the $H_2O$ on the left. Finally, balance hydrogen. There are 18 on the left that are "locked in." Thus we need a **6** in front of the $H_2$ to have 18 hydrogen atoms on the right. A quick check confirms that we have a balanced equation.

$$B_2H_6(g) + 6H_2O(l) \longrightarrow 2H_3BO_3(aq) + 6H_2(g)$$

### ANALYSIS

You may run into a case where you can't seem to balance the equation, no matter what combination of coefficients you use. Or perhaps you find yourself continually spiraling through the equation again and again as the numbers get larger and larger. Most chemical reactions balance with relatively small whole numbers. If there is a problem, it very well may be that one or more of your formulas are incorrect. You may have transcribed the problem inaccurately or written a wrong formula yourself. Rechecking formulas would be a logical place to restart.

### SYNTHESIS

Technically, the coefficients should be the smallest set of whole numbers possible. Therefore 4 A + 6 B $\longrightarrow$ 2 C + 8 D should reduce to 2 A + 3 B $\longrightarrow$ C + 4 D. It *is*, however, acceptable to use fractions when balancing, and they can be quite useful for several types of problems whose solutions might not be apparent otherwise. These fractions shouldn't be interpreted as a fraction of a molecule, and if the equation is being used to determine how many molecules of each type react together, then any equation with fractions should be cleared to whole numbers. See Example 6-3 in Section 6-2.1 for this type of problem.

▶ **ASSESSING THE OBJECTIVE FOR SECTION 6-1**

**EXERCISE 6-1{a} LEVEL 1:** Fill in the blanks.

A chemical reaction is represented with symbols and formulas by means of a chemical _____. The arrow in an equation separates the _____ on the left from the _____ on the right. To conform to the law of conservation of mass, an equation must be _____. This is accomplished by introducing _____ in front of formulas rather than changing subscripts in a formula.

**EXERCISE 6-1{b} LEVEL 2:** Write unbalanced chemical equations for the following.
**(a)** Lithium and oxygen react to form lithium oxide.
**(b)** Aluminum and sulfuric acid yield aluminum sulfate and hydrogen.
**(c)** Copper reacts with nitric acid to produce copper(II) nitrate, nitrogen monoxide, and water.

**EXERCISE 6-1{c} LEVEL 2:** In what order should the atoms in the following equations be balanced?
**(a)** $H_3BCO + H_2O \longrightarrow H_3BO_3 + CO + H_2$
**(b)** $NH_3 + O_2 \longrightarrow NO + H_2O$
**(c)** $I_2 + Na_2S_2O_3 \longrightarrow NaI + Na_2S_4O_6$

**EXERCISE 6-1{d} LEVEL 2:** Balance the following reactions.
**(a)** $Cr + O_2 \longrightarrow Cr_2O_3$
**(b)** $Co_2S_3 + H_2 \longrightarrow H_2S + Co$
**(c)** $C_3H_8 + O_2 \longrightarrow CO_2 + H_2O$

**EXERCISE 6-1{e} LEVEL 3:** Write a balanced equation including symbols from the following descriptions.
**(a)** Solid ammonium carbonate decomposes into gaseous ammonia, carbon dioxide, and steam.
**(b)** Gaseous ammonia reacts with liquid chlorine trifluoride to form nitrogen gas, chlorine gas, and hydrogen fluoride gas.

*For additional practice, work chapter problems 6-2, 6-4, 6-10, and 6-11.*

# 6-2 Combustion, Combination, and Decomposition Reactions

▶ **OBJECTIVE FOR SECTION 6-2**
Classify certain chemical reactions as being combustion, combination, or decomposition reactions.

**LOOKING AHEAD!** All the millions of known chemical changes can be represented by balanced equations. Many of these chemical reactions have aspects in common, so they can be grouped into specific classifications. In the remainder of this chapter, we do this with five basic types of reactions. We will notice that each type has a characteristic chemical equation. These five types are not the only ways that reactions can be grouped. In later chapters we will find other convenient classifications that will suit our purpose at that time. The first three types are the simplest and will be considered in this section. ■

Fire is certainly dramatic evidence of the occurrence of a chemical reaction. What we see as fire is the hot, glowing gases of a combustion reaction. The easiest way to put out a fire is to deprive the burning substance of a reactant (oxygen) by dousing it with water or carbon dioxide from a fire extinguisher. The reaction of elements or compounds with oxygen is the first of three types of reactions that we will discuss in this section.

## 6-2.1 Combustion Reactions

One of the most important types of reactions that we may refer to in the future is known as a **combustion reaction**. This type of reaction refers specifically to the reaction of an element or compound with elemental oxygen ($O_2$). Combustion usually liberates considerable heat energy and is accompanied by a flame. It is typically referred to as "burning." When elements undergo combustion, generally only one product (the oxide) is formed. Examples are the combustion of carbon and aluminum shown here.

$$C(s) + O_2(g) \longrightarrow CO_2(g)$$
$$4Al(s) + 3O_2(g) \longrightarrow 2Al_2O_3(s)$$

When compounds undergo combustion, however, two or more combustion products are formed. When carbon–hydrogen or carbon–hydrogen–oxygen compounds undergo combustion in an excess of oxygen, the combustion products are carbon dioxide and water. (Combustion reactions involving carbon–hydrogen or carbon–hydrogen–oxygen compounds are balanced in the order C, H, O).

$$CH_4(g) + 2O_2(g) \longrightarrow CO_2(g) + 2H_2O(l)$$

The metabolism of glucose ($C_6H_{12}O_6$, blood sugar) occurs in our bodies to produce the energy to sustain our life. We will discuss the energy liberated by this reaction in Chapter 7. But we are now concerned with the product compounds. This combustion reaction occurs at a steady, controlled rate.

$$C_6H_{12}O_6(aq) + 6O_2(g) \longrightarrow 6CO_2(g) + 6H_2O(l)$$

When insufficient oxygen is present (as in the combustion of gasoline, $C_8H_{18}$, in an automobile engine), some carbon monoxide (CO) also forms. This incomplete combustion reaction is shown below.

$$2C_8H_{18}(l) + 17O_2(g) \longrightarrow 16CO(g) + 18H_2O(l)$$

---

## EXAMPLE 6-3   Balancing a Combustion Equation

Most fuels are composed of carbon and hydrogen (known as a hydrocarbon), and some may also contain oxygen. When they react with oxygen gas (burn), they form as products carbon dioxide gas and water. Write a balanced equation showing the burning of liquid rubbing alcohol ($C_3H_8O$).

**PROCEDURE**

First, represent the names of the species involved as reactants and products with formulas and indicate their physical states. Remember that oxygen gas is diatomic. Then balance the atoms in the order of C, H, and O. Use fractions where necessary, and scale up.

**SOLUTION**

The unbalanced equation is written as follows:

$$C_3H_8O(l) + O_2(g) \longrightarrow CO_2(g) + H_2O(l)$$

Now, balance carbon. Place a coefficient of **3** in front of $CO_2$ to balance the carbons in $C_3H_8O$. Next, balance the 8 hydrogen atoms in $C_3H_8O$ by adding a coefficient of **4** in front of $H_2O$.

$$C_3H_8O(l) + O_2(g) \longrightarrow 3CO_2(g) + 4H_2O(l)$$

Notice that there are 10 oxygen atoms on the right. On the left 1 oxygen is in $C_3H_8O$, so 9 are needed from $O_2$. To get an odd number of oxygen atoms from $O_2$, we need to use a fractional coefficient, in this case $\frac{9}{2}$ (i.e., $\frac{9}{2} \times 2 = 9$)

$$C_3H_8O(l) + \frac{9}{2} O_2(g) \longrightarrow 3CO_2(g) + 4H_2O(l)$$

Finally, we need to clear the fraction so that all coefficients are whole numbers. Multiply the whole equation through by 2 and do a quick check.

$$\underline{2C_3H_8O(l) + 9O_2(g) \longrightarrow 6CO_2(g) + 8H_2O(l)}$$

**ANALYSIS**

Generally, in a combustion reaction, the total number of oxygen atoms on the product side of an equation will be odd or even. If the number is odd, as in the above example, the use of a fraction makes the balancing easier. The fraction will be some half value (3/2, 7/2, 9/2, etc.). Afterwards, simply double each coefficient to arrive at the appropriate balanced equation. If the number of oxygen atoms is even, it is even easier. A whole number is all that is required to balance things from the start.

**SYNTHESIS**

During any combustion reaction, oxygen combines with the elements present in the fuel. In cleaner-burning fuels, containing only carbon and hydrogen, and possibly oxygen, the only products of *complete* combustion are carbon dioxide and water. When there isn't enough oxygen present (such as in a poorly performing combustion engine), incomplete combustion results, with products containing fewer oxygen atoms than are optimal. This typically means CO (carbon monoxide—a deadly gas) and C (in the form of smoke, soot, or ash). When dirtier fuels are used, ones containing contaminants such as high-sulfur coal, the oxygen combines with these elements, too, to form by-products. $SO_2$ is the unpleasant result of combustion of sulfur-containing compounds. Combustion at high enough temperatures in the presence of nitrogen in the air can lead to the formation of nitrogen oxides such as NO and $NO_2$, components of smog, which themselves have harmful health effects.

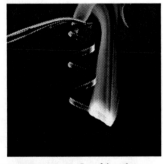

**FIGURE 6-2 Combination or Combustion Reaction** When magnesium burns in air, the reaction can be classified as either a combination or a combustion reaction.

## 6-2.2 Combination Reactions

The chemical properties of an element describe how it does, or in some cases does not, combine with other elements or compounds. One type of reaction, known as a **combination reaction**, concerns *the formation of one compound from two or more elements and/or simpler compounds*. For example, an important chemical property of the metal magnesium is that it reacts with elemental oxygen to form magnesium oxide. (See Figure 6-2.) The synthesis (i.e., production of a substance) of MgO is represented at the end of this paragraph by a balanced equation and an illustration of the magnesium and oxygen atoms in the reaction. Notice in the reaction that an ionic compound is formed from neutral atoms. The $Mg^{2+}$ cation is smaller than the parent atom, while the $O^{2-}$ anion is larger than the parent atom. The reason for this is discussed in Chapter 8. Since one of the reactants is elemental oxygen, this reaction, and others like it, can also be classified as combustion reactions.

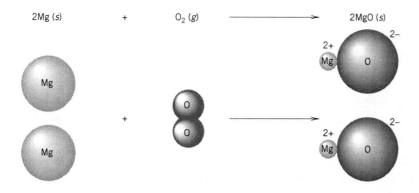

The following equations represent some other important combination reactions.

$$2Na(s) + Cl_2(g) \longrightarrow 2NaCl(s)$$
$$C(s) + O_2(g) \longrightarrow CO_2(g)$$
$$CaO(s) + CO_2(g) \longrightarrow CaCO_3(s)$$

## 6-2.3 Decomposition Reactions

A chemical property of a compound may be its tendency to decompose into simpler substances. This type of reaction is simply the reverse of combination reactions. That is, one compound is decomposed into two or more elements or simpler compounds. Many of these reactions take place only when heat is supplied, which is indicated by a $\Delta$ above the arrow. An example of this type of reaction is the decomposition of carbonic acid ($H_2CO_3$). This **decomposition reaction** causes the fizz in carbonated beverages. The reaction is illustrated here and is followed by other examples. (See also Figure 6-3.)

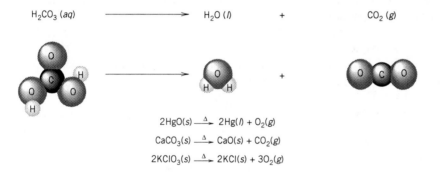

$$2HgO(s) \xrightarrow{\Delta} 2Hg(l) + O_2(g)$$
$$CaCO_3(s) \xrightarrow{\Delta} CaO(s) + CO_2(g)$$
$$2KClO_3(s) \xrightarrow{\Delta} 2KCl(s) + 3O_2(g)$$

▶ **ASSESSING THE OBJECTIVE FOR SECTION 6-2**

**EXERCISE 6-2(a) LEVEL 1:** Label each statement as applying to a decomposition, combination, and/or combustion reaction.
**(a)** Oxygen is a reactant.             **(d)** The equation must be balanced.
**(b)** There are two or more products.  **(e)** Reaction usually requires heating to occur.
**(c)** There are two or more reactants.

**EXERCISE 6-2(b) LEVEL 1:** Label each of the following reactions as being an example of a combustion, combination, or decomposition reaction.
**(a)** $Cu(OH)_2(s) \longrightarrow CuO(s) + H_2O(l)$
**(b)** $2CH_4O(l) + 3O_2(g) \longrightarrow 2CO_2(g) + 4H_2O(g)$
**(c)** $Ba(s) + F_2(g) \longrightarrow BaF_2(s)$
**(d)** $(NH_4)_2Cr_2O_7(s) \longrightarrow N_2(g) + 4H_2O(g) + Cr_2O_3(s)$
**(e)** $Na_2O(s) + H_2O(l) \longrightarrow NaOH(aq)$

**FIGURE 6-3 Decomposition Reaction** The fizz of carbonated water is the result of a decomposition reaction.

**EXERCISE 6-2(c) LEVEL 2:** Represent each of the following word equations with a balanced chemical equation, including state symbols.

**(a)** Disilane gas ($Si_2H_6$) undergoes combustion to form solid silicon dioxide and water.

**(b)** Solid aluminum hydride is formed by a combination reaction of its two elements.

**(c)** When solid calcium bisulfite is heated, it decomposes to solid calcium oxide, sulfur dioxide gas, and water.

**EXERCISE 6-2(d) LEVEL 3:** Write out the complete reaction for the following:

**(a)** The complete combustion of liquid hexane.

**(b)** The combination of elements to form solid sodium iodide.

**(c)** The decomposition of aqueous sulfurous acid into a common liquid and gas.

*For additional practice, work chapter problems 6-16, 6-18, and 6-20*

---

## MAKING IT REAL

### Life Where the Sun Doesn't Shine—Chemosynthesis

Miles deep in the ocean a phenomenal discovery profoundly changed the way we view the life forms on this planet and perhaps other planets far away. Previously, we understood life as totally dependent on energy from the sun. The chlorophyll in plants produces carbohydrates in a process known as *photosynthesis*, as illustrated below. (Carbohydrates are represented by their empirical formula, $CH_2O$.)

$$(\text{solar energy}) + CO_2(g) + H_2O(l) \longrightarrow CH_2O(s) + O_2(g)$$

We use these carbohydrates from plants, or animals that eat these plants, to sustain life. So our energy is indirectly solar energy.

In 1977, scientists in the research submarine *Alvin* were exploring the mile-deep ocean bottom near the Galapagos Islands in the Pacific. Suddenly, they came upon an unbelievable diversity of life that existed in scalding water (350°C). The colony of life extended from bacteria to giant clams, mussels, and tube-worms 8 feet long. The *Alvin* had come upon ocean vents discharging huge amounts of hot water from deep in the Earth. The water was rich in minerals and chemicals.

One of those chemicals was hydrogen sulfide ($H_2S$). This gas is very poisonous to surface life but turned out to be the main source of energy for the bacteria, which serve as the bottom of the food chain. These bacteria are able to produce carbohydrates with the chemical energy from hydrogen sulfide rather than the light energy from the sun. This process is called *chemosynthesis*. The equation illustrating this reaction to produce a carbohydrate is

$$2O_2(g) + 8H_2S(aq) + 2CO_2(aq) \longrightarrow$$
$$2CH_2O(aq) + 2S_8(s) + 6H_2O(l)$$

In the late 1990s, even more startling discoveries were reported. Living bacteria have been found 3000 feet deep in the solid earth. These life-forms seem to use the chemical energy from $H_2$ to maintain life. They do not even need $O_2$, which is produced as a by-product of photosynthesis, as was found in the chemosynthesis in the deep-sea vents.

Life is much more resilient than we ever thought. Because of these discoveries, many scientists feel much more confident that life could exist on other planets, especially Mars.

Currently, we are intensely studying the conditions on that planet. Recent discoveries of the presence of large amounts of water at the poles and buried beneath the surface of Mars have heightened expectations. The Mars explorers have more recently found that bodies of water once existed on the surface of this planet. More exciting discoveries about the robustness of life await us.

## PART A SUMMARY

### KEY TERMS

6-1.1   Chemical reactions are represented by **chemical equations**. p. 180

6-1.1   **Reactants** and **products** in an equation are separated by an arrow. p. 180

6-1.1   Equations are **balanced** by use of **coefficients** in front of a compound or element. p. 181

6-2.1   **Combustion reactions** involve oxygen as a reactant. p. 185

6-2.2   **Combination reactions** have one product. p. 186

6-2.3   **Decomposition reactions** have one reactant. p. 187

### SUMMARY CHART

*Sequence of Balancing Equations*

1. Most complex element $\longrightarrow$ 2. Any element (or polyatomic ion) other than H and O $\longrightarrow$

3. Usually H next if present in the most species $\longrightarrow$ 4. Finally balance O $\longrightarrow$ 5. Check

*Three Types of Reactions*

| Combustion | Combination | Decomposition |
|---|---|---|
| $O_2$ is a reactant; oxides are products. | Elements and/or compounds combine to form one product. | One reactant forms elements and/or compounds. |

## Part B

### Ions In Water and How They React

**SETTING A GOAL**

* You will learn how ions are formed in aqueous solution and how these ions interact in two important types of chemical reactions.

**OBJECTIVES**

6-3 Write the ions formed when ionic compounds or acids dissolve in water.

6-4 Given the activity series, complete several single-replacement reactions as balanced molecular, total ionic, and net ionic equations.

6-5 Write balanced molecular, total ionic, and net ionic equations for precipitation reactions.

6-6 Write balanced molecular, total ionic, and net ionic equations for neutralization reactions.

# 6-3 The Formation of Ions in Water

▶ **OBJECTIVE FOR SECTION 6-3**
Write the ions formed when ionic compounds or acids dissolve in water.

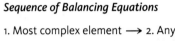 **LOOKING AHEAD!** Before we discuss some general types of reactions that occur in aqueous solution we will examine how ions are formed in water. ■

## 6-3.1 Salts in Aqueous Solution

When one adds a sprinkle of table salt (sodium chloride) to water, the salt soon disappears into the aqueous medium. We observe that the table salt is soluble in water forming a homogeneous mixture known as a *solution, w*hich was first described

**FIGURE 6-4 A Soluble Compound** Table salt dissolves as it is added to hot water.

in Chapter 3. (See Figure 6-4.) However, if we add some powdered chalk (calcium carbonate) to water, it forms a suspension that slowly settles to the bottom of the container without apparent change. *When an appreciable amount of a substance dissolves in a liquid medium, we say that the substance is* **soluble**. *If very little or none of the substance dissolves, we say that the compound is* **insoluble**. Recall that *a* **solution** *is composed of a* **solvent** *(usually a liquid such as water) and a* **solute** *(a solid, a liquid, or even a gas).*

In Chapters 2 and 4, we described table salt (NaCl) as an ionic compound composed of $Na^+$ cations and $Cl^-$ anions in the solid state. When an ionic compound dissolves in water, in nearly all cases the compound is separated into individual ions. The solution of NaCl in water can be represented by the equation

$$NaCl(s) \xrightarrow{H_2O} Na^+(aq) + Cl^-(aq)$$

The $H_2O$ shown above the arrow indicates the presence of water as a solvent. The solution of another ionic compound, calcium perchlorate, can be represented by the equation

$$Ca(ClO_4)_2\,(s) \xrightarrow{H_2O} Ca^{2+}\,(aq) + 2ClO_4^-\,(aq)$$

Notice that all the atoms in the perchlorate ion remain together in solution as a complete entity. That is, they do not separate into chlorine and oxygen atoms. This is true for all of the polyatomic ions that we have mentioned.

## 6-3.2 Strong Acids in Aqueous Solution

In Chapter 4, a class of compounds known as acids was introduced and named. These are molecular compounds, but like ionic compounds, they also produce ions when dissolved in water. In this case, the neutral molecule is "ionized" by the water molecules. (We will examine how this happens in a later chapter.) Acids are so named because *they all form the $H^+$ (aq) ion when dissolved in water.* **Strong acids**, such as hydrochloric acid (HCl), *are completely ionized in water.* We will consider only the action of the six common strong acids (HCl, HBr, HI, $HNO_3$, $HClO_4$, and $H_2SO_4$) in water at this time. The solutions of the strong acids, hydrochloric and nitric acid, are illustrated by the equations

$$HCl(aq) \xrightarrow{H_2O} H^+(aq) + Cl^-(aq)$$
$$HNO_3(aq) \xrightarrow{H_2O} H^+(aq) + NO_3^-(aq)$$

### EXAMPLE 6-4  Forming Ions in Aqueous Solution

Write equations illustrating the solution of the following compounds in water: **(a)** $Na_2CO_3$, **(b)** $CaCl_2$, **(c)** $(NH_4)_2Cr_2O_7$, **(d)** $HClO_4$, and **(e)** $H_2SO_4$. (Although it is not exactly correct, consider sulfuric acid as completely separated into two $H^+(aq)$ ions in aqueous solution.)

**PROCEDURE**

If necessary, refer to Table 4-2 or the periodic table for the charges on the ions.

**SOLUTION**

**(a)** $Na_2CO_3$ is composed of $Na^+$ and $CO_3^{2-}$ ions.

$$Na_2CO_3 \longrightarrow 2Na^+(aq) + CO_3^{2-}(aq)$$

**(b)** $CaCl_2$ is composed of $Ca^{2+}$ and $Cl^-$ ions.

$$CaCl_2 \longrightarrow Ca^{2+}(aq) + 2Cl^-(aq)$$

**(c)** $(NH_4)_2Cr_2O_7$ is composed of $NH_4^+$ and $Cr_2O_7^{2-}$ ions.

$$(NH_4)_2Cr_2O_7 \longrightarrow 2NH_4^+(aq) + Cr_2O_7^{2-}(aq)$$

**(d)** $HClO_4$ is a strong acid that produces $H^+(aq)$ and $ClO_4^-$ ions.

$$HClO_4 \longrightarrow H^+(aq) + ClO_4^-(aq)$$

**(e)** $H_2SO_4$ is a strong acid that produces $H^+(aq)$ and $SO_4^{2-}$ ions.

$$H_2SO_4 \longrightarrow 2H^+(aq) + SO_4^{2-}(aq)$$

**ANALYSIS**

The meaning of the subscript again becomes crucial to your ability to perform this task. Distinguish between the 3 in $CO_3^{2-}$ and the 3 in $FeCl_3$. In the carbonate ion, the subscript 3 is a part of the formula of the ion. You could almost consider it part of the "symbol" of carbonate. The symbol for chlorine is just Cl. Therefore, the subscript 3 in $FeCl_3$ tells us how many ions of chloride there are. To show three ions of carbonate, the entire formula would have to be in parenthesis with a subscripted 3 on the outside.

**SYNTHESIS**

We will learn in Chapter 12 that the number of aqueous ions an ionic compound breaks into can affect some of that solution's properties. Order the following compounds by number of ions they'll form in solution: $Al(ClO_3)_3$, $Na_2CO_3$, $NH_4Cl$, $Fe_2(SO_4)_3$. The correct order is $NH_4Cl$ (with two), $Na_2CO_3$ (three), $Al(ClO_3)_3$ (four), and $Fe_2(SO_4)_3$ (five).

▶ **ASSESSING THE OBJECTIVES FOR SECTION 6-3**

**EXERCISE 6-3(a) LEVEL 1:** List the cations and the anions present when the following compounds dissolve in water.
**(a)** $HClO_4$ **(b)** $K_3PO_4$ **(c)** $NH_4NO_3$ **(d)** $Zn(ClO_4)_2$

**EXERCISE 6-3(b) LEVEL 2:** How many ions will the following species form when one formula unit of each dissolves in water?
**(a)** $MgBr_2$ **(b)** $Na_3PO_4$ **(c)** $Fe(NO_3)_3$ **(d)** $KClO_3$

**EXERCISE 6-3(c) LEVEL 2:** Write the equations illustrating the formation of solutions of the following compounds. Indicate state symbols.
**(a)** $Na_2SO_4$ **(b)** $HNO_3$ **(c)** $Al(C_2H_3O_2)_3$ **(d)** $Ca(OH)_2$

*For additional practice, work chapter problems 6-24, 6-25, and 6-26.*

# 6-4 Single-Replacement Reactions

**LOOKING AHEAD!** Solutions containing metal cations may undergo chemical reactions when a solid sample of some other metal comes into contact with this solution. In this section, we will examine this type of reaction. ■

▶ **OBJECTIVE FOR SECTION 6-4**
Given the activity series, represent several single-replacement reactions with balanced molecular, total ionic, and net ionic equations.

An interesting thing happens when we immerse a strip of zinc metal in a blue aqueous solution of a copper(II) salt such as $CuSO_4(aq)$. When we remove the zinc, it now looks as if it has changed into copper. The blue solution has also lost some of its color. Actually, what happened is that a coating of copper formed on the metal strip. Silver and gold will also form a coating on a strip of zinc immersed in solutions of compounds containing these metal ions. (See Figure 6-5.) These and similar reactions are known as **single-replacement reactions**. In this type of reaction, which most often occurs in aqueous solution, one free element substitutes for another element already combined in a chemical compound. The replacement of zinc ions for the copper ions and the copper metal for the zinc metal is illustrated here; other examples follow.

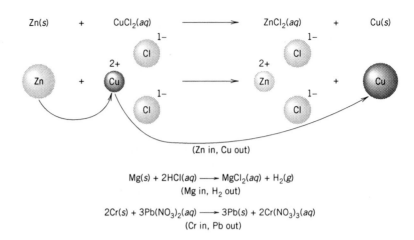

$$Zn(s) + CuCl_2(aq) \longrightarrow ZnCl_2(aq) + Cu(s)$$

(Zn in, Cu out)

$$Mg(s) + 2HCl(aq) \longrightarrow MgCl_2(aq) + H_2(g)$$
(Mg in, $H_2$ out)

$$2Cr(s) + 3Pb(NO_3)_2(aq) \longrightarrow 3Pb(s) + 2Cr(NO_3)_3(aq)$$
(Cr in, Pb out)

**FIGURE 6-5 Single-Replacement Reaction** The formation of a layer of copper on a piece of zinc is a single-replacement reaction.

## 6-4.1 Types of Equations

The equation illustrating the replacement of Zn by Cu is known as the molecular form of the equation. *In a* **molecular equation**, *all reactants and products are shown as neutral compounds.* To represent the nature of soluble ionic compounds and strong acids in water, it is helpful to show the separate ions as they actually exist in aqueous solution. *When the cations and anions of a compound in solution are shown separately, the resulting equation is known as a* **total ionic equation**. It is illustrated as follows.

(molecular equation) $Zn(s) + CuCl_2(aq) \longrightarrow ZnCl_2(aq) + Cu(s)$

(total ionic equation) $Zn(s) + Cu^{2+}(aq) + 2Cl^-(aq) \longrightarrow Zn^{2+}(aq) + 2Cl^-(aq) + Cu(s)$

Notice that in this equation, the $Cl^-$ ions appear on both sides of the equation unchanged. Their role is to provide the anions needed to counteract the positive charge of the cations. The presence of the $Cl^-$ ions is certainly necessary because any compound, whether in the pure state or dispersed in solution, must be electrically neutral. However, they do not actually affect the chemical change that is occurring. *Ions that are in an identical state on both sides of a total ionic equation are called* **spectator ions**. *If spectator ions are subtracted from both sides of the equation, the remaining equation is known as the* **net ionic equation**. This equation focuses only on the species that have undergone a change in the reaction. By subtracting the two $Cl^-$ spectator ions from both sides of the equation we have the net ionic equation. It is the net ionic equation that actually shows us the reaction that is occurring in the beaker.

(net ionic) $Zn(s) + Cu^{2+}(aq) \longrightarrow Zn^{2+}(aq) + Cu(s)$

A reaction is spontaneous in one direction only, so the reverse reaction does not occur. That is, if we were to immerse a copper strip in a $ZnCl_2$ solution, a coating of Zn would not form on the copper. (See Figure 6-6.)

## 6-4.2 The Activity Series

Series of experiments performed on different metal–solution combinations allow us to compare the ability of one metal to replace the ions of other metals in solution. The **activity series** shown in Table 6-2 *lists some common metals in decreasing order of their ability to replace metal ions in aqueous solution.* (The metal cations present in solution are shown to the right of the metal.) The metal at the top (K) replaces all of the metal ions below it and is therefore the *most* reactive. The second metal replaces all below it, while its ions will be replaced only by K. In fact, K, Na, Mg, and Al are all so reactive that they react with water itself. (Aluminum *appears* unreactive with water because it is coated with $Al_2O_3$, which protects the metal from contact with water.) They replace other metal ions only when the solids are mixed,

**FIGURE 6-6 Copper in a Zinc Sulfate Solution** When a strip of copper is immersed in a zinc ion solution, no reaction occurs.

not when the ions are in water solution. The following balanced equation illustrates such a reaction.

$$2Al(s) + Fe_2O_3(s) \longrightarrow Al_2O_3(s) + 2Fe(l)$$

The previous reaction is known as the *thermite reaction* because it liberates so much heat that the iron formed is molten. As a result, this reaction has application in welding.

In the activity series $H_2$ is treated as a metal and $H^+$ $(aq)$ (from one of the six strong acids) as its metal ion. The activity series can be used to predict which reactions are expected to occur. For example, notice in Table 6-2 that nickel is ranked higher than silver. This allows us to predict that elemental nickel metal replaces the $Ag^+$ ion in solution. Thus, if we immerse a strip of nickel in a solution of aqueous $AgNO_3$, we find that a coating of silver forms on the nickel. The balanced molecular equation and net ionic equation illustrating this reaction are as follows. Note that the nitrate ion $(NO_3^-)$ is a spectator ion.

$$Ni(s) + 2AgNO_3(aq) \longrightarrow 2Ag(s) + Ni(NO_3)_2(aq)$$
$$Ni(s) + 2Ag^+(aq) \longrightarrow 2Ag(s) + Ni^{2+}(aq) \text{ (net ionic)}$$

**TABLE 6-2**

**The Activity Series**

|  | METAL | METAL ION |
|---|---|---|
| (most active) | K | $K^+$ |
|  | Na | $Na^+$ |
|  | Ca | $Ca^{2+}$ |
|  | Mg | $Mg^{2+}$ |
|  | Al | $Al^{3+}$ |
|  | Zn | $Zn^{2+}$ |
|  | Cr | $Cr^{3+}$ |
|  | Fe | $Fe^{2+}$ |
|  | Ni | $Ni^{2+}$ |
|  | Sn | $Sn^{2+}$ |
|  | Pb | $Pb^{2+}$ |
|  | $H_2$ | $H^+$ |
|  | Cu | $Cu^{2+}$ |
|  | Ag | $Ag^+$ |
| (least active) | Au | $Au^{3+}$ |

## EXAMPLE 6-5  Predicting Spontaneous Single-Replacement Reactions

Consider the following two possible reactions. If a reaction does occur, write the balanced molecular, total ionic, and net ionic equations illustrating the reactions.

**(a)** A strip of tin metal is placed in an aqueous $AgNO_3$ solution.

**(b)** A strip of silver metal is placed in an aqueous perchloric acid solution.

PROCEDURE

**(a)** Notice in the activity series that Sn is higher in the series than Ag. Therefore Sn replaces $Ag^+$ ions from solution.

**(b)** In the activity series, $H_2$ is higher than Ag. Therefore, $H_2$ replaces $Ag^+$, but the reverse reaction, the replacement of $H^+$ by Ag, does not occur.

SOLUTION

**(a)**
$$Sn(s) + 2AgNO_3(aq) \longrightarrow 2Ag(s) + Sn(NO_3)_2(aq) \text{ (molecular)}$$
$$Sn(s) + 2Ag^+(aq) + 2NO_3^-(aq) \longrightarrow 2Ag(s) + Sn^{2+}(aq) + 2NO_3^-(aq) \text{ (total ionic)}$$
$$Sn(s) + 2Ag^+(aq) \longrightarrow 2Ag(s) + Sn^{2+}(aq) \text{ (net ionic)}$$

**(b)** No reaction occurs.

ANALYSIS

To say that a metal is reactive means that it has a tendency to exist as an ion, not a free metal. To say that a metal is stable means that it is more often found in its metallic, or free, state. So compare Al and Pb. Which is more reactive? Which is more likely to be found in its free state? Which will replace which in a single-replacement reaction? The aluminum is more reactive. The lead is more stable. Therefore, solid aluminum will switch places with, or replace, aqueous lead ion in a single-replacement reaction. It's worth noting that Table 6-2 also reflects the ease with which metals are recovered in mining. You can proceed up the list from the bottom and have a roughly accurate historical record of the order in which important metals were put into service by various cultures.

According to Table 6-2, which metals won't react with acid? Cu, Ag, and Au. How are the uses of these metals related to this chemical property? We use them to make metallic objects that we wouldn't want to corrode or dissolve. Obvious examples are coins, wiring, and jewelry. Why, then, is iron used so extensively in structural building? It is in the middle of the chart, and fairly reactive. It's because it is strong, abundant, and easy to mine and process. We then have to make allowances for the fact that we'll need to protect or replace structures made from iron, and its alloy steel, on a regular basis because of the constant chemical corrosion that occurs. If iron is exposed to the weather, for instance, it will need periodic painting.

▶ **ASSESSING THE OBJECTIVE FOR SECTION 6-4**

**EXERCISE 6-4(a) LEVEL 1:** Choose the metal that will replace the other one (as an ion) in solution.

**(a)** Ag or Ni  **(b)** Al or Cu  **(c)** Cr or Mg  **(d)** Sn or acid

**EXERCISE 6-4(b) LEVEL 2:** Given the following molecular equations, write the total and the net ionic equations for the reactions:

**(a)** $Cu(NO_3)_2(aq) + Zn(s) \longrightarrow Zn(NO_3)_2(aq) + Cu(s)$
**(b)** $2Al(s) + 3PbCl_2(aq) \longrightarrow 2AlCl_3(aq) + 3Pb(s)$

**EXERCISE 6-4(c) LEVEL 2:** Complete balanced molecular equations for the following reactants.

**(a)** $Mg(s) + AgNO_3(aq) \longrightarrow$
**(b)** $Sn(s) + KI(aq) \longrightarrow$
**(c)** $Na(s) + HCl(aq) \longrightarrow$

**EXERCISE 6-4(d) LEVEL 3:** Write total and net ionic equations for the following reactants.

**(a)** $CuCl_2(aq) + Fe(s) \longrightarrow$
**(b)** $Mg(s) + Au(NO_3)_3(aq) \longrightarrow$

*For additional practice, work chapter problems 6-28, 6-30, and 6-31.*

▶ **OBJECTIVE FOR SECTION 6-5**
Write balanced molecular, total ionic, and net ionic equations for precipitation reactions.

# 6-5 Double-Replacement Reactions—Precipitation

**LOOKING AHEAD!** In a single-replacement reaction, only cations are involved. In a double-replacement reaction, both cations and anions are involved. The driving force of these reactions is the formation of a product from the exchange of ions that is insoluble in water, is a molecular compound, or, in a few cases, is both. The first type of double-replacement reaction, formation of a solid, is discussed in this section. ∎

## 6-5.1 Soluble and Insoluble Ionic Compounds

Marble statues have suffered the ravages of weather, for thousands of years in some cases. Marble, limestone, and chalk are essentially the same compound, calcium carbonate. Obviously, this ionic compound is insoluble in water. It formed when calcium ions ($Ca^{2+}$) and carbonate ions ($CO_3^{2-}$) present in some ancient sea came together to form a solid deposit. Before we look at this type of reaction, we should bring some order and guidelines to the determination of which ionic compounds are soluble in water and which are not. In Table 6-3, some rules for the solubility of compounds containing common anions are listed. Although this table focuses only on anions, it will help to know that compounds formed from cations of Group IA (i.e., $Na^+$, $K^+$) and the $NH_4^+$ ion are all water soluble regardless of the anion.

TABLE 6-3

## Solubility Rules for Some Ionic Compounds

| ANION | SOLUBILITY RULE |
|---|---|
| **Mostly Soluble** | |
| $Cl^-$, $Br^-$, $I^-$ | All cations form *soluble* compounds except $Ag^+$, $Hg_2^{2+}$, and $Pb^{2+}$. ($PbCl_2$ and $PbBr_2$ are slightly soluble.) |
| $NO_3^-$, $ClO_4^-$, $C_2H_3O_2^-$ | All cations form *soluble* compounds. ($KClO_4$ and $AgC_2H_3O_2$ are slightly soluble.) |
| $SO_4^{2-}$ | All cations form *soluble* compounds except $Pb^{2+}$, $Ba^{2+}$, and $Sr^{2+}$. ($Ca^{2+}$ and $Ag^+$ form slightly soluble compounds.) |
| **Mostly Insoluble** | |
| $CO_3^{2-}$, $PO_4^{3-}$ | All cations form *insoluble* compounds except Group IA metals and $NH_4^+$. |
| $S^{2-}$ | All cations form *insoluble* compounds except Group IA and IIA metals and $NH_4^+$. |
| $OH^-$ | All cations form *insoluble* compounds except Group IA metals, $Ba^{2+}$, $Sr^{2+}$, and $NH_4^+$. [$Ca(OH)_2$ is slightly soluble.] |

## EXAMPLE 6-6    Predicting Whether an Ionic Compound is Soluble

Use Table 6-3 to predict whether the following compounds are soluble or insoluble.

(a) NaI        (b) CdS        (c) $Ba(NO_3)_2$        (d) $SrSO_4$

PROCEDURE

Apply the solubility rules to the anion. Check to see that the cation is mentioned as an exception.

SOLUTION

(a) According to Table 6-3, all alkali metal (Group IA) compounds of the anions listed are soluble. Therefore, NaI is soluble.
(b) All $S^{2-}$ compounds are insoluble except those formed with Group IA and IIA metals and $NH_4^+$. Since Cd is in Group IIB, it is not one of the exceptions. CdS is insoluble.
(c) All $NO_3^-$ compounds are soluble. Therefore, $Ba(NO_3)_2$ is soluble.
(d) The $Sr^{2+}$ ion is one of the exceptions to soluble $SO_4^{2-}$ compounds. Therefore, $SrSO_4$ is insoluble.

ANALYSIS

In order for an ionic compound to be insoluble, both the cation and the anion have to form at least some insoluble compounds. If either of them forms only soluble compounds, then the specific compounds containing these cations or anions are soluble (with the noted exceptions). Consider the following compounds: $NH_4Cl$, $Na_3PO_4$, $Fe(NO_3)_3$, and $Cu(OH)_2$. In $NH_4Cl$, $Cl^-$ is a listed soluble anion, and $NH_4^+$ is one of the universally soluble cations. Clearly the compound is soluble. In the case of $Na_3PO_4$, the presence of $Na^+$ (a soluble cation) overrides the presence of the typically insoluble $PO_4^{3-}$. Just the reverse is true in $Fe(NO_3)_3$, where the presence of the soluble $NO_3^-$ makes the compound soluble. $Cu(OH)_2$, however, is insoluble, since the $Cu^{2+}$ ion is not one of the exceptions.

SYNTHESIS

Occasionally it is useful to remove a particular cation or anion from solution by formation of a solid compound containing that ion. What anion could you add to a solution containing $Zn^{2+}$ to make it insoluble? There are several possibilities. Anything in the lower half of Table 6-3 would work to precipitate the zinc—$S^{2-}$, for example. This leads us to the discussion of these types of reactions.

### 6-5.2 Formation of a Precipitate

What happens when we mix solutions containing soluble ionic compounds? It depends. If we mix a solution of $CuCl_2$ (green) and $KNO_3$ (clear), we simply have a mixture of the four ions in solution, as illustrated in Figure 6-7; no cation is associated with a particular anion.

Now let's consider a case of two solutions, one containing the soluble compound $CuCl_2$ and the other containing the soluble compound $AgNO_3$. When we mix these two solutions, something obviously occurs. The mixture immediately becomes cloudy, and eventually a white solid settles to the bottom of the container. *The solid that is formed by the reaction of the two solutions is called a* **precipitate**. In this case it is the insoluble compound, $AgCl$. In fact, whenever $Ag^+$ and $Cl^-$ are mixed into the same solution, they come together to form solid $AgCl$. This leaves the $Cu^{2+}$ (which forms a blue color) and the $NO_3^-$ ions in solution, since $Cu(NO_3)_2$ is soluble. (See Figure 6-8.)

*The formation of a precipitate by mixing solutions of two soluble compounds is known as a* **precipitation reaction**. This is one of three types of **double-replacement reactions** where the two cations involved exchange anions. The reaction is illustrated by the following molecular equation.

$$2AgNO_3(aq) + CuCl_2(aq) \longrightarrow 2AgCl(s) + Cu(NO_3)_2(aq)$$

In the total ionic equation, the soluble ionic compounds are represented as separate ions on both sides of the equation, but the solid precipitate (i.e., $AgCl$) is shown as a neutral compound since the two ions come together to produce the insoluble solid.

$$2Ag^+(aq) + 2NO_3^-(aq) + Cu^{2+}(aq) + 2Cl^-(aq) \longrightarrow$$
$$2AgCl(s) + Cu^{2+}(aq) + 2NO_3^-(aq)$$

**FIGURE 6-7 A Mixture of $CuCl_2$ and $KNO_3$ Solutions** No reaction occurs when these solutions are mixed.

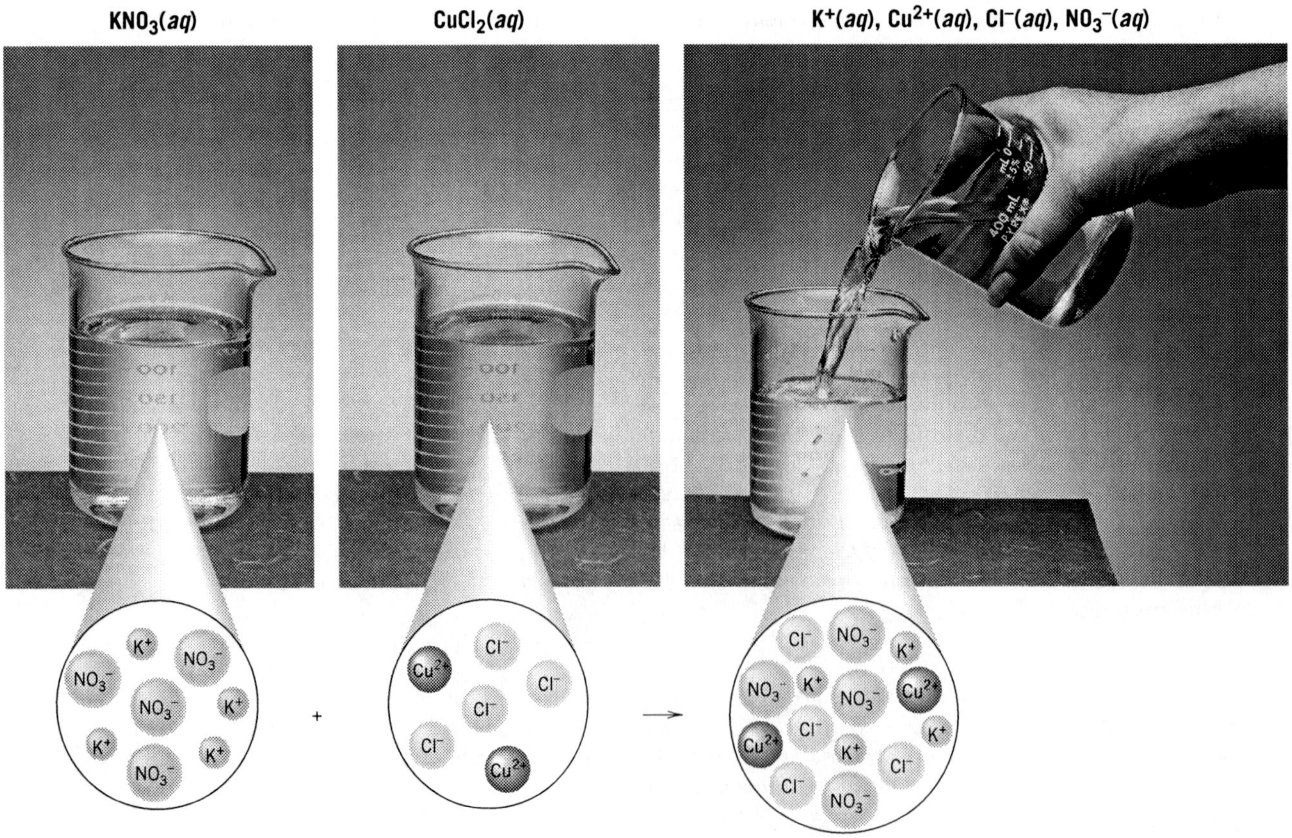

KNO$_3$(aq)          CuCl$_2$(aq)          K$^+$(aq), Cu$^{2+}$(aq), Cl$^-$(aq), NO$_3^-$(aq)

AgNO₃(aq)          CuCl₂(aq)          AgCl(s) + Cu²⁺(aq), NO₃⁻(aq)

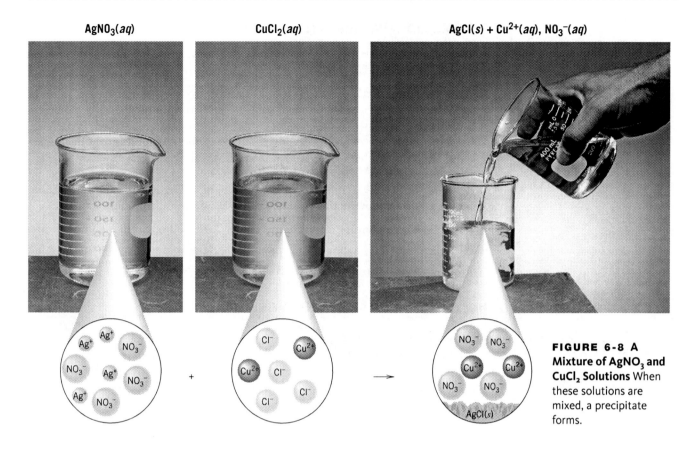

**FIGURE 6-8 A Mixture of AgNO₃ and CuCl₂ Solutions** When these solutions are mixed, a precipitate forms.

Notice that there are two spectator ions, $Cu^{2+}$ and $NO_3^-$. After spectator ions are subtracted from the equation, we have the net ionic equation for the reaction. As before, the net ionic equation shows us the real reaction occurring in the system.

$$Ag^+ (aq) + Cl^- (aq) \longrightarrow AgCl(s)$$

As in the single-replacement reactions discussed previously, the net ionic equation focuses on the driving force for the reaction, which is the formation of solid AgCl from two soluble compounds.

There are some very practical applications of precipitation reactions in industry as well as in the laboratory. Our example is of particular value. Silver is widely used in the development of film. It is obviously worthwhile to recover this precious metal whenever possible. Silver metal in film can be dissolved in aqueous nitric acid to form the water-soluble compound $AgNO_3$. [This is not a single-replacement reaction (which by itself would not work) but involves the nitrate ion in a more complex reaction.] Although the solution contains many other dissolved substances, addition of a soluble compound containing the $Cl^-$ ion (e.g., NaCl) leads to the formation of solid AgCl, as shown in Figure 6-8. As you notice from Table 6-3, very few other cations form precipitates with $Cl^-$, so this is a reaction more or less specific to removing $Ag^+$ from aqueous solution. The AgCl can then be filtered from the solution and silver metal eventually recovered.

In other precipitation reactions, we may want to recover the soluble compound and discard the insoluble compound. In such a case, we would remove the precipitate by filtration and then recover the soluble compound by boiling away the solvent water. See the "Making It Real: Hard Water and Water Treatment" for a discussion on how this concept can be used to improve the quality of a community's water supply.

### 6-5.3 Rules for Writing Precipitation Reactions

By careful use of Table 6-3, we can predict the occurrence of many precipitation reactions. To accomplish this, we follow this procedure:

1. Write the compounds produced in the reaction by "switching partners," changing subscripts as necessary to make sure that the compounds have the correct formulas based on the ions' charges (which do not change).
2. Examine Table 6-3 to determine whether one of these compounds is insoluble. Label the soluble chemicals (*aq*) for *aqueous* and the insoluble ones (*s*) for *solid.*
3. If one of the two new compounds is insoluble in water, a precipitation reaction occurs and we can write the equation illustrating the reaction.

The following examples illustrate the use of Table 6-3 to predict and write precipitation reactions.

### EXAMPLE 6-7   Writing a Possible Precipitation Reaction

A solution of $Na_2CO_3$ is mixed with a solution of $CaCl_2$. Predict what happens. If a precipitate forms, write the balanced molecular, total ionic, and net ionic equations.

#### PROCEDURE
Follow the steps outlined above.

#### SOLUTION
The four ions involved are $Na^+$, $CO_3^{2-}$, $Ca^{2+}$, and $Cl^-$. The combinations of the $Na^+$ and $Cl^-$ and the $Ca^{2+}$ and $CO_3^{2-}$ produce the compounds NaCl and $CaCO_3$. If both of these compounds are soluble, no reaction occurs. In this case, however, reference to Table 6-3 indicates that $CaCO_3$ is insoluble. Thus, a reaction occurs that we can illustrate with a balanced reaction written in molecular form.

$$Na_2CO_3(aq) + CaCl_2(s) \longrightarrow CaCO_3(s) + 2NaCl(aq)$$

The equation written in total ionic form is

$$2Na^+(aq) + CO_3^{2-}(aq) + Ca^{2+}(aq) + 2Cl^-(aq) \longrightarrow CaCO_3(s) + 2Na^+(aq) + 2Cl^-(aq)$$

Note that the $Na^+$ and the $Cl^-$ ions are spectator ions. Elimination of the spectator ions on both sides of the equation leaves the net ionic equation.

$$Ca^{2+}(aq) + CO_3^{2-}(aq) \longrightarrow CaCO_3(s)$$

(This would be an example of the formation of limestone in an ancient sea.)

#### ANALYSIS
Working as many of these types of problems as possible is the key to seeing the patterns that develop. Typically, the anion of one of the reactants will combine with the cation of the second to form the insoluble product. A quick glance at the anions present will give you an idea of the likelihood that they will form an insoluble compound. Then analyze the cation of the other reactant. Will it combine with the first anion to precipitate? Consider $Ni(NO_3)_2$ and $Li_3PO_4$. Do we expect an insoluble product to form? Of the two anions, the phosphate is the one likely to form a precipitate. The cation of the first compound, $Ni^{2+}$, is not in the Group IA column, so it, too, is a good candidate. We'd expect the combination of the two, $Ni_3(PO_4)_2$ (nickel(II) phosphate), to be a precipitate.

#### SYNTHESIS
Can you go further and find a compound that would react with a given reactant? What compound (and there are several) would form a precipitate with KOH? Here it is the anion that likely will precipitate. Let's pick a cation that will do the job. $Cu^{2+}$ would work. Now we need an anion that will ensure the $Cu^{2+}$ to be initially soluble. Nitrate, chloride, and acetate fit the bill. $Cu(NO_3)_3$, for one, would dissolve in water and then form a precipitate with KOH. Following that same reasoning, any of these would also work: $FeCl_3$, $Al(C_2H_3O_2)_3$, $NiSO_4$, and many others. Consider the following example.

## EXAMPLE 6-8    Writing a Possible Precipitation Reaction

A solution of KOH is mixed with a solution of $MgI_2$. Predict what happens. If a precipitate forms, write the balanced molecular, total ionic, and net ionic equations.

### SOLUTION

The four ions involved are $K^+$, $OH^-$, $Mg^{2+}$ and $I^-$. An exchange of ions in the reactants produces the compounds KI and $Mg(OH)_2$. Reference to Table 6-3 indicates that $Mg^{2+}$ forms an insoluble compound with $OH^-$. Therefore, a precipitation reaction does occur and is illustrated with the following molecular equation.

$$2KOH(aq) + MgI_2(aq) \longrightarrow Mg(OH)_2(s) + 2KI(aq)$$

The total ionic equation is

$$2K^+(aq) + 2OH^-(aq) + Mg^{2+}(aq) + 2I^-(aq) \longrightarrow Mg(OH_2)(s) + 2K^+(aq) + 2I^-(aq)$$

Elimination of spectator ions gives the net ionic equation.

$$Mg^{2+}(aq) + 2OH^-(aq) \longrightarrow Mg(OH)_2(s)$$

### ANALYSIS

When writing the total ionic equation, simply go through your equation to all the ionic compounds or acids labeled "aqueous," and break them apart into their ions. Any other chemical, labeled as "solid," "liquid," or "gas," should be written exactly the same way it was in the molecular equation.

### SYNTHESIS

It is almost always the case that the combination of the four possible ions from a double-replacement reaction will at most form one insoluble compound. In several cases, *no* insoluble compound forms and there is no reaction (see the next example). By studying Table 6-3, particularly the exceptions, can you come up with a combination of two soluble compounds that will react to form two insoluble products? There are very few choices. Notice that $Ba(OH)_2$ is soluble, whereas most hydroxides are insoluble. Furthermore, $BaSO_4$ is insoluble, whereas most sulfates are soluble. Does that give you an idea? As an example, how about combining solutions of $Ba(OH)_2(aq)$ and $CuSO_4(aq)$? What would that net ionic equation look like?

$$Ba^{2+}(aq) + 2OH^-(aq) + Cu^{2+}(aq) + SO_4^{2-}(aq) \longrightarrow BaSO_4(s) + Cu(OH)_2(s)$$

## EXAMPLE 6-9    Writing a Possible Precipitation Reaction

A solution of KBr is mixed with a solution of $Sr(ClO_4)_2$. Predict what happens. If a precipitate forms, write the balanced molecular, total ionic, and net ionic equations.

### SOLUTION

The four ions involved are $K^+$, $Br^-$, $Sr^{2+}$, and $ClO_4^-$. An exchange of ions produces the compounds $KClO_4$ and $SrBr_2$. Both of these compounds are soluble, so no reaction occurs. The solution contains a mixture of these four ions.

### ANALYSIS

Visually, what would we expect to see in these examples? In the case of the precipitation reactions, we initially begin with two clear, though not necessarily colorless, solutions. Upon mixing, cloudiness appears due to particles that should eventually settle to the bottom of the reaction vessel. For this last reaction, the two solutions are simply mixed together into one large vessel; they look essentially the same as before mixing. If one solution was colored, the combination might appear to be a lighter hue, but this is just due to diluting. It doesn't indicate a chemical reaction. (See also the example in Figure 6-7.)

### SYNTHESIS

The following reaction works, for reasons to be discussed in the following section. What would you predict to be the visual indication of a reaction?

$$Fe(OH)_3 + 3HCl \longrightarrow 3H_2O + FeCl_3$$

According to the solubility rules, $Fe(OH)_3$ is a solid. HCl and $FeCl_3$ are in aqueous solutions. $H_2O$ is, of course, a liquid. So we are starting off with a solid and aqueous solution, and ending with a mixture of a soluble salt in water. Therefore, upon the addition of hydrochloric acid, we should see our solid "disappear," as its soluble product dissolves in water.

## MAKING IT REAL

### Hard Water and Water Treatment

Hard water is water that contains significant concentrations of $Fe^{3+}$, $Ca^{2+}$ and $Mg^{2+}$. These are picked up when rainwater filters down through soil rich in these ions. Most areas of the country, other than the South, East Coast, and Pacific Northwest, suffer from very hard water. Hard water has a strong tendency to form insoluble compounds with the compounds found in soap. This reduces the soap's ability to clean by forming an insoluble residue that deposits on sinks, tubs, dishes, and clothes. This leaves them gray, gritty, and dingy. Insoluble carbonates may also precipitate within water pipes and water heaters, forming what is called *scale*. Scale reduces water flow, insulates the water in heaters from the heat source, and lowers the lifetime of the plumbing.

Hard water can be fixed by using detergents with added softening agents. These compounds remain soluble despite the presence of the hard ions, making lathering and cleaning more effective. The instillation of a water-softening system in a house also solves the problem of hard water. This system exchanges the soft soluble cation $Na^+$ for the hard ions that form precipitates in the water. (Recall that sodium compounds are all soluble.) This must be done to preserve the total charge, so it takes two sodium ions to remove one calcium ion or one magnesium ion, and three sodium ions to remove one iron ion [e.g., $3Na^+(aq)$ has the same total charge as one $Fe^{3+}$]. However, the large amount of sodium added to the water can make it unhealthy, especially for those on a low-sodium diet. So water-softening systems are installed only on pipes leading to showers and other cleaning devices. Typically the kitchen and bathroom sinks receive the harder, but healthier, water.

Municipalities in areas that have hard water try to reduce the problem by removing some of the ions at the source before the water goes to commercial and residential areas. They do this by adding CaO and $Na_2CO_3$ to the water. These compounds cause the hard ions to precipitate at the site as their insoluble hydroxide or carbonate salts. These salts are then allowed to settle out of the water and are periodically removed.

Each treatment option described relies on chemists and engineers understanding the chemical reactions that lead to the problems caused, and then employing other reactions, based on solubility, that allow them to alleviate the problem.

▶ **ASSESSING THE OBJECTIVE FOR SECTION 6-5**

**EXERCISE 6-5{a} LEVEL 1:** Do the following refer to soluble or insoluble compounds?
**(a)** It forms a precipitate.
**(b)** It is labeled "$(aq)$."
**(c)** It dissolves in water.
**(d)** Its formation is the driving force in the reaction.
**(e)** It breaks apart into its individual cations and anions.

**EXERCISE 6-5{b} LEVEL 2:** Label the following as being soluble ($aq$) or insoluble ($s$).
**(a)** $(NH_4)_2SO_4$      **(b)** $Sn(OH)_2$      **(c)** $Pb(NO_3)_2$
**(d)** $Fe_2(SO_4)_3$      **(e)** $MgCO_3$      **(f)** $Ag_3PO_4$

**EXERCISE 6-5{c} LEVEL 2:** Determine whether the following reactants will form a precipitate.
**(a)** $K_2CO_3$ and $Na_2SO_4$      **(b)** $AlBr_3$ and NaOH      **(c)** $(NH_4)_2S$ and $CaI_2$

**EXERCISE 6-5(d) LEVEL 2:** Write the balanced molecular formula, complete with the state symbols $(aq)$ and $(s)$, for the following reactants.

**(a)** $CrI_3(aq) + Li_3PO_4(aq) \longrightarrow$        **(b)** $Cs_2CO_3(aq) + FeBr_3(aq) \longrightarrow$

**EXERCISE 6-5(e) LEVEL 3:** A solution of $AgNO_3$ is mixed with a solution of $K_2S$. Write the molecular, total ionic, and net ionic equations illustrating the reaction.

**EXERCISE 6-5(f) LEVEL 3:** What soluble compounds could you mix together to create a precipitate of:

**(a)** $CaCO_3$        **(b)** $FePO_4$

*For additional practice, work chapter problems 6-34, 6-37, 6-39, 6-44, and 6-46.*

# 6-6 Double-Replacement Reactions–Neutralization

▶ **OBJECTIVE FOR SECTION 6-6**
Write balanced molecular, total ionic, and net ionic equations for neutralization reactions.

**LOOKING AHEAD!** In a second type of double-replacement reaction, the ions combine to form a molecular compound. Although there are several examples of this, we will focus on the formation of the simple molecular compound water. This is discussed next. ∎

## 6-6.1 Strong Acids and Strong Bases

Strong acids and bases are two compounds that can be difficult, if not dangerous, to handle. They are very corrosive and can cause severe burns. (See Figure 6-9.) When carefully (i.e., slowly) mixed together in the right proportions, however, they become harmless. The corrosive properties of both are "neutralized." In Section 4-6 we defined a class of compounds known as strong acids. They are characterized by their complete ionization in water to form $H^+(aq)$ and an anion. A second class of compounds, **strong bases**, *dissolve in water to form the hydroxide ion [$OH^-(aq)$]*. Unlike acids, these compounds are ionic in the solid state and the ions are simply separated in the aqueous solution as in any soluble ionic compound. The strong bases are hydroxides formed by the Group IA and IIA metal ions (except for $Be^{2+}$). Examples include sodium hydroxide (lye) and barium hydroxide. Their solution in water is illustrated by the following equations.

$$NaOH(s) \xrightarrow{H_2O} Na^+(aq) + OH^-(aq)$$
$$Ba(OH)_2(s) \xrightarrow{H_2O} Ba^{2+}(aq) + 2OH^-(aq)$$

**FIGURE 6-9 Strong Acids and Bases** Containers of these compounds usually include a warning about their corrosive properties.

## 6-6.2 Neutralization Reactions

When solutions of strong acids and bases are mixed, the $H^+(aq)$ from the acid combines with the $OH^-(aq)$ from the base to form the molecular compound water. *The reaction of an acid and a base is known as a* **neutralization reaction**. The neutralization of hydrochloric acid and sodium hydroxide is illustrated below with the molecular, total ionic, and net ionic equations. The ionic compound remaining in solution, NaCl, is known as salt. A **salt** *is formed from the cation of the base and the anion of the acid.* If the salt is soluble, its ions are spectator ions and are subtracted from the equation to form the net ionic equation.

$$HCl(aq) + NaOH(aq) \longrightarrow NaCl(aq) + H_2O(l)$$
$$H^+(aq) + Cl^-(aq) + Na^+(aq) + OH^-(aq) \longrightarrow Na^+(aq) + Cl^-(aq) + H_2O(l)$$
$$H^+(aq) + OH^-(aq) \longrightarrow H_2O(l)$$

Unlike precipitation reactions, the net ionic equation for all neutralization reactions between strong acids and strong bases is the same. The driving force for these reactions is the formation of water, a molecular compound, from two ions. The balanced molecular equations for two additional neutralization reactions follow.

$$HBr(aq) + KOH(aq) \longrightarrow KBr(aq) + H_2O(l)$$
$$2HNO_3(aq) + Ca(OH)_2(aq) \longrightarrow Ca(NO_3)_2(aq) + 2H_2O(l)$$

The interactions of other types of acids and bases, known as weak acids and bases, are somewhat more involved and are discussed in more detail in Chapter 13.

---

### EXAMPLE 6-10   Writing Neutralization Reactions

Write the molecular, total ionic, and net ionic equations for the neutralization of **(a)** $HClO_4$ and LiOH and **(b)** $H_2SO_4$ and KOH.

#### PROCEDURE

Follow the steps outlined in Section 6-5.3. Water is a product in neutralization reactions and should be labeled with an (*l*) and not ionized.

#### SOLUTION

To balance the equations, one should make sure that there is one $H^+(aq)$ for each $OH^-(aq)$. Another way is to write the formula of the salt formed and then balance the number of reactant cations (from the base) and reactant anions (from the acid).

**(a)**
$$HClO_4(aq) + LiOH(aq) \longrightarrow LiClO_4(aq) + H_2O(l)$$
$$H^+(aq) + ClO_4^-(aq) + Li^+(aq) + OH^-(aq) \longrightarrow Li^+(aq) + ClO_4^-(aq) + H_2O(l)$$
$$H^+(aq) + OH^-(aq) \longrightarrow H_2O(l)$$

**(b)**
$$H_2SO_4(aq) + 2KOH(aq) \longrightarrow K_2SO_4(aq) + 2H_2O(l)$$
$$2H^+(aq) + SO_4^{2-}(aq) + 2K^+(aq) + 2OH^-(aq) \longrightarrow 2K^+(aq) + SO_4^{2-}(aq) + 2H_2O(l)$$
$$H^+(aq) + OH^-(aq) \longrightarrow H_2O(l)$$

#### ANALYSIS

The water that is produced in the reaction is in addition to the water used as a solvent to dissolve the reactants. So, unlike a precipitation reaction, where the formation of the solid shows us that there is an obvious reaction occurring, neutralization reactions are harder to recognize in the lab. There are many times where no discernible physical change occurs. If the concentrations of reactants are high enough, a significant amount of heat can be produced in the neutralization process and the solution's temperature will rise. Alternatively, you can follow the course of the reaction with chemical indicators that change color as the reactants are neutralized, or the reaction can be followed by electrical meters that track the concentrations of ions in solution. Beyond that, it's just our knowledge of the chemistry of the reaction that tells us that anything is occurring.

#### SYNTHESIS

It will be useful in upcoming chapters to know the balancing coefficients for chemical reactions. Neutralization reactions provide us with a shortcut to determine the needed coefficients for the reactants. Every acid provides a given number of $H^+$s. Every base provides a given number of $OH^-$s. Together they'll combine in a 1-to-1 ratio to form water. So how many of the acid molecules and how many of the base molecules are needed to produce the same number of $H^+$s and $OH^-$s? Consider a reaction between $H_3PO_4$ and $Ba(OH)_2$. What will be the balancing coefficient in front of each molecule?

$H_3PO_4$ delivers $3H^+$. $Ba(OH)_2$ delivers $2OH^-$. Two acids and three bases will produce a total of six waters. The balancing coefficients are 2 and 3, respectively.

---

### 6-6.3 Gas-Forming Neutralization Reactions

Calcium carbonate is the solid ingredient in several products commonly advertised that effectively neutralizes stomach acid. Although it is not a strong base, as we described earlier, it does do the job. In this case the double-displacement reaction produces a molecular compound other than water. The molecular compound formed in this case is carbonic acid, which then decomposes to carbon dioxide gas and water as described earlier in this chapter. The salt acts as a base-neutralizing stomach acid (HCl) as shown below.

$$2HCl(aq) + CaCO_3(s) \longrightarrow CaCl_2(aq) + H_2CO_3(aq)$$

The carbonic acid formed is a molecular compound that then decomposes to carbon dioxide gas and water.

$$H_2CO_3 \longrightarrow CO_2(g) + H_2O(l)$$

The complete reaction is illustrated below.

$$2HCl(aq) + CaCO_3(s) \longrightarrow CaCl_2(aq) + CO_2(g) + H_2O(l)$$

The net ionic equation for this reaction is

$$CO_3{}^{2-}(aq) + 2H^+(aq) \longrightarrow CO_2(g) + H_2O(l)$$

Salts containing the following anions neutralize strong acids by forming a gas.

- $HCO_3{}^-$ and $CO_3{}^{2-}$ salts produce $H_2CO_3$, which decomposes to $CO_2(g) + H_2O$.
- $HSO_3{}^-$ and $SO_3{}^{2-}$ salts produce $H_2SO_3$, which decomposes to $SO_2(g) + H_2O$.
- $HS^-$ and $S^{2-}$ salts produce $H_2S(g)$.
- $CN^-$ salts produce $HCN(g)$.

Another example for a **gas-forming reaction** is shown below.

$$K_2S(aq) + 2HNO_3(aq) \longrightarrow 2KNO_3(aq) + H_2S(g)$$

The net ionic equation for this reaction is

$$S^{2-}(aq) + 2H^+(aq) \longrightarrow H_2S(g)$$

The hydrogen sulfide gas formed is poisonous but in very small amounts produces the obnoxious smell of rotten eggs.

▶ **ASSESSING THE OBJECTIVE FOR SECTION 6-6**

**EXERCISE 6-6{a} LEVEL 1:** Write out how the following compounds exist when placed in water. Use appropriate state symbols.
**(a)** KOH          **(b)** $Fe(OH)_3$          **(c)** HI          **(d)** $NaHSO_3$

**EXERCISE 6-6{b} LEVEL 2:** Write out the balanced molecular equation, complete with the state symbols $(aq)$ and $(l)$, for the following reactants.
**(a)** $H_2SO_4(aq) + LiOH(aq) \longrightarrow$
**(b)** $Ca(OH)_2(aq) + HClO_4(aq) \longrightarrow$
**(c)** $HCl(aq) + NaHCO_3(aq) \longrightarrow$
**(d)** $K_2S(aq) + HBr(aq) \longrightarrow$

**EXERCISE 6-6{c} LEVEL 3:** Write the balanced molecular, total ionic, and net ionic equations illustrating the neutralization of nitric acid with strontium hydroxide.

**EXERCISE 6-6{d} LEVEL 3:** The lethal gas used in the gas chamber is hydrogen cyanide (HCN). It is produced by adding a strong acid to a solid salt. Write a balanced molecular equation illustrating such a reaction using sulfuric acid along with its net ionic equation.

*For additional practice, work chapter problems 6-55, 6-57, and 6-60.*

# PART B SUMMARY

## KEY TERMS

6-3.1    Ionic compounds may be **soluble** or **insoluble** in water. p. 190

6-3.1    A **solution** is formed by a **solute** dissolving in a **solvent**. p. 190

6-3.2    **Strong acids** are completely ionized in aqueous solution. p. 190

6-4    A **single-replacement reaction** involves the exchange of a free metal for a different metal ion. p. 191

6-4.1    Reactions in aqueous solution can be represented by **molecular** and **total ionic equations**. p. 192

6-4.1    When **spectator ions** are subtracted out, a **net ionic equation** results. p. 192

6-4.2    The **activity series** relates the ability of a metal to replace other metal ions. p. 192

6-4.2    A **precipitate** is a solid formed from solution. p. 196

6-5    A **precipitation reaction** is a type of **double-replacement reaction**. p. 196

6-6.1    **Strong bases** are ionic compounds that produce the hydroxide ion in solution. p. 201

6-6.2    A **neutralization reaction** is a second type of double-replacement reaction that produces a **salt** and water. p. 201

6-6.3    A type of neutralization reaction called a **gas-forming reaction** involves the combination of a strong acid with certain salts to produce a gas. p. 203

## SUMMARY CHART

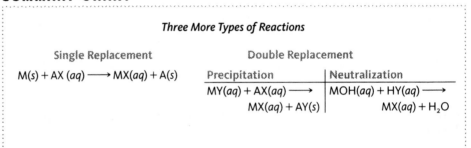

*Three More Types of Reactions*

Single Replacement

$$M(s) + AX\,(aq) \longrightarrow MX(aq) + A(s)$$

Double Replacement

| Precipitation | Neutralization |
|---|---|
| $MY(aq) + AX(aq) \longrightarrow$ $MX(aq) + AY(s)$ | $MOH(aq) + HY(aq) \longrightarrow$ $MX(aq) + H_2O$ |

## CHAPTER 6 SYNTHESIS PROBLEM

Copper metal is a stable metal along with other coinage metals such as silver and gold. As mentioned in this chapter, even most acids do not react with these metals. The one exception is nitric acid, which reacts with copper but not by an ordinary single-replacement reaction as described here. The reaction is somewhat more complex and will be discussed further in Chapter 13. In a well-known laboratory experiment we can take metallic copper, dissolve it in nitric acid and through a series of reactions that we have discussed in this chapter, return it to its metallic form. There are five reactions involved in this series.

| PROBLEM | SOLUTION |
|---|---|
| **a.** Copper dissolves in nitric acid forming copper(II) nitrate and toxic nitrogen dioxide:<br>$Cu(s) + HNO_3(aq) \longrightarrow Cu(NO_3)_2(aq) + NO_2(g) + H_2O(l)$<br>Balance this equation by inspection using the guidelines described. | **a.** The copper is balanced, so consider the nitrogens. On the right there are three, so balance with three nitric acids on the left.<br><br>$Cu(s) + 3HNO_3(aq) \longrightarrow Cu(NO_3)_2(aq) + NO_2(g) + H_2O(l)$<br>Now consider the hydrogens. To balance water we obviously need an even number of nitric acids. If we add one nitric acid on the left, we can now balance the hydrogens on the right.<br>$Cu(s) + 4HNO_3(aq) \longrightarrow Cu(NO_3)_2(aq) + NO_2(g) + 2H_2O(l)$<br>Notice that we now have one extra nitrogen and two extra oxygens on the left. We can fix this easily by adding one more nitrogen dioxide on the right and we are finished.<br>$Cu(s) + 4HNO_3(aq) \longrightarrow Cu(NO_3)_2(aq) + 2NO_2(g) + 2H_2O(l)$ |

| PROBLEM | SOLUTION |
|---|---|
| **b.** Aqueous sodium hydroxide reacts with the copper(II) nitrate solution from above to form copper(II) hydroxide. Write the balanced molecular, total ionic, and net ionic equations for this reaction. Identify the type of reaction. | **b.** $Cu(NO_3)_2(aq) + 2NaOH(aq) \longrightarrow Cu(OH)_2(s) + 2NaNO_3(aq)$<br>$Cu^{2+}(aq) + 2NO_3^-(aq) + 2Na^+(aq) + 2OH^-(aq) \longrightarrow$<br>$Cu(OH)_2(s) + 2NO_3^-(aq) + 2Na^+(aq)$<br>$Cu^{2+}(aq) + 2OH^-(aq) \longrightarrow Cu(OH)_2(s)$ This is a precipitation reaction. |
| **c.** The solid copper(II) hydroxide is filtered and then is heated, releasing water. Write the balanced equation for this reaction. Identify the type of reaction. | **c.** $Cu(OH)_2(s) \longrightarrow CuO(s) + H_2O(l)$ By removing a $H_2O$ from $Cu(OH)_2$ we have CuO. This is a decomposition reaction. |
| **d.** A solution of sulfuric acid reacts with the solid copper(II) oxide, producing copper(II) sulfate. Write the balanced equation illustrating this reaction. Identify the type of reaction. | **d.** $CuO(s) + H_2SO_4(aq) \longrightarrow CuSO_4(aq) + H_2O(l)$ This is a neutralization reaction where solid CuO can be considered the base. Recall that $CuSO_4$ is soluble. |
| **e.** Aluminum metal is added to the copper(II) sulfate solution, re-forming metallic copper. Write the balanced molecular, total ionic, and net ionic equations for this reaction. Identify the type of reaction. | **e.** $2Al(s) + 3CuSO_4(aq) \longrightarrow Al_2(SO_4)_3(aq) + 3Cu(s)$<br>$2Al(s) + 3Cu^{2+}(aq) + 3SO_4^{2-}(aq) \longrightarrow$<br>$2Al^{3+}(aq) + 3SO_4^{2-}(aq) + 3Cu(s)$<br>$2Al(s) + 3Cu^{2+}(aq) \longrightarrow 2Al^{3+}(aq) + 3Cu(s)$ This is a single-replacement reaction. |

**YOUR TURN**

Complete where necessary and balance the following reactions.

**a.** Magnesium metal reacts with a gold(III) nitrate solution in a single-replacement reaction.

**b.** Magnesium hydroxide reacts with $HClO_4$. Write the balanced molecular, total ionic, and net ionic equations. Identify the type of reaction.

**c.** $C_2H_6O$ undergoes combustion.

**d.** A solution of magnesium bromide is mixed with a solution of potassium hydroxide. Write the balanced molecular, total ionic, and net ionic equations. Identify the type of reaction.

**e.** Fluorine reacts with aluminum. Identify the type of reaction.

Answers are on p. 207.

# CHAPTER SUMMARY

A concise statement of a chemical property is relayed by the **chemical equation**. With symbols, formulas, and other abbreviations, a sizable amount of chemical information can be communicated. This includes the elements or compounds involved as **reactants** and **products**, their physical states, and the number of molecules of each compound involved in the reaction. When the numbers of atoms of each element are made the same on both sides of the equation by use of **coefficients**, the equation is considered **balanced**.

In this chapter, we considered five different types of reactions that can be conveniently represented by equations. Each type has a general equation that characterizes that kind of reaction. The first three types discussed in this chapter are **combustion reactions**, **combination reactions**, and **decomposition reactions**.

In addition to these three types of reactions, two other types usually involve reactions that occur in an aqueous solution. When a substance (a **solute**) is dispersed by a liquid (a **solvent**), it forms a homogeneous mixture known as a **solution**. Substances that dissolve in water are said to be **soluble** and those that do not are **insoluble**. Soluble ionic compounds are separated into their individual ions in aqueous solution.

In **single-replacement reactions**, a metal exchanges places with the cation of a different metal. The ability of metals to replace other metal ions can be compared and ranked in the **activity series**. Hydrogen, although not a metal, is usually included in this series.

**Double-replacement reactions** involve the exchange of ions between two soluble compounds. In a **precipitation reaction**, the two ions combine to form a solid ionic compound known as a **precipitate**, which separates from the solution. In a **neutralization reaction**, the two ions form a molecular compound.

In neutralization reactions, **strong acids** [molecular compounds that dissolve in water to form $H^+(aq)$ ions] react with **strong bases** [ionic compounds that dissolve in water to form $OH^-(aq)$ ions]. The reaction produces water and a **salt**. **Gas-forming reactions** involve the reaction of a strong acid with certain salts to produce molecular compounds that are either gases or decompose to gases.

Single- and double-replacement reactions can be illustrated by three types of equations. In a **molecular equation**, all species are represented as neutral compounds. In a **total ionic equation**, soluble ionic compounds and strong acids are represented as separate ions. If the **spectator ions** (those ions that are not directly involved in the reaction) are removed, the result is a **net ionic equation**. The three types of equations for a typical precipitation reaction are shown here.

$$Pb(NO_3)_2(aq) \quad + \quad 2KCl(aq) \quad \longrightarrow \quad PbCl_2(s) \quad + \quad 2KNO_3(aq)$$

$$Pb^{2+}(aq) + 2\cancel{NO_3^-}(aq) \quad + \quad 2K^+(aq) + 2Cl^-(aq) \quad \longrightarrow \quad PbCl_2(s) \quad + \quad 2K^+(aq) + 2\cancel{NO_3^-}(aq)$$

$$Pb^{2+}(aq) + 2Cl^-(aq) \quad \longrightarrow \quad PbCl_2(s)$$

## OBJECTIVES

| SECTION | YOU SHOULD BE ABLE TO... | EXAMPLES | EXERCISES | CHAPTER PROBLEMS |
|---|---|---|---|---|
| 6-1 | Write balanced chemical equations for simple reactions from inspection. | 6-1, 6-2, 6-3 | 1a, 1b, 1c, 1d, 1e, 2c | 2, 3, 4, 5, 10, 11, 12, 13 |
| 6-2 | Classify certain chemical reactions as being combustion, combination, or decomposition reactions. | 6-3 | 2a, 2b, 2c | 14, 15, 16, 18, 19, 20, 21, 22, 23 |
| 6-3 | Write the ions formed when ionic compounds or acids dissolve in water. | 6-4 | 3a, 3b, 3c | 24, 25, 26, 27 |
| 6-4 | Given the activity series, complete several single-replacement reactions as balanced molecular, total ionic, and net ionic equations. | 6-5 | 4a, 4b, 4c, 4d | 28, 29, 30, 33 |
| 6-5 | Write balanced molecular, total ionic, and net ionic equations for precipitation reactions. | 6-6, 6-7, 6-8, 6-9 | 5a, 5b, 5c, 5d, 5e | 34, 35, 40, 42, 44, 45, 46, 47, 48, 49 |
| 6-6 | Write balanced molecular, total ionic, and net ionic equations for neutralization reactions | 6-10 | 6a, 6b | 55, 56, 57, 58 |

## ANSWERS TO ASSESSING THE OBJECTIVES

### Part A
**EXERCISES**

**6-1(a)** A chemical reaction is represented with symbols and formulas by means of a chemical equation. The arrow in an equation separates the reactants on the left from the products on the right. To conform to the law of conservation of mass, an equation must be balanced. This is accomplished by introducing coefficients in front of formulas rather than changing subscripts in a formula.

**6-1(b)** (a) $Li(s) + O_2(g) \longrightarrow Li_2O(s)$

(b) $Al(s) + H_2SO_4(l) \longrightarrow Al_2(SO_4)_3(aq) + H_2(g)$

(c) $Cu(s) + HNO_3(aq) \longrightarrow Cu(NO_3)_2(aq) + NO(g) + H_2O(l)$

**6-1(c)** (a) B, C, O, H (b) N, H, N(again), O (c) S, O, Na, I

**6-1(d)** (a) $4Cr + 3O_2 \longrightarrow 2Cr_2O_3$

(b) $Co_2S_3 + 3H_2 \longrightarrow 3H_2S + 2Co$

(c) $C_3H_8 + 5O_2 \longrightarrow 3CO_2 + 4H_2O$

**6-1(e)** (a) $(NH_4)_2CO_3(s) \longrightarrow 2NH_3(g) + CO_2(g) + H_2O(g)$

(b) $2NH_3(g) + 2ClF_3(l) \longrightarrow N_2(g) + Cl_2(g) + 6HF(g)$

**6-2(a)** (a) combination, combustion (b) decomposition, combustion (c) combination, combustion (d) all reactions (e) decomposition

**6-2(b)** (a) decomposition (b) combustion (c) combination (d) decomposition (e) combination

**6-2(c)** (a) $2Si_2H_6(g) + 7O_2(g) \longrightarrow 4SiO_2(s) + 6H_2O(l)$

(b) $2Al(s) + 3H_2(g) \longrightarrow 2AlH_3(s)$

(c) $Ca(HSO_3)_2(s) \longrightarrow CaO(s) + H_2O(l) + 2SO_2(g)$

**6-2(d)** (a) $2C_6H_{14}(l) + 19O_2(g) \longrightarrow 12CO_2(g) + 14H_2O(l)$

(b) $2Na(s) + I_2(s) \longrightarrow 2NaI(s)$

(c) $H_2SO_3(aq) \longrightarrow H_2O(l) + SO_2(g)$

## Part B
### EXERCISES

6-3(a) $H^+$ and $ClO_4^-$ (b) $K^+$ and $PO_4^{3-}$ (c) $NH_4^+$ and $NO_3^-$ (d) $Zn^{2+}$ and $ClO_4^-$

6-3(b) (a) three (b) four (c) four (d) two

6-3(c) (a) $Na_2SO_4(s) \longrightarrow 2Na^+(aq) + SO_4^{2-}(aq)$

(b) $HNO_3(l) \longrightarrow H^+(aq) + NO_3^-(aq)$

(c) $Al(C_2H_3O_2)_3(s) \longrightarrow Al^{3+}(aq) + 3C_2H_3O_2^-(aq)$

(d) $Ca(OH)_2(s) \longrightarrow Ca^{2+}(aq) + 2OH^-(aq)$

6-4(a) (a) Ni replaces Ag (b) Al replaces Cu (c) Mg replaces Cr (d) Sn replaces H

6-4(b) (a) total: $Cu^{2+}(aq) + 2NO_3^-(aq) + Zn(s) \longrightarrow$
$$Zn^{2+}(aq) + 2NO_3^-(aq) + Cu(s)$$
net: $Cu^{2+}(aq) + Zn(s) \longrightarrow Zn^{2+}(aq) + Cu(s)$

(b) total: $2Al(s) + 3Pb^{2+}(aq) + 6Cl^-(aq) \longrightarrow$
$$2Al^{3+}(aq) + 6Cl^-(aq) + 3Pb(s)$$
net: $2Al(s) + 3Pb^{2+}(aq) \longrightarrow 2Al^{3+}(aq) + 3Pb(s)$

6-4(c) (a) $Mg(s) + 2AgNO_3(aq) \longrightarrow Mg(NO_3)_2(aq) + 2Ag(s)$

(b) no reaction (Sn is less reactive than K)

(c) $2Na(s) + 2HCl(aq) \longrightarrow 2NaCl(aq) + H_2(g)$

6-4(d) (a) total: $Cu^{2+}(aq) + 2Cl^-(aq) + Fe(s) \longrightarrow$
$$Fe^{2+}(aq) + 2Cl^-(aq) + Cu(s)$$
net: $Cu^{2+}(aq) + Fe(s) \longrightarrow Fe^{2+}(aq) + Cu(s)$

(b) total: $3Mg(s) + 2Au^{3+}(aq) + 6NO_3^-(aq) \longrightarrow$
$$2Au(s) + 3Mg^{2+}(aq) + 6NO_3^-(aq)$$
net: $3Mg(s) + 2Au^{3+}(aq) \longrightarrow 2Au(s) + 3Mg^{2+}(aq)$

6-5(a) (a) insoluble (b) soluble (c) soluble (d) insoluble (e) soluble

6-5(b) (a) soluble (b) insoluble (c) soluble (d) soluble (e) insoluble (f) insoluble

6-5(c) No. Both the $K^+$ and the $Na^+$ will produce soluble products.

(b) Yes. $Al(OH)_3$ is insoluble.

(c) Yes. CaS is insoluble.

6-5(d) $CrI_3(aq) + Li_3PO_4(aq) \longrightarrow CrPO_4(s) + 3LiI(aq)$

(b) $3Cs_2CO_3(aq) + 2FeBr_3(aq) \longrightarrow 6CsBr(aq) + Fe_2(CO_3)_3(s)$

6-5(e) molecular: $2AgNO_3(aq) + K_2S(aq) \longrightarrow$
$$Ag_2S(s) + 2KNO_3(aq)$$
total: $2Ag^+(aq) + 2NO_3^-(aq) + 2K^+(aq) + S^{2-}(aq) \longrightarrow$
$$Ag_2S(s) + 2K^+(aq) + 2NO_3^-(aq)$$
net: $2Ag^+(aq) + S^{2-}(aq) \longrightarrow Ag_2S(s)$

6-5(f) There are several possibilities for each product. The following examples illustrate the general concept of the problem.

(a) $CaCl_2(aq) + Na_2CO_3(aq)$   (b) $Fe(NO_3)_3(aq) + K_3PO_4(aq)$

6-6(a) (a) $K^+(aq) + OH^-(aq)$

(b) $Fe(OH)_3(s)$   (c) $H^+(aq) + I^-(aq)$

(d) $Na^+(aq) + HSO_3^-(aq)$

6-6(b) (a) $H_2SO_4(aq) + 2LiOH(aq) \longrightarrow Li_2SO_4(aq) + 2H_2O(l)$

(b) $Ca(OH)_2(aq) + 2HClO_4(aq) \longrightarrow$
$$Ca(ClO_4)_2(aq) + 2H_2O(l)$$

(c) $HCl(aq) + NaHCO_3(aq) \longrightarrow NaCl(aq) + H_2O(l) + CO_2(g)$

(d) $K_2S(aq) + 2HBr(aq) \longrightarrow 2KBr(aq) + H_2S(g)$

6-6(c) molecular: $2HNO_3(aq) + Sr(OH)_2(aq) \longrightarrow$
$$Sr(NO_3)_2(aq) + 2H_2O(l)$$
total: $2H^+(aq) + 2NO_3^-(aq) + Sr^{2+}(aq) + 2OH^-(aq) \longrightarrow$
$$Sr^{2+}(aq) + 2NO_3^-(aq) + 2H_2O(l)$$
net: $H^+(aq) + OH^-(aq) \longrightarrow H_2O(l)$

6-6(d) molecular: $2NaCN(s) + H_2SO_4(aq) \longrightarrow$
$$Na_2SO_4(aq) + 2HCN(g)$$
net: $CN^-(aq) + H^+(aq) \longrightarrow HCN(g)$

---

## ANSWERS TO CHAPTER SYNTHESIS PROBLEM

a. $3Mg(s) + 2Au(NO_3)_3(aq) \longrightarrow$
$$3Mg(NO_3)_2(aq) + 2Au(s)$$

b. $Mg(OH)_2(s) + HClO_4(aq) \longrightarrow$
$$Mg(ClO_4)_2(aq) + 2H_2O(l)$$
$Mg(OH)_2(s) + 2H^+(aq) + 2ClO_4^-(aq) \longrightarrow$
$$Mg^{2+}(aq) + 2ClO_4^-(aq) + 2H_2O(l)$$
$Mg(OH)_2(s) + 2H^+(aq) \longrightarrow$
$$Mg^{2+}(aq) + 2H_2O(l)$$
This is a neutralization reaction.

c. $C_2H_6O + 3O_2 \longrightarrow$
$$2CO_2 + 3H_2O$$

d. $MgBr_2(aq) + 2KOH(aq) \longrightarrow$
$$Mg(OH)_2(s) + 2KBr$$
$Mg^{2+}(aq) + 2NO_3^-(aq) + 2K^+(aq) + 2OH^-(aq)$
$\longrightarrow Mg(OH)_2(s) + 2K^+(aq) + 2Br^-(aq)$
$Mg^{2+}(aq) + 2OH^-(aq) \longrightarrow Mg(OH)_2(s)$
This is a precipitation reaction.

e. $2Al(s) + 3F_2(g) \longrightarrow 2AlF_3(s)$ This is a combination reaction. Notice that $AlF_3$ is ionic so it is a solid.

# CHAPTER PROBLEMS

*Throughout the text, answers to all exercises in color are given in Appendix E. The more difficult exercises are marked with an asterisk.*

## Chemical Equations (SECTION 6-1)

6-1. The physical state of an element is included in a chemical equation. Each of the following compounds is a gas, a solid, or a liquid under normal conditions. Indicate the proper physical state by adding (g), (s), or (l) after the formula.

(a) $Cl_2$        (d) $H_2O$        (g) $Br_2$        (j) Na

(b) C        (e) $P_4$        (h) NaBr        (k) Hg

(c) $K_2SO_4$        (f) $H_2$        (i) $S_8$        (l) $CO_2$

6-2. Balance the following equations.

(a) $CaCO_3 \xrightarrow{\Delta} CaO + CO_2$

(b) $Na + O_2 \longrightarrow Na_2O$

(c) $H_2SO_4 + NaOH \longrightarrow Na_2SO_4 + H_2O$

(d) $H_2O_2 \longrightarrow H_2O + O_2$

6-3. Balance the following equations.

(a) $NaBr + Cl_2 \longrightarrow NaCl + Br_2$

(b) $KOH + H_3AsO_4 \longrightarrow K_2HAsO_4 + H_2O$

(c) $Ti + Cl_2 \longrightarrow TiCl_4$

(d) $Al + H_2SO_4 \longrightarrow Al_2(SO_4)_3 + H_2$

6-4. Balance the following equations.

(a) $Al + H_3PO_4 \longrightarrow AlPO_4 + H_2$

(b) $Ca(OH)_2 + HCl \longrightarrow CaCl_2 + H_2O$

(c) $Mg + N_2 \longrightarrow Mg_3N_2$

(d) $C_2H_6 + O_2 \longrightarrow CO_2 + H_2O$

6-5. Balance the following equations.

(a) $Ca(CN)_2 + HBr \longrightarrow CaBr_2 + HCN$

(b) $C_3H_6 + O_2 \longrightarrow CO + H_2O$

(c) $P_4 + S_8 \longrightarrow P_4S_3$

(d) $Cr_2O_3 + Si \longrightarrow Cr + SiO_2$

6-6. Balance the following equations.

(a) $Mg_3N_2 + H_2O \longrightarrow Mg(OH)_2 + NH_3$

(b) $H_2S + O_2 \longrightarrow S + H_2O$

(c) $Si_2H_6 + H_2O \longrightarrow Si(OH)_4 + H_2$

(d) $C_2H_6 + Cl_2 \longrightarrow C_2HCl_5 + HCl$

6-7. Balance the following equations.

(a) $Na_2NH + H_2O \longrightarrow NH_3 + NaOH$

(b) $CaC_2 + H_2O \longrightarrow C_2H_2 + Ca(OH)_2$

(c) $XeF_6 + H_2O \longrightarrow XeO_3 + HF$

(d) $PCl_5 + H_2O \longrightarrow H_3PO_4 + HCl$

6-8. Balance the following equations.

(a) $B_4H_{10} + O_2 \longrightarrow B_2O_3 + H_2O$

(b) $SF_6 + SO_3 \longrightarrow O_2SF_2$

(c) $CS_2 + O_2 \longrightarrow CO_2 + SO_2$

(d) $BF_3 + NaH \longrightarrow B_2H_6 + NaF$

6-9. Balance the following equations.

(a) $NH_3 + Cl_2 \longrightarrow NHCl_2 + HCl$

(b) $PBr_3 + H_2O \longrightarrow HBr + H_3PO_3$

(c) $Mg + Fe_3O_4 \longrightarrow MgO + Fe$

(d) $Fe_3O_4 + H_2 \longrightarrow Fe + H_2O$

6-10. Write balanced chemical equations from the following word equations. Include the physical state of each element or compound.

(a) Sodium metal plus water yields hydrogen gas and an aqueous sodium hydroxide solution.

(b) Potassium chlorate when heated yields potassium chloride plus oxygen gas. (Ionic compounds are solids.)

(c) An aqueous sodium chloride solution plus an aqueous silver nitrate solution yields a silver chloride precipitate (solid) and a sodium nitrate solution.

(d) An aqueous phosphoric acid solution plus an aqueous calcium hydroxide solution yields water and solid calcium phosphate.

6-11. Write balanced chemical equations from the following word equations. Include the physical state of each element or compound.

(a) Solid phenol ($C_6H_6O$) reacts with oxygen to form carbon dioxide gas and liquid water.

(b) An aqueous calcium hydroxide solution reacts with gaseous sulfur trioxide to form a solid of calcium sulfate and water.

(c) Lithium is the only element that combines with nitrogen at room temperature. The reaction forms lithium nitride.

(d) Magnesium dissolves in an aqueous chromium (III) nitrate solution to form chromium and a magnesium nitrate solution.

6-12. Nickel (II) nitrate is prepared by heating nickel metal with liquid dinitrogen tetroxide. In addition to the nitrate, gaseous nitrogen monoxide is formed. Write the balanced equation.

6-13. One of the steps in the production of iron involves the reaction of $Fe_3O_4$ with carbon monoxide to produce FeO and carbon dioxide. Write the balanced equation.

## Combustion, Combination, and Decomposition Reactions (SECTION 6-2)

6-14. Which reactions in problems 6-2 and 6-4 can be classified as a combustion, a combination, or a decomposition reaction?

6-15. Which reactions in problems 6-3 and 6-5 can be classified as either a combustion, a combination, or a decomposition reaction?

**6-16.** Write balanced combustion reactions when the following compounds react with excess oxygen.

**(a)** $C_7H_{14}(l)$

**(b)** $LiCH_3(s)$
(a product is $Li_2O$)

**(c)** $C_4H_{10}O(l)$

**(d)** $C_2H_5SH(g)$
(a product is $SO_2$)

**6-17.** Write balanced combustion reactions when the following compounds react with excess oxygen.

**(a)** $C_2H_6O_2(l)$

**(b)** $B_6H_{12}(g)$ [a product is $B_2O_3(s)$]

**(c)** $C_6H_{12}(l)$

**(d)** $Pb(C_2H_5)_4(s)$ [a product is $PbO_2(s)$]

**6-18.** Write balanced combination reactions that occur when the metal barium reacts with the following nonmetals.

**(a)** hydrogen

**(b)** sulfur

**(c)** bromine

**(d)** nitrogen

**6-19.** Write balanced combination reactions that occur when the metal aluminum reacts with the following nonmetals.

**(a)** hydrogen

**(b)** oxygen

**(c)** iodine

**(d)** nitrogen

**6-20.** Write balanced decomposition reactions for the following compounds. Recall that ionic compounds are solids.

**(a)** $Ca(HCO_3)_2$ into calcium oxide, carbon dioxide, and water

**(b)** $Ag_2O$ into its elements

**(c)** $N_2O_3$ gas into nitrogen dioxide gas and nitrogen monoxide gas

**6-21.** Write balanced decomposition reactions for the following compounds. Recall that ionic compounds are solids.

**(a)** liquid $SbF_5$ into fluorine and solid antimony trifluoride

**(b)** $PtO_2$ into its elements

**(c)** gaseous $BrF$ into bromine and gaseous bromine trifluoride

**6-22.** Write balanced equations by predicting the products of the following reactions. Include the physical state of each element or compound.

**(a)** the combination of potassium and chlorine

**(b)** the combustion of liquid benzene ($C_6H_6$)

**(c)** the decomposition of gold(III) oxide into its elements by heating

**(d)** the combustion of propyl alcohol ($C_3H_8O$)

**(e)** the combination of phosphorus ($P_4$) and fluorine gas to produce solid phosphorus pentafluoride

**6-23.** Write balanced equations by predicting the products of the following reactions. Include the physical state of each element or compound.

**(a)** the combustion of liquid butane ($C_4H_{10}$)

**(b)** the decomposition of aqueous sulfurous acid to produce water and a gas

**(c)** the combination of sodium and oxygen gas to form sodium peroxide (the peroxide ion is $O_2^{2-}$)

**(d)** the decomposition of copper(I) oxide into its elements by heating

## Ions in Aqueous Solution (SECTION 6-3)

**6-24.** Write equations illustrating the solution of each of the following compounds in water.

**(a)** $Na_2S$

**(b)** $Li_2SO_4$

**(c)** $K_2Cr_2O_7$

**(d)** $CaS$

**(e)** $(NH_4)_2S$

**(f)** $Ba(OH)_2$

**6-25.** Write equations illustrating the solution of each of the following compounds in water.

**(a)** $Ca(ClO_3)_2$

**(b)** $CsBr$

**(c)** $AlCl_3$

**(d)** $Cs_2SO_3$

**6-26.** Write equations illustrating the solution of the following compounds in water.

**(a)** $HNO_3$

**(b)** $Sr(OH)_2$

**6-27.** Write equations illustrating the solution of the following compounds in water.

**(a)** $LiOH$

**(b)** $HI$

## Single-Replacement Reactions (SECTION 6-4)

**6-28.** If any of the following reactions occur spontaneously, write the balanced net ionic equation. If not, write "no reaction." (Refer to Table 6-2.)

**(a)** $Pb + Zn^{2+} \longrightarrow Pb^{2+} + Zn$

**(b)** $Fe + H^+ \longrightarrow Fe^{2+} + H_2$

**(c)** $Cu + Ag^+ \longrightarrow Cu^{2+} + Ag$

**(d)** $Cr + Zn^{2+} \longrightarrow Cr^{3+} + Zn$

**6-29.** If any of the following reactions occur spontaneously, write the balanced net ionic equation. If not, write "no reaction." (Refer to Table 6-2.)

**(a)** $Pb + Sn^{2+} \longrightarrow Pb^{2+} + Sn$

**(b)** $H_2 + Ni^{2+} \longrightarrow H^+ + Ni$

**(c)** $Cr + Ni^{2+} \longrightarrow Cr^{3+} + Ni$

**(d)** $H_2 + Au^{3+} \longrightarrow H^+ + Au$

**6-30.** In the following situations, a reaction may or may not take place. If it does, write the balanced molecular, total ionic, and net ionic equations illustrating the reaction. Assume all involve aqueous solutions.

**(a)** Some iron nails are placed in a $CuCl_2$ solution.

**(b)** Silver coins are dropped in a hydrochloric acid solution.

**(c)** A copper wire is placed in a $Pb(NO_3)_2$ solution.

**(d)** Zinc strips are placed in a $Cr(NO_3)_3$ solution.

**6-31.** In the following situations, a reaction may or may not take place. If it does, write the balanced molecular, total ionic, and net ionic equations illustrating the reaction. Assume all involve aqueous solutions.

**(a)** A solution of nitric acid is placed in a tin can.

**(b)** Iron nails are placed in a $ZnBr_2$ solution.

**(c)** A chromium-plated auto accessory is placed in an $SnCl_2$ solution.

**(d)** A silver bracelet is placed in a $Cu(ClO_4)_2$ solution.

**6-32.** When heated, sodium metal reacts with solid $Cr_2O_3$. Write the balanced molecular and the net ionic equations for this single-replacement reaction.

**6-33.** When heated, aluminum metal reacts with solid PbO. Write the balanced molecular and net ionic equations for this single-replacement reaction.

## Solubility and Precipitation Reactions
### (SECTION 6-4)

**6-34.** Referring to Table 6-3, determine which of the following compounds are insoluble in water.

(a) $Na_2S$      (d) $Ag_2S$
(b) $PbSO_4$      (e) $(NH_4)_2S$
(c) $MgSO_4$      (f) $HgI_2$

**6-35.** Referring to Table 6-3, determine which of the following compounds are insoluble in water.

(a) NiS      (d) $Rb_2SO_4$
(b) $Hg_2Br_2$      (e) CaS
(c) $Al(OH)_3$      (f) $BaCO_3$

**6-36.** Write the formulas of the precipitates formed when $Ag^+$ combines with the following anions.

(a) $Br^-$      (b) $CO_3^{2-}$      (c) $PO_4^{3-}$

**6-37.** Write the formulas of the precipitates formed when $Pb^{2+}$ combines with the following anions.

(a) $SO_4^{2-}$      (b) $PO_4^{3-}$      (c) $I^-$

**6-38.** Write the formulas of the precipitates formed when $CO_3^{2-}$ combines with the following cations.

(a) $Cu^{2+}$      (b) $Cd^{2+}$      (c) $Cr^{3+}$

**6-39.** Write the formulas of the precipitates formed when $OH^-$ combines with the following cations

(a) $Ag^+$      (b) $Ni^{2+}$      (c) $Co^{3+}$

**6-40.** Which of the following chlorides is insoluble in water? (Refer to Table 6-3.)

(a) NaCl      (c) $AlCl_3$
(b) $Hg_2Cl_2$      (d) $BaCl_2$

**6-41.** Which of the following sulfates is insoluble in water? (Refer to Table 6-3.)

(a) $K_2SO_4$      (c) $SrSO_4$
(b) $ZnSO_4$      (d) $MgSO_4$

**6-42.** Which of the following phosphates is insoluble in water? (Refer to Table 6-3.)

(a) $K_3PO_4$      (c) $(NH_4)_3PO_4$
(b) $Ca_3(PO_4)_2$      (d) $Li_3PO_4$

**6-43.** Which of the following hydroxides is insoluble in water? (Refer to Table 6-3.)

(a) $Mg(OH)_2$      (c) $Ba(OH)_2$
(b) CsOH      (d) NaOH

**6-44.** Write the balanced molecular equation for any reaction that occurs when the following solutions are mixed. (Refer to Table 6-3.)

(a) KI and $Pb(C_2H_3O_2)_2$      (d) BaS and $Hg_2(NO_3)_2$
(b) $AgClO_4$ and $KNO_3$      (e) $FeCl_3$ and KOH
(c) $Sr(ClO_4)_2$ and $Ba(OH)_2$

**6-45.** Write the balanced molecular equation for any reaction that occurs when the following solutions are mixed. (Refer to Table 6-3.)

(a) $Ba(C_2H_3O_2)_2$ and $Na_2SO_4$      (c) $Mg(NO_3)_2$ and $Na_3PO_4$
(b) $NaClO_4$ and $Pb(NO_3)_2$      (d) SrS and $NiI_2$

**6-46.** Write the total ionic and net ionic equations for any reactions that occurred in problem 6-44.

**6-47.** Write the total ionic and net ionic equations for any reactions that occurred in problem 6-45.

**6-48.** Write the total ionic equation and the net ionic equation for each of the following reactions.

(a) $K_2S(aq) + Pb(NO_3)_2(aq) \longrightarrow PbS(s) + 2KNO_3(aq)$
(b) $(NH_4)_2CO_3(aq) + CaCl_2(aq) \longrightarrow$
$$CaCO_3(s) + 2NH_4Cl(aq)$$
(c) $2AgClO_4(aq) + Na_2CrO_4(aq) \longrightarrow$
$$Ag_2CrO_4(s) + 2NaClO_4(aq)$$

**6-49.** Write the total ionic equation and the net ionic equations for each of the following reactions.

(a) $Hg_2(ClO_4)_2(aq) + 2HBr(aq) \longrightarrow$
$$Hg_2Br_2(s) + 2HClO_4(aq)$$
(b) $2AgNO_3(aq) + (NH_4)_2SO_4(aq) \longrightarrow$
$$Ag_2SO_4(s) + 2NH_4NO_3(aq)$$
(c) $CuSO_4(aq) + 2KOH(aq) \longrightarrow Cu(OH)_2(s) + K_2SO_4(aq)$

*6-50. Write the balanced molecular equations indicating how the following ionic compounds can be prepared by a precipitation reaction using any other ionic compounds. In some cases, the equation should reflect the fact that the desired compound is soluble and must be recovered by vaporizing the solvent water after removal of a precipitate.

(a) $CuCO_3$      (c) $Hg_2I_2$      (e) $KC_2H_3O_2$
(b) $PbSO_4$      (d) $NH_4NO_3$

## Neutralization Reactions (SECTION 6-5)

**6-51.** Which of the following is not a strong acid?
(a) HBr      (c) $HNO_3$
(b) HF      (d) $HClO_4$

**6-52.** Which of the following is not a strong acid?
(a) $HNO_3$      (c) $H_2SO_4$
(b) HI      (d) $HNO_2$

**6-53.** Which of the following is not a strong base?
(a) NaOH      (c) $Al(OH)_3$
(b) $Ba(OH)_2$      (d) CsOH

**6-54.** Which of the following is not a strong base?

**(a)** $Be(OH)_2$ **(b)** $Ba(OH)_2$ **(c)** LiOH **(d)** KOH

**6-55.** Write balanced molecular equations for the neutralization reactions between the following compounds.

**(a)** HI and CsOH **(c)** $H_2SO_4$ and $Sr(OH)_2$

**(b)** $HNO_3$ and $Ca(OH)_2$

**6-56.** Write balanced molecular equations for the neutralization reactions between the following compounds.

**(a)** $Ca(OH)_2$ and HI **(c)** $HClO_4$ and $Ba(OH)_2$

**(b)** $H_2SO_4$ and LiOH

**6-57.** Write the total ionic and net ionic equations for the reactions in problem 6-55.

**6-58.** Write the total ionic and net ionic equations for the reactions in problem 6-56.

**\*6-59.** Magnesium hydroxide is considered a strong base but has very low solubility in water. It is known as milk of magnesia and is used to neutralize stomach acid (HCl). Write the balanced molecular, total ionic, and net ionic equations illustrating this reaction. (Since magnesium hydroxide is a solid, the total and net ionic equations will be somewhat different.)

**\*6-60.** When calcium hydroxide is neutralized with sulfuric acid, the salt produced is insoluble in water. Write the balanced molecular, total ionic, and net ionic equations illustrating this reaction.

## General Problems

**6-61.** Write the balanced equations representing the combustion of propane gas ($C_3H_8$), butane liquid ($C_4H_{10}$), octane ($C_8H_{18}$) in liquid gasoline, and liquid ethyl alcohol ($C_2H_5OH$) found in alcoholic beverages.

**6-62.** In the combination reaction between sodium and chlorine and in the combustion reaction of magnesium, why could these also be considered electron exchange reactions?

**6-63.** Iron replaces gold ions in solution. Can you think of any practical application of this reaction?

**6-64.** Write balanced equations by predicting the products of the following reactions. Include the physical state of each element or compound.

**(a)** the combination of barium and iodine

**(b)** the neutralization of aqueous rubidium hydroxide with hydrobromic acid

**(c)** a single-replacement reaction of calcium metal with a nitric acid solution

**(d)** the combustion of solid naphthalene ($C_{10}H_8$)

**(e)** a precipitation reaction involving aqueous ammonium chromate and aqueous barium bromide

**(f)** the decomposition of solid aluminum hydroxide into solid aluminum oxide and gaseous water

**6-65.** Write the total ionic and net ionic equations for parts (b), (c), and (e) of problem 6-64.

**6-66.** Write balanced equations by predicting the products of the following reactions. Include the physical state of each element or compound.

**(a)** the decomposition of solid sodium azide ($NaN_3$) into solid sodium nitride and nitrogen gas

**(b)** a precipitation reaction involving aqueous potassium carbonate and aqueous copper(II) sulfate

**(c)** the combustion of solid benzoic acid ($C_7H_6O_2$)

**(d)** a single-replacement reaction of iron metal and an aqueous gold(III) nitrate solution

**(e)** the combination of aluminum and solid sulfur ($S_8$)

**(e)** the neutralization of aqueous sulfuric acid with aqueous barium hydroxide

**6-67.** Write the total ionic and net ionic equations for parts (b), (d), and (f) of problem 6-66.

**6-68.** Consider a mixture of the following ions in aqueous solution: $Na^+$, $H^+$, $Ba^{2+}$, $ClO_4^-$, $OH^-$, $SO_4^{2-}$. Write the net ionic equations for any reaction or reactions that occur between a cation and an anion.

**6-69.** Consider a mixture of the following ions in aqueous solution: $NH_4^+$, $Mg^{2+}$, $Ni^{2+}$, $Cl^-$, $S^{2-}$, $CO_3^{2-}$. Write the net ionic equations for any reaction or reactions that occur between a cation and an anion.

**6-70.** Consider a mixture of the following ions in aqueous solution: $K^+$, $Fe^{3+}$, $Pb^{2+}$, $I^-$, $PO_4^{3-}$, and $S^{2-}$. Write the net ionic equations for any reaction or reactions that occur between a cation and an anion.

## STUDENT WORKSHOP

### Chemical Reactions

**Purpose: To write and balance several different classes of chemical reactions. (Work in groups of three or four. Estimated time: 20 min.)**

Use the following ions, elements, and molecular compounds to write as many molecular equations as possible:

$$Ba^{2+}, Na^+, H^+, OH^-, CO_3^{2-}, Cl^-, O^{2-},$$
$$Ba, Na, H_2, O_2, CO_2, H_2O$$

- Assign state symbols [(s), (l), (g), and (aq)] to all reactants and products.

- Balance the chemical reactions.

- Label each reaction by its type (decomposition, combination, combustion, single replacement, precipitation, neutralization).

Each group should be allowed to put one unique equation on the board. How many different reactions was the class able to come up with?

# Aqueous Solutions

The woman floats like a cork in the Dead Sea in Israel. The water in this lake contains high concentrations of solutes, so it is denser than pure water. The properties of aqueous solutions are discussed in this chapter.

# SETTING THE STAGE

The sound and sensation that we feel from the rhythmic pounding of waves against a silvery ocean beach are among nature's most tranquil gifts. This endless body of liquid seems to extend forever past the horizon. Actually, the ocean covers two-thirds of the surface of Earth and in places it is nearly 6 miles deep. But we can't drink this water, nor can we use it to irrigate crops. This water is far from pure; it contains a high concentration of dissolved compounds as well as suspended matter. The blood coursing in our veins is an example of how our life also depends on this same ability of water to dissolve substances. This red waterway dissolves oxygen and nutrients for life processes and then carries away dissolved waste products for removal by the lungs and kidneys. In fact, water is indispensable for any life-form as we know it.

The ability of water to act as a solvent is the emphasis of this chapter. In the last chapter, we examined the unusual properties of this important compound. Most of the unique properties of water can be attributed to hydrogen bonding between molecules.

In Part A in this chapter, we will examine how water acts as such a versatile solvent for many ionic and polar covalent compounds. The importance of measuring the amount of solute present in a given amount of solvent and how this relates to the stoichiometry of reactions that take place in aqueous solution will be detailed. In Part B we will discuss how the presence of a solute changes the physical properties of a solvent.

## Part A

## Solutions and the Quantities Involved

**SETTING A GOAL**

■ You will learn how water acts to dissolve specific types of compounds and how concentrations of solutes are expressed and used.

**OBJECTIVES**

12-1 Describe the forces that interact during the formation of aqueous solutions of ionic compounds, strong acids, and polar molecules.

12-2 Describe the effects of temperature and pressure on the solubility of solids and gases in a liquid.

12-3 Perform calculations of concentration involving percent by mass, ppm, and ppb.

12-4 Perform calculations of concentration involving molarity and the dilution of solution.

12-5 Perform calculations involving titrations and other solution stoichiometry.

▶ **OBJECTIVE FOR SECTION 12-1**
Describe the forces that interact during the formation of aqueous solutions of ionic compounds, strong acids, and polar molecules.

# 12-1 The Nature of Aqueous Solutions

**LOOKING AHEAD!** The composition of a solution is familiar territory. In Chapter 3, we defined a solution as a homogeneous mixture of a solute (that which dissolves) in a solvent (the medium that dissolves the solute—usually a liquid). In this section we will look into the process of how and why a solute is dispersed into a solvent. ■

## 12-1.1 Mixtures of Two Liquids

Consider two possibilities when two liquids are mixed. *If homogeneous mixing occurs when the solvent and solute are both liquids, we say that the two liquids are* **miscible**. *If two liquids do not mix to form a solution, we say that they are* **immiscible** and remain as a heterogeneous mixture with two liquid phases. Oil and water, for example, are immiscible and thus form a heterogeneous mixture with two visible phases. Alcohol and water are miscible and form a solution with one phase. This was previously discussed in Section 3-3.2 and illustrated in Figure 3-5. In Chapter 10, we discussed mixtures of gases, which are also homogeneous. Mixtures of gases are subject to the same gas laws as pure gases. Alloys are solids that are mainly homogeneous mixtures of metals.

## 12-1.2 The Formation of Aqueous Solutions of Ionic Compounds

Water is a fantastic solvent. It has a unique ability to dissolve many solids and liquids. (See Figure 12-1.) First, we will consider the aqueous solution of an ionic solid such as table salt, NaCl. It is a typical example of how ionic compounds dissolve in water. Recall that solid NaCl is composed of alternating $Na^+$ ions and $Cl^-$ ions in a three-dimensional crystal lattice. It is held together by the rather strong electrostatic attractions known as ion-ion forces. Water is a polar molecular compound with positive dipoles located on the hydrogen atoms and negative dipoles located on the unshared pairs of electrons on the oxygen. In pure water, the molecules are moderately attracted to each other by hydrogen bonds. When solid NaCl is placed in water, competing forces develop between the ions and the dipoles of water. (See Figure 12-2.) *The interactions between the ions and dipoles of solvent molecules are referred to as* **ion–dipole forces**. An individual ion–dipole force is not as strong as one ion–ion force, but there are many ion–dipole forces at work. As a result, a tug-of-war

**FIGURE 12-1 A Solution**
The red-tinted solution is a homogeneous mixture of solute (the solid, red chromium compound) and solvent (water). The solution is in the same physical state as the solvent.

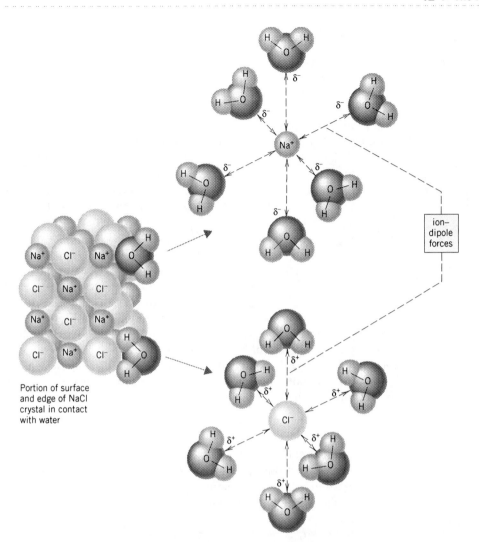

**FIGURE 12-2 Interaction of Water and Ionic Compounds**
There is an electrostatic interaction between the polar water molecules and the ions. This is an ion–dipole force.

Portion of surface and edge of NaCl crystal in contact with water

ion–dipole forces

develops between the forces holding the crystal together and the ion–dipole forces that are pulling the ions into solution. In the case of NaCl, the ion-dipole forces are stronger and the ions on the surface of the solid are separated from the rest of the crystal lattice and pulled into the aqueous medium. Since the ions in solution are now surrounded by water molecules, we say that the ions are *hydrated*. In solution, the positive and negative ions are no longer associated with one another. In fact, the charges on the ions are diminished or insulated from each other by the "escort" of hydrating water molecules around each ion. As before, we represent the solution of the ionic compound as going from the ions in the crystal lattice on the left to the hydrated ions on the right. Two examples of the solution of ionic compounds are as follows.

$$NaCl(s) \xrightarrow{H_2O} Na^+(aq) + Cl^-(aq)$$

$$K_2SO_4(s) \xrightarrow{H_2O} 2K^+(aq) + SO_4^{2-}(aq)$$

The $H_2O$ (above the reaction arrow) represents a large, undetermined number of water molecules needed to break up the crystal and hydrate the ions. The (*aq*) after the symbol of each ion indicates that it is hydrated in the solution. Of course, not all ionic compounds dissolve to an appreciable extent in water. In these cases, the ion–ion forces are considerably stronger than the ion–dipole attractions, so the solid crystal remains largely intact when placed in water. For example, ancient marble (i.e., $CaCO_3$) sculptures have suffered the indignities of weather for centuries with little deterioration.

### 12-1.3 Formation of Aqueous Solutions of Molecular Compounds

Polar molecular compounds, such as acids, may also dissolve in water. An example is the HCl molecule. In the pure gaseous state the two atoms are held together by a single covalent bond. However, HCl is a very polar molecule where the chlorine is the site of a partial negative charge and the hydrogen is the site of a partial positive charge. When dissolved in water, a tug-of-war develops between the covalent bond in HCl holding the molecule together and the dipole-dipole forces between $H_2O$ and HCl pulling the molecule apart. In this case, the dipole-dipole forces are clearly stronger so the covalent bond breaks. When this bond breaks the electron pair in the bond remains with the more electronegative Cl, which produces ions rather than neutral atoms. Hydrated $H^+$ and $Cl^-$ ions are formed in the process. *The process of forming ions from molecular compounds is known as* **ionization**.

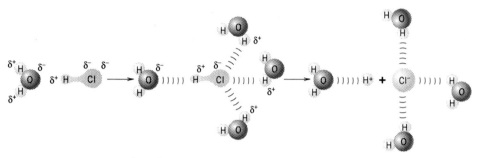

**FIGURE 12-3 Interaction of HCl and H₂O** The dipole–dipole interaction between H₂O and HCl leads to breaking of the HCl bond.

The ionization process is illustrated in Figure 12-3. For clarity, we have shown only four water molecules, but actually many more are involved in the interaction. We will have much more to say about the reaction of acids in water in the next chapter. Ionization is represented by the following equation.

$$HCl(g) \xrightarrow{\text{H}_2\text{O}} H^+ (aq) + Cl^- (aq)$$

Other polar molecules dissolve in water without the formation of ions. In these cases, the dipole–dipole interactions between solute and solvent do not lead to ionization, so the neutral solute molecule remains intact in solution. Methyl alcohol, a liquid, is a polar molecular compound that is miscible with water without ionization. (See Figure 12-4.)

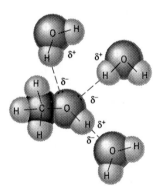

**FIGURE 12-4 Methyl Alcohol in Water** For some polar covalent molecules in water, there are only dipole–dipole attractions between solute and water molecules.

If a molecule is nonpolar, there are no sites of positive and negative charge to interact with the dipoles of water. Since the water molecules are moderately attracted to one another by hydrogen bonding, there is no tendency for the water molecules to interact with a solute molecule. *As a result, most nonpolar compounds do not dissolve in polar solvents such as water.* Nonpolar compounds do tend to dissolve in nonpolar solvents such as benzene or carbon tetrachloride. This occurs because neither solvent nor solute molecules are held together by particularly strong forces, so they mix freely. For example, if we wish to dissolve a grease stain (i.e., grease is composed of nonpolar molecules), we know that plain water does not work but a nonpolar solvent such as gasoline does. Within chemistry circles, a well-known phrase sums up the tendency of one chemical to dissolve another: "Like dissolves like." This simply means that, in most cases, *polar solvents dissolve ionic or polar molecular compounds, and nonpolar solvents dissolve nonpolar compounds.*

Why should we be concerned with the dissolving of substances? A great deal of time and effort are spent trying to find the right solvent for all sorts of chemical compounds in industry. Chemical reactions occur more readily when reactants are in solution. The close packing of molecules in a solid hinders the reacting molecules or ions from coming together. The proper solvent is needed so the solid can enter into the liquid phase and its molecules or ions mix thoroughly.

▶ **ASSESSING THE OBJECTIVE FOR SECTION 12-1**

**EXERCISE 12-1(a) LEVEL 1:** Are the following compounds soluble in water?
**(a)** NaI      **(b)** $H_2SO_4$      **(c)** $CCl_4$      **(d)** $NH_2CH_3$      **(e)** $FeCl_3$

**EXERCISE 12-1(b) LEVEL 2:** Write symbols for the aqueous form of each compound, including state symbols [for example, $Na^+$ (*aq*) + $Cl^-$ (*aq*)]. All dissolve in water.

(a) $(NH_4)_2Cr_2O_7$     (b) $HNO_3$     (c) $CH_3-\overset{\overset{\text{O}}{\|}}{C}-CH_3$     (d) $ZnBr_2$

**EXERCISE 12-1(c) LEVEL 2:** What kinds of forces form between the following?
(a) water and $Zn(NO_3)_2$     (b) water and $CH_3CH_2OH$     (c) $CCl_4$ and $C_6H_{14}$

**EXERCISE 12-1(d) LEVEL 3:** When a compound like KF(*s*) dissolves in water, we say that it dissociates. When a compound like $HNO_3$(*l*) dissolves in water, we say that it ionizes. What do these terms mean, and why is there a difference?

*For additional practice, work chapter problems 12-1, 12-3, 12-4, and 12-6.*

# 12-2 The Effects of Temperature and Pressure on Solubility

▶ OBJECTIVE
FOR SECTION 12-2
Describe the effects of temperature and pressure on solubility of solids and gases in a liquid.

 **LOOKING AHEAD!** The terms used to define the relative amount of a substance that dissolves almost constitute a separate vocabulary. Besides the terms that we use, in this section we are also interested in how temperature affects the solubility of compounds. ■

## 12-2.1 The Solubility of Compounds

*The* **solubility** *of a solute is defined as the maximum amount that dissolves in a given amount of solvent at a specified temperature.* The terms *soluble* and *insoluble* were introduced in Section 5-5.1. In fact, these terms are somewhat arbitrary since every compound has a maximum solubility and many compounds that we designate as insoluble actually do have a limited solubility. So there is no clear boundary between soluble and insoluble compounds.

Now consider the amount of solute that dissolves in a solvent. *When a defined amount of solvent contains the maximum amount of dissolved solute, the solution is considered to be* **saturated**. *If less than the maximum amount is present, the solution is* **unsaturated**. In certain unusual situations, *an unstable condition may exist in which there is actually more solute present in solution than its solubility would indicate. Such a solution is said to be* **supersaturated**. They are formed when saturated solutions are slowly cooled. Supersaturated solutions often shed the excess solute if a tiny "seed" crystal of solute is added or if the solution is shaken. The excess solute rapidly solidifies and collects at the bottom of the container as a precipitate.

Given that certain compounds are soluble in water, how do we express the **concentration**, *which is the amount of solute present in a given amount of solvent or solution?* Several units are available, and the one we choose depends on the application involved. Some units emphasize the mass of solute and some the number of particles (moles) of solute. Some relate the solute to the mass of solvent, the mass of the solution, or the volume of the solution. We will introduce these units later as they are applied.

The first concentration unit that we will discuss is used to compare solubilities of different compounds. This unit expresses the amount of solute present in a saturated solution as mass of solute present in 100 g of solvent (g solute/100 g $H_2O$ in the case of aqueous solutions). The solubilities of several compounds in water are listed in Table 12-1. For example, note that 205 g of sugar dissolved in 100 g (100 mL) of water produces a saturated solution at 20°C. Also notice that $PbSO_4$, $Mg(OH)_2$, and AgCl have very low

| TABLE 12-1 | |
|---|---|
| **Solubilities of Compounds (at 20°C)** | |
| **COMPOUND** | **SOLUBILITY (g SOLUTE/100 g $H_2O$)** |
| sucrose (table sugar) | 205 |
| HCl | 63 |
| NaCl | 36 |
| $KNO_3$ | 28 |
| $PbSO_4$ | 0.04 |
| $Mg(OH)_2$ | 0.01 |
| AgCl | $1.9 \times 10^{-4}$ |

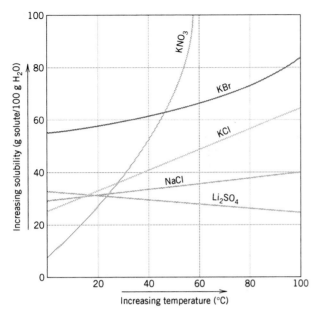

FIGURE 12-5 Solubility and Temperature The solubility of most solids increases as temperature increases.

solubilities and thus are usually considered as insoluble (or, more accurately, *sparingly soluble*). In Chapter 6, we indicated that whenever both ions involved in one of these insoluble compounds (e.g., $Mg^{2+}$ and $OH^-$) are mixed from separate solutions, a precipitate of that compound forms [e.g., $Mg(OH)_2$]. The other compounds listed are considered *soluble*, although to various extents. Table 5-3 can be used as an aid in determining whether compounds of some common anions are considered soluble or generally insoluble.

## 12-2.2 The Effect of Temperature on the Solubility of Solids in Water

It is apparent that the nature of a solute affects its solubility in water. Temperature is also an important factor. From practical experience, most of us know that more sugar or salt dissolves in hot water than in cold. This is generally true. *Most solids and liquids are more soluble in water at higher temperatures.* In Figure 12-5, the solubilities of several ionic compounds are graphed as a function of temperature. Note that all except $Li_2SO_4$ are more soluble as the temperature increases. The information shown in Figure 12-5 has important laboratory implications. An impure solid can be purified by a process called **recrystallization**. In this procedure, a solution is saturated with the solute to be purified at a high temperature, such as the boiling point of the solution. Insoluble impurities are then filtered from the hot solution. As the solution is allowed to cool, the solvent can hold less and less solute. The excess solute precipitates from the solution as it cools (if it does not become supersaturated). This solid, now more pure, can then be filtered from the cold solution. The soluble impurities, as well as some of the original compound still in solution, pass through the filter. For example, if 100 g of water is saturated with KBr at its boiling point near 100°C, it contains 85 g of dissolved KBr. If the solution is cooled to 0°C in an ice bath, the water can now contain only 55 g of dissolved salt. The difference (i.e., 85 g − 55 g = 30 g) forms a precipitate. (See Figure 12-6.)

## 12-2.3 The Effect of Temperature on the Solubility of Gases in Water

Despite their nonpolar nature, many gases also dissolve in water to a small extent (e.g., $O_2$, $N_2$, and $CO_2$). Indeed, the presence of dissolved oxygen in water provides the means of life for fish and other aquatic animals. *Unlike solids, gases become less*

FIGURE 12-6 Recrystallization A hot, saturated solution of KBr is being prepared on the left. A precipitate has formed in the cold solution on the right because of its lower solubility.

*soluble as the temperature increases.* This can be witnessed by observing water being heated. As the temperature increases, the water tends to fizz somewhat as the dissolved gases are expelled. High temperatures in lakes can be a danger to aquatic animals and may cause fish kills. The lower solubility of oxygen at the higher temperatures can lead to an oxygen-depleted lake.

Fish maintain life by extracting dissolved oxygen from water.

### 12-2.4 The Effect of Pressure on Solubility

The solubility of solids and liquids in a liquid is not affected to any extent by the external pressure. However, this is not true of the solubility of gases in liquids. The solubility of a gas in a liquid relates to the partial pressure of that gas above the liquid. This is known as **Henry's law**, *which states that the solubility of a gas is proportional to the partial pressure of that gas above the solution.*

$$\text{solubility} = k\,P_{\text{gas}}$$

If you have ever opened a carbonated beverage, you have experienced Henry's law. A sealed can of soda contains carbon dioxide gas above the liquid under modest pressure. When the can is opened, the pressure of carbon dioxide above the liquid decreases as it escapes. The lowering of the partial pressure of the carbon dioxide results in the decreased solubility of carbon dioxide, and bubbles of $CO_2$

---

**MAKING IT REAL**

## Hyperbaric Therapy

Hyperbaric cylinder.

A scuba diver needs to be very much aware of Henry's law. As a diver descends in the ocean, the pressure of the water increases. As a result, the diver must inhale air under high pressure from a tank. However, the high pressure of air that is inhaled increases the concentration of dissolved $N_2$ in the blood. If the diver comes to the surface too quickly (high pressure to low pressure), the lower pressure in the lungs causes $N_2$ to come out of solution and form bubbles of $N_2$ in the blood and cells. This is a condition known as *the bends* and can be fatal if the lungs are not quickly repressurized. A careful diver knows to return to the surface very slowly, pausing at specific intervals until the excess nitrogen is expelled from the blood.

Treatment of the bends requires that the patient be placed in a hyperbaric chamber as soon as possible. The person is completely enclosed in the chamber, where pressures of 2–3 atm of pure oxygen are applied. The higher pressure forces the nitrogen back into solution in the blood, and the pure oxygen speeds the purging of the system of nitrogen. The pressure in the chamber is slowly brought back to normal.

Hyperbaric chambers are also used in the treatment of carbon monoxide and cyanide poisoning. Both of these substances attach to the hemoglobin in the blood, thus blocking it from attaching to molecular oxygen in the lungs. In effect, the victim suffocates. The partial pressure of oxygen in the chamber is 10 to 15 times the normal partial pressure in the atmosphere (about 0.20 atm). Under these conditions, the concentration of dissolved oxygen in the blood is from 10 to 15 times normal. Oxygen is transported to the tissues in solution, thus bypassing the normal hemoglobin transport. The high concentration of oxygen in the blood also helps purge the system of carbon monoxide. Eventually, the patient is revived through blood transfusions or the regeneration of new red blood cells.

Hyperbaric treatment has a large variety of other uses, especially in treating hard-to-heal wounds, such as those found in diabetics, or wounds in remote areas, such as the ankles and feet. The high concentration of oxygen destroys bacteria, which thrive in a low-oxygen environment. This treatment is becoming more popular to treat more and more conditions that seem to respond to a high concentration of oxygen.

gas evolve from the solution. As time goes on, the carbon dioxide will continue to escape and the soda eventually goes flat. (Keeping an open can in a refrigerator will extend its carbonated life—see Section 12-2.3.) An understanding of Henry's law is also very important for scuba divers, as discussed in Making it Real, "Hyperbaric Therapy."

Bottled carbonated beverages fizz when the bottle is opened because the sudden drop in pressure causes a sudden drop in gas solubility. (Andy Washnik)

▶ **ASSESSING THE OBJECTIVE FOR SECTION 12-2**

**EXERCISE 12-2{a} LEVEL 1:** Fill in the blanks.
If a soluble compound dissolves to the limit of its solubility at a given temperature, the solution is _____; if the solute is not dissolved to the limit, the solution is _____. If more solute is present than indicated by its solubility, the solution is_____ and the excess solute may eventually form a _____. Solids generally become _____ soluble at higher temperatures, whereas gases become _____ soluble. An increase in partial pressure of a gas above a liquid _____ its solubility.

**EXERCISE 12-2{b} LEVEL 1:** Under what conditions of temperature and pressure will the following be most soluble?
**(a)** $Cl_2$ **(b)** $Na_2SO_4$

**EXERCISE 12-2{c} LEVEL 2:** Refer to Table 12-1. Describe the following as saturated, unsaturated, or supersaturated:
**(a)** 25.0 g of sugar in 10.0 g of $H_2O$
**(b)** 9.0 g of NaCl in 25.0 g of $H_2O$
**(c)** 12.0 g of $KNO_3$ in 50.0 g of $H_2O$

**EXERCISE 12-2{d} LEVEL 3** Referring to Figure 12-5, describe each of the following solutions as saturated, unsaturated, or supersaturated. (All are in 100 g of $H_2O$.)
**(a)** 60 g of KBr at 20°C   **(c)** 50 g of KCl at 60°C
**(b)** 40 g of $KNO_3$ at 40°C   **(d)** 20 g of NaCl at 40°C

**EXERCISE 12-2{e} LEVEL 3:** While working in lab, you want to dissolve a large crystal (about 3 g in size) of $CaCl_2$. What types of things could you do to speed the dissolving process?

*For additional practice, work chapter problems 12-9, 12-11, and 12-12.*

▶ **OBJECTIVE FOR SECTION 12-3**
Perform calculations of concentration involving percent by mass, ppm and ppb.

# 12-3 Concentration: Percent by Mass

**LOOKING AHEAD!** A *concentrated* solution means that a large amount of a given solute is present in a given amount of solvent. A *dilute* solution means that comparatively little of the same solute is present. Obviously, we need more quantitative methods of expressing concentrations for laboratory situations. ∎

In the previous discussion, the concentration unit (g solute/100 g solvent) related mass of solute to *solvent*. A second type of unit relates mass of solute to mass of *solution*, which contains both solute and solvent. **Percent by mass** *expresses the mass of solute per 100 grams of solution.* Consider 100 g of a solution that is 25% by mass HCl. There are 25 g of HCl and 75 g of $H_2O$ present. The unit allows us to convert between mass of solute, mass of solvent, and mass of solution. We actually introduced mass percent in Section 3-3.3, which included Examples 3-5 and 3-6. However, we will also review the unit in this section and include an additional worked-out example as well as chapter-end practice problems. The formula for percent by mass is

$$\% \text{ by mass (solute)} = \frac{\text{mass of solute}}{\text{mass of solute} + \text{mass of solvent}} \times 100\%$$

$$= \frac{\text{mass of solute}}{\text{mass of solution}} \times 100\%$$

## EXAMPLE 12-1 Calculating the Mass of Solution from Mass Percent

A solution is 14.0% by mass $H_2SO_4$. There are 0.221 moles of $H_2SO_4$ in the solution. What is the mass of the solution?

### PROCEDURE

**1.** Convert moles of $H_2SO_4$ to mass.

**2.** Convert mass of $H_2SO_4$ to mass of the solution.

### SOLUTION

**1.** The molar mass is

$$2.016 \text{ g (H)} + 32.07 \text{ g (S)} + 64.00 \text{ g (O)} = 98.09 \text{ g/mol}$$

$$0.221 \text{ mol } H_2SO_4 \times \frac{98.09 \text{ g } H_2SO_4}{\text{mol } H_2SO_4} = 21.7 \text{ g } H_2SO_4$$

**2.** $21.7 \text{ g } H_2SO_4 \times \dfrac{100 \text{ g solution}}{14.0 \text{ g } H_2SO_4} = \underline{155 \text{ g solution}}$

### ANALYSIS

Notice we are using the conversion factor

$$\frac{100 \text{ g solution}}{14.0 \text{ g solute}}$$

as we were given the mass of solute and were looking for the total mass of solution. What conversion factor would you use if the question asked for the mass of solvent instead? It would be

$$\frac{86.0 \text{ g solvent}}{14.0 \text{ g solute}}$$

### SYNTHESIS

Percent solutions can also be described by the term "parts per hundred," or pph. In this example, 14 mass units out of every 100 mass units in the solution are due to $H_2SO_4$. The other 86 mass units are due to water molecules. As solutions become more and more dilute, and the mass percent of solute becomes smaller and smaller, other concentration units become necessary. Read on.

## 12-3.1 Parts per Million and Parts per Billion

Percent by mass is equivalent to *parts per hundred*. When concentrations are very low, however, two closely related units become more convenient. These units are **parts per million (ppm)** and **parts per billion (ppb)**. For example, the concentration of carbon dioxide in the atmosphere is currently 0.0380%. It is more conveniently represented as 380 ppm. (It is unfortunately increasing by about 3 ppm each year.) Dioxin, a synthetic chemical linked to cancer, is measured in the soil in units of ppb.

Parts per million is obtained by multiplying the ratio of the mass of solute to mass of solution by $10^6$ ppm rather than 100%. Parts per billion is obtained by multiplying the same ratio by $10^9$ ppb. For example, if a solution has a mass of 1.00 kg and contains only 3.0 mg of a solute, it has the following concentration in percent by mass, ppm, and ppb.

$$\frac{3.0 \times 10^{-3} \text{ g (solute)}}{1.0 \times 10^{3} \text{ g (solution)}} \times 100\% = \underline{3.0 \times 10^{-4}\%}$$

$$\frac{3.0 \times 10^{-3} \text{ g}}{1.0 \times 10^{3} \text{ g}} \times 10^{6} \text{ ppm} = \underline{3.0 \text{ ppm}}$$

$$\frac{3.0 \times 10^{-3} \text{ g}}{1.0 \times 10^{3} \text{ g}} \times 10^{9} \text{ ppb} = \underline{3.0 \times 10^{3} \text{ ppb}}$$

In this case, the most convenient expression of concentration is in units of ppm. In the examples cited, the units, ppm and ppb, refer to the mass of the solution. In the case of the concentration of $CO_2$ in the atmosphere, the ppm refers to 1 million particles (molecules of compounds or atoms of noble gases) in the atmosphere. Thus, there are currently 380 $CO_2$ molecules per million molecules.

## EXAMPLE 12-2   Calculating ppm and ppb of a Solution

What is the concentration in ppm and ppb of a solution if it is $8.8 \times 10^{-5}\%$ by mass solute?

**PROCEDURE**

Find the mass of solute per gram of solution and multiply by $10^6$ for ppm or $10^9$ for ppb.

**SOLUTION**

$$\frac{8.8 \times 10^{-5}\%}{100\%} = \frac{8.8 \times 10^{-7} \text{ g solute}}{\text{g solution}}$$

$$\frac{8.8 \times 10^{-7} \text{ g solute}}{\text{g solution}} \times 10^{6} \text{ ppm} = \underline{0.88 \text{ ppm}}$$

$$\frac{8.8 \times 10^{-7} \text{ g solute}}{\text{g solution}} \times 10^{9} \text{ ppb} = \underline{880 \text{ ppb}}$$

**ANALYSIS**

The units of ppm and ppb can look quite imposing, but if you're comfortable using percents, then conversions become natural. The procedures are virtually identical. If you scored 80% on a test, and the test had 60 questions, you'd multiply $60 \times \frac{80\%}{100\%}$, to see how many you got right (48 questions). If you had 25 g of water that had an 880-ppb concentration of lead in it, you'd multiply $25\text{g} \times \frac{880 \text{ ppb}}{10^9 \text{ ppb}}$ to see the mass of toxin ($2.2 \times 10^{-5}$ g of Pb).

**SYNTHESIS**

Choosing the appropriate concentration unit (%, ppm, ppb, or even ppt!) is a choice left to the scientist to discern the most reasonable unit. People are most comfortable dealing with numbers that fall between 1 and 1000. Beyond that range, they begin to look too large and unwieldy. Once they become decimals, their significance diminishes with size. But in the 1 to 1000 range, we are mentally prepared to compare and react to them in comparison to other data. As a rule of thumb, then, most scientists, agencies, health professionals, and others presenting data will choose units so that the data fall comfortably in that range. With our choices above, concentrations of most things that we measure can be manipulated into one of those units.

▶ **ASSESSING THE OBJECTIVE FOR SECTION 12-3**

**EXERCISE 12-3(a) LEVEL 1:** What are the three ratios that can be written involving the masses of solute, solvent, and solution for an 8.0% aqueous solution of KBr?

**EXERCISE 12-3(b) LEVEL 2:** What is the percent by mass if 15.0 g of $NH_4Cl$ is dissolved in 45.0 g of water?

**EXERCISE 12-3(c) LEVEL 2:** What mass of solvent is needed to make a 14.0% by mass solution using 25.0 g of solute?

**EXERCISE 12-3(d) LEVEL 2:** What mass of *solute* is required to make 300.0 g of a 6.0% solution?

**EXERCISE 12-3(e) LEVEL 3:** A sample of river water contained 2.50 mg of $Ba^{2+}$ contaminant in a 10.0-kg sample. What is the amount of $Ba^{2+}$ expressed in the following measurements?
**(a)** percent      **(b)** ppm      **(c)** ppb
Which of these is the most appropriate way to report the concentration?

**EXERCISE 12-3(f) LEVEL 3:** The EPA allows 15 ppb lead in drinking water. How many mg of lead are allowed in 50.0 kg of water?

*For additional practice, work chapter problems 12-13, 12-16, 12-17, 12-18, and 12-19.*

# 12-4 Concentration: Molarity

► **OBJECTIVE FOR SECTION 12-4**
Perform calculations involving molarity and the dilution of solutions.

**LOOKING AHEAD!** In the laboratory, it is more convenient to measure the volume of a solution rather than its mass. In stoichiometry, recall that we are interested primarily in the mole relationships, so it is also important to have a unit that expresses the solute in moles rather than mass. Such a unit is discussed in this section. ∎

## 12-4.1 Calculations Involving Molarity

When a substance is in an aqueous solution, the most convenient way to measure the amount is by measuring the volume of the solution. Graduated cylinders, burets, or other readily available laboratory apparatus allow this to be a convenient measurement. **Molarity (M)** *is defined as the number of moles of solute* (n) *per volume in liters* (V) *of solution.* Although molarity may be shown without units, it is understood to have units of *mol/L*. This is expressed as follows in equation form.

$$M = \frac{n \text{ (moles of solute)}}{V \text{ (liters of solution)}}$$

The following examples illustrate the calculation of molarity and its use in determining the amount of solute in a specific solution.

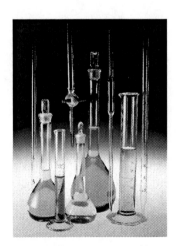

Solution volume is measured by burets, pipettes, and volumetric flasks.

## EXAMPLE 12-3  Calculating Molarity

What is the molarity of $H_2SO_4$ in a solution if 49.0 g of $H_2SO_4$ is present in 250 mL of solution?

**PROCEDURE**
Write down the formula for molarity and what you have been given, and then solve for what's requested. Recall that the volume is expressed in liters in this calculation.

**SOLUTION**

$$M = \frac{n}{V}$$

$$n = 49.0 \text{ g H}_2\text{SO}_4 \times \frac{1 \text{ mol}}{98.09 \text{ g H}_2\text{SO}_4} = 0.500 \text{ mol}$$

$$V = 250 \text{ mL} \times \frac{10^{-3} \text{ L}}{\text{mL}} = 0.250 \text{ L}$$

$$\frac{n}{V} = \frac{0.500 \text{ mol}}{0.250 \text{ L}} = \underline{\underline{2.00 \text{ M}}}$$

## EXAMPLE 12-4    Calculating the Amount of Solute from Molarity

What mass of HCl is present in 155 mL of a 0.540-M solution?

**PROCEDURE**

Volume must be expressed in liters. Molarity has units of mol/L. A quantity in grams requires the molar mass of HCl to convert to moles.

**SOLUTION**

$$M = \frac{n}{V} \quad n = M \times V$$

$$M = 0.540 \text{ mol/L}$$

$$V = 155 \text{ mL} = 0.155 \text{ L}$$

$$n = 0.540 \text{ mol/L} \times 0.155 \text{ L} = 0.0837 \text{ mol HCl}$$

$$0.0837 \text{ mol HCl} \times \frac{36.46 \text{ g}}{\text{mol HCl}} = \underline{\underline{3.05 \text{ g HCl}}}$$

## EXAMPLE 12-5    Calculating Molarity from Percent by Mass

Concentrated laboratory acid is 35.0% by mass HCl and has a density of 1.18 g/mL. What is its molarity?

**PROCEDURE**

Since a volume was not given, you can start with any volume you want since this is an intensive property. The molarity will be the *same* for 1 mL as for 25 L. To make the problem as simple as possible, assume that you have exactly 1 L of solution ($V = 1.00$ L) and go from there. We just need to find the number of moles of HCl in that 1 L. This is obtained as follows.

1. Find the mass of 1 L from the density.
2. Find the mass of HCl in 1 L using the percent by mass and the mass of 1 L.
3. Convert the mass of HCl to moles of HCl.

**SOLUTION**

Assume that $V = 1.00$ L

1. The mass of 1.00 L ($10^3$ mL) is

$$10^3 \text{ mL} \times 1.18 \text{ g/mL} = 1180 \text{ g solution}$$

2. The mass of HCl in 1.00 L is

$$1180 \text{ g solution} \times \frac{35.0 \text{ g HCl}}{100 \text{ g solution}} = 413 \text{ g HCl}$$

3. The number of moles of HCl in 1.00 L is

$$431 \text{ g} \times \frac{1 \text{ mol}}{36.46 \text{ g}} = 11.3 \text{ mol HCl}$$

$$\frac{n}{V} = \frac{11.3 \text{ mol}}{1.00 \text{ L}} = \underline{\underline{11.3 \text{ M}}}$$

### ANALYSIS

All the examples above are solved by dimensional analysis. If you've mastered that problem-solving technique, then by this time the calculations should be straightforward. Remember to write down all the given information and the units. Also, remember to express molarity as mol/L. Most importantly, remember that the liters in molarity are liters of solution, not solvent. This has implications for the formation of solutions, as we will see in future discussions.

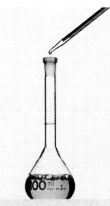

A student adds solvent with a pipette to a volumetric flask.

### SYNTHESIS

What if you were sent into the laboratory to make a specific molarity of solution? How would you do it? First, of course, you'd calculate the amount of solute you'd need for the required volume. Generally, the volumes we make are very specific, such as 100 mL, 250 mL, 500 mL, or 1000 mL. That is because we use volumetric flasks to ensure that our volumes are as accurate as possible. Then just mix the amount of solute in the required amount of solvent and stir? No! The solid itself takes up some volume. Until it has been made into a solution, we can't be sure how its volume will be accounted for. So you should transfer the solid into the flask as quantitatively as possible (use a funnel, rinse the weighing boat), and then fill up the flask halfway with solvent. This allows you to swirl until *all* the solute is dissolved. Then and only then can you fill the remainder of the flask with solvent. Toward the top, it is crucial that you do not exceed the line marked on the volumetric flask. You can always add more pure solvent, but you won't be able to remove it. Most scientists would use an eyedropper or disposable pipette to get the solvent exactly to the volume line. At this point, simply cap the flask and invert it several times to ensure thorough mixing, and your (very accurate) solution is made.

## 12-4.2 Dilution of Concentrated Solutions

From soft drinks to medicine, many products are transported as concentrated solutions. Before being sold, these products are carefully diluted to the desired concentration. Dilution is a straightforward procedure requiring a simple calculation. For example, in our laboratory situations, assume we are asked to prepare 200 mL of a 2.0-M solution from a large supply of a 6.0 M-HCl solution. We simply need to know what volume of the more concentrated solution is needed. (See Figure 12-7.)

In the following relationships, the variables of the dilute solution are designated $M_d$, $V_d$, and $n_d$. The variables of the concentrated solution are designated $M_c$, $V_c$, and $n_c$. It is important to understand that in a dilution process the moles of solute present in the dilute solution will be equal to those transferred from the concentrated solution. Thus we have the relationship

moles solute = $n_d = n_c$

**FIGURE 12-7 Dilution of Concentrated HCl** (*Note:* Never add water directly to concentrated acid, because it may splatter and cause severe burns.)

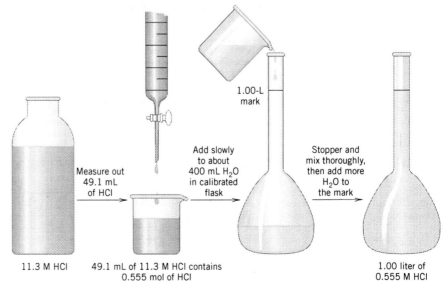

11.3 M HCl   49.1 mL of 11.3 M HCl contains 0.555 mol of HCl

Measure out 49.1 mL of HCl

Add slowly to about 400 mL H₂O in calibrated flask

1.00-L mark

Stopper and mix thoroughly, then add more H₂O to the mark

1.00 liter of 0.555 M HCl

Recall that $M_d \times V_d = n_d$ and $M_c \times V_c = n_c$ Since $n_c$ and $n_d$ are the same quantity, we can construct a simple equation relating the volume and molarity of the dilute solution to the volume and molarity of the concentrated solution:

$$M_c \times V_c = M_d \times V_d$$

## EXAMPLE 12-6    Calculating the Volume of a Concentrated Solution

What volume of 11.3 M HCl must be mixed with water to make 1.00 L of 0.555 M HCl? (See also Figure 12-7.)

**PROCEDURE**

Recall that the same number of moles of HCl will be measured from the concentrated solution as needed in the dilute solution. Thus we can simply rearrange the dilution equation to solve for the requested variable.

$$M_c \times V_c = M_d \times V_d \qquad V_c = \frac{M_d \times V_d}{M_c}$$

**SOLUTION**

$$M_c = 11.3 \text{ M} \qquad M_d = 0.555 \text{ M}$$

$$V_c = ? \qquad V_d = 1.00 \text{L}$$

$$V_c = \frac{0.555 \text{ mol/L} \times 1.00 \text{ L}}{11.3 \text{ mol/L}} = 0.0491 \text{ L} = \underline{\underline{49.1 \text{ mL}}}$$

**ANALYSIS**

We have the same issue here that we had when we were making solutions from solutes directly. The total volume calculated is the volume of the solution. So, in this problem, 49.1 mL of HCl would be measured out (probably with a buret) and then added to a 1.0-L volumetric flask. The volume of water added would then be the amount necessary to bring the total volume up to 1.0 L. This will, of course, be very close to 950.9 mL, but because volumes are not necessarily additive, the exact amount may be a little off from this value. Filling up to the 1.0-L line on the volumetric flask assures that the proper amount is added.

**SYNTHESIS**

This problem illustrates a concept that you learned in lab: When diluting an acid (or other concentrated compound), do you pour the concentrated solution into the water or pour the water into the concentrated solution? The catchphrase is "add acid." Diluting acids is often very exothermic, and splattering may occur. The proper procedure of pouring the concentrated solution into the solvent ensures that any splatter is from a more dilute solution, rather than a more concentrated one; it is therefore considered the safer route.

## EXAMPLE 12-7    Calculating the Molarity of Dilute Solution

What is the molarity of a solution of KCl that is prepared by dilution of 855 mL of a 0.475 M solution to a volume of 1.25 L?

**PROCEDURE**

Again, we can use the dilution equation. Solve the algebraic equation for $M_d$.

$$M_c \times V_c = M_d \times V_d \qquad M_d = \frac{M_c \times V_c}{V_d}$$

**SOLUTION**

$$M_c = 0.475 \text{ M} \qquad M_d = ?$$

$$V_c = 855 \text{ mL} = 0.855 \text{ L} \qquad V_d = 1.25 \text{ L}$$

$$M_d = \frac{0.475 \text{ M} \times 0.855 \cancel{L}}{1.25 \cancel{L}} = \underline{0.325 \text{ M}}$$

### ANALYSIS

The key concept in working dilution problems is that while the volume of solution goes up, and the concentration of solution goes down, the overall number of moles of solute never changes. The same number of moles are present before the dilution and afterward. Though it goes beyond the scope of this text, this concept can be stretched to allow calculations when the dilution is not occurring with water but instead with a more dilute solution of the compound. For instance, if you wanted to turn your 1.0 M $NH_3$ into 3.0 M $NH_3$ by adding 9.0 M $NH_3$, determining the total number of moles before and after the dilution, and then converting into the $M \times V$ relationship, would allow you to solve the problem.

### SYNTHESIS

Dilution is a process that occurs frequently in lab. Why so prevalent? Because manufacturers find that it is more convenient to produce and ship solutions that are concentrated. It makes a more convenient use of space and weight and costs less. Furthermore, end users can use the dilution formula to scale-down the concentrations to whatever value is needed for their particular use. We can always dilute, but without the original solute, we can't make commercial solutions more concentrated. As a result, acids are sold at very high concentrations (18 M for $H_2SO_4$, 12 M for HCl). Hence, there are numerous safety procedures in place whenever we deal with commercial bottles.

▶ ASSESSING THE OBJECTIVE FOR SECTION 12-4

**EXERCISE 12-4(a) LEVEL 1:** What is the concentration if 0.500 mol of NaOH is present in 0.250 L of solution?

**EXERCISE 12-4(b) LEVEL 1:** What is the concentration if 1.00 L of 0.400 M HCl is diluted to 2.00 L?

**EXERCISE 12-4(c) LEVEL 2:** What mass of KI is needed to make 500 mL of 0.0750 M solution?

**EXERCISE 12-4(d) LEVEL 2:** What volume of water must you *add* to 50.0 ml of 2.00 M $Cu(NO_3)_2$ solution to dilute it to 0.800 M? (Assume volumes are additive.)

**EXERCISE 12-4(e) LEVEL 2:** What volume of 6.00 M $H_2SO_4(aq)$ is needed to prepare 250 mL of 0.400 M $H_2SO_4(aq)$?

**EXERCISE 12-4(f) LEVEL 3:** Describe how you would make 250.0 mL of 0.500 M NaCl solution using the following:

**(a)** solid NaCl                    **(b)** a 3.00 M solution of NaCl(*aq*)

**EXERCISE 12-4(g) LEVEL3:** What is the molarity of a 2.0% KCl solution? (Assume the density of the solution is 1.0 g/ml.)

*For additional practice, work chapter problems 12-23, 12-27, and 12-30.*

# 12-5 Stoichiometry Involving Solutions

▶ OBJECTIVE
FOR SECTION 12-5
Perform calculations involving titrations and other solution stoichiometry.

**LOOKING AHEAD!** In Chapter 5, we related the moles of a substance to its molar mass and the number of molecules. The volume of a gas at a specific temperature and pressure also relates to moles, so gases could be included in the general stoichiometry scheme in Chapter 10. Since molarity also relates to moles, solutions can be now be added to our general stoichiometry scheme as discussed in this section. ■

**FIGURE 12-8 General Procedure for Stoichiometry Problems**

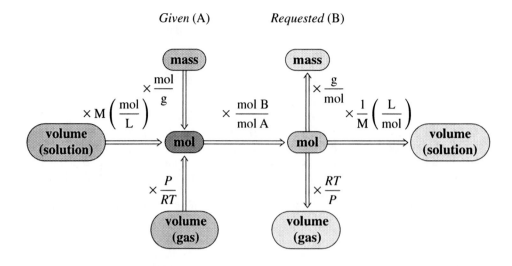

## 12-5.1 Stoichiometry and Molarity

It is obvious by now that a large number of important chemical reactions take place in aqueous solution. With the use of molarity, the volume of a solution provides a direct path to the number of moles of a reactant or product. Conversion of the given information into moles has always been the first step in solving a stoichiometry problem. In Figure 12-8, the general scheme for working stoichiometry problems has been extended to include volumes of solutions. The following examples also illustrate the inclusion of solutions in stoichiometry problems.

## EXAMPLE 12-8 Calculating the Volume of a Reactant

Given the balanced equation

$$3NaOH(aq) + H_3PO_4(aq) \rightarrow Na_3PO_4(aq) + 3H_2O(l)$$

what volume of 0.250 M NaOH is required to react completely with 4.90 g of $H_3PO_4$?

**PROCEDURE**

1. Convert mass of $H_3PO_4$ to moles using the molar mass of $H_3PO_4$.

2. Convert moles of $H_3PO_4$ to moles of NaOH using the mole ratio from the balanced equation.

3. Convert moles of NaOH to volume using the equation for molarity.

The complete unit map for this problem is shown below.

*Given* (g $H_3PO_4$)                                    *Requested* [L(aq) NaOH]

$$\times \frac{mol\ H_3PO_4}{g\ H_3PO_4} \quad \times \frac{mol\ NaOH}{mol\ H_3PO_4} \quad \times \frac{1}{M}\left[\frac{L\ NaOH}{mol\ NaOH}\right]$$

$$\boxed{mass\ H_3PO_4} \Rightarrow \boxed{mol\ H_3PO_4} \Rightarrow \boxed{mol\ NaOH} \Rightarrow \boxed{volume\ NaOH}$$

**SOLUTION**

$$4.90\ g\ H_3PO_4 \times \frac{1\ mol\ H_3PO_4}{97.99\ g\ H_3PO_4} \times \frac{3\ mol\ NaOH}{1\ mol\ H_3PO_4} = 0.150\ mol\ NaOH$$

$$vol\ NaOH = \frac{mol\ NaOH}{M} = \frac{0.150\ mol}{0.250\ mol/L} = \underline{0.600\ L}$$

In Section 7-1, we introduced the mass-to-mass stoichiometry problem. This problem is an example of a mass-to-volume (solution) calculation. The similarities are important. Compare the unit map in Example 7-3 in Section 7-1.3 to the one in this example. The only difference in units is in the last conversion factor, where molarity is used to calculate volume, rather than molar mass for the purpose of converting to grams. Otherwise, the procedure is identical. Substitution of a second molarity value for the second reactant would allow for a volume-to-volume calculation, negating the need to calculate a molar mass entirely. See Example 12-9.

### SYNTHESIS

These problems are actually more common than the original stoichiometry problems presented in Chapter 7 simply because they represent reactions occurring in solution. The vast majority of chemical reactions are solution reactions rather than solid-phase reactions because of the mixing that occurs in solution. It's hard for solids to react together at all, and if they do, reaction times are generally slow. Solutions allow dissolved chemicals to mix thoroughly, bringing reactant molecule right up to reactant molecule and significantly increasing reaction rates.

## EXAMPLE 12-9   Calculating the Volume of a Gas from a Solution Reaction

Given the balanced equation

$$2HCl(aq) + K_2S(aq) \rightarrow H_2S(g) + 2KCl(aq)$$

what volume of $H_2S$ measured at STP would be evolved from 1.65 L of a 0.552 M HCl solution with excess $K_2S$ present?

### PROCEDURE

1. Convert volume and molarity of HCl to moles of HCl.

2. Convert moles of HCl to moles of $H_2S$ using mole ratio from the balanced equation.

3. Convert moles of $H_2S$ to volume of $H_2S$ using the molar volume.

The complete unit map for the problem is shown below.

### SOLUTION

$$V \text{ (Solution)} \times M(HCl) = n \text{ (HCl)}$$

$$1.65 \, \cancel{L} \times \frac{0.552 \, \text{mol}}{\cancel{L}} = 0.911 \, \text{mol HCl}$$

Since the volume of the gas is at STP, the molar volume relationship can be used rather than the ideal gas law.

$$0.911 \, \cancel{\text{mol HCl}} \times \frac{1 \, \cancel{\text{mol H}_2\text{S}}}{2 \, \cancel{\text{mol HCl}}} \times \frac{22.4 \, \text{L (STP)}}{\cancel{\text{mol H}_2\text{S}}} = \underline{10.2 \, \text{L (STP)}}$$

### ANALYSIS

This problem combines two different volume problems. One is a volume of solution and requires the use of molarity. The other is a volume of a gas and requires a gas law relationship, which was discussed in Chapter 10. Sometimes students get the two confused. Try to visualize the aqueous solution and the gas being evolved as the HCl solution is added. The solution to any stoichiometry problem lies in using the proper conversion factor: molar mass for grams, 22.4 L/mol for gases at STP, the ideal gas law for volumes at other conditions, and molarity for solutions.

**SYNTHESIS**

Which conversion factors would be necessary to determine the number of *molecules* of a product that could be produced from a given volume of reactant solution? Starting with the volume, we would need the molarity of the solution, the mole ratio between reactant and product, and finally Avogadro's number. The unit map for this calculation is

$$\frac{mol \ (reactant)}{L} \times \frac{mol \ (product)}{mol \ (reactant)} \times \frac{6.022 \times 10^{23} \ molecules}{mol \ (product)}$$

### 12-5.2 Titrations

Quite often, laboratory experiments require that we establish the molarity of a solution from stoichiometry data. For example, environmental scientists encounter this situation frequently when they sample river water. To know whether the water is safe to drink, the concentrations of $Pb^{2+}$, or $Hg^{2+}$, or some other heavy metal contaminant has to be established. The concentrations are determined through a stoichiometric procedure known as a *titration.*

**Titrations** *are usually volume-to-volume stoichiometry problems where a concentration is the unknown variable.* A measured volume of one reactant of known molarity is added to a known volume of the other reactant. The end of the reaction is generally noted by the addition of an *indicator*, which is a compound that provides a visual clue, such as a color change, that a reaction has been completed. When the indicator changes color, the titration is said to be at its *end point.* This occurs when a stoichiometric balance occurs between reactants. The molarity of the unknown solution can then be calculated. This is illustrated in Example 12-10.

---

**EXAMPLE 12-10    Calculating an Unknown Concentration from Titration Data**

---

Given the reaction: $3HCl(aq) + K_3PO_4(aq) \longrightarrow H_3PO_4(aq) + 3KCl(aq)$

What is the concentration of an HCl solution if 25.0 mL reacts with 38.5 mL of 0.145 M $K_3PO_4$ solution?

**PROCEDURE**

**1.** Convert volume in mL to volume in L.

**2.** Convert L and M of $K_3PO_4$ to moles of $K_3PO_4$ and then moles of $K_3PO_4$ to moles of HCl using the mole ratio from the balanced equation. The unit map for this conversion is shown below.

*Given* [L $K_3PO_4$]                          *Requested* [mol HCl]

$$\times \ M \ \frac{mol \ K_3PO_4}{L \ K_3PO_4} \qquad \times \ \frac{mol \ HCl}{mol \ K_3PO_4}$$

$$\boxed{volume \ K_3PO_4 \ (solution)} \Rightarrow \boxed{mol \ K_3PO_4} \Rightarrow \boxed{mol \ HCl}$$

**3.** Convert moles and volume of HCl to molarity of HCl.

**SOLUTION**

$$38.5 \ mL \times \frac{1 \ L}{10^3 \ mL} = 0.0385 \ L \ K_3PO_4$$

$$25.0 \ mL \times \frac{1 \ L}{10^3 \ mL} = 0.250 \ L \ HCl$$

$$0.0385 \ L \ K_3PO_4 \times \frac{0.145 \ mol \ K_3PO_4}{L \ K_3PO_4} \times \frac{3 \ mol \ HCl}{1 \ mol \ K_3PO_4} = 0.0167 \ mol \ HCl$$

$$\text{molarity} = \frac{\text{mol}}{\text{L}} = \frac{0.0167 \text{ mol}}{0.250 \text{ L}} = \underline{\underline{0.668 \text{ M}}}$$

**ANALYSIS**

As a rule of thumb, concentrations above 1 M are considered fairly concentrated solutions. Concentrations below 0.1 M are considered dilute. The range between those two is what is frequently (though not exclusively) encountered. So when a value of 0.668 M is calculated for the molarity of a solution, it falls right in the range of common concentrations. The answer is very reasonable.

**SYNTHESIS**

Titrations find their biggest application in chemistry during acid–base reactions. There is generally a favorable reaction, and the accompanying change in the $H^+$ ($aq$) concentration (see Chapter 13) is the primary factor that causes the indicator to change color. Most indicators change color very close to the end point, making for a wide range of available indicators. The stoichiometry of the reaction is usually very straightforward and can be determined easily from the formulas of the acid and base.

▶ **ASSESSING THE OBJECTIVE FOR SECTION 12-5**

**EXERCISE 12-5(a) LEVEL 1:** What is the conversion factor needed to convert each of the following into moles?
**(a)** volume of a gas (at STP)   **(c)** mass of a solid
**(b)** volume of a solution       **(d)** number of molecules

**EXERCISE 12-5(b) LEVEL 2:** For the reaction
$$Ca(OH)_2(aq) + 2HNO_3(aq) \longrightarrow Ca(NO_3)_2(aq) + 2H_2O(l)$$
What volume of 0.125 M of $Ca(OH)_2$ reacts with 15.0 mL of 0.225 M $HNO_3$?

**EXERCISE 12-5(c) LEVEL 2:** For the reaction
$$Fe(OH)_3(s) + 3HCl(aq) \longrightarrow FeCl_3(aq) + 3H_2O(l)$$
What is the concentration of a solution of HCl if 33.5 mL reacts with 1.50 g of $Fe(OH)_3$?

**EXERCISE 12-5(d) LEVEL 3:** Sodium carbonate and hydrochloric acid react together to form carbon dioxide, water, and sodium chloride. If 50.0 mL of an HCl solution reacts with an excess of sodium carbonate to form 3.50 L of $CO_2$ at STP, what is the concentration of the HCl solution?

**EXERCISE 12-5(e) LEVEL 3:** What volume of 0.125 M phosphoric acid will react with 25.0 mL of 0.0850 M potassium hydroxide?

*For additional practice, work chapter problems 12-43, 12-46, 12-49, and 12-51.*

**PART A SUMMARY**

**KEY TERMS**

| | |
|---|---|
| 12-1.1 | Two liquids are **miscible** if they form one phase and **immiscible** if they remain in two phases. p. 398 |
| 12-1.2 | Ionic compounds dissolve in water as a result of **ion–dipole forces**. p. 398 |
| 12-1.3 | Strong acids undergo **ionization** when dissolved in water. p. 400 |
| 12-2.1 | **Solubility** is maximum amount of a solute that dissolves at a specific temperature. p. 401 |
| 12-2.1 | Depending on the amount of solute dissolved and its solubility, the solution may be **unsaturated**, **saturated**, or, in certain circumstances, **supersaturated**. p. 401 |
| 12-2.1 | The **concentration** of a solute refers to the amount present in a certain amount of solvent or solution. p. 401 |
| 12-2.2 | **Recrystallization** takes advantage of the difference in solubility of a substance at different temperatures. p. 402 |

12-2.4     According to **Henry's law**, the solubility of gases in a liquid relates to the pressure above the liquid. p. 403

12-3        Concentration may be measured as **percent by mass**. p. 404

12-3.1    **Parts per million (ppm)** or **parts per billion (ppb)** are used for small concentrations. p. 405

12-4.1    **Molarity (M)** is a concentration unit that emphasizes the volume of the solution. p. 407

12-5.2    During a **titration**, an indicator can be used to determine the end point of the experiment. p. 414

## SUMMARY CHART

| Concentration Units | | | |
|---|---|---|---|
| *Concentration Unit* | *Name* | *Relationship of solute* | *Use* |
| $\dfrac{\text{g solute}}{100 \text{ g solvent}}$ | ——— | Mass of solvent | Solubility tables |
| $\dfrac{\text{g solute}}{\text{g solution}} \times 100\%$ | Percent by mass | Mass of solution | High concentrations (above 0.01%) |
| $\dfrac{\text{g solute}}{\text{g solution}} \times 10^6 \text{ ppm}$ | Parts per million (ppm) | Mass of solution | Low concentrations ($>10^{-4}$ %) |
| $\dfrac{\text{g solute}}{\text{g solution}} \times 10^9 \text{ ppb}$ | Parts per billion ppb | Mass of solution | Extremely low concentrations ($>10^{-7}$ %) |
| $\dfrac{\text{mole solute}}{\text{L solution}}$ | Molarity (M) | Volume of solution | Measuring molar amount with volume and in stoichiometry problems |

## Part B

## The Effects of Solutes on the Properties of Water

**SETTING A GOAL**

■ You will learn how the physical properties of aqueous solutions differ from those of pure water.

**OBJECTIVES**

12-6 Explain the differences between nonelectrolytes, strong electrolytes, and weak electrolytes.

12-7 Calculate the boiling and melting points of aqueous solutions of electrolytes and nonelectrolytes.

▶ **OBJECTIVE FOR SECTION 12-6**
Explain the differences between nonelectrolytes, strong electrolytes, and weak electrolytes.

# 12-6 Electrical Properties of Solutions

**LOOKING AHEAD!** The use of a hair dryer in the bathtub is extremely dangerous. Even though pure water is not a good conductor of electricity, ordinary tap water is because it contains a variety of dissolved compounds. It has long been known that the presence of a solute in water may affect its ability to conduct electricity. In this section, we will examine the electrical properties of water and aqueous solutions. ■

## 12-6.1 Conduction of Electricity

We have probably all been zapped at one time or another by touching a live wire. The culprit, naturally, was electricity. *Electricity is simply a flow of electrons through a substance called a* **conductor**. Metals are the most familiar conductors and, as such, find use in electrical wires. Because the outer electrons of metals are loosely held, they can be made to flow through a continuous length of wire. *Other substances resist the flow of electricity and are known as* **nonconductors** *or* **insulators**. Glass and wood are examples of nonconductors of electricity. When wires are attached to an automobile battery and then to a lightbulb, the light shines brightly. If the wire is cut, the light goes out because the circuit is broken. If the two ends of the cut wire are now immersed in pure water (distilled or rain), the light stays out, indicating that water does not conduct electricity under these circumstances. Now let's dissolve certain solutes in water and examine what happens. When compounds such as $CuSO_4$ or HCl are dissolved in water, the effect is obvious. The light immediately begins to shine, indicating that the solution is a good conductor of electricity. (See Figure 12-9b.) *Compounds whose aqueous solutions conduct electricity are known as* **electrolytes**. (Some ionic compounds have limited solubility in water, but if their molten state conducts electricity, they are also classified as electrolytes.)

*We now understand that it is the presence of ions in the aqueous solution that allows the solution to conduct electricity.* It is the movement of these ions that carries the electrical charge and completes the circuit. Soluble ionic compounds form ions in solution, and some polar covalent compounds dissociate upon dissolving to form ions. For example, both NaCl (ionic) and HCl (polar covalent) are classified as electrolytes because they form ions in aqueous solution. As you will recall, HCl is a molecular compound in the pure state. However, in water it is ionized as described earlier in this chapter.

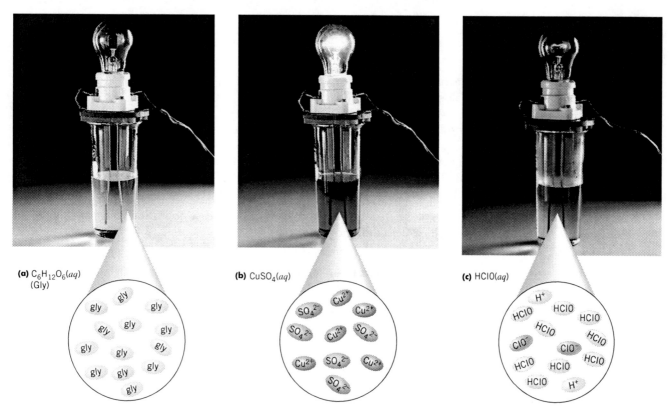

**(a)** $C_6H_{12}O_6(aq)$ (Gly)

**(b)** $CuSO_4(aq)$

**(c)** HClO(aq)

**FIGURE 12-9 Nonelectrolytes, Strong Electrolytes, and Weak Electrolytes** (a) A solution of glucose sugar ($C_6H_{12}O_6$) does not conduct electricity. (b) A $CuSO_4$ solution is a strong electrolyte and conducts electricity. (c) A hypochlorous acid solution [HClO(aq)] is a weak electrolyte and conducts a limited amount of electricity.

### 12-6.2 Nonelectrolytes and Electrolytes

Other compounds such as sucrose (table sugar), glucose (blood sugar), and alcohol dissolve in water, but their solutions do not conduct electricity. *Compounds whose aqueous solutions do not conduct electricity are known as* **nonelectrolytes**. Nonelectrolytes are molecular compounds that dissolve in water without formation of ions. (See Figure 12-9a.)

There are two classes of electrolytes: strong electrolytes and weak electrolytes. *Solutions of* **strong electrolytes** *are good conductors of electricity.* Almost all salts and strong acids are present only as ions in aqueous solution (e.g., NaCl, $CuSO_4$, and HCl) and are thus classified as strong electrolytes. (See Figure 12-9b.) *Solutions of* **weak electrolytes** *allow a limited amount of conduction.* When wires are immersed in solutions of weak electrolytes, the lightbulb glows, but very faintly. (See Figure 12-9c.) Even adding more of the solute does not cause increased conduction. Examples of weak electrolytes are ammonia ($NH_3$) and hypochlorous acid (HClO). As shown in Figure 12-9c, most of the HClO molecules in the solution remain as neutral molecules with only a small fraction present as ions. The ionization of HClO is an example of a reversible reaction that reaches a point of equilibrium and can be represented by the following equation. The equilibrium in this case lies far to the left.

$$HClO(aq) \rightleftharpoons H^+(aq) + ClO^-(aq)$$

The concept of equilibrium was discussed in relation to vapor pressure (Section 11-4.3) but will be discussed in more detail in Chapter 15. The identification of strong and weak acids will be explored in the next chapter.

(*Note*: Pure water actually does contain a very small concentration of ions, as we will discuss in the next chapter. The concentration of these ions in pure water is too low to detect by conduction of electrical current by the method described above.)

▶ **ASSESSING THE OBJECTIVE FOR SECTION 12-6**

**EXERCISE 12-6(a) LEVEL 1:** Are the following descriptions of strong electrolytes, weak electrolytes, or nonelectrolytes?
**(a)** describes all ionic compounds
**(b)** solution causing a lightbulb to glow dimly
**(c)** describes most molecular compounds
**(d)** conducts electricity well
**(e)** will not conduct electricity
**(f)** made from compounds that partially ionize in water

**EXERCISE 12-6(b) LEVEL 2:** Which of the following is the strong electrolyte, the weak electrolyte, and the nonelectrolyte?
**(a)** $NH_3$        **(b)** $KNO_3$        **(c)** $CH_3OH$

**EXERCISE 12-6(c) LEVEL 3:** If water is a poor conductor of electricity, why is it important to get out of a pool during an electrical storm?

*For additional practice, work chapter problems 12-51 and 12-52.*

---

▶ **OBJECTIVE FOR SECTION 12-7**
Calculate the boiling and melting points of aqueous solutions of electrolytes and nonelectrolytes.

# 12-7 Colligative Properties of Solutions

**LOOKING AHEAD!** We melt ice on the street by spreading salt and put antifreeze in our car's radiator—we take these actions because the presence of solutes alters some important physical properties of pure water. In this section we will examine why and how much the presence of solutes affects certain properties. ■

The presence of a solute in water may or may not affect its conductivity, depending on whether the solute is an electrolyte or a nonelectrolyte. There are other properties of water, however, that are always affected to some extent by the presence of a solute. Consider again what was mentioned in Chapter 3 as characteristic of a pure substance. Recall that a pure substance has a distinct and unvarying melting point and boiling point (at a specific atmospheric pressure). Mixtures, such as aqueous solutions, freeze and boil over a range of temperatures that are lower (for freezing) and higher (for boiling) than those of the pure solvent. The effect of these changes is to extend the liquid range for the solvent. The more solute, the more the melting and boiling points are affected. *A property that depends only on the relative amounts of solute in relation to the solvent is known as a* **colligative property**.

Colligative properties depend only on the amount or number of moles of particles present in solution, not their identity. The particles may be small molecules, large molecules, or ions—only the total number is relevant. This is like many of the gas laws, which, you may recall, also depend only on the total number of moles of gas present.

## 12-7.1 Vapor Pressure

The Dead Sea in Israel and the Great Salt Lake in the United States contain large concentrations of solutes. Since these bodies of water have no outlets to the ocean, dissolved substances have accumulated, forming saturated solutions. Even though both bodies of water exist in semiarid regions with high summer temperatures, they evaporate very slowly compared with a freshwater lake or even the ocean. If water in these lakes evaporated at the same rate as fresh water, both would nearly dry up in a matter of years. Why do they evaporate so slowly?

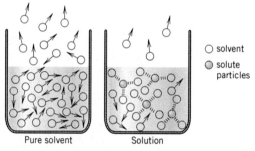

**FIGURE 12-10 Vapor Pressure Lowering** A nonvolatile solute reduces the number of solvent molecules escaping to the vapor.

*The presence of a nonvolatile solute*[*] *in a solvent lowers the equilibrium vapor pressure from that of the pure solvent.* (See Section 11-4.3.) It is not hard to understand why this occurs based on what we have discussed about the interactions between solute and solvent. Because of various attractive forces, solvent molecules surround solute molecules or ions. Solute molecules or ions thus tend to tie up the solvent molecules, which in effect prevents them from escaping to the vapor. An increase in solute particles causes more solvent molecules to be held in the liquid phase. This results in a solution with a lower equilibrium vapor pressure than the pure solvent. (See Figure 12-10.) As we might predict from this model, the more solute particles present, the lower the vapor pressure of the solution. The resulting **vapor pressure lowering** affects the boiling point of the solution, as described next.

## 12-7.2 Boiling Point

*A direct effect of the lowered vapor pressure of a solution is a higher boiling point than that of the solvent.* Recall that the normal boiling point of water is 100°C, which is the temperature at which its vapor pressure is equal to 760 torr. An aqueous salt solution, however, would have a vapor pressure lower than 760 torr. Thus, the solution would have to be heated above 100°C for the vapor pressure to reach 760 torr and begin boiling. Again, the more concentrated the solution, the lower is its vapor pressure and the higher is its boiling point.

The amount of **boiling-point elevation** is given by the equation

$$\Delta T_b = K_b m$$

---

[*]A nonvolatile solute is one that has essentially no vapor pressure at the relevant temperatures.

where

$\Delta T_b$ = the number of Celsius (or Kelvin) degrees that the boiling point is raised

$K_b$ = a constant characteristic of the solvent [for water $K_b = 0.512$ (°C · kg)/mol; other values of $K_b$ are given for particular solvents as needed in the problems]

$m$ = a concentration unit called molality

For these calculations we need one more unit of concentration, which is known as molality. The definition of **molality** is shown below.

$$\text{molality } (m) = \frac{\text{moles of solute}}{\text{kg of solvent}}$$

This is a convenient concentration unit for this purpose since it emphasizes the relationship between the relative amounts of solute (expressed in moles) and mass of solvent (expressed in kg) present rather than the volume of the solution, as does molarity. Also, temperature does not affect the molality of a solution. Molarity, however, is affected by temperature as the volume of most liquids changes in response to the temperature.

## EXAMPLE 12-11　Calculating Molality

What is the molality of methyl alcohol in a solution made by dissolving 18.5 g of methyl alcohol ($CH_3OH$) in 850 g of water?

### PROCEDURE

**1.** Convert mass of solute to mol of solute and g of solvent to kg of solvent.

**2.** Use these values to calculate molality.

$$\text{molality} = \frac{\text{mol solute}}{\text{kg solvent}}$$

### SOLUTION

$$\text{mol solute} = \frac{18.5 \text{ g}}{32.04 \text{ g/mol}} = 0.577 \text{ mol}$$

$$\text{kg solvent} = \frac{850 \text{ g}}{10^3 \text{ g/kg}} = 0.850 \text{ kg}$$

$$\text{molality} = \frac{0.577 \text{ mol}}{0.850 \text{ kg}} = \underline{0.679 \text{ } m}$$

### ANALYSIS

When water is the solvent, the value of the molarity and the molality differ by just a fraction of a percent. That is because 1.0 L of aqueous solution has a mass of about 1.0 kg. Should they be closer together for concentrated or dilute solutions? In fact, the more dilute the solution, the closer the mass of 1 L of the solution is to 1.0 kg (the mass of 1.0 L of pure water). Thus, they are closer for dilute solutions. For example, the molarity of a 1.0% solution of LiCl is 0.237, while the molality is 0.238. However, the molarity of a 10% solution of LiCl is 2.49, while the molality is 2.62.

### SYNTHESIS

So what if the solvent isn't water? Most liquids that routinely serve as solvents have densities significantly less than water's. For example, ethyl alcohol, a common solvent, has a density of 0.789 g/mL (0.789 kg/L). If we assume a dilute solution where 1 L of solution weighs about the same as 1 L of solvent, the number of moles of solute would be divided by 1 L for molarity but 0.789 kg for molality. That will cause the molality to be noticeably higher than the molarity. For the few solvents with densities higher than water [e.g., methylene chloride (1.33 g/mL)], the molality would be lower than the molarity.

**EXAMPLE 12-12**    **Calculating the Boiling Point of a Solution**

What is the boiling point of an aqueous solution containing 468 g of sucrose ($C_{12}H_{22}O_{11}$) in 350 g of water at 1 atm?

PROCEDURE

1. Convert g of solute (sucrose) to moles and g of solvent to kg.

2. Use these values and the value of $K_b$ for water to calculate the temperature change.

$$\Delta T_b = K_b\ m = 0.512\ (°C \cdot kg)/mol \times \frac{mol\ solute}{kg\ solvent}$$

3. Calculate the actual boiling point from the temperature change.

SOLUTION

$$mol\ solute = \frac{468\ g}{342.5\ g/mol} = 1.37\ mol$$

$$kg\ solvent = \frac{350\ g}{10^3\ g/kg} = 0.350\ kg$$

$$\Delta T_b = 0.512\ (°C \cdot kg)/mol \times \frac{1.37\ mol}{0.350\ kg} = 2.0\ °C$$

$$normal\ boiling\ point\ of\ water = 100.0°C$$

$$boiling\ point\ of\ the\ solution = 100.0°C + \Delta T_b = 100.0 + 2.0 = \underline{102.0°C}$$

ANALYSIS

In this problem the mass of solute is greater than the mass of solvent, yet it created an increase in boiling point of only 2°C. Why so small a change? In this case, it's because the solute is made of comparatively heavy molecules. The molar mass of the sucrose is 342.5 g/mol. If our solute had a molar mass of only 50 g/mol or so, what would our boiling point have been? 50 is about 7 times less than 342.5, which means there would be seven times as many particles and seven times the rise in temperature. The new boiling point would be closer to 114°C, a significant increase.

SYNTHESIS

This process of boiling-point elevation (or freezing-point depression, discussed in the next section) represented one of the earliest ways chemists had to determine the molar mass of an unknown compound. First, we determine whether the compound is soluble in a polar or a nonpolar solvent. Knowing the proper solvent and its value of $K_b$, we can then do the experiment. It requires that we dissolve a measured mass of the compound in a measured mass of solvent. We then measure the boiling point of the pure solvent, the boiling point of the solution, and, from these two values, the boiling-point elevation. From this we solve for the molality. Since we know the mass of solute and the mass of solvent, the only variable that is left is the molar mass. We could try the experiment using the same compound in other solvents to confirm our values.

## 12-7.3 Freezing Point

The icy, cold winds of winter can be very hard on automobiles. If there is not enough antifreeze in the radiator, the coolant water may freeze. This could ruin the radiator and even crack the engine block, because water expands when it freezes. We illustrate the same principle as antifreeze in radiators when we spread salt on ice-covered streets or sidewalks. In both of these cases, we take advantage of the fact that solutions have lower freezing points than pure solvents. *The freezing point of a solution is lower just as the boiling point is higher than that of the pure solvent.*

The amount of **freezing-point lowering** is given by the equation

$$\Delta T_f = K_f m$$

where

$\Delta T_f =$ the number of Celsius (or Kelvin) degrees that the freezing point is lowered
$K_f =$ a constant characteristic of the solvent [for water, $K_f = 1.86$ $(°C \cdot kg)/mol$]
$m =$ molality of the solution

---

## EXAMPLE 12-13    Calculating the Freezing Point of a Solution

What is the freezing point of the solution in Example 12-12?

**PROCEDURE**

$$\Delta T_f = K_f\, m = 1.86\ (°C \cdot kg)/\,mol \times \frac{mol\ solute}{kg\ solvent}$$

**SOLUTION**

$$\Delta T_f = K_f\, m = 1.86\ (°C \cdot kg)/\,mol \times \frac{1.37\ mol}{0.350\ kg} = 7.3°C$$

freezing point of water $= 0.0°C$

freezing point of the solution $= 0.0°C - \Delta T_f = 0.0°C\ \text{-}7.3°C = \underline{-7.3°C}$

**ANALYSIS**

This problem stresses the concept of a *colligative* property. In Examples 12-12 and 12-13 nothing changed about the solution, since there are the same number of solute particles in each case. Yet notice that the effect on the melting point is more pronounced than the effect on the boiling point. Since $K_f$ of water (1.86) is over three times larger than the $K_b$ of water (0.512), the freezing-point depression is over three times larger as well (7.3°C compared to 2°C). Because of the freezing-point *lowering* and boiling-point *elevation*, the liquid range in this example has been extended by over 9°C (i.e., −7.3°C to 102°C) for the solution compared to pure water. Permanent antifreeze not only protects the engine from freezing but in the summer it protects the water from boiling away. Until the late 1930s, methanol was used as antifreeze, but because it has a low boiling point, it would boil away in hot weather. It had to be removed and replaced with water when the weather warmed. Permanent antifreeze is now composed mostly of ethylene glycol ($C_2H_6O_2$). A 1:1 mixture protects down to −40°C (and up to about 110°C), although less may be used depending on the locality. Ethylene glycol, however, is very poisonous compared to propylene glycol ($C_3H_8O_2$), which is not. The latter is used in water-heating pipes in homes or other places where there is danger of accidental ingestion. (Because of its higher molar mass, however, it takes more propylene glycol to have the same effect as ethylene glycol.)

**SYNTHESIS**

Freezing-point depression is also used by chemists as a laboratory procedure to determine the molar mass of an unknown compound. See if you can calculate the molar mass of the compound in problem 12-91 in the chapter-end problems. Besides solubility, one looks for a solvent with the largest value for $K_f$. When you look at the equation for freezing-point depression, notice that the greater the value of $K_f$, the greater the freezing-point depression and the more precision (i.e., number of significant figures) in the measurement. For example, a measured depression of 12.2°C in one solvent is more precise than one of 1.3°C for the same solute in another solvent. Chloroform ($CHCl_3$) is very effective in this regard, since it has $K_f = 30$. One mole of solute in chloroform causes about 16 times as much freezing-point depression as in water. (This assumes that the solute is soluble in both solvents, which may not be the case.)

### 12-7.4 Osmotic Pressure

Food is preserved in salt water, drinking ocean water causes dehydration, tree and plant roots absorb water—these are all phenomena related to a colligative effect called osmosis. **Osmosis** *is the tendency for a solvent to move through a thin porous membrane from a dilute solution to a more concentrated solution.* The membrane is said to be *semipermeable*, which means that small solvent molecules can pass through but large hydrated solute species cannot. Figure 12-11 illustrates osmosis. On the right is a pure solvent and on the left, a solution. The two are separated by a semipermeable membrane. Solvent molecules can pass through the membrane in both directions, but the rate at which they diffuse to the right is lower because some of the water molecules on the left are held back by solute–solvent

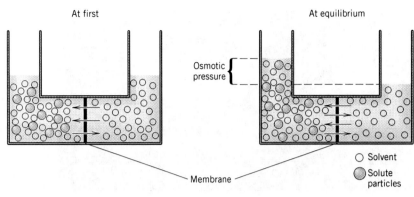

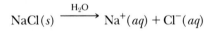

**FIGURE 12-11 Osmotic Pressure** Osmosis causes dilution of the more concentrated solution.

interactions. As a result of the uneven passage of water molecules, the water level rises on the left and drops on the right. This creates increased pressure on the left, which eventually counteracts the osmosis, and equilibrium is established. *The extra pressure required to establish this equilibrium is known as the* **osmotic pressure**. Like other colligative properties, it depends on the concentration of the solute. In Figure 12-11, the more concentrated the solution on the left (less solvent), the higher the osmotic pressure.

In Figure 12-11, if pressure greater than the osmotic pressure is applied on the left, reverse osmosis takes place and solvent molecules move from the solution to the pure solvent. This process is used in desalination plants that convert seawater (a solution) to drinkable water. This is important in areas of the world such as the Middle East, where there is a shortage of fresh water.

### 12-7.5 Electrolytes and Colligative Properties

Our final point concerns the effect of electrolytes on colligative properties. Electrolytes have a more pronounced effect on colligative properties than do nonelectrolytes. The reason is that these properties depend only on how many particles are present regardless of whether the particle is a neutral molecule, a cation, or an anion. For example, one mole of NaCl dissolves in water to produce two moles of particles, one mole of $Na^+$, and one mole of $Cl^-$.

Sodium chloride is used to melt ice from sidewalks, streets, and highways.

$$NaCl(s) \xrightarrow{H_2O} Na^+(aq) + Cl^-(aq)$$

Thus one mole of NaCl lowers the freezing point about twice as much as one mole of a nonelectrolyte. This effect is put to good use in the U.S. Snow Belt, where sodium chloride is spread on snow and ice to cause melting even though the temperature is below freezing. Even more effective in melting ice is calcium chloride ($CaCl_2$). This compound produces three moles of ions ($Ca^{2+} + 2Cl^-$) per mole of solute and therefore is three times as effective per mole as a nonelectrolyte in lowering the freezing point. Calcium chloride is occasionally used on roads when the temperature is too low for sodium chloride to be effective. Aqueous electrolyte solutions are quite corrosive toward metals because of their electrical conductivity. This is why they are not used in automobile radiators as an inexpensive antifreeze.

We see an example of the osmosis process whenever we leave our hands in water for extended periods of time. The oils that protect our skin eventually wash away, allowing water to come in contact with the skin, which is a semipermeable membrane. The movement of excess water molecules from the outside of our skin to the more concentrated fluid in our bodies causes puffy wrinkling. Pickles are wrinkled for the opposite reason. The cells of the cucumber have been dehydrated by the salty brine solution. In fact, brine solutions preserve many foods because the concentrated solution of salt removes water from the cells of bacteria, thus killing the bacteria. Trees and plants obtain water by absorbing water through the semipermeable membranes in their roots into the more concentrated solution inside the root cells.

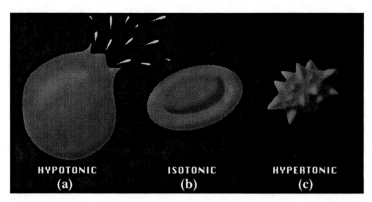

**HYPOTONIC**     **ISOTONIC**     **HYPERTONIC**
    (a)          (b)          (c)

**FIGURE 12-12 Blood Cells** (a) At lower ion concentration, osmotic flow pumps water into the cell and may cause it to burst. (b) In isotonic solution, red blood cells are disk shaped. (c) At higher ion concentration, osmotic flow removes water from the cell interior, shrinking the cell.

The concentration of solutes in the blood and other bodily fluids is important in the hydration and health of cells in our bodies. When the concentration of ions and other solutes in the blood or plasma is the same as that inside of a cell, the solution is said to be *isotonic*. In this case, there is no net movement of water into or out of the cell. If the concentration of solutes in the solutions around the cells is greater in the blood than in the cell, water moves out of the cell and dehydration occurs. If the opposite occurs, water moves into the cell and expands it. (See Figure 12-12.) In either case, destruction of the cells may occur in extreme cases. Intravenous solutions, such as a glucose drip or injections in a saline solution, are isotonic with the blood so as not to dilute or concentrate the solution of the cells. As mentioned earlier in Example 12-1, a 0.89% (wt/v) saline solution is used as an isotonic solution.

## MAKING IT REAL

### Osmosis in a Diaper

Except for the fact that a baby seems to be unusually heavy, one might not realize just how wet a diaper has become. In the old days, a quick touch would tell the condition. Modern superabsorbent diapers make use of a chemical that has a tremendous ability to absorb water. In fact, such diapers contain a white powdery material that can absorb 200 to 500 times its weight in water. Not only is such a diaper convenient for the diaper changer but it is also quite a bit more comfortable for the diaper wearer.

The compound used in these diapers is a polymeric material. The polymer used in diapers (sodium polyacrylate) is made of long chains of an ionic unit (called a monomer), sodium acrylate (shown below). Most familiar plastics such as Styrofoam cups, plastic bottles and bags, PVC pipes, and thousands of other everyday materials are made of various types of polymers. More detail about polymers is provided in Chapter 17.

$$CH_2\!=\!CH \qquad\qquad \{CH_2\!-\!CH\}$$
$$\quad\;|\qquad\qquad\qquad\qquad\quad\;|$$
$$CO_2^-Na^+ \qquad\qquad\quad CO_2^-Na^+$$

*Sodium acrylate*     *Sodium polyacrylate*
    *(Monomer)*

The unique property of the diaper polymer is that its surface is semipermeable. Inside the surface, ions are present. The high concentration of ions inside causes water molecules to cross the membrane in the process of osmosis. The water then stays put inside the polymer. In fact, the diaper does not even feel wet, thus protecting the baby from nasty rashes. It is so effective that special "training diapers" can be used when it is time for baby to move on. These diapers are engineered to allow some wetness and discomfort as an incentive to become "trained."

Consider the absorbent ability of these diapers. A 1-g quantity of the polyacrylate can absorb up to 500 g of water. If one had an 8-oz glass of water, it would take less than 500 mg of superabsorbent to turn the glass of water into a wiggly, gelatinous mass. A 700-lb quantity of superabsorbent would be enough to turn a good-size swimming pool into something like Jell-O.

In 1999, world production of this polymer was 980 million tons. Not all of that went into diapers (fortunately). It is also used in agriculture, crafts, evaporative coolers, firefighting, toothpaste, and cosmetics.

An unpleasant (odiferous), drippy experience has been changed into something much more tolerable. Baby caregivers of the world are grateful for this chemical advance.

▶ **ASSESSING THE OBJECTIVE FOR SECTION 12-7**

**EXERCISE 12-7(a) LEVEL 1:** Liquid A is a pure compound and liquid B contains a nonvolatile solute dissolved in liquid A.
**(a)** Which boils at the higher temperature?
**(b)** Which freezes at the higher temperature?
**(c)** Which has the higher osmotic pressure?
**(d)** Which has the higher vapor pressure?

**EXERCISE 12-7(b) LEVEL 2:** Calculate the molality if 15.0 g of $NaNO_3$ is dissolved in 50.0 g of $H_2O$.

**EXERCISE 12-7(c) LEVEL 2:** What is the freezing point of a solution if 0.750 mol of a nonelectrolyte solute is dissolved in 250.0 g of $H_2O$? What is the freezing point if it's 0.750 mol of $CaCl_2$ that's dissolved?

**EXERCISE 12-7(d) LEVEL 3:** Acetic acid ($HC_2H_3O_2$) is a weak electrolyte. What would be the effect on the boiling point of water of adding one mole of acetic acid compared to 1 mole of some nonelectrolyte molecular solute? What would be the effect compared to adding 1 mole of NaCl?

**EXERCISE 12-7(e) LEVEL 3:** There is a limit as to how cold a salt (NaCl) solution can be lowered before it freezes. At this temperature the salt solution is saturated, which is at about 28 g/100 g $H_2O$. What is this temperature in Celsius and Fahrenheit degrees?

*For additional practice, work chapter problems 12-56, 12-58, 12-60, 12-64, and 12-67.*

**PART B SUMMARY**

## KEY TERMS

12-6.1 A medium that conducts electricity is known as a **conductor**, whereas a medium that does not is an **insulator** (or **nonconductor**). p. 416

12-6.2 A solute that does not change water to a conductor is a **nonelectrolyte**, whereas an **electrolyte** allows the solution to become a conductor. p. 417

12-6.2 A **strong electrolyte** makes water a good conductor, whereas a **weak electrolyte** makes water a weak conductor. p. 418

12-7 A **colligative property** of a solution depends only on the amount of solute present. p. 419

12-7.1 A nonvolatile solute causes a **vapor pressure lowering** compared to the pure solvent. p. 419

12-7.2 A nonvolatile solute causes **boiling-point elevation**, the amount of which depends on the **molality** of the solution. p. 419

12-7.3 A solute causes a **freezing-point lowering**. p. 422

12-7.4 The presence of a solute allows **osmosis** to occur, which causes **osmotic pressure**. pp. 422–423

## SUMMARY CHART

| *Colligative Properties* | | |
|---|---|---|
| Property of Solution | Effect | Result |
| Vapor pressure | Lowered | Solutions evaporate more slowly than pure solvents. |
| Boiling point | Raised | Solutions boil at higher temperatures than pure solvents. |
| Freezing point | Lowered | Solutions freeze at lower temperatures than pure solvents. |
| Osmotic pressure | Raised | Solvent from dilute solutions diffuses through a semi-permeable membrane into concentrated solutions. |

---

## CHAPTER 12 SYNTHESIS PROBLEM

There are two ways we could melt the ice off of the front step on a nasty evening. We could either pour an alcoholic drink on it or spread some calcium chloride. Calcium chloride is more effective but a beverage may be more available in an emergency. In our study of chemistry, an understanding of how we measure concentrations, especially involving chemical reactions, is quite important. Also, how the physical properties of solutions differ from pure solvents answers questions such as the melting of ice referred to previously. In this problem, however, we will focus on these two very different water-soluble compounds to illustrate some of the many topics of this chapter.

| PROBLEM | SOLUTION |
|---|---|
| **a.** What forces are present when ethyl alcohol ($CH_3CH_2OH$) and $CaCl_2$ dissolve in water? | **a.** Ethyl alcohol interacts with water much like methyl alcohol which was described earlier in this chapter. The alcohol has an O—H bond so it interacts with water with hydrogen bonding forces. It does not ionize in water, so the alcohol molecule remains intact in aqueous solution. Calcium chloride interacts with water with ion-dipole forces, which overcome the ion–ion forces in the solid crystal, thus causing solution. The solution process produces one $Ca^{2+}$ and 2 $Cl^-$ ions per formula unit of $CaCl_2$. |
| **b.** A 100.0-g quantity of alcohol and 100.0 g of calcium chloride are each dissolved in 275 mL of water. What is the mass percent of solute in each solution? | **b.** For water, 275 mL has a mass of 275 g since the density of water is nearly 1.00 g/mL. Therefore, both solutions have a mass of 100.0 g + 275 g = 375 g.<br><br>$\dfrac{100.0 \text{ g solute}}{375 \text{ g solution}} \times 100\% = \underline{26.7\% \text{ by mass solute}}$ in both solutions. |
| **c.** A 100.0 g quantity of each of these two compounds is dissolved in enough water to make 275 mL of solution. What is the molarity of these two solutions? | **c.** For alcohol: $100.0 \text{ g} \times \dfrac{1 \text{ mol}}{46.07 \text{ g}} = 2.17 \text{ mol}$<br><br>$\dfrac{2.17 \text{ mol}}{0.275 \text{ L}} = \underline{7.89 \text{ M}}$<br><br>For calcium chloride: $100.0 \text{ g} \times \dfrac{1 \text{ mol}}{111 \text{ g}} = 0.901 \text{ mol}$<br><br>$\dfrac{0.901 \text{ mol}}{0.275 \text{ L}} = \underline{3.28 \text{ M}}$ |
| **d.** What is the molarity of the alcohol solution if 325 mL of water is added to the solution in part **c**? Assume that the volumes are additive. | **d.** Volume of the dilute = 275 mL + 325 mL = 600 mL<br><br>$M_d = \dfrac{M_c \times V_c}{V_d} = \dfrac{7.89 \text{ M} \times 275 \text{ mL}}{600 \text{ mL}} = \underline{3.62 \text{ M}}$ |
| **e.** What mass of $CO_2$ and volume at STP are produced from the complete combustion of 100.0 g of alcohol? | **e.** The balanced equation for the combustion reaction is:<br>$C_2H_5OH(l) + 3O_2(g) \longrightarrow 2CO_2(g) + 3H_2O(l)$<br><br>$\boxed{\text{mol alcohol}} \longrightarrow \boxed{\text{mol } CO_2} \longrightarrow \boxed{\text{g } CO_2}$ (or) $\boxed{\text{Volume } CO_2}$<br><br>$2.17 \text{ mol } C_2H_5OH \times \dfrac{2 \text{ mol } CO_2}{\text{mol } C_2H_5OH} \times \dfrac{44.01 \text{ g } CO_2}{\text{mol } CO_2} = \underline{191 \text{ g } CO_2}$<br><br>$2.17 \text{ mol } C_2H_5OH \times \dfrac{2 \text{ mol } CO_2}{\text{mol } C_2H_5OH} \times \dfrac{22.4 \text{ L } CO_2}{\text{mol } CO_2} = \underline{97.2 \text{ L } CO_2}$ |
| **f.** Describe the electrical conductivity of these two solutions. | **f.** Alcohol does not ionize in water so it is a <u>nonelectrolyte</u> and does not conduct electricity. Calcium chloride is ionized into $Ca^{2+}(aq)$ and $2Cl^-(aq)$ ions so it is a <u>strong electrolyte</u> and is a good conductor of electricity in solution. |
| **g.** What is the melting point of the alcohol solution and the melting point and boiling point of the calcium chloride solution? Use the information from part **b**. | **g.** For the aqueous solutions:<br>$\Delta T_f = K_f m = 1.86 \text{ (°C} \cdot \text{kg)/mol} \times \dfrac{\text{mol solute}}{\text{kg solvent}}$<br><br>For alcohol: $m = \dfrac{2.17 \text{ mol solute}}{\dfrac{275 \text{ g solvent}}{1000 \text{ g solvent}}} = 7.89 \text{ } m$ |

| PROBLEM | SOLUTION |
|---|---|
| | $\Delta T_f = 1.86 \times 7.89\ m = 14.7°C \qquad T_f = 0 - 14.7 = \underline{-14.7°C}$<br>For calcium chloride, recall that there are three moles of ions per mole of compound.<br><br>$m\ \text{(of ions)} = \dfrac{\dfrac{3 \times 0.901\ \text{mol solute}}{275\ \text{g solvent}}}{1000\ \text{g solvent}} = 9.83\ m$<br><br>$\Delta T_f = 1.86 \times 9.83\ m = 18.3°C \qquad T_f = 0 - 18.3 = \underline{-18.3°C}$<br>For the boiling point of the calcium chloride solution:<br><br>$\Delta T_b = K_b m = 0.512\ (°C \cdot kg)\ /\ \text{mol} \times \dfrac{\text{mol solute}}{\text{kg solvent}}$<br><br>$\Delta T_b = 3 \times 0.512 \times \dfrac{0.901\ \text{mol}}{0.275\ \text{kg solvent}} = 5.03°C$<br><br>$T_b = 100.0 + 5.03 = \underline{105.0°C}.$ |

**YOUR TURN**

Consider two water-soluble compounds: acetone, $H_3CCCH_3$ (with $\overset{\displaystyle O}{\overset{\displaystyle \|}{}}$ on the central carbon) and nitric acid, $HNO_3$.

**a.** What forces are present when acetone and nitric acid dissolve in water?

**b.** A 100.0-g quantity of acetone and 100.0 g of nitric acid are each present in 475 mL of water. What is the mass percent of solute in each solution?

**c.** A 100.0-g quantity of each of these two compounds is dissolved in enough water to make 475 mL of solution. What is the molarity of these two solutions?

**d.** What is the molarity of the acetone solution if it is diluted to a new volume of 1.25 L?

**e.** What mass of $O_2$ and volume at STP are required for the complete combustion of 100.0 g of acetone?

**f.** Describe the electrical conductivity of these two solutions.

**g.** What is the melting point of the acetone solution and the melting point and boiling point of the nitric acid solution? Use the information from part **b.**

Answers are on p 429.

# CHAPTER SUMMARY

Water acts as an effective solvent, dispersing solutes into a homogeneous mixture known as a solution. When two liquids are **miscible**, they form a solution, but if they are **immiscible**, they remain a heterogeneous mixture. Some ionic compounds may dissolve in water because the ion–water forces (**ion–dipole**) overcome the forces holding the crystal together. Polar covalent molecular compounds may dissolve in water as discrete molecules, or they may undergo **ionization**. Although many ionic compounds are considered soluble, others are said to be insoluble since a very limited amount dissolves. The amount that dissolves—the **solubility** of a compound—is indicated by some convenient unit of **concentration**.

How much of a compound can dissolve at a certain temperature to make a **saturated** solution varies from compound to compound. **Unsaturated** solutions contain less than the maximum amount of a compound so that more of the compound may dissolve. **Supersaturated** solutions are unstable solutions containing more of a compound than the solubility would indicate. A precipitate often forms in such a solution. Solid compounds are generally more soluble at higher temperatures, whereas gaseous compounds are less soluble at higher temperatures. This property can be used to purify solids in a process called **recrystallization**. External pressure does not affect the solubility of solids but does affect gases, which illustrates **Henry's Law**.

Besides mass of solute per 100 g of solvent, which was used to illustrate comparative solubilities, other units of concentration are **percent by mass, molarity (M),** and **molality. Parts per million (ppm)** and **parts per billion (ppb)** are used for very small concentrations.

Since molarity relates volume of a solution to moles of solute, it can be incorporated into the general scheme for stoichiometry problems along with the mass of a compound (Chapter 9) and the volume of a gas (Chapter 10) (see Figure 12-6). **Titrations** are examples of solution stoichiometry.

We also studied the physical properties of solutions. In the first property mentioned, we found that certain solutes act as **nonelectrolytes** or as either **weak** or **strong electrolytes. Electrolytes** change water from a **nonconductor (insulator)** to a **conductor** of electricity. **Electrolytes** produce ions in solution, which allows water to become a conductor of electricity.

There are also four **colligative properties** of solutions. These are **vapor pressure lowering, boiling-point elevation,** and **freezing-point lowering.** The magnitude of the latter two properties relate to the **molality** of the solution. The process of **osmosis** leads to **osmotic pressure elevation,** the fourth colligative property.

## OBJECTIVES

| SECTION | YOU SHOULD BE ABLE TO... | EXAMPLES | EXERCISES | CHAPTER PROBLEMS |
|---|---|---|---|---|
| 12-1 | Describe the role of water in the formation of aqueous solutions of ionic compounds, strong acids, and polar molecules. | | 1a, 1b, 1c, 1d | 1, 5, 6, 7 |
| 12-2 | Describe the effects of temperature and pressure on the solubility of solids and gases in a liquid. | | 1d, 2a, 2b, 2c, 2d | 2, 3, 9, 10, 11 |
| 12-3 | Perform calculations of concentration involving percent by mass, ppm, and ppb. | 12-1, 12-2 | 3a, 3b, 3c, 3d, 3e, 3f | 14, 15, 16, 20, 22 |
| 12-4 | Perform the calculation involving molarity and the dilution of solutions. | 12-3, 12-4, 12-5, 12-6, 12-7 | 4a, 4b, 4c, 4d, 4e | 23, 24, 25, 26, 27, 34, 35, 37, 40, 42 |
| 12-5 | Perform calculations involving titrations and other solution stoichiometry. | 12-8, 12-9, 12-10 | 5a, 5b, 5c | 44, 45, 47, 49, 50, 51, 53 |
| 12-6 | Explain the differences between non-electrolytes, strong electrolytes, and weak electrolytes. | | 6a, 6b | 56, 57 |
| 12-7 | Calculate the boiling and melting points of aqueous solutions of electrolytes and nonelectrolytes. | 12-11, 12-12, 12-13 | 7a, 7b, 7c, 7d, 7e | 60, 62, 66, 67, 71, 72, 73, 74, 75, 80 |

## ▶ ANSWERS TO ASSESSING THE OBJECTIVES

### PART A

#### EXERCISES

**12-1(a)** (a) yes (b) yes (c) no (d) yes (e) yes

**12-1(b)** (a) $2NH_4^+$ $(aq)$ + $Cr_2O_7^{2-}$ $(aq)$ (b) $H^+$ $(aq)$ + $NO_3^-$ $(aq)$ (c) $CH_3COCH_3$ $(aq)$ (d) $Zn^{2+}$ $(aq)$ + $2Br^-$ $(aq)$

**12-1(c)** (a) ion–dipole (b) hydrogen bonding (c) London force (the only force between nonpolar molecules)

**12-1(d)** The term *dissociates* here means "to break apart." The chemical is already ionic, so the water merely separates the positive ion from the negative ion. In the case of $HNO_3$, the compound was originally molecular in nature. But due to the strong interaction with water, the water was able to *ionize* the acid, or form ions out of the individual particles, so that what ends up dissolved is $H^+$ and $NO_3^-$.

**12-2(a)** If a soluble compound dissolves to the limit of its solubility at a given temperature, the solution is saturated; if the solute is not dissolved to the limit, the solution is unsaturated. If more solute is present than indicated by its solubility, the solution is supersaturated and the excess solute may eventually form a precipitate. Solids generally become more soluble at higher temperatures, whereas gases become less soluble. An increase in partial pressure of a gas above a liquid increases its solubility.

**12-2(b)** (a) $Cl_2$ is a gas. It is more soluble at low temperature and high pressures. (b) $Na_2SO_4$ is an ionic solid. It is more soluble at high temperatures but pressure has no effect.

**12-2(c)** (a) supersaturated (b) saturated (c) unsaturated

**12-2(d)** (a) supersaturated (b) unsaturated (c) saturated (d) unsaturated

12-2{e} Something that large should be ground up into smaller particles to increase the surface area. Since it's an ionic solid, the solvent can be gently heated to help dissolve the solid. Stirring or swirling the flask usually helps as well.

12-3{a} 8.0 g KBr/100 g solution, 8.0 g KBr/92 g $H_2O$, and 92 g $H_2O$/100 g solution

12-3{b} 15.0 g/60.0 g = 25.0% by mass

12-3{c} 154 g of solvent

12-3{d} 18 g

12-3{e} (a) $2.5 \times 10^{-5}\%$ (b) 0.25 ppm (c) 250 ppb

Based on the size of the numbers, the ppb gives the most appropriately sized value.

12-3{f} 0.75 mg lead

12-4{a} 2.00 M

12-4{b} 0.200 M

12-4{c} 6.23 g KI

12-4{d} 75.0 ml of $H_2O$ must be added to bring the total volume to 125 ml.

12-4{e} 16.7 mL of 6.00 M $H_2SO_4$

12-4{f} (a) Using a 250-mL volumetric flask, measure out 7.31 g of NaCl. Transfer the solid into the flask. Fill the flask halfway with water and swirl until all the solid is dissolved. Fill the flask the rest of the way, using a dropper at the end to get the volume to the volumetric line. Cap and invert several times. (b) Using a buret, dispense 41.7 mL of 3.00 M NaCl solution into a 250-mL volumetric flask. Fill the rest of the way with water, swirling to ensure thorough mixing. Use a dropper at the end to get the volume to the volumetric line. Cap and invert several times.

12-4{g} 0.27 M

12-5{a} (a) molar volume (22.4 L/mol)   (b) molarity (c) molar mass   (d) Avogadro's number ($6.022 \times 10^{23}$ molecules/mol)

12-5{b} 13.5 mL of 0.125 M $Ca(OH)_2$

12-5{c} 1.26 M HCl

12-5{d} $Na_2CO_3 + 2HCl \longrightarrow 2\,NaCl + H_2O + CO_2$
6.25 M HCl

12-5{e} 5.67 mL

## Part B

### EXERCISES

12-6{a} (a) strong electrolytes (b) weak electrolytes (c) nonelectrolytes (d) strong electrolytes (e) nonelectrolytes (f) weak electrolytes

12-6{b} (a) weak electrolyte (b) strong electrolyte (c) nonelectrolytes

12-6{c} Swimming pool water has several compounds dissolved in it. Chlorine itself is a nonelectrolyte, but the forms in which it is delivered are mostly ionic strong electrolytes (such as calcium hypochlorite). Further, the water used in the pool naturally has several dissolved ions like $Ca^{2+}$, $Mg^{2+}$ and $Fe^{3+}$ in it already, which increase its conductivity. The compounds used to provide chlorine, though, are the primary conductive medium.

12-7{a} (a) liquid B (b) liquid A (c) liquid B (d) liquid A

12-7{b} 3.53 $m$

12-7{c} $-5.58°C$ for the nonelectrolyte solute; $-16.7°C$ for $CaCl_2$

12-7{d} The effect of acetic acid would be somewhere between a nonelectrolyte solute, which produces one particle per mole, and NaCl, which produces two particles per mole. Acetic acid is a weak electrolyte, which means only a small percent of the molecules are ionized. In fact, its effect would be only slightly greater than that of a nonelectrolyte.

12-7{e} $-17.8°C$. 0.0°F. This is the method used to define zero on the Fahrenheit scale.

## ANSWERS TO CHAPTER SYNTHESIS PROBLEM

a. Acetone is a polar compound that can interact with water molecules by hydrogen bonding between the O on acetone and the H's on water. It does not ionize when dissolved in water. Nitric acid is a strong acid and dissolves through ion-dipole interactions with ionization to form $H^+(aq)$ and $NO_3^-(aq)$ ions.

b. Both solutions are 17.4% solute by mass.

c. Acetone is 3.62 M; nitric acid is 3.35 M.

d. 1.38 M

e. 220 g $O_2$, 154 L $O_2$ (STP)

f. Acetone is a nonelectrolyte since it does ionize. Its solutions do not conduct electricity. Nitric acid is a strong electrolyte since strong acids are completely ionized in aqueous solution. Its solution is a good conductor of electricity.

g. Acetone; melting point = $-6.74°C$. For nitric acid, melting point = $-12.5°C$. The boiling point is 103.4°C.

## CHAPTER PROBLEMS

*Throughout the text, answers to all exercises in color are given in Appendix E. The more difficult exercises are marked with an asterisk.*

### Aqueous Solutions (SECTION 12-1)

12-1. When an ionic compound dissolves in water, what forces in the crystal resist the solution process? What forces between water molecules and the crystal remove the ions from the lattice?

**12-2.** When a sample of KOH is placed in water, a homogeneous mixture of KOH is formed. Which is the solute, which is the solvent, and which is the solution?

12-3. Calcium bromide readily dissolves in water, but lead(II) bromide does not. Liquid benzene and water form a heterogeneous mixture, but liquid isopropyl alcohol and water mix thoroughly. Which of the above is said to be miscible, which immiscible, which insoluble, and which soluble?

12-4. Write equations illustrating the solution of each of the following ionic compounds in water.

**(a)** LiF **(b)** $(NH_4)_3PO_4$ **(c)** $Na_2CO_3$ **(d)** $Ca(C_2H_3O_2)_2$

**12-5.** Write equations illustrating the solution of each of the following ionic compounds in water.

**(a)** $BaCl_2$ **(b)** $Al_2(SO_4)_3$ **(c)** $Cr(NO_3)_3$ **(d)** $Mg(ClO_4)_2$

12-6. Formaldehyde ($H_2CO$) dissolves in water without formation of ions. Write the Lewis structure of formaldehyde and show what types of interactions between solute and solvent are involved.

**12-7.** Nitric acid is a covalent compound that dissolves in water to form ions in the same manner as HCl. Write the equation illustrating the solution of nitric acid in water.

### Temperature and Solubility (SECTION 12-2)

12-8. Referring to Figure 12-5, determine which of the following compounds is most soluble at 10°C: NaCl, KCl, or $Li_2SO_4$. Which is most soluble at 70°C?

**12-9.** Referring to Figure 12-5, determine what mass of each of the following dissolves in 250 g of $H_2O$ at 60°C: KBr, KCl, and $Li_2SO_4$.

12-10. Referring to Figure 12-5, determine whether each of the following solutions is saturated, unsaturated, or supersaturated. (All are in 100 g of $H_2O$.)

**(a)** 40 g of $KNO_3$ at 40°C    **(c)** 75 g of KBr at 80°C

**(b)** 40 g of $KNO_3$ at 20°C    **(d)** 20 g of NaCl at 40°C

**12-11.** A 200-g sample of water is saturated with $KNO_3$ at 50°C. What mass of $KNO_3$ forms as a precipitate if the solution is cooled to the freezing point of water? (Refer to Figure 12-5.)

12-12. A 500-mL portion of water is saturated with $Li_2SO_4$ at 0°C. What happens if the solution is heated to 100°C? (Refer to Figure 12-5.)

### Percent by Mass (SECTION 12-3)

12-13. What is the percent by mass of solute in a solution made by dissolving 9.85 g of $Ca(NO_3)_2$ in 650 g of water?

**12-14.** What is the percent by mass of solute if 14.15 g of NaI is mixed with 75.55 g of water?

12-15. A solution is 10.0% by mass NaOH. How many moles of NaOH are dissolved in 150 g of solution?

**12-16.** A solution contains 15.0 g of $NH_4Cl$ in water and is 8.50% $NH_4Cl$. What is the mass of water present?

12-17. A solution is 23.2% by mass $KNO_3$. What mass of $KNO_3$ is present in each 100 g of $H_2O$?

12-18. A solution contains 1 mol of NaOH dissolved in 9 mol of ethyl alcohol ($C_2H_5OH$). What is the percent by mass NaOH?

12-19. Blood contains 10 mg of calcium ions in 100 g of blood serum (solution). What is this concentration in ppm?

**12-20.** A high concentration of mercury in fish is 0.5 ppm. What mass of mercury is present in each kilogram of fish? What is this concentration in ppb?

12-21. Seawater contains $1.2 \times 10^{-2}$ ppb of gold ions. If all the gold could be extracted, what volume in liters of seawater is needed to produce 1.00 g of gold? (Assume the density of seawater is the same as that of pure water.)

**12-22.** The maximum allowable level of lead in drinking water is 50 ppb. What mass of lead in milligrams is allowed in 5000 gallons of water? (Assume that the density of the water is the same as that of pure water.)

### Molarity (SECTION 12-4)

12-23. What is the molarity of a solution made by dissolving 2.44 mol of NaCl in enough water to make 4.50 L of solution?

12-24. Fill in the blanks.

| Solute | M | Amount of Solute | Volume of Solution |
|---|---|---|---|
| **(a)** KI | _____ | 2.40 mol | 2.75 L |
| **(b)** $C_2H_5OH$ | _____ | 26.5 g | 410 mL |
| **(c)** $NaC_2H_3O_2$ | 0.255 | 3.15 mol | _____ L |
| **(d)** $LiNO_2$ | 0.625 | _____ g | 1.25 L |
| **(e)** $BaCl_2$ | _____ | 0.250 mol | 850 mL |
| **(f)** $Na_2SO_3$ | 0.054 | _____ mol | 0.45 L |
| **(g)** $K_2CO_3$ | 0.345 | 14.7 g | _____ mL |
| **(h)** LiOH | 1.24 | _____ g | 1650 mL |
| **(i)** $H_2SO_4$ | 0.905 | 0.178 g | _____ mL |

**12-25.** What is the molarity of a solution of 345 g of Epsom salts ($MgSO_4 \cdot 7H_2O$) in 7.50 L of solution?

**12-26.** What mass of $CaCl_2$ is in 2.58 L of a solution with a concentration of 0.0784 M?

**12-27.** What volume in liters of a 0.250 M solution contains 37.5 g of KOH?

12-28. What is the molarity of a solution made by dissolving $2.50 \times 10^{-4}$ g of baking soda ($NaHCO_3$) in enough water to make 2.54 mL of solution?

12-29. What are the molarities of the hydroxide ion and the barium ion if 13.5 g of $Ba(OH)_2$ is dissolved in enough water to make 475 mL of solution?

**12-30.** What is the molarity of each ion present if 25.0 g of $Al_2(SO_4)_3$ is present in 250 mL of solution?

*12-31. A solution is 25.0% by mass calcium nitrate and has a density of 1.21 g/mL. What is its molarity?

**\*12-32.** A solution of concentrated NaOH is 16.4 M. If the density of the solution is 1.43 g/mL, what is the percent by mass NaOH?

*12-33. Concentrated nitric acid is 70.0% $HNO_3$ and 14.7 M. What is the density of the solution?

## Dilution (SECTION 12-4)

12-34. What volume of 4.50 M $H_2SO_4$ should be diluted with water to form 2.50 L of 1.50 M acid?

**12-35.** If 450 mL of a certain solution is diluted to 950 mL with water to form a 0.600 M solution, what was the molarity of the original solution?

12-36. One liter of a 0.250 M solution of NaOH is needed. The only available solution of NaOH is a 0.800 M solution. Describe how to make the desired solution.

**12-37.** What is the volume in liters of a 0.440 M solution if it was made by dilution of 250 mL of a 1.25 M solution?

12-38. What is the molarity of a solution made by diluting 3.50 L of a 0.200 M solution to a volume of 5.00 L?

12-39. What volume of water in milliliters should be *added* to 1.25 L of 0.860 M HCl so that its molarity will be 0.545? Assume additive volumes.

**12-40.** What volume of water in milliliters should be *added* to 400 mL of a solution containing 35.0 g of KBr to make a 0.100 M KBr solution? Assume additive volumes.

*12-41. What volume in milliliters of *pure* acetic acid should be used to make 250 mL of 0.200 M $HC_2H_3O_2$? (The density of the pure acid is 1.05 g/mL.)

*12-42. What would be the molarity of a solution made by mixing 150 mL of 0.250 M HCl with 450 mL of 0.375 M HCl?

## Stoichiometry and Titrations (SECTION 12-5)

12-43. Given the reaction

$$3KOH(aq) + CrCl_3(aq) \longrightarrow Cr(OH)_3(s) + 3KCl(aq)$$

what mass of $Cr(OH)_3$ would be produced if 500 mL of 0.250 M KOH were added to a solution containing excess $CrCl_3$?

**12-44.** Given the reaction

$$2KCl(aq) + Pb(NO_3)_2(aq) \longrightarrow PbCl_2(s) + 2KNO_3(aq)$$

what mass of $Pb(NO_3)_2$ is required to react with 1.25 L of 0.550 M KCl?

12-45. Given the reaction

$$Al_2(SO_4)_3(aq) + 3BaCl_2(aq) \longrightarrow 3BaSO_4(s) + 2AlCl_3(aq)$$

what mass of $BaSO_4$ is produced from 650 mL of 0.320 M $Al_2(SO_4)_3$?

12-46. Given the reaction

$$3Ba(OH)_2(aq) + 2Al(NO_3)_3(aq) \longrightarrow$$
$$2Al(OH)_3(s) + 3Ba(NO_3)_2(aq)$$

what volume of 1.25 M $Ba(OH)_2$ is required to produce 265 g of $Al(OH)_3$?

**12-47.** Given the reaction

$$2AgClO_4(aq) + Na_2CrO_4(aq) \longrightarrow Ag_2CrO_4(s) + 2NaClO_4(aq)$$

what volume of a 0.600 M solution of $AgClO_4$ is needed to produce 160 g of $Ag_2CrO_4$?

12-48. Given the reaction

$$3Ca(ClO_3)_2(aq) + 2Na_3PO_4(aq) \longrightarrow$$
$$Ca_3(PO_4)_2(s) + 6NaClO_3(aq)$$

what volume of a 2.22 M solution of $Na_3PO_4$ is needed to react with 580 mL of a 3.75 M solution of $Ca(ClO_3)_2$?

**12-49.** Consider the reaction

$$2HNO_3(aq) + 3H_2S(aq) \longrightarrow 2NO(g) + 3S(s) + 4H_2O(l)$$

**(a)** What volume of 0.350 M $HNO_3$ will completely react with 275 mL of 0.100 M $H_2S$?

**(b)** What volume of NO gas measured at 27°C and 720 torr will be produced from 650 mL of 0.100 M $H_2S$ solution?

12-50. The concentration of acetic acid in vinegar can be determined by titration with sodium hydroxide. This reaction is represented by the following equation.

$$HC_2H_3O_2(aq) + NaOH(aq) \longrightarrow NaC_2H_3O_2(aq) + H_2O$$

What is the concentration of acetic acid in vinegar if 10.0 mL of vinegar takes 28.8 mL of 0.300 M NaOH to reach the endpoint?

**12-51.** A household antibacterial cleanser is made from a solution of sodium hydroxide. What is its concentration of NaOH if it takes 42.5 mL of 0.0500 M HCl to titrate 25.0 mL of the cleanser to the end point?

12-52. Dilute aqueous solutions of ammonia are used as cleansers, especially for grease stains. What is the concentration of the ammonia in the cleanser if 22.6 mL of 0.220 M sulfuric acid is needed to titrate 10.0 mL of the ammonia solution? The equation for neutralization is

$$2NH_3(aq) + H_2SO_4(aq) \longrightarrow 2NH_4^+(aq) + SO_4^{2-}(aq)$$

**12-53.** What is the molarity of 1.00 L of $HNO_3$ solution if it reacts completely with 25.0 g of $Ca(OH)_2$?

*12-54. Given the reaction

$$2NaOH(aq) + MgCl_2(aq) \longrightarrow Mg(OH)_2(s) + 2NaCl(aq)$$

what mass of $Mg(OH)_2$ would be produced by mixing 250 mL of 0.240 M NaOH with 400 mL of 0.100 M $MgCl_2$?

**\*12-55.** Given the reaction

$$CO_2(g) + Ca(OH)_2(aq) \longrightarrow CaCO_3(s) + H_2O(l)$$

what is the molarity of a 1.00 L solution of $Ca(OH)_2$ that would completely react with 10.0 L of $CO_2$ measured at 25°C and 0.950 atm?

## Properties of Solutions (SECTIONS 12-6 AND 12-7)

12-56. Three hypothetical binary compounds dissolve in water. AB is a strong electrolyte, AC is a weak electrolyte, and AD is a nonelectrolyte. Describe the extent to which each of these solutions conducts electricity and how each compound exists in solution.

**12-57.** Chlorous acid ($HClO_2$) is a weak electrolyte, and perchloric acid ($HClO_4$) is a strong electrolyte. Write equations illustrating the different behaviors of these two polar covalent molecules in water.

**12-58.** Explain the difference in the following three terms: 1 mole NaBr, 1 molar NaBr, and 1 molal NaBr.

**12-59.** What is the molality of a solution made by dissolving 25.0 g of NaOH in **(a)** 250 g of water and **(b)** 250 g of alcohol ($C_2H_5OH$)?

**12-60.** What is the molality of a solution made by dissolving 1.50 kg of KCl in 2.85 kg of water?

**12-61.** What mass of NaOH is in 550 g of water if the concentration is 0.720 $m$?

**12-62.** What mass of water is in a 0.430 $m$ solution containing 2.58 g of $CH_3OH$?

**12-63.** What is the freezing point of a 0.20 $m$ aqueous solution of a nonelectrolyte?

**12-64.** What is the boiling point of a 0.45 $m$ aqueous solution of a nonelectrolyte?

**12-65.** When immersed in salty ocean water for an extended period, a person gets very thirsty. Explain.

**12-66.** Dehydrated fruit is wrinkled and shriveled up. When put in water, the fruit expands and becomes smooth again. Explain.

**12-67.** Explain how pure water can be obtained from a solution without boiling.

**12-68.** In industrial processes, it is often necessary to concentrate a dilute solution (much more difficult than diluting a concentrated solution). Explain how the principle of reverse osmosis can be applied.

*12-69. What is the molality of an aqueous solution that is 10.0% by mass $CaCl_2$?

*12-70. A 1.00 $m$ KBr solution has a mass of 1.00 kg. What is the mass of the water?

*12-71. Ethylene glycol ($C_2H_6O_2$) is used as an antifreeze. What mass of ethylene glycol should be added to 5.00 kg of water to lower the freezing point to −5.0°C? (Ethylene glycol is a nonelectrolyte.)

*12-72. What is the boiling point of the solution in problem 12-71?

*12-73. Methyl alcohol can also be used as an antifreeze. What mass of methyl alcohol ($CH_3OH$) must be added to 5.00 kg of water to lower its freezing point to −5.0°C?

**12-74.** What is the molality of an aqueous solution that boils at 101.5°C?

**12-75.** What is the boiling point of a 0.15 $m$ solution of a solute in liquid benzene? (For benzene, $K_b = 2.53$, and the boiling point of pure benzene is 80.1 °C.)

**12-76.** What is the boiling point of a solution of 75.0 g of naphthalene ($C_{10}H_8$) in 250 g of benzene? (See problem 12-75.)

**12-77.** What is the freezing point of a solution of 100 g of $CH_3OH$ in 800 g of benzene? (For benzene, $K_f = 5.12$, and the freezing point of pure benzene is 5.5°C.)

**12-78.** What is the freezing point of a 10.0% by mass solution of $CH_3OH$ in benzene? (See problem 12-77.)

**12-79.** A 1 $m$ solution of HCl lowers the freezing point of water almost twice as much as a 1 $m$ solution of HF. Explain.

**12-80.** What is the freezing point of automobile antifreeze if it is 40.0% by mass ethylene glycol ($C_2H_6O_2$) in water? (Ethylene glycol is a nonelectrolyte.)

**12-81.** In especially cold climates, methyl alcohol ($CH_3OH$) may be used as an automobile antifreeze. Would 40.0% by mass of an aqueous solution of methyl alcohol remain a liquid at −40°C? (Methyl alcohol is a nonelectrolyte.)

*12-82. Give the freezing point of each of the following in 100 g of water.

**(a)** 10.0 g of $CH_3OH$  **(b)** 10.0 g of NaCl  **(c)** 10.0 g of $CaCl_2$

## General Problems

**12-83.** A mixture is composed of 10 g of $KNO_3$ and 50 g of KCl. What is the approximate amount of KCl that can be separated using the difference in solubility shown in Figure 12-5.

**12-84.** KBr and $KNO_3$ have equal solubilities at about 42°C. What is the composition of the precipitate if 100 g of $H_2O$ saturated with these two salts at 42°C is then cooled to 0°C? (Refer to Figure 12-5.)

**12-85.** What is the percent composition by mass of a solution made by dissolving 10.0 g of sugar and 5.0 g of table salt in 150 mL of water?

**12-86.** What is the molarity of each ion in a solution that is 0.15 M $CaCl_2$, 0.22 M $Ca(ClO_4)_2$, and 0.18 M NaCl?

*12-87. 500 mL of 0.20 M $AgNO_3$ is mixed with 500 mL of 0.30 M NaCl. What is the concentration of $Cl^-$ ion in the solution? The net ionic equation of the reaction that occurs is

$$Ag^+(aq) + Cl^-(aq) \longrightarrow AgCl(s)$$

*12-88. 400 mL of 0.15 M $Ca(NO_3)_2$ is mixed with 500 mL of 0.20 M $Na_2SO_4$. Write the net ionic equation of the precipitation reaction that occurs. What is its concentration of $SO_4^{2-}$ remaining in solution?

*12-89. A certain metal (M) reacts with HCl according to the equation

$$M(s) + 2HCl(aq) \longrightarrow MCl_2(aq) + H_2(g)$$

1.44 g of the metal reacts with 225 mL of 0.196 M HCl. What is the metal?

*12-90. Another metal (Z) also reacts with HCl according to the equation

$$2Z(s) + 6HCl(aq) \longrightarrow 2ZCl_3(aq) + 3H_2(g)$$

24.0 g of Z reacts with 0.545 L of 2.54 M HCl. What is the metal? What volume of $H_2$ measured at STP is produced?

*12-91. A certain compound dissolves in a solvent, nitrobenzene. For nitrobenzene, $K_f = 8.10$. A solution with 3.07 g of the compound dissolved in 120 g of nitrobenzene freezes at 2.22°C. The freezing point of pure nitrobenzene is 5.67°C. Analysis of the compound shows it to be 40.0% C, 13.3% H, and 46.7% N. What is the formula of the compound?

**12-92.** Given 1.00 $m$ aqueous solutions of **(a)** $Na_3PO_4$, **(b)** $CaCl_2$, **(c)** urea (a nonelectrolyte), **(d)** $Al_2(SO_4)_3$, and

**(e)** LiBr. Order these solutions from highest to lowest freezing points and explain.

12-93. Order the following solutions from lowest to highest boiling points.

**(a)** 0.30 $m$ sugar (a nonelectrolyte)   **(d)** 0.12 $m$ KCl

**(b)** pure water   **(e)** 0.05 $m$ CrCl$_3$

**(c)** 0.05 $m$ K$_2$CO$_3$

**\*12-94.** One mole of an electrolyte dissolves in water to form three moles of ions. A 9.21-g quantity of this compound is dissolved in 175 g of water. The freezing point of this solution is −1.77°C. The compound is 47.1% K, 14.5% C, and 38.6% O. What is the formula of this compound?

\*12-95. A sample of a metal reacts with water to form 487 mL of a 0.120-M solution of the metal hydroxide along with 1.10 L of hydrogen gas measured at 25°C and 0.650 atm. Is the metal Na or Ca?

12-96. What volume of NH$_3$ measured at 0.951 atm and 25°C is needed to form 250 mL of 0.450 M aqueous ammonia?

**12-97.** A 1.82-L volume of gaseous H$_2$S measured at 1.08 atm and 20°C is dissolved in water. What is the molarity of the aqueous H$_2$S if the volume of the solution is 2.00 L?

12-98. Sodium bicarbonate reacts with hydrochloric acid to form water, sodium chloride, and carbon dioxide gas. What volume of CO$_2$ measured at 35°C and 1.00 atm could be released by the reaction of 1.00 L of a 0.340 M solution of sodium bicarbonate with excess hydrochloric acid solution?

**12-99.** Aqueous calcium hydroxide solutions absorb gaseous carbon dioxide to form calcium bicarbonate solutions. What mass of calcium bicarbonate would be formed by reaction of 125.0 mL of 0.150 M calcium hydroxide with 450 mL of gaseous carbon dioxide measured at STP?

\*12-100. The molecules of a compound are composed of one phosphorus and multiple chlorine atoms. A molecule of the compound is described as a trigonal pyramid. This gaseous compound dissolves in water to form a hydrochloric acid solution and phosphorus acid (H$_3$PO$_3$). What is the molarity of the hydrochloric acid if 750 mL of the gas, measured at STP, dissolves in 250 mL of water?

**\*12-101.** A phosphorus-oxygen compound is 43.7% phosphorus. When the compound dissolves in water, it forms one compound, phosphoric acid. If 0.100 mol of the phosphorus-oxygen compound dissolves in 4.00 L of water to form a 0.100 M solution of phosphoric acid, what is the formula of the original compound?

\*12-102. A 10.0-g quantity of a compound is dissolved in 100 g of water. The solution formed has a melting point of −7.14°C. Is the compound KCl, Na$_2$S, or CaCl$_2$?

**12-103.** An aqueous solution has a freezing point of −2.50°C. What is its boiling point?

\*12-104. An aqueous solution of a nonelectrolyte is made by dissolving the solute in 1.00 L of water. The solution has a freezing point of −1.50°C. What volume of water must be added to change the freezing point to −1.15°C?

---

STUDENT WORKSHOP

### Determining the Dipole of Planar Molecules

**Purpose: To estimate the dipole moment of several simple molecules based on molecular shape and bond polarity. (Work in groups of three or four. Estimated time: 25 min.)**

As we have seen in this chapter, polarity plays a major role in determining what compounds will dissolve in what solvents. "Like dissolves like" is a saying that indicates that polar solutes dissolve in polar solvents and nonpolar solutes dissolve in nonpolar solvents. Slightly polar solutes might dissolve in either, but certainly slightly polar solvents would be our first choice. The degree of polarity of a molecule can be estimated by the following activity. We will use only linear and planar molecules for simplicity. As an example, we will evaluate the polarity of formaldehyde, CH$_2$O.

1. Draw the Lewis structure of the molecule, attempting to be faithful to the bond angles predicted by VSEPR theory.

2. Draw arrows next to each bond, pointing in the direction of the more electronegative atom. The length of the arrow should be proportional to the difference in electronegativity between the two atoms. In this case, oxygen is significantly more electronegative than carbon, which is slightly more electronegative than hydrogen.

3. Next to the structure on the paper, redraw the arrows, tail to tip, in any order, maintaining their exact orientation.

4. Connect the tail of the first arrow to the tip of the last with another arrow. This last arrow represents the dipole of the molecule. The longer it is, the more polar the molecule, and it points toward the molecule's negative end. If the tail and tip are exactly in the same place, then there is no dipole, and the molecule is nonpolar.

Using the above procedure, evaluate the dipoles of the following molecules or ions:

- H$_2$O
- CO$_2$
- SO$_2$
- COCl$_2$
- HCN
- NO$_3^-$

# Chapter 13

# Acids, Bases, and Salts

The lemon is known for its sour taste, which is caused by citric acid. Acids are a unique class of compounds that are discussed in this chapter.

# SETTING THE STAGE

It can make your mouth pucker, your body shudder, and your eyes water. That's the reaction one gets from taking a bite of a fresh lemon. A taste of vinegar has the same effect. Even carbonated beverages produce a subtle sour taste that peps up the drink. All these substances have a similar effect because of the presence of a compound that produces a sour taste (but to different degrees). These compounds, known as acids, were characterized over 500 years ago, during the Middle Ages, in the chemical laboratories of alchemists. Substances were classified as acids because of their common properties (such as sourness) rather than a certain chemical composition. Acids are well known to the general population. They are very common in foods and drugs, such as citric acid in lemons, acetic acid in vinegar, lactic acid in sour milk, or acetylsalicylic acid in aspirin. Some must be handled with caution, such as sulfuric acid used in car batteries, or hydrochloric acid, used to clean concrete. We also relate the word *acid* to the serious environmental hazard of acid rain. When rain is acidic, reactions characteristic of acids lead to the degradation of stone used in buildings and the liberation of poisonous metal ions locked in soil.

We briefly introduced acids, bases, and the reaction between them in Section 6-6-2. At that time we restricted our discussion to strong acids and bases. We have covered quite a bit of chemistry since Chapter 6, so we will reexamine this important topic in more detail. We can expand on our discussion of these compounds by including weak acids and bases.

In Part A of this chapter, we will review and expand on the concept of acids and bases introduced in earlier chapters. How acidity is measured and reported is the emphasis of Part B. Finally, we expand the concept of acids and bases even further to include salts, buffers, and oxides in Part C.

Part A

## Acids, Bases, and the Formation of Salts

**SETTING A GOAL**

■ You will expand your knowledge of acids and bases with more general definitions that allow us to examine their comparative strengths.

**OBJECTIVES**

13-1 List the general properties of acids and bases.

13-2 Identify Brønsted acids and bases and conjugate acid–base pairs in a proton exchange reaction.

13-3 Calculate the hydronium ion concentration in a solution of a strong acid and a weak acid given the initial concentration of the acid and the percent ionization of the weak acid.

13-4 Write the molecular, total ionic, and net ionic equations for neutralization reactions.

▶ **OBJECTIVE FOR SECTION 13-1**
List the general properties of acids and bases.

# 13-1 Properties of Acids and Bases

**LOOKING AHEAD!** Historically, well before scientists knew much about their compositions, acids and bases were classified as such based on their common properties. These common properties relate to a specific "active ingredient." The nature of these properties and the active ingredients are the topics of this section. ■

The sour taste of acids accounts for the origin of the word itself. The word *acid* originates from the Latin *acidus,* meaning "sour," or the closely related Latin *acetum,* meaning "vinegar." This ancient class of compounds has several characteristic chemical properties. Acids are compounds that do the following:

1. Taste sour (of course, one *never* tastes laboratory chemicals)
2. React with certain metals (e.g., Zn and Fe), with the liberation of hydrogen gas (see Figure 13-1)
3. Cause certain organic dyes to change color (e.g., litmus paper turns from blue to red in acids)
4. React with limestone ($CaCO_3$), with the liberation of carbon dioxide gas (see Figure 13-1)
5. React with bases to form salts and water

Some familiar acids, their common names, and their formulas are shown below.

| CHEMICAL NAME | COMMON NAME | FORMULA |
| --- | --- | --- |
| hydrochloric acid | muriatic acid | HCl |
| sulfuric acid | oil of vitriol, battery acid | $H_2SO_4$ |
| acetic acid | vinegar (sour ingredient) | $HC_2H_3O_2$ |
| carbonic acid | carbonated water | $H_2CO_3$ |

The counterparts to acids are bases. Bases are compounds that do the following:

1. Taste bitter
2. Feel slippery or soapy
3. Dissolve oils and grease
4. Cause certain organic dyes to change color (e.g., litmus paper turns from red to blue in bases)
5. React with acids to form salts and water

**FIGURE 13-1 Zinc and Limestone in Acid** Zinc (top) reacts with acid to liberate hydrogen; limestone ($CaCO_3$, bottom) reacts with acid to liberate carbon dioxide.

## 13-1.1 Arrhenius Acids and Bases

The properties listed above relate to what acids and bases do, not to their chemical composition. It was not until 1884 that a Swedish chemist, Svante Arrhenius, suggested that the particular composition of these compounds determined their behavior. *He proposed that acids produced $H^+$ ions and bases produced $OH^-$ ions in water.*

## 13-1.2 Strong Acids in Water

The ionization process of acids in water was illustrated in Figure 12-3 in the previous chapter. To illustrate the importance of water in the ionization process, the reaction of an acid with water can be represented as

$$HCl + H_2O \longrightarrow H_3O^+(aq) + Cl^-(aq)$$

*Instead of $H^+$, the acid species is often represented as $H_3O^+$, which is known as the* **hydronium ion**. The hydronium ion is simply a representation of the $H^+$ ion in a hydrated form. The acid species is represented as $H_3O^+$ rather than $H^+$ because it is somewhat closer to what is believed to be the actual species. In fact, the nature of $H^+$ in aqueous solution is even more complex than $H_3O^+$ (i.e., $H_5O_2^+$, $H_7O_3^+$, etc.). In any case, the acid species can be represented as $H^+(aq)$ or $H_3O^+(aq)$, depending on the convenience of the particular situation. *Just remember that both refer to the same species in aqueous solution.* If $H^+(aq)$ is used, it should be understood that it is not just a bare proton in aqueous solution but is associated with water molecules. (It is hydrated.)

It is the current practice to list on the label the active ingredient in medicines or drugs. In this regard, the active ingredient of acids is the $H^+(aq)$ ion. We can now see how this ion accounts for some of the behavior of acids listed previously. Equation 1 in the list below illustrates the reaction of an acid with a metal. In equation 2, the reaction of an acid with limestone is illustrated. And in equation 3, we show a neutralization reaction. The net ionic equations of these reactions are also shown, which emphasizes the role of the $H^+(aq)$ ion in each case.

**1.** Acids react with metals (e.g., Zn) and give off hydrogen gas.

$$Zn(s) + 2HCl(aq) \longrightarrow ZnCl_2(aq) + H_2(g)$$

$$Zn(s) + \underline{2H^+(aq)} \longrightarrow Zn^{2+}(aq) + H_2(g)$$

**2.** Acids react with limestone to give off carbon dioxide gas.

$$CaCO_3(s) + 2HNO_3(aq) \longrightarrow Ca(NO_3)_2(aq) + H_2O(l) + CO_2(g)$$

$$CaCO_3(s) + \underline{2H^+(aq)} \longrightarrow Ca^{2+}(aq) + H_2O(l) + CO_2(g)$$

**3.** Acids react with bases.

$$ACID + BASE \longrightarrow SALT + WATER$$

$$HClO_4(aq) + NaOH(aq) \longrightarrow NaClO_4(aq) + H_2O(l)$$

$$\underline{H^+(aq)} + OH^-(aq) \longrightarrow H_2O(l)$$

The last reaction is of prime importance and is discussed in more detail in Section 13-4.

## 13-1.3 Strong Bases in Water

Now let's turn our attention to bases. Bases are compounds that produce $OH^-$ ions in water, forming what are known as basic solutions, sometimes referred to as *alkaline* or *caustic* solutions. Some of the commonly known bases are sodium hydroxide (also known as caustic soda, or lye), potassium hydroxide (caustic potash), calcium hydroxide (slaked lime), and ammonia. Except for ammonia, these compounds are all solid ionic compounds. Forming a solution in water simply releases the $OH^-$ ion into the aqueous medium.

$$NaOH(s) \xrightarrow{H_2O} Na^+(aq) + OH^-(aq)$$

$$Ba(OH)_2(s) \xrightarrow{H_2O} Ba^{2+}(aq) + 2OH^-(aq)$$

The action of ammonia ($NH_3$) as a base is somewhat different from that of the ionic hydroxides and is better described by a more detailed look at acids and bases in the following section.

▶ **ASSESSING THE OBJECTIVE FOR SECTION 13-1**

**EXERCISE 13-1(a) LEVEL 1:** Fill in the blanks.
An acid is a compound that produces the _____ ion in solution, which is also written as the hydronium ion (_____). A base is a compound that produces an ion with the formula _____ and the name _____ ion.

**EXERCISE 13-1(b) LEVEL 2:** Write the formula and name of the acid or base formed from the following ions.
(a) $ClO_4^-$      (b) $Fe^{2+}$      (c) $S^{2-}$      (d) $Li^+$

**EXERCISE 13-1(c) LEVEL 2:** Write an equation for the reaction that occurs when the following compounds are placed in water:
(a) HI      (b) LiOH

**EXERCISE 13-1(d) LEVEL 3:** Based on the list of properties of acids and bases, which of the two do the following most likely contain?
(a) drain cleaner      (d) dishwashing detergent
(b) orange juice      (e) bleach
(c) salad dressing      (f) antacid

*For additional practice, work chapter problems 13-1, 13-3, 13-5, and 13-6*

▶ **OBJECTIVE FOR SECTION 13-2**
Identify Brønsted acids and bases and conjugate acid–base pairs in a proton exchange reaction.

# 13-2 Brønsted–Lowry Acids and Bases

**LOOKING AHEAD!** Besides neutral compounds that act as acids or bases in water, certain ions have acid or base behavior. However, to better describe the action of ions in water, we need a more inclusive definition of acids and bases. We do this in the following discussion. ∎

Limestone ($CaCO_3$) is quite a versatile compound. We can use it as solid rock in the construction of huge buildings or we can use it as a powder in chalk. It is also the major ingredient of many antacids, which are consumed to neutralize excess stomach acid. In this reaction, the carbonate ion ($CO_3^{2-}$) is the ingredient that reacts as a base (i.e., an antacid). We previously discussed this reaction as a *gas-forming neutralization reaction* in Section 6-6.3. However, from our previous definition of acids and bases, it is not immediately obvious how an anion such as $CO_3^{2-}$ behaves as a base. In order to include anions as bases, we would be aided by a broader, more inclusive definition than that of Arrhenius, which focused mainly on molecular compounds. We will now focus on the role of the $H^+$ ion in solution. *In the **Brønsted–Lowry** definition, an **acid** is a proton ($H^+$) donor and a **base** is a proton acceptor.* To illustrate this definition, we again look at the reaction of HCl as an acid to form the $H_3O^+$ ion.

$$HCl(aq) + H_2O(l) \longrightarrow H_3O^+(aq) + Cl^-(aq)$$

## 13-2.1 Conjugate Acid–Base Pairs

HCl is an acid by the Arrhenius definition because it produces the $H_3O^+$ ion. It is also an acid by the Brønsted–Lowry definition because *it donates an $H^+$ to $H_2O$*. In this definition, however, the $H_2O$ molecule also takes the role of a base because it accepts an $H^+$ from the HCl. The reaction of an acid and a base in water can be considered as an exchange of the proton. The two products formed could then conceivably act as an acid and a base in the reverse reaction. So, in our example, an acid (HCl) reacts with a base ($H_2O$) to form another acid ($H_3O^+$) and another base ($Cl^-$). *The base that remains when an acid donates a proton is known as the* **conjugate base** *of the acid. Likewise, the acid that is formed when the base accepts a proton is known as the* **conjugate acid** *of the base.* Thus $HCl$–$Cl^-$ and $H_3O^+$–$H_2O$ are known as *conjugate acid–base pairs*. The exchange of $H^+$ is illustrated below, where $A_1$ and $B_1$ refer to a specific conjugate acid–base pair and $A_2$ and $B_2$ refer to the other acid–base pair.

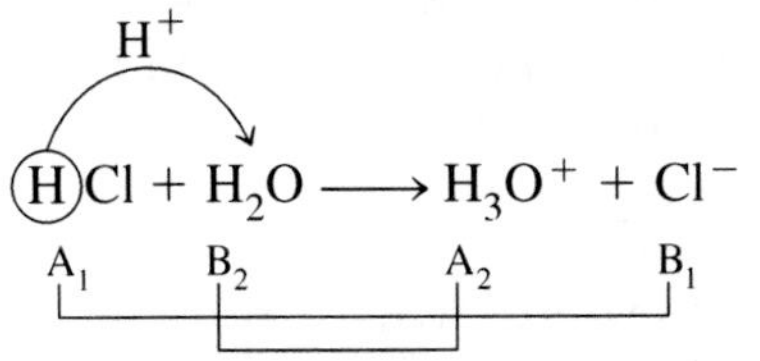

$$\text{(H)}Cl + H_2O \longrightarrow H_3O^+ + Cl^-$$
$$A_1 \qquad B_2 \qquad\quad A_2 \qquad B_1$$

Now consider the reaction of ammonia ($NH_3$) in water. Ammonia is a base in the Arrhenius definition because it forms $OH^-$ in aqueous solution even though the ammonia molecule itself does not contain the $OH^-$ ion. If we examine its behavior in water as a Brønsted–Lowry base, however, it becomes more obvious how $OH^-$ ions are produced.

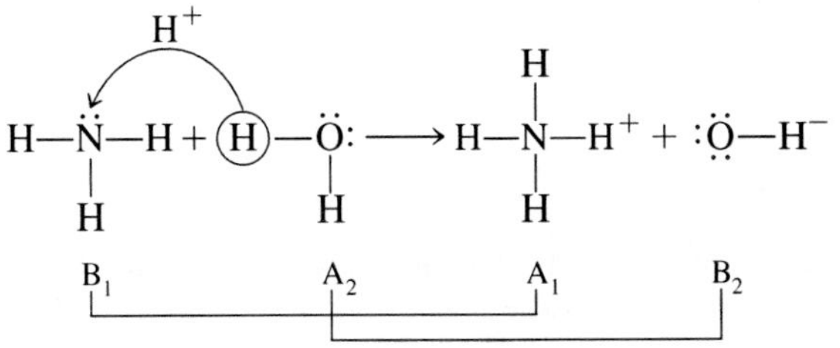

$$H-\overset{H}{\underset{H}{N}}-H + \text{(H)}-\overset{}{\underset{H}{\ddot{O}}}: \longrightarrow H-\overset{H}{\underset{H}{N}}-H^+ + :\ddot{O}-H^-$$
$$B_1 \qquad\qquad A_2 \qquad\qquad A_1 \qquad\qquad B_2$$

In the Brønsted–Lowry sense, the reaction can be viewed as simply an exchange of an $H^+$. When the base ($NH_3$) reacts, it adds $H^+$ to form its conjugate acid ($NH_4^+$). When the acid ($H_2O$) reacts, it loses an $H^+$ to form its conjugate base ($OH^-$). The $NH_3$, $NH_4^+$ ($B_1$ and $A_1$) and the $H_2O$, $OH^-$ ($A_2$ and $B_2$) pairs are conjugate acid–base pairs.

## 13-2.2 Amphiprotic Ions

In the previous reaction, $H_2O$ is an acid since it donates an $H^+$ to form $NH_4^+$. Recall that $H_2O$ acts as a *base* when HCl is present. *A compound or ion that can either donate or accept $H^+$ ions is called* **amphiprotic**. Water is amphiprotic since it can accept $H^+$ ions when an acid is present or donate $H^+$ when a base is present. An amphiprotic substance has both a conjugate acid and a conjugate base. Examples of other amphiprotic substances include $HS^-$ and $H_2PO_4^-$.

Before we look at other examples of Brønsted–Lowry acid–base reactions, we should emphasize the identification of conjugate acids and bases. *The conjugate base of a compound or ion results from removal of an $H^+$. The conjugate acid of a compound or ion results from the addition of an $H^+$.*

$$\text{conjugate acid} \underset{+H^+}{\overset{-H^+}{\rightleftarrows}} \text{conjugate base}$$

For example,

$$\underset{\text{acid}}{H_3PO_4} \underset{+H^+}{\overset{-H^+}{\rightleftarrows}} \underset{\text{base}}{H_2PO_4^-}$$

Notice that in the formation of a conjugate base, the base species ($H_2PO_4^-$) has one less hydrogen and the charge decreases by one from the acid ($H_3PO_4$). The reverse is true for formation of a conjugate acid from a base. That is, the acid has one additional hydrogen and the charge increases by one.

We are now ready to examine how the carbonate ion in calcium carbonate behaves as a base in antacid tablets. The $CO_3^{2-}$ ion relieves acidic stomachs (containing excess $H_3O^+$) as illustrated by the following proton exchange reaction.

$$CO_3^{2-} + H_3O^+ \longrightarrow HCO_3^- + H_2O$$

Notice that the carbonate ion acts as a base by accepting the proton from $H_3O^+$ to form its conjugate acid ($HCO_3^-$), while the $H_3O^+$ ion forms its conjugate base ($H_2O$). Decreasing the hydronium ion concentration in the stomach is what is meant by "relief of stomach distress."

## EXAMPLE 13-1  Determining Conjugate Bases of Compounds

What are the conjugate bases of **(a)** $H_2SO_3$ and **(b)** $H_2PO_4^-$?

**PROCEDURE**

Remove a hydrogen and subtract a positive charge from the remaining ion.

$$acid - H^+ = conjugate\ base$$

**SOLUTION**

**(a)** $H_2SO_3 - H^+ = \underline{HSO_3^-}$    **(b)** $H_2PO_4^- - H^+ = \underline{HPO_4^{2-}}$

**ANALYSIS**

Notice that the two conjugate bases in this example each have a hydrogen remaining on the structure. In these cases, the hydrogens can be removed to produce another conjugate base—$SO_3^{2-}$ and $PO_4^{3-}$.

**SYNTHESIS**

It gets progressively more difficult to remove second and third hydrogen ions from acids. This makes sense, as you are now trying to pull something with a positive charge away from something with a negative charge. As a result, it takes a stronger and stronger base to remove the $H^+$. Said another way, each successive species becomes weaker and weaker.

## EXAMPLE 13-2  Determining Conjugate Acids of Compounds

What are the conjugate acids of **(a)** $CN^-$ and **(b)** $H_2PO_4^-$?

**PROCEDURE**

$$base + H^+ = conjugate\ acid$$

**SOLUTION**

**(a)** $CN^- + H^+ = \underline{HCN}$    **(b)** $H_2PO_4^- + H^+ = \underline{H_3PO_4}$

**ANALYSIS**

Notice that in this example the conjugate bases have negative charges and the conjugate acids are neutral. Another example of a conjugate acid–base pair is $NH_4^+$–$NH_3$, where the acid is positively charged and the base is neutral. This illustrates a fairly consistent pattern found in acids and bases. Acids are usually neutral or positively charged species. Bases are usually neutral or negatively charged species. In the case of amphiprotic anions, however, the anion can act as an acid because it contains an acidic hydrogen (e.g., $H_2PO_4^-$).

### SYNTHESIS

Proteins consist of long chains of amino acids. Amino acids are interesting compounds in regard to acid–base pairs and amphiprotism. Just from the name, you might suspect that something is unique. *Amino* is similar to the name *ammonia,* which we know to be a base, and the term *acid* is unambiguous. Amino acids are well-known amphiprotic compounds. What makes them unique is that the acid–base reactions they undergo can occur within the same molecule! The neutral structure of a simple amino acid is

$$\begin{array}{ccccc} & H & & O & \\ & | & & \| & \\ H\!-\!N\!-\!&C&\!-\!C&\!-\!O\!-\!H \\ & | & | & & \\ & H & H & & \end{array}$$

Under most natural conditions, the acid part on the right of the molecule donates a proton to the base part on the left. This produces the conjugate acid and base on each end of the molecule.

$$\begin{array}{ccccc} & H & H & O & \\ & | & | & \| & \\ H\!-\!N^+\!-\!&C&\!-\!C&\!-\!O^- \\ & | & | & & \\ & H & H & & \end{array}$$

Amino acids thus have properties more typical of ionic compounds (i.e., high melting points). Can you identify the structural regions in the amino acid that form the conjugate acid–base pairs?

## EXAMPLE 13-3  Writing Acid–Base Reactions

Write the equations illustrating the following Brønsted–Lowry acid–base reactions.
(a) $H_2S$ as an acid with $H_2O$
(b) $H_2PO_4^-$ as an acid with $OH^-$
(c) $H_2PO_4^-$ as a base with $H_3O^+$
(d) $CN^-$ as a base with $H_2O$

### PROCEDURE

A Brønsted–Lowry acid–base reaction produces a conjugate acid and base. Remove an $H^+$ from the acid and transfer it to the base to form the products.

### SOLUTION

| Acid | | Base | | Conjugate Acid | | Conjugate Base |
|------|---|------|---|------|---|------|
| (a) $H_2S$ | + | $H_2O$ | $\longrightarrow$ | $H_3O^+$ | + | $HS^-$ |
| (b) $H_2PO_4^-$ | + | $OH^-$ | $\longrightarrow$ | $H_2O$ | + | $HPO_4^{2-}$ |
| (c) $H_3O^+$ | + | $H_2PO_4^-$ | $\longrightarrow$ | $H_3PO_4$ | + | $H_2O$ |
| (d) $H_2O$ | + | $CN^-$ | $\longrightarrow$ | $HCN$ | + | $OH^-$ |

### ANALYSIS

Acid–base reactions always move from the stronger acid–base pair to the weaker pair. So we can examine reactions that work well to help rank acids and bases relative to each other. For instance, $H_3O^+$ reacts completely with $H_2PO_4^-$ to produce the conjugate acid $H_3PO_4$ [part (c)]. This tells us that the hydronium cation is a stronger acid than phosphoric acid. It's also not that surprising that a cation is more acidic than a neutral molecule. We will discuss the relative strengths of acids and bases in more detail in the next section.

**SYNTHESIS**

Note that equations (b) and (c) indicate that the $H_2PO_4^-$ is amphiprotic. Another question that could be asked, especially in equation (a), is what makes $H_2S$ the acid and $H_2O$ the base. Both are neutral, and they're very similar, with sulfur and oxygen both in the Group VIA column. Further, in (b), both species are negative. Why is either an acid? This becomes a question of relative acidic or basic strength of the two species involved, and is explored in the next section.

▶ **ASSESSING THE OBJECTIVE FOR SECTION 13-2**

**EXERCISE 13-2(a) LEVEL 1:** Fill in the blanks.
In the Brønsted–Lowry definition, acids are _____ donors and bases are _____ acceptors. A conjugate acid of a compound or ion results from the _____ of an _____ ion. A substance that has both a conjugate acid and a conjugate base is said to be _____.

**EXERCISE 13-2(b) LEVEL 1:** Use the Brønsted–Lowry definition to identify the acid and the base in the following reaction:

$$SO_3^{2-} + NH_4^+ \longrightarrow NH_3 + HSO_3^-$$

**EXERCISE 13-2(c) LEVEL 2:** Write the conjugate acid and the conjugate base of the $HC_2O_4^-$ ion.

**EXERCISE 13-2(d) LEVEL 2:** Write the reaction of the $HCO_3^-$ ion with water **(a)** where water acts as a base and **(b)** where water acts as an acid.

**EXERCISE 13-2(e) LEVEL 3:** Complete the following reaction of a Brønsted–Lowry proton exchange. What are the two sets of conjugate acid–base pairs?

$$CH_3COOH + (CH_3)_3N: \longrightarrow$$

**EXERCISE 13-2(f) LEVEL 3:** The $NH_2^-$ ion is a powerful base that can remove $H^+$ from many compounds. What is the Brønsted–Lowry acid–base reaction that $NH_2^-$ undergoes with $CH_3OH$?

*For additional practice, work chapter problems 13-7, 13-9, 13-11, and 13-13.*

▶ **OBJECTIVE FOR SECTION 13-3**
Calculate the hydronium ion concentration in a solution of a strong acid and a weak acid given the initial concentration of the acid and the percent ionization of the weak acid.

# 13-3 Strengths of Acids and Bases

**LOOKING AHEAD!** The properties of acids and bases described in Section 13-1 are mostly associated with strong acids and bases. Other substances display these properties but in less dramatic fashion. For example, dilute acetic acid is sour but tame enough to use on a salad, and ammonia dissolves grease but is mild enough to clean oil stains from floors. There is a wide range of behavior that we regard as acidic or basic. This is the subject of this section. ■

Ammonia as a base would do a poor job of unclogging a stopped-up drain, yet we certainly wouldn't want to use lye to clean an oil spot from a carpet. In the former case, the base is too weak; in the latter, it is much too strong. Strong acids and bases are difficult and dangerous to handle and store. Weak acids and bases are quite easy and safe to have around. The large difference in acid or base behavior relates to the concentration of the active ingredient ($H_3O^+$ or $OH^-$) produced by the acid or base in water. This depends on its strength. First, we will consider the strength of acids.

## 13-3.1 The Strength of Acids

In Chapter 6, we indicated that strong acids were 100% dissociated into ions in solution. There are only six common strong acids. In addition to hydrochloric (HCl), which we have already discussed, there are two other binary acids, hydrobromic acid

(HBr) and hydroiodic acid (HI). The other strong acids are sulfuric acid ($H_2SO_4$), nitric acid ($HNO_3$), and perchloric acid ($HClO_4$). Sulfuric acid is a somewhat more complex case but will be considered shortly.

We have been using the 100% ionization criteria to describe a strong acid, but we still haven't formally answered the question "strong compared to what?" In the Brønsted–Lowry definition, the reaction of a molecular acid with water is considered a proton ($H^+$) exchange reaction. In fact, there is a competition between the proton-donating abilities of two acids (e.g., HCl and $H_3O^+$) and, like other competitions, the stronger prevails. *The stronger acid reacts with the stronger base to produce a weaker conjugate acid and conjugate base. In the case of a strong acid in water, the molecular acid (e.g., HCl) is a stronger proton donor than $H_3O^+$.* Therefore, the reaction proceeds essentially 100% to the right.

$$\underset{\text{stronger acid}}{HCl(aq)} + \underset{\text{stronger base}}{H_2O(l)} \longrightarrow \underset{\text{weaker acid}}{H_3O^+(aq)} + \underset{\text{weaker base}}{Cl^-(aq)}$$

Most acids that we may be familiar with, such as acetic acid, ascorbic acid (vitamin C), and citric acid, are all considered weak acids. The weak acids that we will discuss in this section are also neutral molecular acids. *A **weak molecular acid** is partially ionized (usually less than 5% at typical molar concentrations).*

The ionization of a weak acid is limited because it is a reversible reaction. Such a reaction was briefly mentioned in Section 12-6.1, since weak acids are examples of weak electrolytes. We will discuss the concept of reversible reactions and equilibrium in detail in Chapter 15, but a basic understanding of these concepts will help us understand the action of weak acids and bases in water. The ionization of HF, a weak acid, is as follows.

$$HF(aq) + H_2O(l) \rightleftharpoons H_3O^+(aq) + F^-(aq)$$

This is an example of a chemical reaction that reaches a state of equilibrium, which is represented by a double arrow ($\rightleftharpoons$). (A single arrow represents a reaction that essentially goes to completion.) *In a reaction at equilibrium, two reactions are occurring simultaneously.* In the ionization of HF, a forward reaction occurs to the right, producing ions ($H_3O^+$ and $F^-$), and a reverse reaction occurs to the left, producing the original reactants, which are the molecular compounds HF and $H_2O$.

*Forward:* $HF(aq) + H_2O(l) \longrightarrow H_3O^+(aq) + F^-(aq)$

*Reverse:* $H_3O^+(aq) + F^-(aq) \longrightarrow HF(aq) + H_2O(l)$

*At equilibrium, the forward and reverse reactions occur at the same rate* so the concentrations of all species remain constant. However, the identities of the individual molecules and ions do change. The reaction thus *appears* to have gone to a certain extent and then stopped. In fact, at equilibrium, a *dynamic (constantly changing)* situation exists in which two reactions going in opposite directions at the same rate keep the concentrations of all species constant.

For weak acids, the point of equilibrium lies far to the left side of the original ionization equation. This is because the $H_3O^+$ ion is a stronger proton donor than the HF molecular acid, opposite the case for strong acids. Thus, reactants (the molecular compounds on the left) are favored over the ionic products on the right. In other words, most of the fluorine is present in the form of molecular HF rather than fluoride ions. In a weak acid solution the concentration of the active ingredient, $H_3O^+$, and the anion is comparatively small. (See Figure 13-2.)

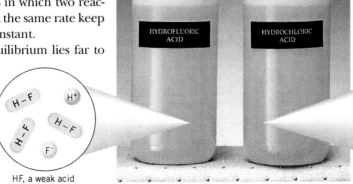

HF, a weak acid

HCl, a strong acid

**FIGURE 13-2 Strong Acids and Weak Acids** Strong acids are completely ionized in water; weak acids are only partially ionized.

In the following discussions and examples we will refer to the percent ionization of the weak acid. Like all percent problems, the actual amount or concentration of ions present is found by multiplying the total amount of acid initially present by the percent expressed in decimal form, which is obtained by dividing the percent ionization by 100%. Thus, if the original concentration of an acid is 0.20 M and it is 5.0% ionized, the concentration of each ion (the $H_3O^+$ cation and the specific anion) is

$$0.20 \text{ M} \times \frac{5.0 \text{ \%}}{100 \text{ \%}} = 0.20 \text{ M} \times 0.050 = 0.010 \text{ M}$$

The following examples illustrate the difference in acidity (the difference in $H_3O^+$ concentration) between a strong acid and a weak acid. In these examples, *the appearance of a species in brackets (e.g., [H₃O⁺]) represents the numerical value of the concentration of that species in moles per liter (M).*

## EXAMPLE 13-4    Calculating the $H_3O^+$ Concentration in a Strong Acid Solution

What is [$H_3O^+$] in a 0.100 M $HNO_3$ solution?

**PROCEDURE**

$HNO_3$ is a strong acid, so the following reaction goes 100% to the right.

$$HNO_3(aq) + H_2O(l) \longrightarrow H_3O^+(aq) + NO_3^-(aq)$$

As in other stoichiometry problems involving complete reactions, the amount (or concentration) of a product is found from the amount (or concentration) of a reactant using a mole ratio conversion factor from the balanced equation.

**SOLUTION**

$$0.100 \text{ mol/L } HNO_3 \times \frac{1 \text{ mol/L } H_3O^+}{1 \text{ mol/L } HNO_3} = 0.100 \text{ mol/L } H_3O^+$$

$$[H_3O^+] = \underline{0.100 \text{ M}}$$

## EXAMPLE 13-5    Calculating the $H_3O^+$ Concentration in a Weak Acid Solution

What is [$H_3O^+$] in a 0.100 M $HC_2H_3O_2$ solution that is 1.34% ionized?

**PROCEDURE**

Calculate the concentration of $H_3O^+$ from the percent ionization and the initial concentration. Since $HC_2H_3O_2$ is a weak acid, the following ionization reaches equilibrium when 1.34% of the initial $HC_2H_3O_2$ is ionized.

$$HC_2H_3O_2(aq) + H_2O(l) \rightleftharpoons H_3O^+(aq) + C_2H_3O_2^-(aq)$$

The [$H_3O^+$] is calculated by multiplying the original concentration of acid by the percent *expressed in fraction form.*

$$[H_3O^+] = [\text{original concentration of acid}] \times \frac{\% \text{ ionization}}{100\%}$$

**SOLUTION**

In this case,

$$[H_3O^+] = [0.100] \times \frac{1.34 \text{ \%}}{100 \text{ \%}} = \underline{1.34 \times 10^{-3} \text{ M}}$$

**ANALYSIS**

So which is more dangerous or reactive, a dilute strong acid or a concentrated weak acid? Of course the terms are vague, and we'd have to know the exact concentrations and the exact percent ionization of the weak acid. Actually, both factors play a role. We will have to come up with some convenient way of measuring the relative strength of such solutions, based on a common component of both. We'll take this up in Section 13-5.

**SYNTHESIS**
A 0.100-M solution seems to us to be relatively dilute. Furthermore, if it is less than 2% ionized, it would appear that the solution in question has very little acid in it at all. As it turns out, a little acid goes a long way. The solution described above is about as acidic as orange juice and more acidic than acid rain. Acid rain kills fish and trees, and eats away at marble buildings and structures. So, even at $1.34 \times 10^{-3}$ M, there's still plenty of hydronium to do the damage associated with acids.

In the two preceding examples, we found that the concentration of $H_3O^+$ is about 100 times greater in the strong acid solution, although both were at the same original concentration. Only in the case of strong acids does the original concentration of the acid equal the concentration of $H_3O^+$ ions.

In Example 13-5 we used acetic acid ($HC_2H_3O_2$) as a typical weak acid. Perhaps one wonders why it is written that way, not as $H_4C_2O_3$. However, if we look at the Lewis representation of acetic acid, we notice that there are two types of hydrogen atoms. The one attached to the oxygen is polar and is potentially acidic. It is ionized (to a limited extent) by the water molecules, as illustrated in Figure 12-3 in the previous chapter. In the case of acetic acid, the three hydrogen atoms attached to the carbon are essentially nonpolar and do not interact with polar water molecules when placed in aqueous solution. Thus, the three hydrogen atoms attached to carbon are not affected by proton exchange and remain as part of the acetate ion. Except for the binary acids the acidic hydrogen in an acid is bonded to an oxygen.

Three H's on the C in acetic acid do not ionize. (The C—H bond is essentially nonpolar.)

The O—H bond is polar, so the H can be ionized.

## 13-3.2 The Strength of Bases

Now we consider the case of bases. They also exhibit a range of strengths depending on the concentration of $OH^-$ produced by the base. Strong bases are ionic compounds that dissolve in water to form $OH^-$ anions. All alkali metal hydroxides are strong bases and are quite soluble in water. The alkaline earth hydroxides [except $Be(OH)_2$] also completely dissociate into ions in solution. However, $Mg(OH)_2$ has a very low solubility in water and so produces a very small concentration of aqueous $OH^-$. Because of its low solubility, it can be taken internally, as a solid suspension, to combat excess stomach acid (milk of magnesia).

The most familiar example of a weak molecular base and the one we will emphasize is ammonia ($NH_3$), whose reaction as a base was discussed in Section 13-2. A **weak molecular base** *is a base that is only partially converted into ions in solution.* The reaction of ammonia as a base is shown by the equation

$$NH_3(aq) + H_2O(l) \rightleftharpoons NH_4^+(aq) + OH^-(aq)$$

The tip-off that ammonia is a weak base is found in the equilibrium arrows rather than the single arrow that implies a complete reaction. As in the case of weak acids, the position of equilibrium lies far to the left. The vast majority of dissolved $NH_3$ molecules remain in the molecular form shown on the left of the double arrows rather than as ions, shown on the right. In the Brønsted–Lowry sense, we note that $NH_4^+$ is a stronger proton donor than $H_2O$ and $OH^-$ is a stronger proton acceptor than $NH_3$. Several other neutral nitrogen-containing compounds, such as methylamine ($CH_3NH_2$) and pyridine ($C_5H_5N$), also react with water in a similar manner to produce weakly basic solutions.

Milk of magnesia is a base taken for indigestion.

▶ **ASSESSING THE OBJECTIVE FOR SECTION 13-3**

**EXERCISE 13-3{a} LEVEL 1:** Fill in the blanks.
Strong acids are essentially _____% ionized in aqueous solution, whereas weak acids are _____ ionized. Sodium hydroxide is a strong base, but ammonia is a _____. When a weak acid reacts with water, the reaction is said to be at _____.

**EXERCISE 13-3{b} LEVEL 2:** A certain 0.10 M solution of an acid is 2.5% ionized. Is this a strong or a weak acid? What is the $[H_3O^+]$ in this solution?

**EXERCISE 13-3{c} LEVEL 2:** An acid with a concentration of 0.25 M contains a hydronium concentration of 0.0050 M. What percent of the acid is ionized? Is it strong or weak?

**EXERCISE 13-3{d} LEVEL 3:** Write the equation for each of the following reacting with water. Be sure to include the proper arrow ($\longrightarrow$ or $\rightleftharpoons$) as appropriate.
**(a)** $HNO_3$      **(b)** $HNO_2$      **(c)** $HClO_2$      **(d)** $HClO_4$

*For additional practice, work chapter problems 13-18, 13-21, 13-23, 13-24, and 13-25.*

▶ **OBJECTIVE FOR SECTION 13-4**
Write the molecular, total ionic, and net ionic equations for neutralization reactions.

# 13-4 Neutralization and the Formation of Salts

**LOOKING AHEAD!** Molecules or ions that act as acids in water have characteristic properties, as do molecules or ions that act as bases. When solutions of acids and bases are mixed in the proper amounts, the characteristic properties are destroyed or neutralized. The products of such a reaction are a salt and water. We will look at the interactions of solutions of acids with solutions of bases next. ■

In Chapter 6 we described a type of double-displacement reaction between acids and bases known as *neutralization*. If we mix the acid and base in stoichiometric amounts, the products are simply water and a salt. We will begin our discussion of neutralization reactions with a review of the reaction between a strong acid (hydrochloric acid) and a strong base (sodium hydroxide) as described in Chapter 6 and then move on to other cases. The molecular, total ionic, and net ionic equations are shown below. In this case, it is more convenient to represent the acid species as simply $H^+(aq)$ rather than $H_3O^+$.

$$ACID + BASE \longrightarrow SALT + WATER$$

*Molecular:* $\quad HCl(aq) + NaOH(aq) \longrightarrow NaCl(aq) + H_2O(l)$

*Total ionic:* $\quad H^+(aq) + \cancel{Cl^-(aq)} + \cancel{Na^+(aq)} + OH^-(aq) \longrightarrow$
$$\cancel{Na^+(aq)} + \cancel{Cl^-(aq)} + H_2O(l)$$

*Net ionic:* $\quad H^+(aq) + OH^-(aq) \longrightarrow H_2O(l)$

The key to what drives neutralization reactions is found in the net ionic equation. The active ingredient from the acid $[H^+(aq)]$ reacts with the active ingredient from the base $[OH^-(aq)]$ to form the molecular compound water. A salt is what is left over—usually present as spectator ions if the salt is soluble.

As a vital mineral needed to maintain good health, "salt" refers to just one substance, sodium chloride, as formed in the preceding reaction. Actually, salts can result from many different combinations of anions and cations from a variety of neutralizations. The following neutralization reactions, written in molecular form, illustrate the formation of some other salts.

| ACID | + | BASE | $\longrightarrow$ | SALT | + | WATER |
|------|---|------|-------------------|------|---|-------|
| **1.** $2HNO_3(aq)$ | + | $Ca(OH)_2(aq)$ | $\longrightarrow$ | $Ca(NO_3)_2(aq)$ | + | $2H_2O(l)$ |
| **2.** $HClO(aq)$ | + | $LiOH(aq)$ | $\longrightarrow$ | $LiClO(aq)$ | + | $H_2O(l)$ |
| **3.** $H_2SO_4(aq)$ | + | $2NaOH(aq)$ | $\longrightarrow$ | $Na_2SO_4(aq)$ | + | $2H_2O(l)$ |

## 13-4.1 Neutralization of a Strong Acid with a Strong Base

Each of these three neutralization reactions represents somewhat different situations, so we will look at these reactions one at a time in ionic form. Reaction 1 in the above list again represents the neutralization of a strong acid with a strong base. In this case, however, the base, $Ca(OH)_2$, dissolves in water to produce two $OH^-$ ions per formula unit. Thus two moles of acid are needed per mole of base for complete neutralization. The total ionic and net ionic equations for reaction 1 are as follows.

$$2H^+(aq) + 2NO_3^-(aq) + Ca^{2+}(aq) + 2OH^-(aq) \longrightarrow Ca^{2+}(aq) + 2NO_3^-(aq) + 2H_2O(l)$$
$$H^+(aq) + OH^-(aq) \longrightarrow H_2O(l)$$

Notice that the net ionic equation is identical to the reaction illustrated at the beginning of this section.

## 13-4.2 Neutralization of a Weak Acid with a Strong Base

Reaction 2 illustrates a neutralization of hypochlorous acid (HClO), a weak acid, with a strong base. Recall that in the case of most weak acids, the overwhelming majority of molecules are present in solution in the molecular form [i.e., $HClO(aq)$] rather than as ions [i.e., $H^+(aq)$ and $ClO^-(aq)$]. Thus, when we write the total ionic and net ionic equations, the acid is displayed in the predominant molecular form. These two equations for reaction 2 are shown as follows.

*Total ionic:* $HClO(aq) + Li^+(aq) + OH^-(aq) \longrightarrow Li^+(aq) + ClO^-(aq) + H_2O(l)$

*Net ionic:* $HClO(aq) + OH^-(aq) \longrightarrow ClO^-(aq) + H_2O(l)$

## 13-4.3 Neutralization of a Polyprotic Acid with a Strong Base

Acids are sometimes designated by the number of $H^+$ ions that are available from each molecule. Thus, HCl, $HNO_3$, and HClO are known as **monoprotic acids**, *since only one $H^+$ is produced per molecule. Those acids that can produce more than one $H^+$ are known as* **polyprotic** acids. More specifically, polyprotic acids may be **diprotic** (*two $H^+$'s*), such as $H_2SO_4$, or **triprotic** (*three $H^+$'s*) as in the case of $H_3PO_4$. Except for sulfuric acid, all other polyprotic acids are weak acids.

Reaction 3 represents the neutralization of the strong diprotic acid $H_2SO_4$. In the case of neutralization of polyprotic acids, the neutralization takes place one acidic hydrogen at a time. Thus addition of one mole of NaOH to $H_2SO_4$ results in a partial neutralization, forming water and $NaHSO_4$ (sodium bisulfate).

$$H_2SO_4(aq) + NaOH(aq) \longrightarrow NaHSO_4(aq) + H_2O(l)$$

Sodium bisulfate (or sodium hydrogen sulfate) is an example of an acid salt. *An* **acid salt** *is an ionic compound containing an anion with one or more acidic hydrogens that can be neutralized by a base.*

A second mole of NaOH added to the $NaHSO_4$ solution completes the neutralization.

$$NaHSO_4(aq) + NaOH(aq) \longrightarrow Na_2SO_4(aq) + H_2O(l)$$

The sum of the two equations produces the overall, complete neutralization of $H_2SO_4$. (See Figure 13-3.)

$$H_2SO_4(aq) + 2NaOH(aq) \longrightarrow Na_2SO_4(aq) + 2H_2O(l)$$

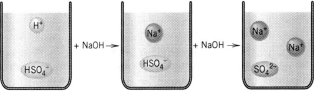

**FIGURE 13-3 Neutralization of $H_2SO_4$** The hydrogens of $H_2SO_4$ can be neutralized one at a time.

The total ionic and net ionic equations for the complete neutralization are represented below. For simplification, we will consider sulfuric acid as completely ionized to produce two $H^+$ ions in aqueous solution. In fact, the bisulfate ion in solution is not completely ionized.

$$2H^+(aq) + SO_4^{2-} + 2Na^+(aq) + 2OH^-(aq) \longrightarrow 2Na^+(aq) + SO_4^{2-}(aq) + 2H_2O(l)$$
$$H^+(aq) + OH^-(aq) \longrightarrow H_2O(l)$$

## EXAMPLE 13-6   Writing a Complete Neutralization Reaction

Write the balanced equation in molecular form illustrating the complete neutralization of $Al(OH)_3$ with $H_2SO_4$.

### PROCEDURE

Complete neutralization requires one $H^+$ for each $OH^-$. Since $Al(OH)_3$ has three available $OH^-$ ions and $H_2SO_4$ can provide only two $H^+$ ions, the reaction requires two moles of $Al(OH)_3$ for three moles of $H_2SO_4$.

### SOLUTION

$$2Al(OH)_3 + 3H_2SO_4 \longrightarrow Al_2(SO_4)_3 + 6H_2O$$

### ANALYSIS

When the goal is complete neutralization, it is easy to determine the mole ratio between acid and base without having to write out the balanced reaction. Just use the procedure above to match up the $H^+$'s produced by the acid with the $OH^-$'s available from the base. What would the mole ratio for complete neutralization be for the reaction between NaOH and $H_3PO_4$? It would take three NaOH's for each acid.

### SYNTHESIS

The experimental procedure used to neutralize an acid and a base is called a *titration,* as discussed in the previous chapter. Here, base solution of a known molarity is slowly added to a known amount of acid using a *buret,* an accurately calibrated glass tube with a stopcock at its base. A chemical indicator added to the original acid solution changes color when there is an excess of base present. Typically, one drop of indicator solution indicates visually when the solution changes from acidic to basic. A commonly used indicator is phenolphthalein. It is colorless when the solution is acidic but changes abruptly to pink when even a slight excess of base is present. The stoichiometric equivalence point is the point where the solution just begins to change color.

## EXAMPLE 13-7   Writing a Partial Neutralization Reaction

Write the balanced molecular, total ionic, and net ionic equations illustrating the reaction of 1 mol of $H_3PO_4$ (a weak acid) with 1 mol of $Ca(OH)_2$.

### PROCEDURE

Although 1 mol of $H_3PO_4$ has three available $H^+$ ions to neutralize, 1 mol of $Ca(OH)_2$ can react with only two of them. This would leave the $HPO_4^{2-}$ ion in solution.

### SOLUTION

*Molecular:* $H_3PO_4(aq) + Ca(OH)_2(aq) \longrightarrow CaHPO_4(aq) + 2H_2O(l)$

*Total ionic:* $H_3PO_4(aq) + Ca^{2+}(aq) + 2OH^-(aq) \longrightarrow Ca^{2+}(aq) + HPO_4^{2-} + 2H_2O(l)$

*Net ionic:* $H_3PO_4(aq) + 2OH^- \longrightarrow HPO_4^{2-}(aq) + 2H_2O(l)$

### ANALYSIS

In most cases, the strength of the first acidic hydrogen in a polyprotic acid is several thousand times greater than the second acidic hydrogen, and if there is a third, the second is several thousand times greater than the third. As a result, when we neutralize acids with bases, we can do so one hydrogen at a time. It would not be the case that two moles of $OH^-$ would form some $PO_4^{3-}$, and an equal amount of $H_2PO_4^-$ would not react. Instead, the reaction essentially takes place one step at a time.

SYNTHESIS

We can apply some common chemical sense to understand why it gets progressively harder to remove each successive $H^+$ from a polyprotic acid and its acid salt. Covalent bonds hold the hydrogens onto the molecule. These bonds must be broken, which requires energy. The first $H^+$ is removed from a neutral molecule. But the second $H^+$ must be removed from a negative ion. It is harder to remove a positive ion from a negative ion than from a neutral molecule. After it is removed, the resulting conjugate base is even more negative. Energetically, it takes progressively more and more energy to remove the next $H^+$. The weaker the acid, the harder it is to remove an $H^+$.

## MAKING IT REAL

# Forensic Chemistry: Salts and Fingerprint Imaging

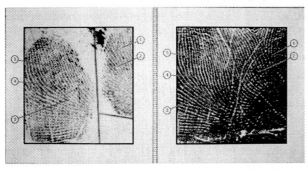

A latent fingerprint (left) is matched with one in a file (right).

The use of fingerprints to identify individuals has been in practice for over 2000 years. In the second century B.C., the Chinese used the imprint of a finger in a wax seal to identify the sender of a document. For over 400 years it has been known that the pattern of a fingerprint is unique to each individual. In modern times, fingerprints can be matched by comparing certain characteristics of the print called loops, whorls, and arches. There are about 20 to 30 characteristics of a fingerprint that are usually classified. Chances are less than one in a billion that two individuals would have more than eight of these characteristics the same.

There are three types of prints that are found at a crime scene. *Visible* prints are obvious when they are in a colored material such as blood, paint, or ink. *Plastic* prints are also obvious when they occur in wax, soap, or even dust. The most difficult to detect are *latent* prints, which are invisible and made by the transfer of perspiration or body oils to the material in question. Detection of latent prints is very difficult and requires special techniques depending on the surface where the print is suspected.

A crime scene that has latent prints is first "dusted for prints." Special powders are used that can be applied with a brush and will contrast with the surface.

The powder adheres to the perspiration or body oil of the print and results in an image. Charcoal and aluminum powder are often used in dusting.

The use of ultraviolet light is also used to detect prints without the use of powders. Ultraviolet light is directed at the surface and reflected back. A sensor detects the difference in reflected light from the surface and the print. The sensor also converts the ultraviolet light to visible light, which can then be recorded or made into a photographic print.

The use of chemicals is also important for some prints that are very hard to detect by other methods. A procedure usually performed in a laboratory in an enclosed container involves subjecting the object containing the print to vapors of an organic compound called cyanoacrylate ester (the major component of *superglue*). Fumes from the chemical adhere to the fingerprint, and eventually it becomes visible.

Lasers that emit an intense beam of light with a specific wavelength are also used to detect fingerprints. The laser causes compounds in the print to fluoresce, or give off light of a different specific wavelength. The investigator wears goggles, which protect the eyes from the laser light and transmit only the light from the print.

So what does all of this have to do with salts? Perspiration contains several salts, mainly sodium chloride and potassium chloride. Even after the perspiration dries, the solid salts are left behind. Recently, at an American Chemical Society Convention in 2005, scientists at Los Alamos National Laboratory reported that a type of X-rays called micro-X-rays cause the elements in the two salts to fluoresce. The light that is given off from the salts can be analyzed by a computer and converted into a print. It is hoped that this technique, combined with others, will provide yet another weapon in the identification of a hard-to-detect latent fingerprint that may be weeks or even months old.

▶ **ASSESSING THE OBJECTIVE FOR SECTION 13-4**

**EXERCISE 13-4(a) LEVEL 1:** Fill in the blanks.
The reaction between an acid and a base is known as a _____ reaction. The net ionic equation of this reaction always has _____ as a product. The spectator ions of the reaction form a _____. The partial neutralization of polyprotic acids produces an _____ _____ and water.

**EXERCISE 13-4(b) LEVEL 2:** Write the balanced molecular, total ionic, and net ionic equations illustrating the neutralization of $HNO_3$ with $Sr(OH)_2$.

**EXERCISE 13-4(c) LEVEL 2:** Write the balanced molecular, total ionic, and net ionic equations for the reaction between the weak base $NH_3$ and the strong acid $HBr$.

**EXERCISE 13-4(d) LEVEL 3:** Write the balanced molecular, total ionic, and net ionic equations illustrating the reaction of 1 mol of $H_2C_2O_4$ (oxalic acid) **(a)** with 1 mol of CsOH and then **(b)** with 2 mol of CsOH.

**EXERCISE 13-4(e) LEVEL 3:** What acid and base react together to form the following?
**(a)** $K_2SO_4$ **(b)** $KHSO_4$ **(c)** $NH_4Cl$

*For additional practice, work chapter problems 13-35, 13-36, 13-41, and 13-45.*

## PART A SUMMARY

### KEY TERMS

| | |
|---|---|
| 13-1.2 | The **hydronium ion** represents the proton in hydrated form. p. 437 |
| 13-2 | In the **Brønsted–Lowry** definition, an **acid** is a proton donor and a **base** is a proton acceptor. p. 438 |
| 13-2.1 | A proton exchange reaction produces **conjugate acid** and **conjugate base** pairs. p. 439 |
| 13-2.2 | An **amphiprotic** substance can act as either a proton acceptor or donor. p. 439 |
| 13-3.1 | **Weak molecular acids** produce limited amounts of hydronium ion in solution. p. 443 |
| 13-3.2 | **Weak molecular bases** produce limited amounts of hydroxide ion in solution. p. 445 |
| 13-4.3 | A **monoprotic acid** can donate one proton. A **diprotic** (two protons) and **triprotic** (three protons) are **polyprotic** acids. p. 447 |
| 13-4.3 | An **acid salt** is produced by the partial neutralization of a polyprotic acid. p. 447 |

### SUMMARY CHART

| Acids and Bases | | | |
|---|---|---|---|
| Substance | Arrhenius | Brønsted–Lowry | Comments |
| Acid | Increases $H^+(aq)$ concentration | Proton donor | Strong—100% ionized Weak—usually less than 10% ionized |
| Base | Increases $OH^-$ concentration | Proton acceptor | Strong—100% ionized Weak—usually less than 10% ionized |

*Neutralization and Partial Neutralization Reactions*

| | Acid | + | Base | ⟶ | Salt | + | Water |
|---|---|---|---|---|---|---|---|
| 1. | $HX(aq)$ | + | $M^+OH^-(aq)$ | ⟶ | $M^+X^-(aq)$ | + | $H_2O(l)$ |
| 2. | $H_2Y(aq)$ | + | $M^+OH^-(aq)$ | ⟶ | $M^+HY^-(aq)$ | + | $H_2O(l)$ |

Part B

## The Measurement of Acid Strength

**SETTING A GOAL**

■ You will learn about how the relative acidities of aqueous solutions are expressed.

**OBJECTIVES**

13-5 Using the ion product of water, relate the hydroxide ion and the hydronium ion concentrations.

13-6 Given the hydronium or hydroxide concentrations, calculate the pH and pOH and vice versa.

# 13-5 Equilibrium of Water

**LOOKING AHEAD!** We still need a convenient way to express the acidity of a solution, which relates to the concentration of $H_3O^+$ ions. To do this we need to take a closer look at water itself. As we will see in this section, there is more going on in pure water than we originally indicated. ■

▶ **OBJECTIVE FOR SECTION 13-5**
Using the ion product of water, relate the hydroxide ion and the hydronium ion concentrations.

## 13-5.1 Autoionization

In the previous chapter, pure water was classified as a nonconductor of electricity. This implied that no ions were present. This isn't exactly true, however. With more sensitive instruments, we find that there actually are very small and equal concentrations of hydronium and hydroxide ions in pure water. The presence of ions in pure water is due to a process known as autoionization. **Autoionization** *produces positive and negative ions from the dissociation of the molecules of the liquid.* For water, this is represented as follows, the double arrow again indicating that the reaction is reversible and reaches a state of equilibrium.

$$H_2O + H_2O \rightleftharpoons H_3O^+ + OH^-$$

Although this equilibrium lies very far to the left, a small but important amount of $H_3O^+$ ions and $OH^-$ ions coexist in pure water. It is this small concentration that we will focus on as a means of expressing acid and base behaviors and their relative strengths.

The concentration of each ion at 25°C has been found by experiment to be $1.0 \times 10^{-7}$ mol/L. This means that only about one out of every 10 million water molecules is actually ionized at any one time. Other experimental results tell us that the product of the ion concentrations is a constant. This phenomenon will be explained in more detail in Chapter 15, but for now we accept it as fact. Therefore, at 25°C

$$[H_3O^+][OH^-] = K_w \text{ (a constant)}$$

Substituting the actual concentrations of the ions, we can now find the numerical value of the constant.

$$[1.0 \times 10^{-7}][1.0 \times 10^{-7}] = 1.0 \times 10^{-14}$$

## 13-5.2 The Ion Product of Water

$K_w$ *($1.0 \times 10^{-14}$) is known as the* **ion product** *of water* at 25°C. The importance of this constant is that it tells us the concentrations of $H_3O^+$ and $OH^-$ not only in pure water but also in acidic and basic solutions. The following example illustrates this relationship. In Figure 13-4, the ion product of water is illustrated. Notice that there is an inverse relationship between the two ion concentrations. That is, the larger the concentration of $H_3O^+$, the smaller the concentration of $OH^-$. In pure water or a neutral solution, the concentrations are both equal to $1.0 \times 10^{-7}$ M. If an acid is added to pure water, the balance is tipped toward the $H_3O^+$ side and the solution becomes acidic to some degree. This means that the concentration of $H_3O^+$ rises above $10^{-7}$ M, while the concentration of $OH^-$ drops below $10^{-7}$ M. It is analogous to the action of a see-saw. As one side goes up, the other goes down.

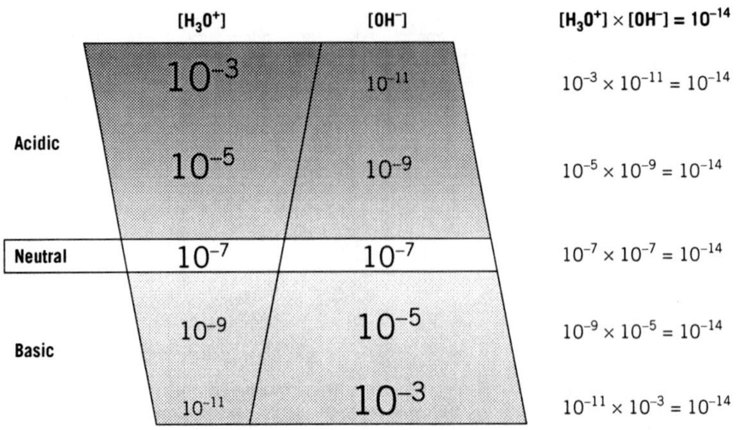

| $[H_3O^+]$ | $[OH^-]$ | $[H_3O^+] \times [OH^-] = 10^{-14}$ |
|---|---|---|
| $10^{-3}$ | $10^{-11}$ | $10^{-3} \times 10^{-11} = 10^{-14}$ |
| $10^{-5}$ | $10^{-9}$ | $10^{-5} \times 10^{-9} = 10^{-14}$ |
| $10^{-7}$ | $10^{-7}$ | $10^{-7} \times 10^{-7} = 10^{-14}$ |
| $10^{-9}$ | $10^{-5}$ | $10^{-9} \times 10^{-5} = 10^{-14}$ |
| $10^{-11}$ | $10^{-3}$ | $10^{-11} \times 10^{-3} = 10^{-14}$ |

Acidic · Neutral · Basic

**FIGURE 13-4 The Relationship Between $H_3O^+$ and $OH^-$ in Water** A large concentration of $H_3O^+$ corresponds to a low concentration of $OH^-$ in a solution, and vice versa.

In summary, an acidic, basic, or neutral solution can now be defined in terms of concentrations of ions.

*Neutral:* $[H_3O^+] = [OH^-] = 1.0 \times 10^{-7}$
*Acidic:* $[H_3O^+] > 1.0 \times 10^{-7}$ and $[OH^-] < 1.0 \times 10^{-7}$
*Basic:* $[H_3O^+] < 1.0 \times 10^{-7}$ and $[OH^-] > 1.0 \times 10^{-7}$

We should now incorporate this information into our understanding of acids and bases. In the Arrhenius definition, an acid is a substance that produces $H_3O^+$ ions in aqueous solution. But now we see that $H_3O^+$ is present in neutral and even basic solutions as well. A slight modification of the definition solves this problem. *An acid is any substance that increases $[H_3O^+]$ in water, and a base is any substance that increases $[OH^-]$ in water.* With our new understanding of the equilibrium, we can see that a substance can be an acid by directly donating $H^+(aq)$ to the solution (e.g., HCl, $H_2S$), or a substance can be an acid by reacting with $OH^-$ ions, thus removing them from the solution.

---

## EXAMPLE 13-8 Calculating [OH⁻] from [H₃O⁺]

In a certain solution, $[H_3O^+] = 1.5 \times 10^{-2}$ M. What is $[OH^-]$ in this solution?

**PROCEDURE**

Use the relationship for $K_w$, $[H_3O^+][OH^-] = 1.0 \times 10^{-14}$, and solve for $[OH^-]$.

**SOLUTION**

$$[H_3O^+][OH^-] = 1.0 \times 10^{-14}$$

$$[OH^-] = \frac{1.0 \times 10^{-14}}{[H_3O^+]} = \frac{1.0 \times 10^{-14}}{1.5 \times 10^{-2}}$$

$$= \underline{6.7 \times 10^{-13} \text{ M}}$$

**ANALYSIS**

Notice that any concentration of acid or base above 1.0 M will lead to the other concentration being below $1.0 \times 10^{-14}$. This is perfectly acceptable, both mathematically and in practice. In the next section, we'll see that it leads to some calculations that many students initially assume are impossible.

**SYNTHESIS**

When the hydronium concentration is high, it requires large amounts of acid or base to change the relative values of the two. When the hydroxide concentration is high, the same situation occurs. However, in the middle range, where both concentrations are around $10^{-7}$, it takes only small amounts of acid or base to dramatically alter the relative concentrations. What's the lesson here? In our typically neutral, or close-to-neutral, world, it doesn't take a lot of acidic or basic substances released into the environment to dramatically change things. Acid rain doesn't have to be very acidic to kill plants or fish. Small amounts will raise the concentration above a level that is toxic.

▶ ASSESSING THE OBJECTIVE FOR SECTION 13-5

**EXERCISE 13-5{a} LEVEL 1:** Fill in the blanks.
Pure water contains a small but important concentration of _____ and
_____ ions. The product of the concentrations of these two ions, known as
the _____ _____ of water, is symbolized by _____ and has a value
of _____ at 25°C. As the concentration of _____ increases in water, the
concentration of $H_3O^+$_____.

**EXERCISE 13-5{b} LEVEL 2:** What is the $[H_3O^+]$ in a solution that has
$[OH^-] = 7.2 \times 10^{-5}$?

**EXERCISE 13-5{c} LEVEL 3:** What are the hydronium and hydroxide concentrations of a 0.125-M solution of weak base that is 0.40% ionized?

**EXERCISE 13-5{d} LEVEL 3:** Is the solution in Exercise 13-5(b) acidic or basic? Is
it strongly or weakly acidic or basic? What is an example of a compound that could
produce a hydronium concentration at that level?

*For additional practice, work chapter problems 13-51, 13-53, and 13-57.*

# 13-6 The pH Scale

▶ OBJECTIVE
FOR SECTION 13-6
Given the hydronium or hydroxide concentrations, calculate the pH and pOH
and vice versa.

**LOOKING AHEAD!** The concentration of hydronium or hydroxide ions in aqueous solution is usually quite small. While scientific notation is a great help in expressing these very
small numbers, it is still awkward in this case. There is another way. This involves expressing the numbers as logarithms, which then gives us a three- or four-digit number that tells us
the same thing. The expression of these numbers in this manner is discussed in this section. ■

## 13-6.1 The Definition of pH

The producers of commercial television advertising assume that the general population is aware not only of the importance of acidity but also of how it is scientifically
expressed. For example, we often hear references to controlled pH in hair shampoo
commercials and other products. In fact, pH is an important and convenient method for expressing acid strength. For example, in a typical acidic solution, assume
$[H_3O^+]$ is equal to $1 \times 10^{-5}$ M. Scientific notation is certainly better than using a
string of nonsignificant zeros (i.e., 0.00001 M), but expressed as pH, the number
is simply 5.0. The pH scale represents the negative exponent of 10 as a positive
number. The exponent of 10 in a number is the number's common logarithm or,
simply, log. **pH** *is a logarithmic expression of* $[H_3O^+]$.

$$pH = -\log [H_3O^+]$$

Therefore, a solution of pH = 1.00 has $[H_3O^+]$ equal to $1.0 \times 10^{-1}$ M, and pure
water has pH = 7.00 ($[H_3O^+] = 1.0 \times 10^{-7}$ M). In expressing pH, the number to
the right of the decimal place should have the same number of significant figures
as the original coefficient or number. That is,

$$\text{if } [H_3O^+] = \underset{\underset{\text{2 significant figures}}{\uparrow}}{1.0} \times 10^{-4} \text{ M, then pH} = \underset{\underset{\substack{\text{2 places to the right} \\ \text{of the decimal}}}{\uparrow}}{4.00}$$

A much less popular but valid way of expressing $[OH^-]$ is **pOH**.

$$pOH = -\log [OH^-]$$

This shampoo is supposedly
desirable because it is "pH
balanced."

A simple relationship between pH and pOH can be derived from the ion product of water.

$$[H_3O^+][OH^-] = 1.0 \times 10^{-14}$$

If we now take −log of both sides of the equation, then we have

$$-\log[H_3O^+][OH^-] = -\log(1.0 \times 10^{-14})$$

Since $\log(A \times B) = \log A + \log B$, the equation can be written as

$$-\log[H_3O^+] - \log[OH^-] = -\log 1.0 - \log 10^{-14}$$

Since $\log 1.0 = 0.00$ and $\log 10^{-14} = -14$, the equation is

$$pH + pOH = 14.00$$

Generally, pOH is not used extensively since pH relates to the $OH^-$ concentration as well as the $H_3O^+$ concentration. The relationships among $[H_3O^+]$, $[OH^-]$, pH, and pOH are summarized as follows.

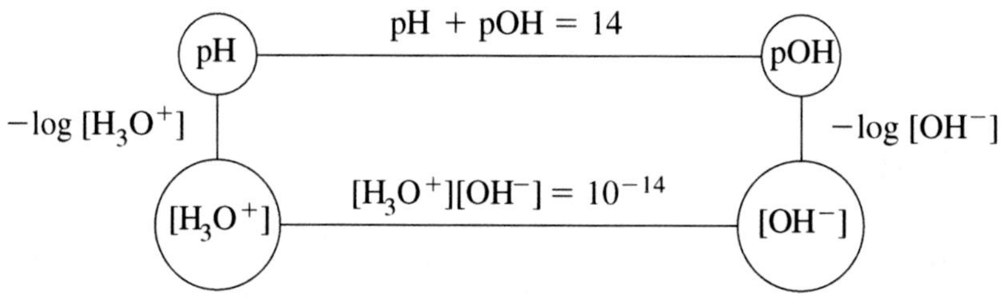

Although most of us are tempted to go straight to our calculators to change from scientific notation to logarithms, it is helpful to review the *meaning* of common logs and some of the rules of their use. You are encouraged to read Appendix C, which contains a brief discussion of common logarithms.

In Figure 13-5 we have included the pH and pOH in addition to the ion concentrations shown in Figure 13-4. Acidic, basic, and neutral solutions can now be defined in terms of pH and pOH.

*Neutral:* pH = pOH = 7.00

*Acidic:* pH < 7.00 and pOH > 7.00

*Basic:* pH > 7.00 and pOH < 7.00

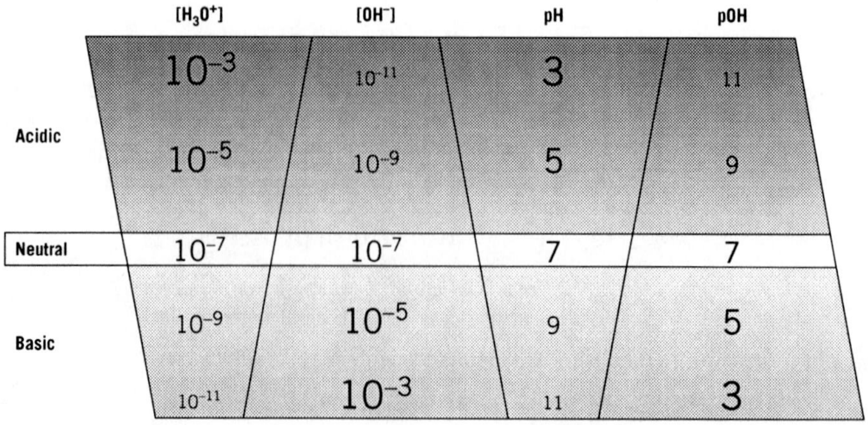

**FIGURE 13-5 Concentrations of ions, pH, and pOH** A low pH in a solution corresponds to a high pOH.

## 13-6.2 pH and the Acidity of Solutions

In the use of pH, one must remember that the *lower* the value for pH, the *higher* the concentration of $H_3O^+$. Also, *a change in one unit in the pH (e.g., from 4 to 3) corresponds to a 10-fold change in concentration (e.g., from $10^{-4}$ to $10^{-3}M$).* Another scientific scale that is logarithmic is the Richter scale for measuring earthquakes. This scale measures the amplitude of seismic waves set off by the tremor. An earthquake with a reading of 9.0 on this scale (such as the huge earthquake in Japan in 2011) indicates the waves are 10 times larger than an earthquake of magnitude 8.0. It is 100 times larger than one measuring 7.0, which is still considered strong.

In Table 13-1, we have listed the pH of some common chemicals, foods, or products. A 1.0-M HCL solution is the most acidic solution listed. Solutions of pH 1 or less are considered *strongly acidic.* Solutions with pH less than 7 but greater than 1 are considered *weakly acidic.* Even then, what we refer to as a weakly acidic solution still covers quite a range. A solution of pH 6 is 100,000 times less acidic than a solution of pH 1. On the other side of the scale, we have a 1-M solution of NaOH, which has a pH of 14. Solutions of pH 13 or greater are considered *strongly basic.* Solutions with pH greater than 7 but less than 13 are considered *weakly basic.*

**TABLE 13-1**

**The pH Scale**

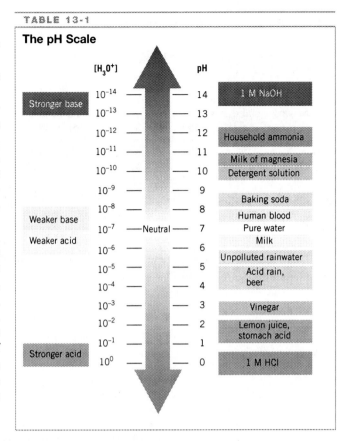

---

## EXAMPLE 13-9   Expressing the pH and pOH of a Solution

What is the pH of a solution with $[H_3O^+] = 1.0 \times 10^{-8}$M? What is the pOH?

**PROCEDURE**

A calculator is not needed for calculations of pH where the coefficient is exactly 1. Understanding the definition is sufficient. The pH is simply the negative of the exponent of 10.

**SOLUTION**

$$[H_3O^+] = 1.0 \times 10^{-8} \text{ M}$$

$$pH = -\log(1.0 \times 10^{-8}) = \underline{8.00}$$

*(Since there are two significant figures, there should be two places to the right of the decimal.)*

$$pH + pOH = 14.00$$

$$pOH = 14.00 - pH$$

$$pOH = 14.00 - 8.00 = \underline{6.00}$$

**ANALYSIS**

The pOH could have been calculated in another way as well. Knowing the inverse relationship of $H_3O^+$ and $OH^-$, we determine that a $1.0 \times 10^{-8}$ M hydronium solution would be $1.0 \times 10^{-14}/1.0 \times 10^{-8} = 1.0 \times 10^{-6}$ M hydroxide. The pOH is equal to $-\log(1.0 \times 10^{-6})$, which is 6.00.

**SYNTHESIS**

What is the pH of a 10.0-M solution of $H_3O^+$? 10.0 in scientific notation is $1.00 \times 10^1$. The pH equals −1.000, since the negative of the exponent in this case is −1. This solution has a pH of less than zero, as would any hydronium concentration greater than 1.0 M. Conversely, the pH scale can range higher than 14 as well, for particularly concentrated hydroxide solutions. They don't extend much beyond those values, though, as a pH of 15 would be 10 M $OH^-$, and a pH of 16 would have to be 100 M. Concentrations this high are unlikely.

## EXAMPLE 13-10 Calculating the [H₃O⁺] from the pH

What is the $[H_3O^+]$ of a solution with a pH = 3.00? What is the pOH? What is $[OH^-]$?

**PROCEDURE**

Again, a calculator is not needed for calculations if the pH is a whole number. The $[H_3O^+]$ is simply the antilog (or inverse log) of the minus value of pH.

**SOLUTION**

$$pH = 3.00$$
$$3.00 = -\log[H_3O^+]$$
$$-3.00 = \log[H_3O^+]$$

This means that the exponent of 10 is –3 and the coefficient should be expressed to two significant figures.

$$[H_3O^+] = \underline{1.0 \times 10^{-3}}$$
$$pOH = 14.00 - 3.00 = \underline{11.00}$$
$$[OH^-] = \text{antilog}[-11.00] = \underline{1.0 \times 10^{-11}}$$

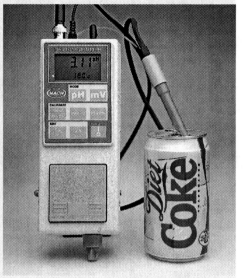

pH is read directly with this common laboratory instrument.

**ANALYSIS**

You must be careful of what you are expressing with pH. You are not necessarily calculating the concentration of the acid itself but only the $H_3O^+$ concentration produced by the specific acid. Whether this translates into the concentration of the acid producing the hydronium depends on whether the acid is strong or weak and therefore on how much of its original concentration is converted into hydronium.

**SYNTHESIS**

Occasionally advertisers will play on the general public's lack of scientific literacy by using terms associated with pH to mislead. Speaking of a substance's pH as being "higher" than normal has opposite meanings when the substance is an acid or a base. Acids with a higher pH are weaker, whereas bases with a higher pH are stronger. Not knowing which an advertiser is referring to can lead a consumer to believe that a chemical in question is more dangerous when in fact it is more benign. When advertisers say that the pH of a woman's perspiration is higher than a man's in order to sell a product, what they are really saying is that it is weaker, as perspiration is mildly acidic. But it sells the antiperspirant.

## EXAMPLE 13-11 Calculating the pH and pOH of a Strong Acid Solution

What is the pH of a $1.5 \times 10^{-2}$ M solution of $HClO_4$? What is the pOH of this solution?

**PROCEDURE**

$HClO_4$ is a strong acid, which means that it is 100% ionized in solution. Therefore, $[H_3O^+]$ is equal to the original $HClO_4$ concentration. Calculators are usually employed to calculate logarithms but there are several styles. The following instructions are valid for a majority of nongraphing calculators. If yours differs, you should consult your user's manual.

**1.** Enter the number. First enter "1.5," then push the exponent key, EXP or EE and enter "2". Push +/− the key to change the exponent to −2.

**2.** Push the log key.

**3.** The display reads −1.82, which is the log of the number you entered.

**4.** Change the reading to 1.82, since the pH is the negative of the log.

**SOLUTION**

$$[H_3O^+] = 1.5 \times 10^{-2} \text{ M}$$

$$\log(1.5 \times 10^{-2}) = -1.82$$

$$pH = -\log(1.5 \times 10^{-2}) = \underline{1.82}$$

$$pH + pOH = 14.00$$

$$pOH = 14.00 - 1.82 = \underline{12.18}$$

**ANALYSIS**

If this were a KOH solution of the same concentration, what would be the pH? The only difference in the solutions, as far as pH is concerned, is that the concentration is hydroxide. So it would be the pOH that would be calculated directly from the starting concentration and the pH that would be determined by subtracting from 14.00. pOH = 1.82 and pH = 12.18. This makes sense. KOH is a base, and therefore its solutions should have pH's greater than 7.0.

**SYNTHESIS**

The calculation above holds true only for a strong acid (or base, with the appropriate changes for pOH). If the acid in question were weak, you would have to know the % ionization to figure out what the concentration of $H_3O^+$ was. There are alternative methods that can be used, which are discussed in Chapter 15.

# EXAMPLE 13-12 Converting pH to [$H_3O^+$]

In a given weakly basic solution, pH = 9.62. What is [$H_3O^+$]?

**PROCEDURE**

In this case, it is necessary to take the antilog (or the inverse log on a calculator).

1. Enter the 9.62 on the calculator.

2. Change the sign ($\boxed{+/-}$ key).

3. Press the $\boxed{\text{inv}}$, $\boxed{\text{shift}}$, or $\boxed{\text{2}^{\text{nd}}}$ key, then the $\boxed{\text{log}}$ key. Consult the instructions for your calculator if these keys are different or not available.

4. The number displayed should be rounded off to two significant figures since there are two numbers to the right of the decimal place in the original number.

**SOLUTION**

$$-\log[H_3O^+] = 9.62 \qquad \log[H_3O^+] = -9.62$$

$$[H_3O^+] = \underline{2.4 \times 10^{-10} \text{ M}}$$

**ANALYSIS**

Remember to make sure that your answers make mathematical and chemical sense. Failure to convert the sign to negative gives a concentration of 4 billion molar. That number can be rejected immediately. Furthermore, if you forget the shift or 2nd key and simply take the log of a negative number, you'll get an error message. It is mathematically meaningless. Typically, acid concentrations will range from 1.0 M down to $10^{-5}$ M for chemically relevant acids. Those represent a pH range from 0 to 5. Bases have the same concentration range, and the pH generally ranges from 14 down to 9. A pH in the middle range, 6–8, tends to be very dilute, and the actual pH is affected by the dissociation of water itself, thus boosting the hydronium or hydroxide concentrations higher than you might expect.

**SYNTHESIS**

The more deeply you get into science, the more prevalent you'll find logarithmic scales. Along with the Richter scale, and, of course, pH, logarithmic scales are used to measure all sorts of phenomena whose values are spread out over several orders of magnitude. Stellar brightness is measured on a logarithmic scale (though not log 10, like pH), as is the decibel in acoustics. In spectroscopy, light absorbance, which is a direct function of concentration, is related logarithmically to the transmittance, or the percentage of light passing through the sample. The voltage of a battery depends on the log of the concentration of the chemicals in the battery. These are just a few examples, but they illustrate the importance of the use of logarithms in the study of science.

▶ **ASSESSING THE OBJECTIVE FOR SECTION 13-6**

**EXERCISE 13-6(a) LEVEL 1:** Fill in the blanks.
The pH of a solution is defined as _____. An acidic solution is one that has an $[H_3O^+]$ greater than _____ and a pH _____ than 7. A basic solution is one that has an $[OH^-]$ greater than _____ and a pH _____ than 7.

**EXERCISE 13-6(b) LEVEL 2:** What is the pH of the solution where $[OH^-] = 7.2 \times 10^{-5}$?

**EXERCISE 13-6(c) LEVEL 2:** What is the concentration of an LiOH solution if the pH is 13.40?

**EXERCISE 13-6(d) LEVEL 2:** For a solution of $HClO_4$ with a pH of 2.20, what are the following?
**(a)** pOH          **(b)** hydronium concentration     **(c)** hydroxide concentration

**EXERCISE 13-6(e) LEVEL 3:** For a solution of NaOH that is 0.075 M, what are the following?
**(a)** hydronium concentration     **(b)** hydroxide concentration     **(c)** pH     **(d)** pOH

**EXERCISE 13-6(f) LEVEL 3:** Which has the higher $[H_3O^+]$, a 0.005-M solution of HCl or a 0.2-M solution of $HC_2H_3O_2$, which is only 0.4% ionized?

*For additional practice, work chapter problems, 13-61, 13-63, 13-69, and 13-71.*

# PART B   SUMMARY

## KEY TERMS

13-5.1    The ionization of the molecules of a solvent into positive and negative ions is known as **autoionization**. p. 451

13-5.2    The **ion product** of water ($K_w$) is the quantitative relationship between the hydronium and hydroxide ions. p. 451

13-6.1    **pH** is the logarithmic measurement of the hydronium ion concentration.
**pOH** is the same measurement of the hydroxide ion concentration. p. 453

## SUMMARY CHART

| *Relative Acidity of Solutions* | | | | |
|---|---|---|---|---|
| **Solution** | **$[H_3O^+]$** | **$[OH^-]$** | **pH** | **pOH** |
| Strongly acidic | $> 10^{-1}$ | $< 10^{-13}$ | $< 1.0$ | $> 13.0$ |
| Weakly acidic | $10^{-4}$ | $10^{-10}$ | 4.0 | 10.0 |
| Neutral | $10^{-7}$ | $10^{-7}$ | 7.0 | 7.0 |
| Weakly basic | $10^{-10}$ | $10^{-4}$ | 10.0 | 4.0 |
| Strongly basic | $< 10^{-13}$ | $> 10^{-1}$ | $> 13.0$ | $< 1.0$ |

## Part C

## Salts and Oxides as Acids and Bases

**SETTING A GOAL**

※ You will learn how salts and oxides can also affect the pH of aqueous solutions.

**OBJECTIVES**

**13-7** Write a hydrolysis reaction, if one occurs, for salt solutions to determine whether they are acidic or basic.

**13-8** Write equations illustrating how a buffer solution can absorb either added acid or base.

**13-9** Determine, if possible, whether a specific oxide is acidic or basic.

# 13-7 The Effect of Salts on pH—Hydrolysis

**LOOKING AHEAD!** Solutions of some salts are neutral, some basic, and some acidic. Why this is so is the subject of this section. ■

▶ **OBJECTIVE FOR SECTION 13-7**
Write a hydrolysis reaction, if one occurs, for salt solutions to determine whether they are acidic or basic.

When a salt dissolves in water, both a cation and an anion are produced. These two ions may or may not react with water. The cation has the potential to act as an acid and the anion as a base. *The reactions of a cation as an acid or an anion as a base are known as* **hydrolysis reactions.** The general hydrolysis reaction of a hypothetical anion (e.g., $X^-$) is represented as follows:

$$X^-(aq) + H_2O(l) \rightleftharpoons HX(aq) + OH^-(aq)$$

The general hydrolysis reaction of a hypothetical cation (e.g., $BH^+$) is shown below.

$$BH^+(aq) + H_2O(l) \rightleftharpoons B(aq) + H_3O^+(aq)$$

We will consider four types of salt solutions. To understand why certain ions undergo hydrolysis we will first examine the ions that *do not* undergo this reaction.

## 13-7.1 Neutral Solutions of Salts

First, consider the $Cl^-$ ion, which is the anion (conjugate base) of the strong acid HCl. Recall that in the ionization process of HCl in water, the forward reaction is 100% complete, so the reverse reaction does not occur (i.e., if it is 100% in one direction, it must be 0% in the other.) Thus we notice that the $Cl^-$ ion, although formally known as a conjugate base, in fact does not exhibit proton-accepting ability in water to form an HCl molecule. *Therefore, the $Cl^-$ion does not undergo hydrolysis. Other anions of strong acids (i.e., $NO_3^-$, $ClO_4^-$, $Br^-$, and $I^-$) also do not undergo hydrolysis reactions so do not affect the pH of the solution.* (The $HSO_4^-$, an acid salt anion, is an exception and is moderately acidic in water.) The anions of strong bases (e.g., $Na^+$, $K^+$, $Ca^{2+}$, and $Mg^{2+}$ and other alkali metal and alkaline earth metal ions) also *do not* undergo hydrolysis in water so do not affect the pH of the solution. These cations and anions exist simply as independent hydrated ion in aqueous solution. If neither the cation nor the anion undergoes a hydrolysis reaction, solutions of these salts do not affect the pH and remain the same as that of pure water (i.e., 7.0). We can identify these salts as having an anion originating from a strong acid and a cation originating from a strong base. [i.e., the alkali and alkaline earth metals (except $Be^{2+}$)]. Examples of neutral salts are $NaCl$, $Ba(ClO_4)_2$, and $KNO_3$.

### 13-7.2 Salts Forming Basic Solutions: Anion Hydrolysis

Now consider the ionization equilibrium for the weak acid HClO.

$$HClO(aq) + H_2O(l) \rightleftharpoons H_3O^+(aq) + ClO^-(aq)$$

This reaction reaches a point of equilibrium that strongly favors the molecular reactants on the left. The reverse reaction shows that the ClO⁻ *does* demonstrate some proton-accepting ability in water. Now consider what happens when this anion is added to water as part of a salt such as in NaClO (bleach). Since ClO⁻ can accept a proton, it exhibits its weakly basic nature by producing a small concentration of hydroxide ion. (If you had a bleach solution on your fingers, you would notice that it is slippery, which is a property typical of bases.) The following equation represents the anion hydrolysis reaction of the hypochlorite ion.

$$ClO^-(aq) + H_2O(l) \rightleftharpoons HClO(aq) + OH^-(aq)$$

The extent of hydrolysis of anions is generally quite small, however, so again the equilibrium lies far to the left. We can now make a general statement. *The anions of weak acids (i.e., their conjugate bases) undergo hydrolysis in aqueous solution, producing weakly basic solutions.* We can make another generalization: the weaker the acid, the stronger is its conjugate base. There are a few anions (e.g., H⁻) that are actually strong bases in water and, as mentioned previously, a few that are so weak (e.g., Cl⁻) that they do not exhibit any basic behavior.

In summary, when the salt originates from the cation of a strong base and the anion of a weak acid, the cation does not affect the pH but the anion does. In the anion hydrolysis reaction, a small equilibrium concentration of OH⁻ makes the solution basic. Examples of basic salts are $KC_2H_3O_2$, $Ca(NO_2)_2$, and NaF. The pH of solutions of these salts will be greater than 7.0.

### 13-7.3 Salts Forming Acidic Solutions: Cation Hydrolysis

Now consider the weak base ammonia. As indicated in Section 13-3, its reaction with water produces small concentrations of $NH_4^+$ and OH⁻ ions. Since this is also an equilibrium situation, we can conclude that the $NH_4^+$ ion demonstrates proton-donating properties in the reverse reaction. When the ammonium ion is placed in water as part of a salt (e.g., $NH_4Cl$), it exhibits a weakly acidic nature by producing a small concentration of hydronium ion. The cation hydrolysis of the ammonium ion is illustrated by the following equation.

$$NH_4^+(aq) + H_2O(l) \rightleftharpoons H_3O^+(aq) + NH_3(aq)$$

We can generalize this behavior also. *Cations (conjugate acids) of weak bases undergo hydrolysis in aqueous solution, producing weakly acidic solutions.*

In summary, when a salt forms from the cation of a weak base and the anion of a strong acid, the anion does not affect the pH but the cation does. The primary example of a cation that undergoes hydrolysis is $NH_4^+$. Since the anions do not undergo hydrolysis, solutions of salts such as $NH_4Br$ and $NH_4NO_3$ are weakly acidic. The pH of such solutions will be less than 7.0. Other examples of acidic cations include transition metal cations and $Al^{3+}$. The neutral hydroxides of these cations are also weak bases but generally insoluble in water. For example, solutions of $FeCl_3$ and $Cu(NO_3)_2$, which produce the $Fe^{3+}$ and $Cu^{2+}$ ions, respectively, form weakly acidic solutions.

### 13-7.4 Complex Cases

There are other salt solutions that are not easy to predict without quantitative data. For example, in a solution of the salt $NH_4NO_2$, both anion and cation undergo hydrolysis, but not to the same extent. In other cases, it is not immediately obvious

Solutions of ordinary bleach (NaClO) are weakly basic.

whether solutions of acid salts are acidic or basic. For example, the $HCO_3^-$ ion is amphiprotic, which means that it is potentially an acid since it has a hydrogen that can react with a base. However, it is also the conjugate base of the weak acid $H_2CO_3$, so it can act as a base by undergoing hydrolysis. Sodium bicarbonate solutions are actually weakly basic and for that reason are sometimes used as an antacid to treat upset stomachs. Solutions of the acid salts $NaHSO_3$ and $NaHSO_4$, however, are acidic. Quantitative information, which is discussed in Chapter 15, would be needed, however, for us to have predicted these facts.

The discussion of the effect on pH when salts dissolve in water is summarized as follows.

| ORIGIN OF CATION | ORIGIN OF ANION | PH OF SOLUTION | EXAMPLES |
|---|---|---|---|
| strong base | strong acid | 7.0 | $KI$, $Sr(ClO_4)_2$ |
| strong base | weak acid | >7.0 | $KNO_2$, $BaS$ |
| weak base | strong acid | <7.0 | $NH_4ClO_4$, $AlCl_3$ |
| weak base | weak acid | more information needed | $NH_4ClO$, $N_2H_5NO_2$ |
| strong base | acid salt | more information needed | $KH_2PO_4$, $Ca(HSO_3)_2$ |

## EXAMPLE 13-13    Predicting the Acidity of Salt Solutions

Indicate whether the following solutions are acidic, basic, or neutral. If the solution is acidic or basic, write the equation illustrating the appropriate reaction.

(a) KCN                    (b) Ca(NO$_3$)$_2$                    (c) $(CH_3)_2NH_2^+Br^-$ [$(CH_3)_2NH$ is a weak base like $NH_3$.]

### PROCEDURE

Identify the ions formed by the solution of each salt. Determine whether the anion originates from a weak or strong acid and the cation from a weak or strong base.

### SOLUTION

(a) KCN: $K^+$ is the cation of the strong base KOH and does not hydrolyze. The $CN^-$ ion, however, is the conjugate base of the weak acid HCN and hydrolyzes as follows.

$$CN^- + H_2O \rightleftharpoons HCN + OH^-$$

Since $OH^-$ is formed in this solution, the solution is $\underline{basic}$.

(b) Ca(NO$_3$)$_2$: $Ca^{2+}$ is the cation of the strong base Ca(OH)$_2$ and does not hydrolyze. $NO_3^-$ is the conjugate base of the strong acid HNO$_3$ and also does not hydrolyze. Since neither ion hydrolyzes, the solution is $\underline{neutral}$.

(c) $(CH_3)_2NH_2^+Br^-$: $(CH_3)_2NH_2^+$ is the conjugate acid of the weak base $(CH_3)_2NH$. It undergoes hydrolysis according to the equation

$$(CH_3)_2NH_2^+ + H_2O \rightleftharpoons (CH_3)_2NH + H_3O^+$$

The $Br^-$ ion is the conjugate base of the strong acid HBr and does not hydrolyze. Since only the cation undergoes hydrolysis, the solution is $\underline{acidic}$.

### ANALYSIS

Another way of evaluating the pH of a salt solution is to think about what compounds would have to be mixed together to make the salt. Consider KCN in (a). It is formed from the neutralization of the strong base KOH with the weak acid HCN. Intuitive sense indicates that a mixture of a *strong* base and a *weak* acid would form a solution that is more basic than acidic, so we'd predict a basic salt. A salt like $NH_4NO_3$ works as the exact opposite. The *weak* base, $NH_3$, neutralized with the *strong* acid, $HNO_3$, should give an acidic salt. Note that this line of reasoning doesn't *explain* where the excess acid or base is coming from, unlike the equations above, but it is a quick way to arrive at the correct answer.

**SYNTHESIS**

A good example of how we take advantage of acidic and basic salts is by using them to alter soil pH. Typically, plants grow better in slightly acidic soils, although a few do better at a higher pH. Ammonium salts lower the pH of soils nicely, while also adding critical nitrogen. Aluminum sulfate is another product used to lower the pH of soils. Calcium, another critical mineral, tends to wash out of acidic soils, so basic calcium carbonate, or lime, is used to treat acidic soil and to increase the calcium content.

▶ **ASSESSING THE OBJECTIVE FOR SECTION 13-7**

**EXERCISE 13-7(a) LEVEL 1:** What type of salt (acidic, basic, or neutral) will the following produce?
**(a)** cation of a weak base with anion of a strong acid
**(b)** cation of a strong base with anion of a strong acid
**(c)** cation of a strong base with anion of a weak acid
**(d)** cation of a weak base with anion of a weak acid

**EXERCISE 13-7(b) LEVEL 2:** Identify the following as forming acidic, basic, or neutral solutions when dissolved in water.
**(a)** $Li_3PO_4$     **(b)** $NH_4ClO_4$     **(c)** $CaBr_2$     **(d)** $K_2SO_3$

**EXERCISE 13-7(c) LEVEL 2:** Write the hydrolysis reaction (if any) of the following salts.
**(a)** $Na_2CO_3$     **(b)** $BaBr_2$     **(c)** $N_2H_5NO_3$ ($N_2H_4$ is a weak base like ammonia.)

**EXERCISE 13-7(d) LEVEL 3:** What are two examples of compounds you could add to NaOH in order to form a basic salt?

**EXERCISE 13-7(e) LEVEL 3:** What are two examples of compounds you could add to ammonia in order to form an acidic salt?

**EXERCISE 13-7(f) LEVEL 3:** $HSO_4^-$ can potentially undergo two reactions in water. Only one occurs. Which one and why?

*For additional practice, work chapter problems 13-78, 13-79, 13-83, and 13-87.*

▶ **OBJECTIVE FOR SECTION 13-8**
Write equations illustrating how a buffer solution can absorb either added acid or base.

# 13-8 Control of pH—Buffer Solutions

**LOOKING AHEAD!** Perhaps the most important chemical system involves the blood coursing through our veins. Our blood has a pH of about 7.4, but a variation of as little as 0.2 pH unit causes coma or even death. How is the pH of the blood so rigidly controlled despite all the acidic and basic substances we ingest? The control of pH is the job of buffers, which are discussed next. ∎

## 13-8.1 The Function of a Buffer

The word *buffer* is usually used in the context of "absorbing a shock." For example, a car bumper serves as a buffer for the passengers by absorbing the energy of an impact. A buffer solution has a similar effect on the pH of a solution. *A* **buffer** *solution resists changes in pH caused by the addition of limited amounts of a strong acid or a strong base.* Commercial products tell us that buffered solutions are important in items such as hair shampoo and aspirin. But to us it is most important because many chemical reactions in our bodies, including those that give us life's energy, must take place in a controlled pH environment.

A buffer works by having a substance in solution that is available to react with any added $H_3O^+$ or $OH^-$. The most logical candidates for this duty are weak bases and weak acids, respectively. Consider how a hypothetical monoprotic weak acid (HX) reacts with added $OH^-$.

$$HX(aq) + OH^-(aq) \longrightarrow X^-(aq) + H_2O(l)$$

In the previous section we found that the conjugate base of the weak acid ($X^-$) can act as a base in water. It reacts with $H_3O^+$ as follows:

$$X^-(aq) + H_3O^+(aq) \longrightarrow HX(aq) + H_2O(l)$$

Both of these reactions are essentially complete. So, if we have a solution that contains a significant concentration of both the weak acid and its conjugate weak base, we have a solution that reacts with either added $H_3O^+$ or $OH^-$. One may think that just the weak acid alone would be a buffer because the ionization produces some of its anion. However, the amount from ionization is very small, so we need additional anion concentration from another source such as a salt.

The buffer in this product controls the pH.

## 13-8.2 The Composition of a Buffer

*Buffer solutions are made from (a) a solution of a weak acid that also contains a salt of its conjugate base or (b) a solution of a weak base that also contains a salt of its conjugate acid.*

A typical buffer solution is put to use in swimming pools. To keep bacteria at bay, we use ordinary household bleach (NaClO) plus a limited amount of strong acid that converts some of the NaClO to HClO. This solution keeps the pH at a comfortable 7.5. If the pH gets too low (acidic), the water can sting the eyes and cause corrosion. If it gets too high (alkaline), the water can become cloudy and algae may thrive. The swimming pool has a significant concentration of both $ClO^-$ and HClO, which together act as a buffer. The solution of these two compounds, one a weak acid and the other a strong electrolyte, is illustrated by the following two equations.

$$HClO(aq) + H_2O(l) \rightleftharpoons H_3O^+(aq) + ClO^-(aq)$$

$$NaClO(s) \longrightarrow Na^+(aq) + ClO^-(aq)$$

Notice that a mixture of these two compounds in water produces a solution containing three ions, $H_3O^+$, $Na^+$, and $ClO^-$, and one molecular compound, HClO. The $Na^+$ is the cation of a strong base and is a spectator ion so it can be neglected. (It does not interact with $H_2O$ so does not affect the pH.) Our main focus, then, is on the significant concentration of molecular HClO and $ClO^-$ ion, along with the small concentration of $H_3O^+$, which are shown in bold above. The relevant equilibrium is again illustrated as

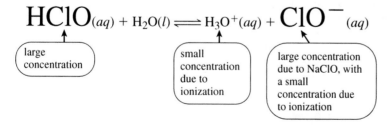

The HClO and the $ClO^-$ ion (from the salt) are available to react with any $H_3O^+$ or $OH^-$ added to the system. When $OH^-$ is added to the system, the molecular HClO removes it as follows:

$$HClO(aq) + OH^-(aq) \longrightarrow ClO^-(aq) + H_2O(l)$$

Should some $H_3O^+$ be added to the system, the $ClO^-$ is available to remove it.

$$ClO^-(aq) + H_3O^+(aq) \longrightarrow HClO(aq) + H_2O(l)$$

**FIGURE 13-6 A Buffer Solution** A buffer can react with added $H_3O^+$ or $OH^-$.

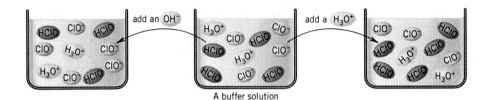

A buffer solution

The addition of a limited amount of acid or base is thus counteracted by species present in the buffer solution, and the pH changes very little. (See Figure 13-6.)

A strong acid and its salt (e.g., HCl and NaCl) cannot act as a buffer because the acid is not present in solution in molecular form—it is completely ionized in water. Therefore, there is no reservoir of HCl molecules that can react with added $OH^-$ ions, nor can the very weak conjugate base ($Cl^-$) react with $H_3O^+$ ions as we indicated previously.

Consider the following analogy. One person has $20 in his pocket with no savings in the bank; another person has $20 in her pocket in addition to $100 in the bank. A $12 expense will change the first person's pocket money drastically, as it will decrease to $8. The second person, however, is "buffered" from this expense and can replenish the loss with the bank savings, maintaining the same amount of pocket money. The molecular HClO is analogous to "money in the bank." It is available to react with added $OH^-$. Thus the original concentration of $H_3O^+$, which is analogous to "money in the pocket," remains essentially unchanged. The person who keeps all his money in his pocket is analogous to a strong acid solution in which there is no molecular acid in reserve. In this case, since all the acid ionizes to $H_3O^+$, any added $OH^-$ decreases the $H_3O^+$ concentration and thus increases the pH.

Solutions of weak bases and salts containing their conjugate acids (e.g., $NH_3$ and $NH_4Cl$) also serve as buffers. The two relevant reactions in this case are

$$\textit{Added acid: } NH_3 + H_3O^+ \longrightarrow NH_4^+ + H_2O$$

$$\textit{Added base: } NH_4^+ + OH^- \longrightarrow H_2O + NH_3$$

The pH of the buffer solution depends on the strength of the acid or base chosen. In Chapter 15, actual pH values of buffer solutions are calculated from quantitative information related to acid strength.

We began this section by mentioning the importance of the buffer system of our blood. The carbonic acid–bicarbonate buffer system is our main protection and is discussed in Making It Real, "The pH Balance in the Blood." However, another buffer system is at work in the cells of our bodies. This is the $H_2PO_4^- - HPO_4^{2-}$ buffer system. In this system the dihydrogen phosphate ion ($H_2PO_4^-$) acts as the acid species and the hydrogen phosphate ion ($HPO_4^{2-}$) acts as the base species. These two ions can remove $H_3O^+$ or $OH^-$ ions produced in the cells as follows:

$$\textit{Added acid: } HPO_4^{2-} + H_3O^+ \longrightarrow H_2PO_4^- + H_2O$$

$$\textit{Added base: } H_2PO_4^- + OH^- \longrightarrow HPO_4^{2-} + H_2O$$

### 13-8.3 Buffer Capacity

There is a limit to how much a buffer system can resist change. If the added amount of $OH^-$ exceeds the reserve of HClO (referred to as the *buffer capacity*), then the pH will rise. This is analogous to a $110 expense for the person with the $100 savings. It is more than she can cover with bank savings, so the amount in her pocket decreases. The buffer capacity also relates to the original amount of the salt (NaClO) present. The best buffers, then, are those that contain large and approximately equal concentrations of acid and conjugate base. They are capable of absorbing significant amounts of either hydronium or hydroxide as necessary.

## MAKING IT REAL

### The pH Balance in the Blood

The chemistry of the blood is a science unto itself. It is our river of life, delivering fuel and oxygen for the muscles, removing waste products, and keeping our body temperature steady. The pH of the blood is 7.40, just barely alkaline. As mentioned in an earlier Making It Real, enzymes run our body but they function only in a very narrow pH range. Deviations of only 0.2 pH unit either way can cause coma or even be fatal. If the pH drops below 7.20, a condition known as *acidosis* results. If the pH rises to above 7.60, the opposite condition is called *alkalosis*. Either situation seriously upsets our body chemistry.

Perhaps one of the most amazing properties of blood is its ability to maintain a nearly constant pH despite the fact that acids and bases find their way into the bloodstream. The pH of our blood is held constant by two buffering systems. We will look closely at the more important system, which is the carbonic acid–bicarbonate buffer. This system is represented by the equation

$$H_2CO_3(aq) + H_2O \rightleftharpoons HCO_3^-(aq) + H_3O^+(aq)$$

The carbonic acid ($H_2CO_3$) part of the buffer reacts with any excess $OH^-$ ion that enters our blood, and

The pH of the blood is an important measurement.

the $HCO_3^-$ ion reacts with any excess $H_3O^+$. For example, exercise produces extra $H_3O^+$ from the lactic acid formed in the muscles. The $H_3O^+$ reacts with $HCO_3^-$ to form carbonic acid. This is transported to the lungs where it decomposes to $CO_2$ gas and $H_2O$, which is then exhaled. Our bodies respond to exercise by faster breathing and faster release of carbon dioxide.

If extra $OH^-$ enters the blood, it reacts with $H_2CO_3$ and more bicarbonate is formed, which is eventually excreted by the kidneys. Sometimes when people get nervous, they breathe too fast, which is called *hyperventilation*. This causes too much carbon dioxide to be exhaled, the blood becomes less acidic and the pH of the blood rises above 7.4. If the person faints, the breathing rate decreases and the pH quickly comes back into balance. Actually, the concentration of bicarbonate is about 10 times the concentration of carbonic acid, so we are more protected against extra acid than extra base, which works out well.

Health problems such as diabetes and kidney disease may disturb the buffers of the blood. Generally, however, we couldn't have a better system to maintain pH and with it the smooth functioning of our body.

▶ ASSESSING THE OBJECTIVE FOR SECTION 13-8

EXERCISE 13-8(a) LEVEL 1: Fill in the blanks.
A buffer solution consists of a weak acid and a salt of its _____ _____. Buffer solutions resist a change in _____ because any hydronium is neutralized with the _____ and any hydroxide is neutralized with the _____. The _____ _____ is a measure of how much strong acid or strong base the buffer can absorb.

EXERCISE 13-8(b) LEVEL 1: Which of these would form a buffer solution?
(a) $HNO_3 + KNO_3$          (c) $HF + NaF$
(b) $HNO_2 + KNO_2$          (d) $HBr + NaBr$

EXERCISE 13-8(c) LEVEL 2: What salt could you add in order to make a buffer solution from each of the following aqueous solutions?
(a) $NH_3$     (b) $Na_2SO_3$     (c) $HClO_2$

EXERCISE 13-8(d) LEVEL 3: A mixture of $H_2C_2O_4$ and $NaHC_2O_4$ can act as a buffer. (a) Write the reaction that occurs when $H_3O^+$ is added to the solution. (b) Write the reaction when $OH^-$ is added to the solution.

EXERCISE 13-8(e) LEVEL 3: The addition of HCl to the weak base $C_5H_5N$ can create a buffer solution if the number of moles of HCl added is less than the number of moles of $C_5H_5N$ present. What two species make up that buffer?

*For additional practice, work chapter problems 13-29, 13-95, and 13-97.*

► OBJECTIVE
FOR SECTION 13-9
Determine, if possible, whether a
specific oxide is acidic or basic.

# 13-9 Oxides as Acids and Bases

**LOOKING AHEAD!** We have one more important question concerning acids. How do they get into the atmosphere so as to make rain acidic? The question of acid rain is a matter of international consequence. ■

## 13-9.1 Acid Anhydrides

One of the more unfortunate consequences of the human race's progress is acid rain. Tall industrial smokestacks disperse exhaust gases high into the atmosphere, where prevailing winds may carry pollutants hundreds of miles before they return to the Earth in the form of acid rain. Since acid rain passes over the boundaries of many countries, it can be a touchy subject between nations. Its effect on lakes and forests can be devastating, and there is little doubt that the problem must be faced and solved. To understand the origin of acid rain, we will examine how the oxides of the elements also lead to acid–base behavior.

Most acid rain originates from the combustion of coal or other fossil fuels that contain sulfur as an impurity. Combustion of sulfur or sulfur compounds produces sulfur dioxide ($SO_2$). In the atmosphere, sulfur dioxide reacts with oxygen to form sulfur trioxide ($SO_3$).

$$2SO_2(g) + O_2(g) \longrightarrow 2SO_3(g)$$

The sulfur trioxide reacts with water in the atmosphere to form sulfuric acid.

$$SO_3(g) + H_2O(l) \longrightarrow H_2SO_4(aq)$$

The sulfuric acid solution that comes down in the rain is a strong acid, which is corrosive and destructive. As mentioned earlier, acids react with metals and limestone, which are both used externally in buildings. (See Figure 13-7.) In the above reaction, sulfur trioxide can be considered as simply the dehydrated form of sulfuric acid. It is thus known as an **acid anhydride**, *which means acid without water*. Many nonmetal oxides are acid anhydrides. When dissolved in water, they form acids. Three other reactions of nonmetal oxides to form acids follow.

$$CO_2(g) + H_2O(l) \rightleftharpoons \underset{\text{carbonic acid}}{H_2CO_3(aq)}$$

$$SO_2(g) + H_2O(l) \rightleftharpoons \underset{\text{sulfurous acid}}{H_2SO_3(aq)}$$

$$N_2O_5(l) + H_2O(l) \longrightarrow \underset{\text{nitric acid}}{2HNO_3(aq)}$$

We have previously mentioned that carbon dioxide, the acid anhydride of carbonic acid, is responsible for the fizz and the tangy taste in carbonated soft drinks and beer. When all the carbon dioxide escapes, the beverage goes flat. Carbon dioxide is also present in the atmosphere and dissolves in rainwater to make rain naturally acidic. Carbon dioxide by itself lowers the pH of rain to only about 5.7. Oxides of sulfur and nitrogen, however, lower the pH to 4.0 or even lower.[*] The oxides of nitrogen originate mainly from engines in automobiles and other heat sources. The high temperature in the engine causes the two elements of air, nitrogen and oxygen, to combine to form nitrogen oxides. In eastern North America and western Europe, the acidity in rain is about two-thirds due to sulfuric acid and the remainder due to nitric acid. The amount of acid rain due to nitrogen oxides seems to be growing, however. There is also a small amount of hydrochloric acid in acid rain.

**FIGURE 13-7 The Effect of Acid Rain** The deterioration of the statue is due to acid rain.

---

[*] On April 10, 1974, a rain fell on Pitlochry, Scotland, that had a pH of 2.4, which is about the same as that of vinegar. This is the most acidic rain ever recorded.

## 13-9.2 Base Anhydrides

*Ionic metal oxides dissolve in water to form bases and thus are known as* **base anhydrides**. Some examples of these reactions are

$$Na_2O(s) + H_2O(l) \longrightarrow 2NaOH(aq)$$

$$CaO(s) + H_2O(l) \longrightarrow Ca(OH)_2(aq)$$

Salt is formed by the reaction between an acid anhydride and a base anhydride. For example, the following reaction and the neutralization of $H_2SO_3$ with $Ca(OH)_2$ in aqueous solution produce the same salt.

$$SO_2(g) + CaO(s) \longrightarrow CaSO_3(s)$$

$$H_2SO_3(aq) + Ca(OH)_2(aq) \longrightarrow CaSO_3(s) + 2H_2O(l)$$

The first reaction represents a way of removing $SO_2$ from the combustion products of an industrial plant so that some of our abundant high-sulfur coal can be used without harming the environment.

---

### MAKING IT REAL

## Acid Rain—The Price of Progress?

Acid rain has had a harmful effect on the environment.

A century ago, it was inconceivable that we could actually change our planet. The human population was less than 2 billion and the world seemed vast and the environment forgiving. Now we know better. Greenhouse gases, ozone holes, and polluted water are serious problems created by people. One problem that we are doing something about is *acid rain*. Acid rain results from the presence of nonmetal oxides such as $SO_2$ and $NO_2$ in the atmosphere as industrial or automobile by-products.

In Canada and Scandinavia some lakes have been seriously affected. The pH of these lakes has become progressively lower as a result of acid rain. Fish and any other aquatic creatures have completely disappeared. In these areas of the world, the soil and rocks contain little of the types of minerals that neutralize acids, such as limestone ($CaCO_3$, the active ingredient in many antacids).

In other situations, the vulnerability of $CaCO_3$ to acid rain causes problems. Marble statues and mortar that have survived for centuries are rapidly deteriorating in the industrialized world. Various attempts are being made to protect these treasures with coatings, but so far nothing completely effective has been found.

The fertility of the soil is being affected by acid rain. Metal oxides are an integral part of the soil. These oxides are insoluble in water but become more soluble at low pH, as illustrated by the following equation.

$$Al_2O_3(s) + 6H_3O^+(aq) \longrightarrow 2Al^{3+}(aq) + 9H_2O(l)$$

Some forests in the world seem to be seriously stressed. Acid rain is the suspected culprit. In addition to oxides, many exposed metals that are not affected by ordinary rain are corroded by acid rain.

There is progress, however. There are strict limits on sulfur emissions from power plants. Catalytic converters on automobiles are reducing the nitrogen emissions. Laws are on the books and more are coming as we attempt to reverse this serious problem. These solutions do not come cheaply, however. We are all paying the billions of dollars necessary to prevent these oxides from entering the atmosphere.

Another concern about the buildup of $CO_2$ in the atmosphere is its effect on the acidity of the oceans. As the partial pressure of $CO_2$ increases in the atmosphere, more dissolves in the ocean (recall Henry's law), decreasing its pH. In fact, it has recently been reported that in the past 200 years the pH of the surface of the ocean has decreased from 8.3 to 8.2. That may not seem like much, but considering that pH is a logarithmic scale, the change represents a 20% increase in $H_3O^+$ concentration (i.e., from $5 \times 10^{-9}$ mol/L to $6 \times 10^{-9}$ mol/L). It is projected that the pH could fall to 7.7 (a 400% increase) by 2100 if the $CO_2$ concentration in the atmosphere increases as projected. It is not possible, at this time, to predict how the increased acidity of the oceans will affect the ocean's ecology or Earth's temperature. But it is a matter of grave concern.

▶ **ASSESSING THE OBJECTIVE FOR SECTION 13-9**

**EXERCISE 13-9{a} LEVEL 1:** Fill in the blanks.
Most nonmetal oxides react with water to form _____ solutions, and ionic metal oxides react with water to form _____ solutions. Compounds like $K_2O$ or $Cl_2O$ are called base or acid _____ because they contain no water.

**EXERCISE 13-9{b} LEVEL 1:** Do you expect the following to be acidic or basic?
**(a)** $P_4O_{10}$ **(b)** $NO_2$ **(c)** MgO **(d)** $B_2O_3$

**EXERCISE 13-9{c} LEVEL 2:** What acid could form directly from $SO_2$?

**EXERCISE 13-9{d} LEVEL 3:** What base could form directly from $Li_2O$?

**EXERCISE 13-9{e} LEVEL 3:** What is the problem with burning high-sulfur coal? Why would we want to do it? What can we do to remove the sulfur from the exhaust?

*For additional practice, work chapter problems 13-99 and 13-101.*

## PART C SUMMARY

### KEY TERMS

**13-7** The reaction of an ion as an acid or base in water is known as a **hydrolysis reaction**. p. 459
**13-8.1** A **buffer** is a solution that resists changes in pH and contains both a weak acid and a weak base. p. 466
**13-9.1** An **acid anhydride** is a nonmetal oxide that forms an acid in water. p. 466
**13-9.2** A **base anhydride** is a metal oxide that forms a base in water. p. 467

### SUMMARY CHART

| *The Identity of Acids and Bases* | | |
|---|---|---|
| **Type** | **Example** | **Reaction** |
| ACIDS | | |
| 1. Molecular hydrogen compounds ($H^+$ + ion) | $HClO_4$ | $HClO_4 + H_2O \longrightarrow H_3O^+ + ClO_4^-$ |
| 2. Cations (conjugate acids of weak bases) | $NH_4^+$ | $NH_4^+ + H_2O \rightleftharpoons H_3O^+ + NH_3$ |
| 3. Nonmetal oxides | $SO_3$ | $SO_3 + H_2O \longrightarrow H_2SO_4$ <br> $H_2SO_4 + H_2O \longrightarrow H_3O^+ + HSO_4^-$ |
| BASES | | |
| 1. Ionic hydroxides | $Ca(OH)_2$ | $Ca(OH)_2 \xrightarrow{H_2O} Ca^{2+} + 2OH^-$ |
| 2. Molecular nitrogen compounds | $(CH_3)_2NH$ | $(CH_3)_2NH + H_2O \rightleftharpoons (CH_3)_2NH_2^+ + OH^-$ |
| 3. Anions (conjugate bases of weak acids) | $CN^-$ | $CN^- + H_2O \rightleftharpoons HCN + OH^-$ |
| 4. Metal oxides | $K_2O$ | $K_2O + H_2O \longrightarrow 2KOH$ <br> $KOH \xrightarrow{H_2O} K^+ + OH^-$ |

### CHAPTER 13 SYNTHESIS PROBLEM

The actions of acids and bases are critical topics in many, if not most, chemical processes including life and the environmental. This chapter has helped us sort out some of these important reactions. In the following problems we will ask questions about the reactions and measurements of two hypothetical acids, one strong and one weak, and two hypothetical bases, one strong and one weak.

| PROBLEM | SOLUTION |
|---|---|
| A hypothetical strong acid has the formula HX and a hypothetical diprotic weak acid has the formula $H_2A$. ($X^-$ and $A^{2-}$ are hypothetical anions. H, as usual, is the symbol for hydrogen.) A hypothetical strong base has the formula LOH and a hypothetical weak base has the formula $NR_3$. ($L^+$ is a hypothetical cation and $NR_3$ is a nitrogen-type base like ammonia.) **a.** Write the reaction of all four of these compounds with water. Show equilibrium arrows where appropriate. | **a.** $HX(aq) + H_2O(l) \longrightarrow H_3O^+(aq) + X^-(aq)$ <br><br> $H_2A(aq) + H_2O(l) \rightleftharpoons H_3O^+(aq) + HA^-(aq)$ <br><br> $LOH(s) \xrightarrow{H_2O} L^+(aq) + OH^-(aq)$ <br><br> $NR_3(aq) + H_2O(l) \rightleftharpoons NR_3H^+(aq) + OH^-(aq)$ |
| **b.** In the reactions of HX and $NR_3$ with water, indicate the conjugate acid–base pairs. | **b.** acid (HX)–conjugate base $X^-$; base $H_2O$–conjugate acid $H_3O^+$ <br> acid $H_2O$–conjugate base $OH^-$; base $NR_3$–conjugate acid $NR_3H^+$ |
| **c.** Write four balanced neutralization reactions between the two acids and the two bases. Write the total ionic and the net ionic reaction between HX and LOH. | **c.** $HX(aq) + LOH(aq) \longrightarrow LX(aq) + H_2O(l)$ <br> $HX(aq) + NR_3(aq) \longrightarrow NR_3H^+X^-(aq)$ <br> $H_2A(aq) + 2LOH(aq) \longrightarrow L_2A(aq) + 2H_2O(l)$ <br> $H_2A(aq) + 2NR_3(aq) \longrightarrow (NR_3H)_2A(aq)$ <br> *Total ionic:* $H^+(aq) + X^-(aq) + L^+(aq) + OH^-(aq) \longrightarrow L^+(aq) + X^-(aq) + H_2O(l)$ <br> *Net ionic:* $H^+(aq) + OH^-(aq) \longrightarrow H_2O(l)$ |
| **d.** What is the $[H_3O^+]$ and the pH of 0.010-M solutions of each of the four compounds? The weak acid ($H_2A$) is 15% ionized. (Ignore the second ionization since it is very small.) The weak base is 2.5% ionized. | **d.** For HX: $[H_3O^+] = 0.010\,M = \underline{1.0 \times 10^{-2}}\,M$    $pH = -\log[1.0 \times 10^{-2}] = \underline{2.00}$ <br> For $H_2A$: $[H_3O^+] = 0.010 \times 0.15 = 0.0015\,M = 1.5 \times 10^{-3}$    $\underline{pH = 2.82}$ <br> For LOH: $[OH^-] = 0.010 = 1.0 \times 10^{-2}$ <br> $[H_3O^+] = \dfrac{Kw}{[OH^-]} = \dfrac{1.0 \times 10^{-14}}{1.0 \times 10^{-2}} = 1.0 \times 10^{-12}; \underline{pH = 12.00}$ <br> For $NR_3$: $[OH^-] = 0.010 \times 0.025 = 0.00025 = \underline{2.5 \times 10^{-4}}$ <br> $[H_3O^+] = \dfrac{1.0 \times 10^{-14}}{2.5 \times 10^{-4}} = 4.0 \times 10^{-11}; \underline{pH = 10.40}$ |
| **e.** There are four salts formed from the reactions in part **c** above. Write the formulas of these salts and describe the acidity of aqueous solutions formed when these four salts are dissolved in water. Write any hydrolysis reactions that may occur involving these four ions. | **e.** $L^+X^-$: A solution of this salt is neutral. Neither ion undergoes hydrolysis. <br> $NR_3H^+X^-(aq)$: This solution is slightly acidic due to cation hydrolysis. <br> $NR_3H^+(aq) + H_2O(l) \rightleftharpoons NR_3(aq) + H_3O^+(l)$ <br> $L_2A(aq)$: This solution is slightly basic due to anion hydrolysis. <br> $A^{2-}(aq) + H_2O(l) \rightleftharpoons HA^-(aq) + OH^-(aq)$ <br> $(NR_3H)_2A(aq)$: Both ions undergo hydrolysis but more information is needed to determine the comparative extent of the hydrolysis reactions. |
| **f.** A solution of $H_2A$ and LHA serves as a buffer solution. Illustrate with two equations how this buffer removes added $H_3O^+$ and $OH^-$ from the solution. Name another combination of acid and conjugate base that would form a buffer. | **f.** *Added acid:* $HA^-(aq) + H_3O^+(l) \longrightarrow H_2A(aq) + H_2O(l)$ <br> *Added base:* $H_2A(aq) + OH^-(aq) \longrightarrow HA^-(aq) + H_2O(l)$ <br> Another buffer would be a solution of $NR_3$ containing the salt: $NR_3H^+X^-$. |

## YOUR TURN

In this case consider two real acids, one strong HBr and the other weak $HC_2H_3O_2$. The two real bases are $Ba(OH)_2$, which is strong, and $CH_3NH_2$, which is weak.

   **a.** Write the reactions of all four species with water. Show equilibrium arrows when appropriate.

   **b.** Write acid–base conjugate pairs for the reactions involving $HC_2H_3O_2$ and $CH_3NH_2$.

   **c.** Write four neutralization reactions involving these four compounds. Write the total ionic and net ionic equations for the reaction between $HC_2H_3O_2$ and $Ba(OH)_2$.

   **d.** What is the $[H_3O^+]$ and the pH of 0.10-M solutions of these four compounds? The weak acid is 1.3% ionized and the weak base is 6.6% ionized.

   **e.** Write the formulas of the four salts formed in part **c** above and describe the acidity of solutions of these salts. Write any hydrolysis reactions that may occur involving these ions.

**f.** A solution of $CH_3NH_2$ and $CH_3NH_3^+Br^-$ is a buffer. Illustrate with two equations how this buffer removes added $H_3O^+$ and $OH^-$ from the solution.

Answers are on p. 472.

## CHAPTER SUMMARY

Compounds have been classified as acids or bases for hundreds of years on the basis of common sets of chemical characteristics. In the twentieth century, however, acid character was attributed to formation of $H^+$ [also represented as the **hydronium ion** $(H_3O^+)$] in aqueous solution. Base character is due to the formation of $OH^-$ in solution.

Our understanding of acid–base behavior can be broadened somewhat by use of the **Brønsted–Lowry** definition, which defines **acids** as proton $(H^+)$ donors and **bases** as proton acceptors. **Amphiprotic** substances can either donate or accept a proton. An acid–base reaction constitutes an $H^+$ exchange between an acid and a base to form a **conjugate base** and **conjugate acid**, respectively.

Acids and bases can also be classified according to strength. Strong acids and strong bases are 100% ionized in water, whereas **weak molecular acids** and **weak molecular bases** are only partially ionized. Partial ionization of a molecular acid occurs when a reaction reaches a point of equilibrium in which both molecules (on the left of the equation) and ions (on the right) are present. For weak molecular acids and bases, the point of equilibrium favors the left, or molecular, side of the equation. Therefore, the $H_3O^+$ concentration in a weak acid solution is considerably lower than in a strong acid solution at the same initial concentration of acid.

When acidic and basic solutions are mixed, the two active ions combine in a neutralization reaction to form water. Complete neutralization of a **monoprotic acid** results in a salt and water. Incomplete neutralization of a **polyprotic acid** (either **diprotic** or **triprotic**) produces an **acid salt** and water.

Even in pure water, there is a very small equilibrium concentration of $H_3O^+$ and $OH^-$ $(1.0 \times 10^{-7}$ M) due to the **autoionization** of water. The product of these concentrations is a constant known as the **ion product** $(K_w)$ of water. The ion product can be used to calculate the concentration of one ion from that of the other in any aqueous solution. A convenient method to express the $H_3O^+$ or $OH^-$ concentrations of solutions involves the use of the logarithmic expressions **pH** and **pOH**.

The ions of a salt may or may not interact with water as acids or bases. If such a reaction of an ion does occur, it is known as **hydrolysis**. To predict the effect of the solution of a salt on the pH, possible hydrolysis reactions of both the cation and the anion must be examined. The resulting solution may be neutral, weakly basic, or weakly acidic, depending on the ion undergoing hydrolysis.

When a solution of a weak acid is mixed with a solution of a salt, providing its conjugate base, a **buffer** solution is formed. Buffer solutions resist changes in pH from addition of limited amounts of a strong acid or base. In a buffer, the reservoir of nonionized acid (e.g., $HC_2H_3O_2$) reacts with added $OH^-$, while the reservoir of the conjugate base (e.g., $C_2H_3O_2^-$) reacts with added $H_3O^+$. Weak bases and salts providing their conjugate acids also act as buffers (e.g., $NH_3$ and $NH_4^+Cl^-$).

Finally, the list of acids and bases was expanded to include oxides, which can be classified as **acid anhydrides** or **base anhydrides**.

## OBJECTIVES

| SECTION | YOU SHOULD BE ABLE TO... | EXAMPLES | EXERCISES | CHAPTER PROBLEMS |
|---------|--------------------------|----------|-----------|------------------|
| 13-1 | List the general properties of acids and bases. | | 1a, 1b, 1c, 1d | 5, 6 |
| 13-2 | Identify Brønsted acids and bases and conjugate acid–base pairs in a proton exchange reaction. | 13-1, 13-2, 13-3 | 2a, 2b, 2c, 2d | 1, 2, 7, 8, 9, 10, 11, 14 |
| 13-3 | Calculate the hydronium ion concentration in a solution of a strong acid and a weak acid given the initial concentration of the acid and the percent ionization of the weak acid. | 13-4, 13-5 | 3a, 3b, 3c | 17, 23, 24, 26, 29 |
| 13-4 | Write the molecular, total ionic, and net ionic equations for neutralization reactions. | 13-6, 13-7 | 4a, 4b, 4c, 4d | 18, 19, 21, 33, 34, 35, 36, 40, 42, 45 |
| 13-5 | Using the ion product of water, relate the hydroxide ion and the hydronium ion concentrations. | 13-8 | 5a, 5b, 5c | 52, 53, 54, 56 |
| 13-6 | Given the hydronium or hydroxide concentrations, calculate the pH and pOH and vice versa. | 13-9, 13-10, 13-11, 13-12 | 6a, 6b, 6c, 6d, 6e, 6f | 60, 62, 64, 66, 67, 70, 73, 76 |

| 13-7 | Write a hydrolysis reaction, if one occurs, for salt solutions to determine whether they are acidic or basic. | 13-13 | 7a, 7b, 7c, 7d, 7e, 7f | 31, 79, 82, 84, 86, 87, 88 |
| 13-8 | Write equations illustrating how a buffer solution can absorb either added acid or base. | | 8a, 8b, 8c, 8d, 8e | 92, 94, 95, 97, 98 |
| 13-9 | Determine, if possible, whether a specific oxide is acidic or basic. | | 9a, 9b, 9c, 9d, 9e | 99, 100 |

# ▶ ANSWERS TO ASSESSING THE OBJECTIVES

## Part A
### EXERCISES

**13-1(a)** An acid is a compound that produces the <u>hydrogen</u> ion in solution, which is also written as the hydronium ion ($H_3O^+$). A base is a compound that produces an ion with the formula <u>$OH^-$</u> and the name <u>hydroxide</u> ion.

**13-1(b)** (a) $HClO_4$, perchloric acid (b) $Fe(OH)_2$, iron(II) hydroxide (c) $H_2S$, hydrosulfuric acid (d) $LiOH$, lithium hydroxide

**13-1(c)** (a) $HI + H_2O \longrightarrow H_3O^+ + I^-$

(b) $LiOH + H_2O \longrightarrow Li^+(aq) + OH^-(aq)$

**13-1(d)** (a) base (b) acid (c) acid (d) base (e) base (f) base

**13-2(a)** In the Brønsted–Lowry definition, acids are <u>proton</u> donors and bases are <u>proton</u> acceptors. A conjugate acid of a compound or ion results from the <u>exchange</u> of an <u>$H^+$</u> ion. A substance that has both a conjugate acid and a conjugate base is said to be <u>amphiprotic</u>.

**13-2(b)** acid: $NH_4^+$; base: $SO_3^{2-}$

**13-2(c)** acid: $H_2C_2O_4$; base: $C_2O_4^{2-}$

**13-2(d)** (a) $HCO_3^- + H_2O \longrightarrow CO_3^{2-} + H_3O^+$

(b) $HCO_3^- + H_2O \longrightarrow H_2CO_3 + OH^-$

**13-2(e)** $CH_3COOH + (CH_3)_3N \longrightarrow CH_3COO^- + (CH_3)_3NH^+$. The two sets of conjugate acid–base pairs are $CH_3COOH–CH_3COO^-$ and $(CH_3)_3NH^+–(CH_3)_3N$

**13-2(f)** $NH_2^- + CH_3OH \longrightarrow NH_3 + CH_3O^-$

**13-3(a)** Strong acids are essentially <u>100</u> % ionized in aqueous solution, whereas weak acids are <u>partially</u> ionized. Sodium hydroxide is a strong base, but ammonia is a <u>weak base</u>. When a weak acid reacts with water, the reaction is said to be at <u>equilibrium</u>.

**13-3(b)** This is a weak acid. $[H_3O^+] = 0.10 \times 0.025 = 0.0025$ M.

**13-3(c)** Since the hydronium concentration is less than the original acid concentration, this is a weak acid. The percent ionization $= 0.0050 \times 100/.25 = 2.0\%$.

**13-3(d)** (a) $HNO_3 + H_2O \longrightarrow H_3O^+ + NO_3^-$

(b) $HNO_2 + H_2O \rightleftharpoons H_3O^+ + NO_2^-$

(c) $HClO_2 + H_2O \rightleftharpoons H_3O^+ + ClO_2^-$

(d) $HClO_4 + H_2O \longrightarrow H_3O^+ + ClO_4^-$

**13-4(a)** The reaction between an acid and a base is known as a <u>neutralization</u> reaction. The net ionic equation of this reaction always has $H_2O$ as a product. The spectator ions of the reaction form a <u>salt</u>. The partial neutralization of polyprotic acids produces an <u>acid salt</u> and water.

**13-4(b)**

*Molecular:* $2HNO_3(aq) + Sr(OH)_2(aq) \longrightarrow$
$$2H_2O(l) + Sr(NO_3)_2(aq)$$

*Total Ionic:* $2H^+(aq) + 2NO_3^-(aq) + Sr^{2+}(aq) + 2OH^-(aq) \longrightarrow$
$$2H_2O(l) + Sr^{2+}(aq) + 2NO_3^-(aq)$$

*Net Ionic:* $H^+(aq) + OH^-(aq) \longrightarrow H_2O(l)$

**13-4(c)**

*Molecular:* $NH_3(aq) + HCl(aq) \longrightarrow NH_4Cl(aq)$

*Total Ionic:* $NH_3(aq) + H^+(aq) + Cl^-(aq) \longrightarrow$
$$NH_4^+(aq) + Cl^-(aq)$$

*Net Ionic:* $NH_3(aq) + H^+(aq) \longrightarrow NH_4^+(aq)$

**13-4(d)** (a) *Molecular:* $H_2C_2O_4(aq) + CsOH(aq) \longrightarrow$
$$CsHC_2O_4(aq) + H_2O(l)$$

*Total Ionic:* $H_2C_2O_4(aq) + Cs^+(aq) + OH^-(aq) \longrightarrow$
$$Cs^+(aq) + HC_2O_4^-(aq) + H_2O(l)$$

*Net Ionic:* $H_2C_2O_4(aq) + OH^-(aq) \longrightarrow HC_2O_4^-(aq) + H_2O(l)$

(b) *Molecular:* $H_2C_2O_4(aq) + 2CsOH(aq) \longrightarrow$
$$Cs_2C_2O_4(aq) + 2H_2O(l)$$

*Total Ionic:* $H_2C_2O_4(aq) + 2Cs^+(aq) + 2OH^-(aq) \longrightarrow$
$$2Cs^+(aq) + C_2O_4^{2-}(aq) + 2H_2O(l)$$

*Net Ionic:* $H_2C_2O_4(aq) + 2OH^-(aq) \longrightarrow C_2O_4^{2-}(aq) + 2H_2O(l)$

**13-4(e)** (a) $H_2SO_4 + 2KOH$ (b) $H_2SO_4 + KOH$ (c) $NH_3 + HCl$

## Part B
### EXERCISES

**13-5(a)** Pure water contains a small but important concentration of $H_3O^+$ and $OH^-$ ions. The product of the concentrations of these two ions, known as the <u>ion product</u> of water, is symbolized by $K_w$ and has a value of <u>$1 \times 10^{-14}$</u> at 25°C. As the concentration of <u>$OH^-$</u> increases in water, the concentration of $H_3O^+$ <u>decreases</u>.

**13-5(b)** $(1.0 \times 10^{-14})/(7.2 \times 10^{-5}) = 1.4 \times 10^{-10}$ M

**13-5(c)** $[OH^-] = 0.00050$ M $= 5.0 \times 10^{-4}$ M   $[H_3O^+] = 2.0 \times 10^{-11}$ M

**13-5(d)** $[OH^-]$ is larger than $1.0 \times 10^{-7}$, so the solution is basic. It would need to be close to $10^{-1}$ to be considered strongly basic, so this is weakly basic. A common weak base that could produce that solution would be $NH_3$.

**13-6(a)** The pH of a solution is defined as $-\log [H_3O^+]$. An acidic solution is one that has an $[H_3O^+]$ greater than $1 \times 10^{-7}$ and a pH <u>less</u> than 7. A basic solution is one that has an $[OH^-]$ greater than $1 \times 10^{-7}$ and a pH <u>greater</u> than 7.

**13-6(b)** pH $= 9.86$

**13-6{c}** $[LiOH] = 0.25$

**13-6{d}** **(a)** 11.80 **(b)** 0.0063 M $H_3O^+$ **(c)** $1.6 \times 10^{-12}$ M $OH^-$

**13-6{e}** **(a)** $1.3 \times 10^{-13}$ M $H_3O^+$ **(b)** 0.075 M $OH^-$
**(c)** pH = 12.88 **(d)** pOH = 1.12

**13-6{f}** The HCl is a strong acid and the $H_3O^+$ is determined directly from the concentration of acid. It is 0.005 M, and the pH is 2.3. The acetic acid's $H_3O^+$ comes only from the part that is ionized, or 0.0008 M, which is about six times less than the HCl solution. The pH of the second solution is 3.1.

## Part C
### EXERCISES

**13-7{a}** **(a)** acidic **(b)** neutral **(c)** basic **(d)** more information is needed

**13-7{b}** **(a)** basic **(b)** acidic **(c)** neutral **(d)** basic

**13-7{c}** **(a)** $CO_3^{2-} + H_2O \rightleftharpoons HCO_3^- + OH^-$

**(b)** No hydrolysis is occurring.

**(c)** $N_2H_5^+ + H_2O \rightleftharpoons N_2H_4 + H_3O^+$

**13-7{d}** Any weak acid would work, such as $HC_2H_3O_2$, $HClO_2$, $HNO_2$, or HF.

**13-7{e}** Any strong acid would work, such as HCl, $HNO_3$, or $H_2SO_4$.

**13-7{f}** $HSO_4^- + H_2O \rightleftharpoons H_3O^+ + SO_4^{2-}$

It can't produce hydroxide because the conjugate acid, sulfuric acid, is strong. Therefore, $HSO_4^-$ has no basic properties.

**13-8{a}** A buffer solution consists of a weak acid and a salt of its <u>conjugate base</u>. Buffer solutions resist a change in <u>pH</u> because any hydronium is neutralized with the <u>base</u> and any hydroxide is neutralized with the <u>acid</u>. The <u>buffer capacity</u> is a measure of how much strong acid or strong base the buffer can absorb.

**13-8{b}** Possible buffers include **(b)** and **(c)**.

**13-8{c}** **(a)** $NH_4Cl$ **(b)** $NaHSO_3$ **(c)** $KClO_2$

**13-8{d}** **(a)** $H_3O^+ + HC_2O_4^- \longrightarrow H_2C_2O_4 + H_2O$
**(b)** $OH^- + H_2C_2O_4 \longrightarrow HC_2O_4^- + H_2O$

**13-8{e}** $C_5H_5NH^+Cl^-$ (the weakly acidic salt) and $C_5H_5N$ (the weak base)

**13-9{a}** Most nonmetal oxides react with water to form <u>acidic</u> solutions, and ionic metal oxides react with water to form <u>basic</u> solutions. Compounds like $K_2O$ or $Cl_2O$ are called base or acid <u>anhydrides</u> because they contain no water.

**13-9{b}** **(a)** acidic **(b)** acidic **(c)** basic **(d)** acidic

**13-9{c}** $H_2SO_3$

**13-9{d}** LiOH

**13-9{e}** High-sulfur coal releases $SO_2$ into the environment, which can lead to the formation of acid rain. High-sulfur coal, though, is abundant and therefore costs less. To keep the $SO_2$ out of the environment, we can use scrubbers that react the acid anhydride $SO_2$ with the base anhydride CaO to form the insoluble salt $CaSO_3$.

## ANSWERS TO CHAPTER SYNTHESIS PROBLEM

**a.** $HBr(aq) + H_2O(l) \longrightarrow H_3O^+(aq) + Br^-(aq)$
$HC_2H_3O_2(aq) + H_2O(l) \rightleftharpoons$
$\qquad H_3O^+(aq) + C_2H_3O_2^-(aq)$
$Ba(OH)_2(s) \xrightarrow{H_2O} Ba^{2+}(aq) + 2\,OH^-(aq)$
$CH_3NH_2(aq) + H_2O(l) \rightleftharpoons$
$\qquad CH_3NH_3^+(aq) + OH^-(aq)$

**b.** acid ($HC_2H_3O_2$)–conjugate base $C_2H_3O_2^-$; base $H_2O$–conjugate acid $H_3O^+$ acid $H_2O$–conjugate base $OH^-$; base $CH_3NH_2$–conjugate acid $CH_3NH_3^+$

**c.** $2HBr(aq) + Ba(OH)_2(aq) \longrightarrow$
$\qquad\qquad BaBr_2(aq) + 2H_2O(l)$
$HBr(aq) + CH_3NH_2(aq) \longrightarrow$
$\qquad\qquad CH_3NH_3^+Br^-(aq)$
$2HC_2H_3O_2(aq) + Ba(OH)_2(aq) \longrightarrow$
$\qquad\qquad Ba(C_2H_3O_2)_2(aq) + 2H_2O(l)$
$HC_2H_3O_2(aq) + CH_3NH_2 \longrightarrow$
$\qquad\qquad CH_3NH_3^+C_2H_3O_2^-(aq)$
*Total ionic:*
$2HC_2H_3O_2(aq) + Ba^{2+}(aq) + 2OH^-(aq)$
$\qquad \longrightarrow Ba^{2+}(aq) + 2C_2H_3O_2^-(aq) + 2H_2O(l)$
*Net ionic:* $2HC_2H_3O_2(aq) + 2OH^-(aq)$
$\qquad \longrightarrow 2C_2H_3O_2^-(aq) + 2H_2O(l)$

**d.** For HBr: $[H_3O^+] = 1.0 \times 10^{-1}$ M pH = <u>1.00</u>
For $HC_2H_3O_2$: $[H_3O^+] = 1.3 \times 10^{-3}$ M pH = <u>2.89</u>
For $Ba(OH)_2$: $[OH^-] = 0.10 \times 2 =$
$\qquad 2.0 \times 10^{-1}$ $[H_3O^+] = 5.0 \times 10^{-14}$;
$\qquad$ pH = <u>13.30</u>
For $CH_3NH_2$: $[OH^-] = 0.0066$ M $[H_3O^+] =$
$\qquad 1.5 \times 10^{-12}$ pH = <u>11.82</u>

**e.** $BaBr_2$: A solution of this salt is neutral. Neither ion undergoes hydrolysis.
$CH_3NH_3^+Br^-(aq)$: This solution is slightly acidic due to cation hydrolysis.
$CH_3NH_3^+(aq) + H_2O(l) \rightleftharpoons$
$\qquad CH_3NH_2(aq) + H_3O^+(l)$
$Ba(C_2H_3O_2)_2(aq)$: This solution is slightly basic due to anion hydrolysis.
$C_2H_3O_2^-(aq) + H_2O(l) \rightleftharpoons$
$\qquad HC_2H_3O_2(aq) + OH^-(aq)$
$CH_3NH_3^+C_2H_3O_2^-(aq)$: Both ions undergo hydrolysis but more information is needed to determine the comparative extent of the hydrolysis reactions.

**f.** *Added acid:* $CH_3NH_2(aq) + H_3O^+(l)$
$\qquad \longrightarrow CH_3NH_3^+(aq) + H_2O(l)$
*Added base:* $CH_3NH_3^+(aq) + OH^-(aq)$
$\qquad \longrightarrow CH_3NH_2(aq) + H_2O(l)$

# CHAPTER PROBLEMS

*Throughout the text, answers to all exercises in color are given in Appendix E. The more difficult exercises are marked with an asterisk.*

## Acids and Bases (SECTION 13-1)

**13-1.** Give the formulas and names of the acid compounds derived from the following anions.

(a) $NO_3^-$  (b) $NO_2^-$  (c) $ClO_3^-$  (d) $SO_3^{2-}$

**13-2.** Give the formulas and names of the acid compounds derived from the following anions.

(a) $CN^-$  (b) $CrO_4^{2-}$  (c) $ClO_4^-$  (d) $Br^-$

**13-3.** Give the formulas and names of the base compounds derived from the following cations.

(a) $Cs^+$  (b) $Sr^{2+}$  (c) $Al^{3+}$  (d) $Mn^{3+}$

**13-4.** Give the formulas and names of the acid or base compounds derived from the following ions.

(a) $Ba^{2+}$  (c) $Pb^{2+}$  (e) $H_2PO_4^-$
(b) $Se^{2-}$  (d) $ClO^-$  (f) $Fe^{3+}$

**13-5.** Write reactions illustrating the acid or base behavior in water for the following.

(a) $HNO_3$  (b) $CsOH$  (c) $Ba(OH)_2$  (d) $HBr$

**13-6.** Write reactions illustrating the acid or base behavior in water for the following.

(a) $HI$  (b) $Sr(OH)_2$  (c) $RbOH$  (d) $HClO_4$

## Brønsted–Lowry Acids and Bases (SECTION 13-2)

**13-7.** What is the conjugate base of each of the following?

(a) $HNO_3$  (c) $HPO_4^{2-}$  (e) $H_2O$
(b) $H_2SO_4$  (d) $CH_4$  (f) $NH_3$

**13-8.** What is the conjugate acid of each of the following?

(a) $CH_3NH_2$  (c) $NO_3^-$  (e) $H^+$
(b) $HPO_4^{2-}$  (d) $O^{2-}$  (f) $H_2O$

**13-9.** Identify conjugate acid-base pairs in the following reactions.

(a) $HClO_4 + OH^- \longrightarrow H_2O + ClO_4^-$
(b) $HSO_4^- + ClO^- \longrightarrow HClO + SO_4^{2-}$
(c) $H_2O + NH_2^- \longrightarrow NH_3 + OH^-$
(d) $NH_4^+ + H_2O \longrightarrow NH_3 + H_3O^+$

**13-10.** Identify conjugate acid-base pairs in the following reactions.

(a) $HCN + H_2O \longrightarrow H_3O^+ + CN^-$
(b) $HClO_4 + NO_3^- \longrightarrow HNO_3 + ClO_4^-$
(c) $H_2S + NH_3 \longrightarrow NH_4^+ + HS^-$
(d) $H_3O^+ + HCO_3^- \longrightarrow H_2CO_3 + H_2O$

**13-11.** Write reactions indicating Brønsted–Lowry acid behavior with $H_2O$ for the following. Indicate conjugate acid-base pairs.

(a) $H_2SO_3$  (c) $HBr$  (e) $H_2S$
(b) $HClO$  (d) $HSO_3^-$  (f) $NH_4^+$

**13-12.** Write reactions indicating Brønsted–Lowry base behavior with $H_2O$ for the following. Indicate conjugate acid-base pairs.

(a) $NH_3$  (c) $HS^-$  (e) $F^-$
(b) $N_2H_4$  (d) $H^-$

**13-13.** Write equations showing how $HS^-$ can act as a Brønsted–Lowry base with $H_3O^+$ and as a Brønsted–Lowry acid with $OH^-$.

**13-14.** Bicarbonate of soda ($NaHCO_3$) acts as an antacid (base) in water. Write an equation illustrating how the $HCO_3^-$ ion reacts with $H_3O^+$. Bicarbonate is amphiprotic. Write the reaction illustrating its behavior as an acid in water.

## Strengths of Acids and Bases (SECTION 13-3)

**13-15.** Describe how a strong acid and a weak acid relate and differ.

**13-16.** When HBr ionizes in water, the reaction is 100% complete. Write the equation illustrating how HBr behaves as an acid. What does this tell us about the strength of the acid? An accepted observation is that *the stronger the acid, the weaker its conjugate base.* Compare the strength of HBr as a proton donor with $Br^-$ as a proton acceptor.

**13-17.** Solutions of $HClO_2$ indicate that the ionization is very limited. Write the reaction illustrating how $HClO_2$ behaves as an acid. What does this tell us about the strength of the acid and the strength of its conjugate base?

**13-18.** Write equations illustrating the reactions with water of the acids formed in problem 13-1. Indicate strong acids with a single arrow and weak acids with equilibrium arrows.

**13-19.** Write equations illustrating the reactions with water of the acids formed in problem 13-2. Indicate strong acids with a single arrow and weak acids with equilibrium arrows.

**13-20.** Dimethylamine $[(CH_3)_2NH]$ is a weak base that reacts in water like ammonia ($NH_3$). Write the equilibrium illustrating this reaction.

**13-21.** Pyridine ($C_5H_5N$) behaves as a weak base in water like ammonia. Write the equilibrium illustrating this reaction.

**13-22.** The concentration of a monoprotic acid (HX) in water is 0.10 M. The concentration of $H_3O^+$ ion in this solution is 0.010 M. Is HX a weak or a strong acid? What percent of the acid is ionized?

**13-23.** A 0.50-mol quantity of an acid is dissolved in 2.0 L of water. In the solution, $[H_3O^+] = 0.25$. Is this a strong or a weak acid? Explain.

**13-24.** What is $[H_3O^+]$ in a 0.55 M $HClO_4$ solution?

**13-25.** What is $[H_3O^+]$ in a 0.55 M solution of a weak acid, HX, that is 3.0% ionized?

**13-26.** What is $[OH^-]$ in a 1.45 M solution of $NH_3$ if the $NH_3$ is 0.95% ionized?

**\*13-27.** What is $[H_3O^+]$ in a 0.354 M solution of $H_2SO_4$? Assume that the first ionization is complete but that the second is only 25% complete.

**13-28.** A 1.0 M solution of HF has $[H_3O^+] = 0.050$. What is the percent ionization of the acid?

**13-29.** A 0.10 M solution of pyridine (a weak base in water) has $[OH^-] = 4.4 \times 10^{-5}$. What is the percent ionization of the base?

13-30. The $HSO_4^-$ ion is not amphiprotic in water. Which species cannot exist in water—its conjugate base or conjugate acid? Why not?

## Neutralization and Salts (SECTION 13-4)

13-31. Identify each of the following as an acid, base, salt, or acid salt.

(a) $H_2S$     (c) $H_3AsO_4$     (e) $KNO_3$

(b) $BaCl_2$     (d) $Ba(HSO_4)_2$     (f) $LiOH$

13-32. Explain why a strong acid is represented in aqueous solution as two ions but a weak acid is represented as one molecule.

13-33. Write the balanced molecular equations showing the complete neutralizations of the following.

(a) $HNO_3$ by $NaOH$     (c) $HClO_2$ by $KOH$

(b) $Ca(OH)_2$ by $HI$

13-34. Write the balanced molecular equations showing the complete neutralizations of the following.

(a) $HNO_2$ by $NaOH$     (c) $H_2S$ by $Ba(OH)_2$

(b) $H_2CO_3$ by $CsOH$

13-35. Write the total ionic and net ionic equations for the reactions in problem 13-33.

13-36. Write the total ionic and net ionic equations for the reactions in problem 13-34.

13-37. Write the molecular, total ionic, and net ionic equations of the complete neutralization of $H_2C_2O_4$ with $NH_3$.

13-38. Write the molecular, total ionic, and net ionic equations for the complete neutralization of $HC_2H_3O_2$ with $NH_3$.

13-39. Write the formulas of the acid and the base that formed the following salts.

(a) $KClO_3$     (c) $Ba(NO_2)_2$

(b) $Al_2(SO_3)_3$     (d) $NH_4NO_3$

13-40. Write the formulas of the acid and the base that formed the following salts.

(a) $Li_2CrO_4$     (c) $Fe(ClO_4)_3$

(b) $NaCN$     (d) $Mg(HCO_3)_2$

13-41. Write balanced acid-base neutralization reactions that would lead to formation of the following salts or acid salts.

(a) $CaBr_2$     (c) $Ba(HS)_2$

(b) $Sr(ClO_2)_2$     (d) $Li_2S$

13-42. Write balanced acid-base neutralization reactions that would lead to formation of the following salts or acid salts.

(a) $Na_2SO_3$     (c) $Mg_3(PO_4)_2$

(b) $AlI_3$     (d) $NaHCO_3$

13-43. Write two equations illustrating the stepwise neutralization of $H_2S$ with $LiOH$.

13-44. Write the two net ionic equations illustrating the two reactions in problem 13-43.

13-45. Write three equations illustrating the stepwise neutralization of $H_3AsO_4$ with $LiOH$. Write the total reaction.

13-46. Write the net ionic equations for the three reactions in problem 13-45.

13-47. Write the equation illustrating the reaction of 1 mol of $H_2S$ with 1 mol of $NaOH$.

*13-48. Write the equation illustrating the reaction between 1 mol of $Ca(OH)_2$ and 2 mol of $H_3PO_4$.

## Equilibrium of Water and $K_w$ (SECTION 13-5)

13-49. If some ions are present in pure water, why isn't pure water considered to be an electrolyte?

13-50. Why can't $[H_3O^+] = [OH^-] = 1.0 \times 10^{-2}$ in water? What would happen if we tried to make such a solution by mixing $10^{-2}$ mol/L of $KOH$ with $10^{-2}$ mol/L of $HCl$?

13-51. (a) What is $[H_3O^+]$ when $[OH^-] = 10^{-12}$ M?

(b) What is $[H_3O^+]$ when $[OH^-] = 10$ M?

(c) What is $[OH^-]$ when $[H_3O^+] = 2.0 \times 10^{-5}$ M?

13-52. (a) What is $[OH^-]$ when $[H_3O^+] = 1.50 \times 10^{-3}$ M?

(b) What is $[H_3O^+]$ when $[OH^-] = 2.58 \times 10^{-7}$ M?

(c) What is $[H_3O^+]$ when $[OH^-] = 5.69 \times 10^{-8}$ M?

13-53. When 0.250 mol of the strong acid $HClO_4$ is dissolved in 10.0 L of water, what is $[H_3O^+]$? What is $[OH^-]$?

13-54. Lye is a very strong base. What is $[H_3O^+]$ in a 2.55 M solution of $NaOH$? In the weakly basic household ammonia, $[OH^-] = 4.0 \times 10^{-3}$ M. What is $[H_3O^+]$?

13-55. Identify the solutions in problem 13-51 as acidic, basic, or neutral.

13-56. Identify the solutions in problem 13-52 as acidic, basic, or neutral.

13-57. Identify each of the following as an acidic, basic, or neutral solution.

(a) $[H_3O^+] = 6.5 \times 10^{-3}$ M     (c) $[OH^-] = 4.5 \times 10^{-8}$ M

(b) $[H_3O^+] = 5.5 \times 10^{-10}$ M     (d) $[OH^-] = 50 \times 10^{-8}$ M

13-58. Identify each of the following as an acidic, basic, or neutral solution.

(a) $[OH^-] = 8.1 \times 10^{-8}$ M     (c) $[H_3O^+] = 4.0 \times 10^{-3}$ M

(b) $[H_3O^+] = 10.0 \times 10^{-8}$ M     (d) $[OH^-] = 55 \times 10^{-8}$ M

## pH and pOH (SECTION 13-6)

13-59. What is the pH of the following solutions?

(a) $[H_3O^+] = 1.0 \times 10^{-6}$ M     (d) $[OH^-] = 2.5 \times 10^{-5}$ M

(b) $[H_3O^+] = 1.0 \times 10^{-9}$ M     (e) $[H_3O^+] = 6.5 \times 10^{-11}$ M

(c) $[OH^-] = 1.0 \times 10^{-2}$ M

13-60. What is the pH of the following solutions?

(a) $[H_3O^+] = 1.0 \times 10^{-2}$ M    (d) $[OH^-] = 3.6 \times 10^{-9}$ M

(b) $[OH^-] = 1.0 \times 10^{-4}$ M    (e) $[OH^-] = 7.8 \times 10^{-4}$ M

(c) $[H_3O^+] = 1.0$ M    (f) $[H_3O^+] = 4.22 \times 10^{-4}$ M

13-61. What are the pH and pOH of the following?

(a) $[H_3O^+] = 0.0001$     (c) $[H_3O^+] = 0.020$

(b) $[OH^-] = 0.00001$     (d) $[OH^-] = 0.000320$

**13-62.** What are the pH and pOH of the following?

**(a)** $[H_3O^+] = 0.0000001$ **(c)** $[OH^-] = 0.0568$

**(b)** $[OH^-] = 0.0001$ **(d)** $[H_3O^+] = 0.00082$

**13-63.** What is $[H_3O^+]$ of the following?

**(a)** pH = 3.00 **(d)** pOH = 6.38

**(b)** pH = 3.54 **(e)** pH = 12.70

**(c)** pOH = 8.00

**13-64.** What is $[H_3O^+]$ of the following?

**(a)** pH = 9.0 **(c)** pH = 2.30

**(b)** pOH = 9.0 **(d)** pH = 8.90

**13-65.** Identify each of the solutions in problems 13-59 and 13-63 as acidic, basic, or neutral.

**13-66.** Identify each of the solutions in problems 13-60 and 13-64 as acidic, basic, or neutral.

**13-67.** A solution has pH = 3.0. What is the pH of a solution that is 100 times less acidic? What is the pH of a solution that is 10 times more acidic?

**13-68.** A solution has pOH = 4. What is the pOH of a solution that is 1000 times more acidic? What is the pOH of a solution that is 100 times more basic?

**13-69.** What is the pH of a 0.075 M solution of the strong acid $HNO_3$?

**13-70.** What is the pH of a 0.0034 M solution of the strong base KOH?

**13-71.** What is the pH of a 0.018 M solution of the strong base $Ca(OH)_2$?

**13-72.** A weak monoprotic acid is 10.0% ionized in solution. What is the pH of a 0.10 M solution of this acid?

**13-73.** A weak base is 5.0% ionized in solution. What is the pH of a 0.25 M solution of this base? (Assume one $OH^-$ per formula unit.)

**13-74.** Identify each of the following solutions as strongly basic, weakly basic, neutral, weakly acidic, or strongly acidic.

**(a)** pH = 1.5 **(d)** pH = 13.0 **(g)** pOH = 7.5

**(b)** pOH = 13.0 **(e)** pOH = 7.0 **(h)** pH = −1.0

**(c)** pH = 5.8 **(f)** pH = 8.5

**13-75.** Arrange the following substances in order of increasing acidity.

**(a)** household ammonia, pH = 11.4

**(b)** vinegar, $[H_3O^+] = 2.5 \times 10^{-3}$ M

**(c)** grape juice, $[OH^-] = 1.0 \times 10^{-10}$ M

**(d)** sulfuric acid, pOH = 13.6

**(e)** eggs, pH = 7.8

**(f)** rainwater, $[H_3O^+] = 2.0 \times 10^{-6}$ M

**13-76.** Arrange the following substances in order of increasing acidity.

**(a)** lime juice, $[H_3O^+] = 6.0 \times 10^{-2}$ M

**(b)** antacid tablet in water, $[OH^-] = 2.5 \times 10^{-6}$ M

**(c)** coffee, pOH = 8.50

**(d)** stomach acid, pH = 1.8

**(e)** saliva, $[H_3O^+] = 2.2 \times 10^{-7}$ M

**(f)** a soap solution, pH = 8.3

**(g)** a solution of lye, pOH = 1.2

**(h)** a banana, $[OH^-] = 4.0 \times 10^{-10}$ M

***13-77.** What is the pH of a 0.0010 M solution of $H_2SO_4$? (Assume that the first ionization is complete but the second is only 25% complete.)

## Hydrolysis of Salts (SECTION 13-7)

**13-78.** Two of the following act as weak bases in water. Write the appropriate reactions illustrating the weak base behavior.

**(a)** $ClO_4^-$ **(b)** $C_2H_3O_2^-$ **(c)** $NH_3$ **(d)** HF

**13-79.** Two of the following act as weak acids in water. Write the appropriate reactions illustrating the weak acid behavior.

**(a)** $H_2CrO_4$ **(b)** $NH_4^+$ **(c)** $NH_2CH_3$ **(d)** $CrO_4^{2-}$

**13-80.** Three of the following molecules or ions do not affect the pH of water. Which are they and why do they not affect the pH?

**(a)** $K^+$ **(c)** $HCO_3^-$ **(e)** $O_2$

**(b)** $NH_3$ **(d)** $NO_3^-$ **(f)** $N_2H_5^+$

**13-81.** Complete the following hydrolysis equilibria.

**(a)** $S^{2-} + H_2O \rightleftharpoons \_\_\_\_ + OH^-$

**(b)** $N_2H_5^+ + H_2O \rightleftharpoons N_2H_4 + \_\_\_\_$

**(c)** $HPO_4^{2-} + H_2O \rightleftharpoons H_2PO_4^- + \_\_\_\_$

**(d)** $(CH_3)_2NH_2^+ + H_2O \rightleftharpoons \_\_\_\_ + H_3O^+$

**13-82.** Complete the following hydrolysis equilibria.

**(a)** $CN^- + H_2O \rightleftharpoons HCN + \_\_\_\_$

**(b)** $NH_4^+ + H_2O \rightleftharpoons \_\_\_\_ + H_3O^+$

**(c)** $B(OH)_4^- + H_2O \rightleftharpoons H_3BO_3 + \_\_\_\_$

**(d)** $Al(H_2O)_6^{3+} + H_2O \rightleftharpoons Al(H_2O)_5(OH)^{2+} + \_\_\_\_$

**13-83.** Write the hydrolysis equilibria (if any) for the following ions.

**(a)** $F^-$ **(d)** $HPO_4^{2-}$

**(b)** $SO_3^{2-}$ **(e)** $CN^-$

**(c)** $(CH_3)_2NH_2^+[(CH_3)_2NH]$ **(f)** $Li^+$

[is a weak base like ammonia.]

**13-84.** Write the hydrolysis equilibria (if any) for the following ions.

**(a)** $Br^-$ **(b)** $HS^-$ **(c)** $ClO_4^-$ **(d)** $H^-$ **(e)** $Ca^{2+}$

**13-85.** Calcium hypochlorite is used to purify water. When dissolved, it produces a slightly basic solution. Write the equation illustrating the solution of calcium hypochlorite in water and the equation illustrating its basic behavior.

**13-86.** Aqueous NaF solutions are slightly basic, whereas aqueous NaCl solutions are neutral. Write the appropriate equation that illustrates this. Why aren't NaCl solutions also basic?

**13-87.** Predict whether aqueous solutions of the following salts are acidic, neutral, or basic.

**(a)** $Ba(ClO_4)_2$ **(d)** KBr

**(b)** $N_2H_5^+NO_3^-$ ($N_2H_4$ is a weak base.) **(e)** $NH_4Cl$

**(c)** $LiC_2H_3O_2$ **(f)** $BaF_2$

**13-88.** Predict whether aqueous solutions of the following salts are acidic, neutral, or basic.

**(a)** $Na_2CO_3$ **(b)** $K_3PO_4$ **(c)** $NH_4ClO_4$ **(d)** $SrI_2$

*13-89. Both $C_2^{2-}$ and its conjugate acid $HC_2^-$ hydrolyze 100% in water. From this information, complete the following equation.

$$CaC_2(s) + 2H_2O(l) \longrightarrow \underline{\quad}(g) + Ca^{2+}(aq) + 2\underline{\quad}(aq)$$

(The gas formed—acetylene—can be burned as it is produced. This reaction was once important for this purpose as a source of light in old miners' lamps.)

*13-90. Aqueous solutions of $NH_4CN$ are basic. Write the two hydrolysis reactions and indicate which takes place to the greater extent.

13-91. Aqueous solutions of $NaHSO_3$ are acidic. Write the two equations (one hydrolysis and one ionization) and indicate which takes place to the greater extent.

## Buffers (SECTION 13-9)

13-92. Identify which of the following form buffer solutions when 0.50 mol of each compound is dissolved in 1 L of water.

(a) $HNO_2$ and $KNO_2$      (f) HCN and KClO

(b) $NH_4Cl$ and $NH_3$      (g) $NH_3$ and $BaBr_2$

(c) $HNO_3$ and $KNO_2$      (h) $H_2S$ and LiHS

(d) $HNO_3$ and $KNO_3$      (i) $KH_2PO_4$ and $K_2HPO_4$

(e) HClO and $Ca(ClO)_2$

13-93. A certain solution contains dissolved HCl and NaCl. Why can't this solution act as a buffer?

13-94. Write the equilibrium involved in the $N_2H_4$, $N_2H_5Cl$ buffer system. ($N_2H_4$ is a weak base.) Write equations illustrating how this system reacts with added $H_3O^+$ and added $OH^-$.

13-95. Write the equilibrium involved in the $HCO_3^-$, $CO_3^{2-}$ buffer system. Write equations illustrating how this system reacts with added $H_3O^+$ and added $OH^-$.

13-96. Write the equilibrium involved in the $HPO_4^{2-}$, $PO_4^{3-}$ buffer system. Write equations illustrating how this system reacts with added $H_3O^+$ and added $OH^-$.

13-97. If 0.5 mol of KOH is added to a solution containing 1.0 mol of $HC_2H_3O_2$, the resulting solution is a buffer. Explain.

13-98. A solution contains 0.50 mol each of HClO and NaClO. If 0.60 mol of KOH is added, will the buffer prevent a significant change in pH? Explain.

## Oxides as Acids and Bases (SECTION 13-9)

13-99. Write the formula of the acid or base formed when each of the following anhydrides is dissolved in water.

(a) SrO      (c) $P_4O_{10}$      (e) $N_2O_3$

(b) $SeO_3$      (d) $Cs_2O$      (f) $Cl_2O_5$

13-100. Write the formula of the acid or base formed when each of the following anhydrides is dissolved in water.

(a) BaO      (b) $SeO_2$      (c) $Cl_2O$      (d) $Br_2O$      (e) $K_2O$

13-101. Carbon dioxide is removed from the space shuttle by bubbling the air through a LiOH solution. Show the reaction and the product formed.

13-102. Complete the following equation.

$$Li_2O + N_2O_5(g) \longrightarrow \underline{\quad\quad} (s)$$

## General Problems

13-103. Iron reacts with an acid, forming an aqueous solution of iron(II) iodide and a gas. Write the equation illustrating the reaction.

13-104. Aluminum reacts with perchloric acid. Write the equation illustrating this reaction.

13-105. Nitric acid reacts with sodium sulfite, forming sulfur dioxide gas, a salt, and water. Write the equation illustrating the reaction.

13-106. Perbromic acid reacts with sodium sulfide to form a pungent gas, hydrogen sulfide. Write the equation illustrating the reaction.

13-107. There are acid-base systems based on solvents other than $H_2O$. One is ammonia ($NH_3$), which is also amphiprotic. Write equations illustrating each of the following.

(a) the reaction of HCN with $NH_3$ acting as a base

(b) the reaction of $H^-$ with $NH_3$ acting as an acid

(c) the reaction of $HCO_3^-$ with $NH_3$ acting as a base

(d) the reaction between $NH_4Cl$ and $NaNH_2$ in ammonia

13-108. The conjugate base of methyl alcohol ($CH_3OH$) is $CH_3O^-$. Its conjugate acid is $CH_3OH_2^+$. Write equations illustrating each of the following.

(a) the reaction of HCl with methyl alcohol acting as a base

(b) the reaction of $NH_2^-$ with methyl alcohol acting as an acid

13-109. Sulfite ion ($SO_3^{2-}$) and sulfur trioxide ($SO_3$) look similar at first glance, but one forms a strongly acidic solution whereas the other is weakly basic. Write equations illustrating this behavior.

13-110. Tell whether each of the following compounds forms an acidic, basic, or neutral solution when added to pure water. Write the equation illustrating the acidic or basic behavior where appropriate.

(a) $H_2S$      (e) $N_2H_5^+Br^-$      (i) $H_2SO_3$

(b) KClO      (f) $Ba(OH)_2$      (j) $Cl_2O_3$

(c) NaI      (g) $Sr(NO_3)_2$

(d) $NH_3$      (h) $LiNO_2$

13-111. Tell whether each of the following compounds forms an acidic, basic, or neutral solution when added to pure water. Write the equation illustrating the acidic or basic behavior where appropriate.

(a) HBrO      (d) $N_2H_4$      (g) RbBr

(b) CaO      (e) $SO_2$

(c) $NH_4ClO_4$      (f) $Ba(C_2H_3O_2)_2$

13-112. In a lab there are five different solutions with pH's of 1.0, 5.2, 7.0, 10.2, and 13.0. The solutions are LiOH, $SrBr_2$, KClO, $NH_4Cl$, and HI, all at the same concentration. Which pH corresponds to which compound? What must be the concentration of all of these solutions?

13-113. When one mixes a solution of baking soda ($NaHCO_3$) with vinegar ($HC_2H_3O_2$), bubbles of gas appear. Write equations for two reactions that indicate the identity of the gas.

*13-114. High-sulfur coal contains 5.0% iron pyrite ($FeS_2$). When the coal is burned, the iron pyrite also burns according to the equation

$$4FeS_2(s) + 11O_2(g) \longrightarrow 2Fe_2O_3(s) + 8SO_2(g)$$

What mass of sulfuric acid can eventually form from the combustion of 100 kg of coal? Sulfuric acid is formed according to the following equations.

$$2SO_2(g) + O_2(g) \longrightarrow 2SO_3(g)$$

$$SO_3(g) + H_2O(l) \longrightarrow H_2SO_4(aq)$$

13-115. A 2.50-g quantity of HCl is dissolved in 245 mL of water and then diluted to 890 mL. What is the pH of the concentrated and the dilute solution?

13-116. A 0.150-mole quantity of NaOH is dissolved in 2.50 L of water. In a separate container, 0.150 mole of HCl is present in 2.50 L of water. What is the pH of each solution? What is the pH of a solution made by mixing the two?

*13-117. A solution is prepared by mixing 10.0 g of HCl with 10.0 g of NaOH. What is the pH of the solution if the volume is 1.00 L?

**13-118.** A solution is prepared by mixing 25.0 g of $H_2SO_4$ with 50.0 g of KOH. What is the pH of the solution if the volume is 500 mL?

*13-119. A solution is prepared by mixing 500 mL of 0.10 M $HNO_3$ with 500 mL of 0.10 M $Ca(OH)_2$. What is the pH of the solution after mixing?

## STUDENT WORKSHOP

### Plotting the Titration of a Strong Acid with a Strong Base

**Purpose: To calculate pH, and create a graph which demonstrates how the pH of an acid solution changes as it is titrated with a base. (Work in groups of three or four. Estimated time: 25 min.)**

In this activity, you will make a graph showing how the pH of a solution changes as you titrate a strong acid with a strong base. The graph paper (sideways) should be scaled from 0 to 14 on the y-axis (this will be the pH) and from 0 mL to 50 mL on the x-axis (the volume of added NaOH). The data for this experiment are for 25.0 mL of 0.10 M $HNO_3$ being titrated with 0.10 M NaOH.

At 25.0 mL of added NaOH, you will be at the equivalence point in the titration, and the pH will be 7.00. Prior to that, we expect acidic pH's, and past that point, pH's should be in the base range, as we add more base than there is acid to neutralize. The accompanying table records the acid or base concentration for each amount of added NaOH, after the reaction is complete. You should determine the pH at each point, plot the graph of pH versus added NaOH, and answer the following questions.

| mL of NaOH added | mol/L [Acid] | mol/L [Base] |
|---|---|---|
| 0.0 | 0.10 | |
| 5.0 | 0.067 | |
| 10.0 | 0.043 | |
| 15.0 | 0.025 | |
| 20.0 | 0.011 | |
| 24.0 | 0.0020 | |
| 25.0 | 0 | 0 |
| 26.0 | | 0.0020 |
| 30.0 | | 0.0091 |
| 35.0 | | 0.017 |
| 40.0 | | 0.023 |
| 50.0 | | 0.033 |

1. Over what range(s) of added base is the pH changing the least?
2. Around what volume is the pH changing the most?
3. If the indicator changes color from pH 8 to pH 10, how much base does it take to cause the color to change?
4. The plot you have created is referred to as an S curve.
5. Using the Internet, can you find other areas where S-curve behavior applies?

# Chapter
# 14
# Oxidation-Reduction Reactions

E lectricity generated by this large Tesla coil is dramatic and awesome. In fact, electricity has been essential to our lives for well over a century. In this chapter, we are concerned with how electricity is generated and put to use by chemical reactions.

# SETTING THE STAGE

A distant rumble signals the ominous gathering of thunderstorms. We may cast a cautious eye toward the sky and think of shelter. The roll of thunder warns us about one force of nature for which we have a great respect, so we try to get out of its way. That, of course, is lightning. Lightning has no doubt caused fear as well as amazement in the human race since people first looked to the sky and wondered about its nature. But this force was not harnessed until modern times. The use of electricity (the same force as lightning) is so common to us now that it is taken for granted. Huge generating plants dot the rural landscape with towering smokestacks discharging smoke and steam. Not many decades ago, however, electricity was mainly a laboratory curiosity, until the experiments of inventors such as James Watt, Alexander Graham Bell, and Thomas Edison tapped its limitless potential. Even now, when we turn on a cell phone or an iPod or start a car, a flow of electrons (electricity) from a battery is put to immediate use. The electricity used by these devices originates from chemical reactions that involve an exchange of electrons between reactants.

Electron exchanges have not previously been defined as a specific type of reaction, but many of the classifications discussed in Chapter 6 fit into this broad category. Most combination, all combustion, and all single-replacement reactions can also be categorized as electron exchange reactions.

In Part A, we will examine the nature of these reactions and how the equations representing these reactions are balanced. The practical applications of redox reactions, such as the generation of electricity in batteries or to release metals from their ores, are among the topics discussed in Part B.

## Part A

## Redox Reactions—The Exchange of Electrons

**SETTING A GOAL**

■ You will learn of an important classification of chemical reactions that involve an exchange of electrons.

**OBJECTIVES**

14-1 Using oxidation states, determine the species oxidized, the species reduced, the oxidizing agent, and the reducing agent in an electron exchange reaction.

14-2 Balance redox reactions by the oxidation state (bridge) method.

14-3 Balance redox reactions by the ion-electron (half-reaction) method in both acidic and basic media.

▶ **OBJECTIVE FOR SECTION 14-1**
Using oxidation states, determine the species oxidized, the species reduced, the oxidizing agent, and the reducing agent in an electron exchange reaction.

# 14-1 The Nature of Oxidation and Reduction and Oxidation States

**LOOKING AHEAD!** There are two general types of reactions that involve the hydrogen atom. One involves the proton and the other involves the electron. In Chapter 13, we described the actions of acids and bases in water as an exchange of a proton. In this chapter, we describe reactions involving the electron. First, we examine this exchange and the terms used to describe it. ■

Sodium metal and chlorine gas react in a spectacular demonstration of chemical power. A small chunk of sodium placed in a flask filled with chlorine gas immediately glows white hot as the elements combine to form ordinary table salt. (See Figure 14-1.) We will examine the reaction of sodium and chlorine to illustrate the process of an electron exchange reaction. The equation for this reaction is as follows.

$$2Na(s) + Cl_2(g) \longrightarrow 2NaCl(s)$$

In Section 9-2, we briefly explained what was happening in the reaction. A sodium atom loses one electron, which is gained by a chlorine atom, resulting in the formation of two ions. The gain and loss of an electron were predicted as a logical consequence of the octet rule.

$$Na\cdot \quad + \quad \cdot \ddot{C}l\!:\ \longrightarrow Na^+ \ :\!\ddot{C}l\!:^-$$

### 14-1.1 Half-Reactions

In the acid–base reactions discussed in the previous chapter, the atoms in the reactants keep their quota of electrons in changing to products. Such is not the case in the reaction shown above, however. We will now take a closer look at what happens as reactants change into products. An electron exchange reaction can be viewed as the sum of two half-reactions. *A* **half-reaction** *represents either the loss of electrons or the gain of electrons as a separate balanced equation.* Thus the half-reaction involving only sodium is

$$Na \longrightarrow Na^+ + e^-$$

In this half-reaction, notice that the neutral sodium atom has lost an electron to form a positive sodium ion. *A substance that loses electrons in a chemical reaction is said to be* **oxidized**.

Now consider what happens to the chlorine molecule in going from reactant to product.

$$2e^- + Cl_2 \longrightarrow 2Cl^-$$

**FIGURE 14-1 Formation of NaCl** An active metal reacts with a poisonous gas to form ordinary table salt (NaCl).

In this half-reaction, the neutral chlorine molecule has gained two electrons to form two chloride ions. *A substance that gains electrons in a chemical reaction is said to be* **reduced**. A simple mnemonic helps us remember these two terms: OIL RIG can be used to recall **O**xidation **I**s **L**oss (of electrons)—**R**eduction **I**s **G**ain.

## 14-1.2 Redox Reactions

Obviously, the two processes (oxidation and reduction) complement each other similar to how acids and bases complement each other in a neutralization reaction. If there is an oxidation occurring, then there must also be a reduction, giving us the basis for this classification of chemical reaction. *Reactions involving an exchange of electrons are known as* **oxidation–reduction**, *or simply,* **redox reactions**.

Now consider how the two half-reactions add together to make a complete, balanced equation. *An important principle of a redox reaction is that the electrons gained in the reduction process must equal the electrons lost in the oxidation process.* Note in our sample reaction that the reduction process involving $Cl_2$ requires two electrons. Therefore, the oxidation process must involve two Na's to provide these two electrons. The electrons on both sides of the equation must be equal so that they can be eliminated by subtraction when the two half-reactions are added.

$$\begin{aligned}
\textit{Oxidation half-reaction:} \quad & 2Na \longrightarrow 2Na^+ + 2e^- \\
\textit{Reduction half-reaction:} \quad & 2e^- + Cl_2 \longrightarrow 2Cl^- \\
\textit{Total reaction:} \quad & 2Na + Cl_2 \longrightarrow 2Na^+ + 2Cl^- \text{ (or 2NaCl)}
\end{aligned}$$

Instead of identifying a reactant by what happened to it (i.e., it was oxidized or reduced), in this type of reaction it is sometimes more useful to emphasize what it does. *The substance that causes the oxidation (i.e., by accepting electrons) is called the* **oxidizing agent**, *and the substance that causes the reduction (i.e., by providing the electrons) is called the* **reducing agent**. Thus, the substance reduced is the oxidizing agent and the substance oxidized is the reducing agent.

In the example above, Na is the *reducing agent* and is oxidized to $Na^+$. $Cl_2$ is the *oxidizing agent* and is reduced to $Cl^-$.

Many other familiar chemical changes are redox reactions. For example, the corrosion of iron to form rust involves an exchange of electrons. The formation of rust [iron(III) oxide] is illustrated below.

$$4Fe(s) + 3O_2(g) \longrightarrow 2Fe_2O_3(s)$$

Originally, the term *oxidation* referred specifically to reactions where a substance like iron adds oxygen. In the reverse reaction, oxygen is removed from iron(III) oxide, which "reduces" its mass. Thus, the removal of oxygen was known as "reduction." Now we define the process in terms of the exchange of electrons, so the terms are used regardless of whether oxygen is involved. In many redox reactions, however, the species undergoing electron exchange are not as obvious as the two examples that we have used in this section. So we need a tool to help us. This leads us to a concept known as oxidation states.

 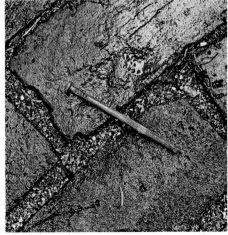

An iron nail soon forms a coating of rust when exposed to moisture and air.

### 14-1.3 Oxidation States

In Chapter 9 we presented Lewis structures for molecules and ions where electrons were shared between two atoms. With the concept of electronegativity (see Section 9-6), however, we found that electrons are not shared equally. The greater share of the electron pair in the bond is closer to the more electronegative atom, which gives it a partial negative charge. As a convenient method of keeping track of electrons in redox reactions, we will now assign *all* of the electrons in a bond to the more electronegative atom. *The* **oxidation state** (*or* **oxidation number**) *of an atom in a molecule or ion is the charge that atom would have if all electrons in its bonds were assigned to the more electronegative atom.* The most electronegative element is fluorine, oxygen is second, and the electronegativity of the elements then decreases diagonally to the left on the periodic table in the direction of the metal–nonmetal borderline in the periodic table. We actually don't need to know all the electronegativities of elements in order to assign oxidation states, however. A few general rules will suffice. These rules and some practice exercises follow.

1. The oxidation state of an element in its free (natural) state is zero [e.g., $Cu(s)$, $B(s)$]. This includes polyatomic elements [e.g., $Cl_2(g)$, $P_4(s)$].
2. The oxidation state of a monatomic ion is the same as the charge on that ion (e.g., $Na^+ = +1$ oxidation state, $O^{2-} = -2$, $Al^{3+} = +3$).
   a. Alkali metal ions are always $+1$ (same as the group number).
   b. Alkaline earth metal ions are always $+2$ (same as the group number).
3. The halogens are in a $-1$ oxidation state in binary (two-element) compounds, whether ionic or covalent, *when bound to a less electronegative element.*
4. Oxygen in a compound is usually $-2$. Certain compounds (which are rare) called peroxides or superoxides contain oxygen in a less negative oxidation state. Oxygen is positive only when bound to the more electronegative fluorine.
5. Hydrogen in a compound is usually $+1$. When combined with a less electronegative element (usually a metal), hydrogen has a $-1$ oxidation state (e.g., $LiH$).
6. The sum of the oxidation states of all the atoms in a neutral compound is zero. For a polyatomic ion, the sum of the oxidation states equals the charge on the ion.

---

**EXAMPLE 14-1   Calculating Oxidation States**

What is the oxidation state of the following?

**(a)** Fe in FeO        **(b)** N in $N_2O_5$        **(c)** S in $H_2SO_3$        **(d)** As in $AsO_4{}^{3-}$

PROCEDURE

An algebraic equation can be constructed from rule 6. For example, assume that we have a hypothetical compound $M_2A_3$. Then, from rule 6,

$$[2 \times (\text{oxidation state of M})] + [3 \times (\text{oxidation state of A})] = 0$$

or, to simplify,

$$2(\text{ox. state M}) + 3(\text{ox. state A}) = 0$$

If the formula represents a polyatomic ion, the quantity on the left is equal to the charge rather than zero.

SOLUTION

**(a)** FeO: The oxidation states of the two elements add to zero (rule 6).

$$(\text{ox. state Fe}) + (\text{ox. state O}) = 0$$

Since the oxidation of state of oxygen is $-2$ (rule 4),

$$\text{ox. state Fe} + (-2) = 0$$

$$\text{ox. state Fe} = \underline{+2}$$

**(b)** $N_2O_5$: The oxidation states add to zero (rule 6), as shown by the equation

$$2(\text{ox. state N}) + 5(\text{ox. state O}) = 0$$

Since ox. state O is −2 (rule 4),

$$2(\text{ox. state N}) + 5(-2) = 0$$
$$2(\text{ox. state N}) = +10$$
$$\text{ox. state N} = \underline{\underline{+5}}$$

**(c)** $H_2SO_3$: The oxidation states add to zero (rule 6).

$$2(\text{ox. state H}) + (\text{ox. state S}) + 3(\text{ox. state O}) = 0$$

H is usually +1 and O is usually −2 (rules 4 and 5).

$$2(+1) + \text{ox. state S} + 3(-2) = 0$$
$$\text{ox. state S} = \underline{\underline{+4}}$$

**(d)** $AsO_4^{3-}$: The sum of the oxidation states of the atoms equals the charge on the ion (rule 6).

$$(\text{ox. state As}) + 4(\text{ox. state O}) = -3$$

Since O is −2 (rule 4),

$$\text{ox. state As} + 4(-2) = -3$$
$$\text{ox. state As} = \underline{\underline{+5}}$$

### ANALYSIS

All charges on monatomic ions are oxidation states, though not all oxidation states are charges. The oxidation state of an atom in a molecule or ion would be the charge on the atom if all the other atoms were present as ions. For example, in the sulfate ion ($SO_4^{2-}$), if all atoms were ions, we would have $[S^{6+}4O^{2-}]^{2-}$. This is certainly not the case, since electrons are shared between the sulfur and oxygen atoms, as we illustrated in Chapter 9. However, even though the sulfur is not present as a +6 ion, the +6 assigned to the sulfur represents its oxidation state. We will see why we need this important information next.

### SYNTHESIS

Sometimes, in assigning oxidation states, we have to choose between a rule that says "always" and one that says "usually." For example, in the compound magnesium hydride ($MgH_2$) all atoms cannot have positive oxidation states. However, magnesium is "always" +2, so the hydrogen, which is "usually" +1, must have a −1 oxidation state in this case. In the compound $O_2F_2$, all atoms could not have negative oxidation states. In this case, fluorine is the more electronegative, so it has a −1 oxidation state. This means that each oxygen must be in a +1 oxidation state. There are even a few cases where we find oxidation states that are not even numbers. What would the oxidation state of the iron atoms be in $Fe_3O_4$? If the oxygens are −2 each, then their total is −8. The three iron atoms must have oxidation states that add to +8, so each one is +2.67. (In fact, $Fe_3O_4$ is a one-to-one combination of FeO and $Fe_2O_3$.) Fortunately, all the odd exceptions are not enough to worry about, so our rules will hold in almost all cases that we will encounter.

## 14-1.4 Using Oxidation States in Redox Reactions

By noting the change of oxidation state of the same atom in going from a reactant to a product, we can trace the exchange of electrons in the reaction. We can now add to our definition of oxidation and reduction in terms of oxidation state. *Oxidation is a loss of electrons as indicated by an increase in the oxidation state. Reduction is a gain of electrons as indicated by a decrease (or reduction) in the oxidation state.* In the reaction of sodium with chlorine discussed in Section 14-1, notice that the oxidation state of the sodium increased from zero to +1, indicating oxidation, and that of chlorine decreased from zero to −1, indicating reduction.

In most compounds, usually only one of the elements undergoes a change in redox reactions. Thus, it is often necessary to calculate the oxidation states of all the elements in all compounds so that we can see which ones have undergone the change. With experience, however, the oxidized and reduced species are more easily recognized. In the following examples, we will find all the oxidation states so that we can identify the changes and label them appropriately.

## EXAMPLE 14-2  Identifying Oxidized and Reduced Species

In the following unbalanced equations, indicate the reactant oxidized, the reactant reduced, the oxidizing agent, and the reducing agent. Indicate the products that contain the elements that were oxidized or reduced.

**(a)** $Al + HCl \longrightarrow AlCl_3 + H_2$

**(b)** $CH_4 + O_2 \longrightarrow CO_2 + H_2O$

**(c)** $MnO_2 + HCl \longrightarrow MnCl_2 + Cl_2 + H_2O$

**(d)** $K_2Cr_2O_7 + SnCl_2 + HCl \longrightarrow CrCl_3 + SnCl_4 + KCl + H_2O$

### PROCEDURE

In the equations, we wish to identify the species that contain atoms of an element undergoing a change in oxidation state. At first, it may be necessary to calculate the oxidation state of every atom in the equation until you can recognize the changes by inspection.

### SOLUTION

**(a)** Oxidation states of elements:

$$\overset{0}{Al} + \overset{+1-1}{HCl} \longrightarrow \overset{+3-1}{AlCl_3} + \overset{0}{H_2}$$

| Reactant | Change | Agent | Product |
|----------|--------|-------|---------|
| Al | oxidized | reducing | AlCl$_3$ |
| HCl | reduced | oxidizing | H$_2$ |

**(b)** Oxidation states of elements:

$$\overset{-4+1}{CH_4} + \overset{0}{O_2} \longrightarrow \overset{+4-2}{CO_2} + \overset{+1-2}{H_2O}$$

| Reactant | Change | Agent | Product |
|----------|--------|-------|---------|
| CH$_4$ | oxidized | reducing | CO$_2$ |
| O$_2$ | reduced | oxidizing | CO$_2$, H$_2$O |

**(c)** Oxidation states of elements:

$$\overset{+4-2}{MnO_2} + \overset{+1-1}{HCl} \longrightarrow \overset{+2-1}{MnCl_2} + \overset{0}{Cl_2} + \overset{+1-2}{H_2O}$$

| Reactant | Change | Agent | Product |
|----------|--------|-------|---------|
| HCl | oxidized | reducing | Cl$_2$ |
| MnO$_2$ | reduced | oxidizing | MnCl$_2$ |

**(d)** Oxidation states of elements:

$$\overset{+1 +6 -2}{K_2Cr_2O_7} + \overset{+2 -1}{SnCl_2} + \overset{+1-1}{HCl} \longrightarrow \overset{+3-1}{CrCl_3} + \overset{+1-1}{KCl} + \overset{+4 -1}{SnCl_4} + \overset{+1-2}{H_2O}$$

| Reactant | Change | Agent | Product |
|----------|--------|-------|---------|
| SnCl$_2$ | oxidized | reducing | SnCl$_4$ |
| K$_2$Cr$_2$O$_7$ | reduced | oxidizing | CrCl$_3$ |

You will notice that any substance present as a free element in a reaction is involved in either the oxidation or the reduction process. Also, hydrogen and oxygen are generally not oxidized or reduced if they remain part of compounds. They are involved only if present as free elements in either the reactants or products. Further note that none of the analysis done for this problem requires a balanced reaction. It is sufficient simply to know the identities of the reactants and their products.

### SYNTHESIS

Consider the equation illustrating the decomposition of hydrogen peroxide:

$$2H_2O_2(aq) \longrightarrow 2H_2O(l) + O_2(g)$$

What has been oxidized and what has been reduced? In this case $H_2O_2$ plays both roles. In one molecule of $H_2O_2$, the oxidation state of the oxygen has decreased from $-1$ to $-2$ to form $H_2O$, so it has been reduced. In the other molecule of $H_2O_2$, the oxygen has increased from $-1$ to $0$, so it has been oxidized. One molecule of hydrogen peroxide is the oxidizing agent and one is the reducing agent. In such a case, we say that the $H_2O_2$ has been *disproportionated*.

## MAKING IT REAL

## Lightning Bugs (Fireflies)—Nature's Little Night-Lights

Tiny little flashes of light on a summer night–those of us east of the Rockies know the sources as lightning bugs, also called fireflies. They have been a source of curiosity since ancient times, but only recently have we known how these tiny creatures can light up.

Glowsticks—an example of chemiluminescence.

In photochemical reactions, such as photosynthesis, light energy *initiates* a chemical reaction. In the firefly, we have just the opposite situation. That is, light energy is *produced* by a chemical reaction. The production of light energy by a chemical reaction is known as *chemiluminescence*. If it is produced by living organisms, such as the firefly, it is known as *bioluminescence*.

We now have some understanding of what goes on in the firefly. The chemical reaction is an oxidation–reduction reaction, with $O_2$ from the air serving as the oxidizing agent. The other compounds are complex molecules, so we will simply refer to them by name (luciferin) or initials (ATP). Also involved is an enzyme (luciferase), which acts as a catalyst. This reaction is represented as follows:

$$\text{luciferin} + \text{ATP} + O_2(g) \xrightarrow{\text{luciferase}} \text{products} + h\upsilon \text{ (cold light)}$$

By studying the bioluminescent chemistry of the firefly, we also discovered that all fireflies have the same luciferin, but each species produces a different color of light. The color was found to be determined by the luciferase that is unique to each species of firefly. An amazing discovery about this reaction is that the production of light is incredibly efficient. Eighty out of 100 molecules that react produce light, thus giving it an 80% efficiency.

It wasn't until 1928 that a scientist, H. O. Albrecht, first described a nonbiological chemical reaction that could be conducted in a laboratory to generate chemiluminescence, but with only 0.1% efficiency. The reaction is similar to the one shown above except that nonbiological chemicals available to the scientist were used along with hydrogen peroxide ($H_2O_2$) as the oxidizing agent. In the early 1960s, other chemiluminescent reactions were discovered and patented. Today a substance called Cyalume™, a trademark product of American Cyanamid, is used to produce light with about 5% efficiency.

When you see children with glowsticks or other decorative jewelry that glows in the dark, thank the firefly for its amazing contribution to our world of chemistry.

▶ ASSESSING THE OBJECTIVE FOR SECTION 14–1

**EXERCISE 14-1(a) LEVEL 1:** Fill in the blanks.

If all the atoms in a compound were ions, the charge on the ions would be the same as their _____ _____. For oxygen in compounds, this is usually _____. Hydrogen is usually _____ in compounds. A substance oxidized undergoes a _____ of electrons and an _____ in oxidation state. This substance is also known as a _____ agent.

**EXERCISE 14-1(b) LEVEL 1:** What is the oxidation state of **(a)** B in $H_3BO_3$ and **(b)** S in $S_2O_3^{2-}$?

**EXERCISE 14-1(c) LEVEL 1:** What is the oxidation state of carbon in each of the following compounds?

**(a)** $CO_3^{2-}$      **(b)** $CH_3Cl$      **(c)** $CF_4$      **(d)** $CH_2O$

**EXERCISE 14-1(d) LEVEL 2:** In the following reaction, indicate the substance oxidized, the substance reduced, the oxidizing agent, and the reducing agent.

$$ClO_2 + H_2O_2 \longrightarrow O_2 + Cl^-$$

**EXERCISE 14-1(e) LEVEL 2:** Consider the following unbalanced equation:

$$CrI_3 + OH^- + Cl_2 \longrightarrow CrO_4^{2-} + IO_4^- + Cl^- + H_2O$$

What has been oxidized and what has been reduced?

**EXERCISE 14-1(f) LEVEL 3:** Is it possible to have a reduction without an oxidation or an oxidation without a reduction? Why or why not?

**EXERCISE 14-1(g) LEVEL 3:** Is the compound $KMnO_4$ more likely to be an oxidizing or reducing agent? Why?

*For additional practice, work chapter problems 14-1, 14-6, 14-10, and 14-12.*

▶ OBJECTIVE
FOR SECTION 14-2
Balance redox reactions by the oxidation state (bridge) method.

# 14-2 Balancing Redox Equations: Oxidation State Method

**LOOKING AHEAD!** An important principle of redox reactions is that "electrons lost equal electrons gained." In the next two sections, we will put this concept to use as the key to balancing some rather complex reactions that would be quite difficult to balance by inspection, as we did in Chapter 6. There are two procedures for this endeavor. The oxidation state method, discussed in this section, is useful for balancing equations in molecular form. ■

In a typical redox reaction, only two atoms undergo a change in their oxidation states. By identifying these two atoms and calculating the change in the oxidation state, we can arrive at a balanced equation. *The **oxidation state**, or **bridge method**, focuses on the atoms of the elements undergoing a change in oxidation state.*

The following reaction will be used to illustrate the procedures for balancing equations by the oxidation state method.

$$HNO_3(aq) + H_2S(aq) \longrightarrow NO(g) + S(s) + H_2O(l)$$

1. Identify the atoms whose oxidation states have changed.

$$\overset{+5}{H\underline{N}O_3} + \overset{-2}{H_2\underline{S}} \longrightarrow \overset{+2}{\underline{N}O} + \overset{0}{\underline{S}} + H_2O$$

2. Draw a bridge between the same atoms whose oxidation states have changed, indicating the electrons gained or lost. This is the change in oxidation state.

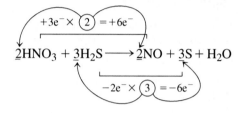

3. Multiply the two numbers (+ 3 and −2) by whole numbers that produce a common multiple. For 3 and 2 the common multiple is 6. (For example, $+3 \times \underline{2} = +6$; $-2 \times \underline{3} = -6$.) Use these multipliers as coefficients of the respective compounds or elements.
   Note that six electrons are lost (bottom) and six are gained (top).

$$\overset{+3e^- \times \,\textcircled{2}\, = +6e^-}{2HNO_3 + 3H_2S \longrightarrow 2NO + 3S + H_2O} \underset{-2e^- \times \,\textcircled{3}\, = -6e^-}{}$$

4. Balance the rest of the equation by inspection. Note that there are eight H's on the left, so *four* $H_2O$'s are needed on the right. If the equation has been balanced correctly, the O's should balance. Note that they do.

$$2HNO_3 + 3H_2S \longrightarrow 2NO + 3S + 4H_2O$$

## EXAMPLE 14-3   Balancing Equations by the Oxidation State Method

Balance the following equations by the oxidation state method.

**(a)** $Zn + AgNO_3 \longrightarrow Zn(NO_3)_2 + Ag$

**(b)** $Cu + HNO_3 \longrightarrow Cu(NO_3)_2 + H_2O + NO_2$

**(c)** $O_2 + HI \longrightarrow H_2O + I_2$

PROCEDURE (a)

**(1)** Determine the elements that have been oxidized and reduced. **(2)** From the oxidation state change, determine the common multiple and use the two multipliers as coefficients in the equation.

SOLUTION (a)

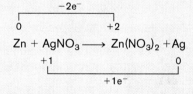

When a copper penny reacts with nitric acid, nitrogen dioxide gas (brown) is formed.

The oxidation (top) should be multiplied by 1, and the reduction process (bottom) should be multiplied by 2.

$$\overset{-2e^- \times 1 = -2e^-}{Zn + 2AgNO_3 \longrightarrow Zn(NO_3)_2 + 2Ag} \underset{+1e^- \times 2 = +2e^-}{}$$

The final balanced equation is

$$Zn + 2AgNO_3 \longrightarrow Zn(NO_3)_2 + 2Ag$$

**PROCEDURE (b)**

Write a bridge between Cu and N, which have undergone oxidation state changes.

**SOLUTION (b)**

$$\overset{\displaystyle -2e^- \times 1 = -2e^-}{\underset{\text{0}\qquad\qquad\qquad +2}{Cu + HNO_3 \longrightarrow Cu(NO_3)_2 + H_2O + NO_2}}$$

with $+5$ and $+4$ bridge $+1e^- \times 2 = +2e^-$

The equation, so far, is

$$Cu + 2HNO_3 \longrightarrow Cu(NO_3)_2 + H_2O + 2NO_2$$

Note, however, that four N's are present on the right, but only two are on the left. The addition of two more $HNO_3$'s balances the N's, and the equation is completely balanced with two $H_2O$'s on the right.

$$Cu + 4HNO_3 \longrightarrow Cu(NO_3)_2 + 2H_2O + 2NO_2$$

(In this aqueous reaction, $HNO_3$ serves two functions. Two $HNO_3$'s are reduced to two $NO_2$'s, and the other two $HNO_3$'s provide anions for the $Cu^{2+}$ ion. These latter $NO_3^-$ ions are present in the solution as spectator ions. Spectator ions are not oxidized, reduced, or otherwise changed during the reaction.)

**PROCEDURE (c)**

The elements undergoing a change in oxidation state are oxygen and iodine. *If an atom that has changed is in a compound where it has a subscript other than 1, first balance these atoms by adding a temporary coefficient.*

**SOLUTION (c)**

$$2HI \longrightarrow I_2 \quad \text{and} \quad O_2 \longrightarrow 2H_2O$$

$$\overset{\displaystyle 2(-1e^-) \times 2 = -4e^-}{\underset{\text{0}\qquad\qquad\qquad -2}{O_2 + 2HI \longrightarrow 2H_2O + I_2}}$$

$$2(+2e^-) \times 1 = +4e^-$$

The final balanced equation is

$$O_2 + 4HI \longrightarrow 2H_2O + 2I_2$$

**ANALYSIS**

In (c), a common mistake is failing to ensure that the element undergoing a change is balanced first. If one neglected to do this, the change would be from 0 in $O_2$ to $-2$ in $H_2O$, for a loss of two electrons. Notice that there is actually a loss of four electrons, since the $O_2$ is reduced to two $H_2O$ molecules. Likewise, there is a gain of two electrons when 2HI is oxidized to $I_2$.

**SYNTHESIS**

Consider the following reaction: $C_6H_{12}O_6 \longrightarrow C_2H_6O + CO_2$. This is the process of fermentation to form alcohol ($C_2H_6O$) from sugar ($C_6H_{12}O_6$), and it is significantly more complex than shown here. Based on this reaction, the carbon in $C_6H_{12}O_6$ would be assigned an oxidation state of zero. The carbons in the products would be $-2$ and $+4$, respectively. If you follow the procedure, you would predict that this equation balances thusly:

$$3\,C_6H_{12}O_6 \longrightarrow 6\,C_2H_6O + 6\,CO_2$$

or, simplified,

$$C_6H_{12}O_6 \longrightarrow 2\,C_2H_6O + 2\,CO_2$$

The point here, though, is that while the average oxidation states of the carbons were 0, $-2$, and $+4$, respectively, the actual oxidation states of the six carbons in sugar and the two carbons in alcohol vary. They merely average to those respective values. To be specific, in alcohol the oxidation states of the two carbons are actually $-3$ and $-1$, due to having different surrounding atoms. In the sugar, the oxidation states vary from $-1$ to $+2$, depending on the type of sugar. Be careful, whenever there are multiple atoms of the same type in a molecule, not to necessarily assume that all have the same oxidation state.

▶ **ASSESSING THE OBJECTIVE FOR SECTION 14-2**

**EXERCISE 14-2(a) LEVEL 2:** Balance the following equations by the bridge method.

**(a)** $Fe(s) + HCl(aq) \longrightarrow FeCl_3(aq) + H_2(g)$

**(b)** $HNO_3(aq) + HCl(aq) \longrightarrow NO_2(g) + Cl_2(g) + H_2O$

**EXERCISE 14-2(b) LEVEL 3:** In an alkaline dry cell (battery), manganese(IV) oxide reacts with water and zinc to produce manganese(III) oxide and zinc(II) hydroxide. Write the equation illustrating this reaction and balance the equation by the bridge method.

*For additional practice, work chapter problems 14-16 and 14-17.*

# 14-3 Balancing Redox Equations: Ion-Electron Method

▶ **OBJECTIVE FOR SECTION 14-3**
Balance redox reactions by the ion-electron (half-reaction) method in both acidic and basic media.

**LOOKING AHEAD!** One problem with the oxidation state method is that it may give the impression that some atoms exist as ions when they are actually *part* of a compound or ion (e.g., $N^{5+}$). The second method that we will discuss focuses on the entire ion or molecule containing the atom undergoing a change. This is a more realistic representation of the species involved. ■

While it is generally true that only two atoms actually undergo oxidation state changes, we can also consider the entire species that changes (e.g., $NO_3^-$ rather than $N^{5+}$). *In the* **ion-electron method** *(also known as the half-reaction method), the total reaction is separated into half-reactions, which are balanced individually and then added back together.* The ion-electron method recognizes the complete change of an ion or molecule as it goes from reactant to products. As we will see later in this chapter, a balanced half-reaction is how we represent a specific change that occurs in a battery.

The rules for balancing equations are somewhat different in acidic solution [containing $H^+(aq)$ ion] than in basic solution [containing $OH^-(aq)$ ion]. The two solutions are considered separately, with acid solution reactions discussed first. To simplify the equations, only the net ionic equations are balanced.

## 14-3.1 Balancing Reactions in Acidic Solution

The balancing of an equation in aqueous acid solution is illustrated with the following unbalanced equation.

$$H^+(aq) + Cl^-(aq) + Cr_2O_7^{2-}(aq) \longrightarrow Cr^{3+}(aq) + Cl_2(g) + H_2O(l)$$

1. Separate out the molecule or ion that contains atoms of an element that has been oxidized or reduced and the product containing atoms of that element. If necessary, calculate the oxidation states of individual atoms until you are able to recognize the species that changes. In this method, it is actually not necessary to know the oxidation state. The reduction process is

$$Cr_2O_7^{2-} \longrightarrow Cr^{3+}$$

2. If a subscript of the atoms of the element undergoing a change in oxidation state is more than 1, balance those atoms with a temporary coefficient. In this case, it is the Cr.

$$Cr_2O_7^{2-} \longrightarrow 2Cr^{3+}$$

3. Balance the oxygens by adding $H_2O$ on the side needing the oxygens (one $H_2O$ for each O needed).

$$Cr_2O_7^{2-} \longrightarrow 2Cr^{3+} + 7H_2O$$

4. Balance the hydrogens by adding $H^+$ on the other side of the equation from the $H_2O$'s ($2H^+$ for each $H_2O$ added). Note that the H and O have not undergone a change in oxidation state.

$$14H^+ + Cr_2O_7^{2-} \longrightarrow 2Cr^{3+} + 7H_2O$$

5. The atoms in the half-reaction are now balanced. Check to make sure. Now comes the important step of balancing the charge on both sides of the equation. The charge is determined separately on each side of the equation. This is accomplished by multiplying the coefficient of any ion present times the charge on that ion. Neutral molecules are excluded from charge determination. Notice that there are 14 $H^+$ ions. The charge due to $H^+$ is 14 times the charge on the proton (+1), or +14. This is then added to the charge on the dichromate (−2), which makes a total charge on the left (i.e., the reactant side) of +12 [i.e., $(14 \times +1) + (−2) = +12$]. On the right (i.e., the product side), the charge on the Cr (+3) is multiplied by its coefficient (2), making a charge of +6 on the right. The $H_2O$ is a neutral molecule, so it is not included. The total charge on the left is +12, and on the right it is +6. The charges on both sides of the reaction must now be balanced. To do this, add the appropriate number of *negative* electrons (−1 each) to the more *positive* side. Adding $6e^-$ on the left (the more positive side) balances the charges on both sides, and the half-reaction is balanced (i.e., $+12 − 6 = +6$).

$$6e^- + 14H^+ + Cr_2O_7^{2-} \longrightarrow 2Cr^{3+} + 7H_2O$$

6. Repeat the same procedure for the other half-reaction.

$$Cl^- \longrightarrow Cl_2$$
$$2Cl^- \longrightarrow Cl_2$$
$$2Cl^- \longrightarrow Cl_2 + 2e^-$$

7. Before the two half-reactions are added, we must make sure that electrons gained equal electrons lost. Sometimes the half-reactions must be multiplied by factors that give the same number of electrons. In this case, if the oxidation process is multiplied by 3 (and the reduction process by 1), there will be an exchange of $6e^-$. When these two half-reactions are added, the $6e^-$ can be subtracted from both sides of the equation.

$$3(2Cl^- \longrightarrow Cl_2 + 2e^-)$$
$$6Cl^- \longrightarrow 3Cl_2 + 6e^-$$

Addition produces the balanced net ionic equation.

$$6e^- + 14H^+ + Cr_2O_7^{2-} \longrightarrow 2Cr^{3+} + 7H_2O$$

$$6Cl^- \longrightarrow 3Cl_2 + 6e^-$$

$$\overline{14H^+(aq) + 6Cl^-(aq) + Cr_2O_7^{2-}(aq) \longrightarrow 2Cr^{3+}(aq) + 3Cl_2(g) + 7H_2O(l)}$$

An excellent way to check our answer is to make sure the net charges on both sides of the equation are the same. The net charge on the left side of the equation is $(14 \times +1) + (6 \times -1) + (-2) = \underline{+6}$. On the right the charge is $(2 \times +3) = \underline{+6}$. Recall that neutral molecules have no net charge.

## EXAMPLE 14-4    Balancing Redox Equations in Acidic Solution

Balance the following equations for reactions occurring in acid solution by the ion-electron method.

(a) $MnO_4^-(aq) + SO_2(g) + H_2O(l) \longrightarrow Mn^{2+}(aq) + SO_4^{2-}(aq) + H^+(aq)$

(b) $Cu(s) + NO_3^-(aq) \longrightarrow Cu^{2+}(aq) + H_2O + NO(g)$

## PROCEDURE

Balance each half-reaction in the following order: (1) the element that changes, (2) oxygens, (3) hydrogens, and (4) the charge. Add the two half-reactions together, and subtract out anything that appears on both sides.

## SOLUTION (a)

$$\text{Reduction:} \qquad MnO_4^- \longrightarrow Mn^{2+}$$

$$H_2O: \qquad MnO_4^- \longrightarrow Mn^{2+} + 4H_2O$$

$$H^+: \qquad 8H^+ + MnO_4^- \longrightarrow Mn^{2+} + 4H_2O$$

$$e^-: \qquad 5e^- + 8H^+ + MnO_4^- \longrightarrow Mn^{2+} + 4H_2O$$

$$\text{Oxidation:} \qquad SO_2 \longrightarrow SO_4^{2-}$$

$$H_2O: \qquad 2H_2O + SO_2 \longrightarrow SO_4^{2-}$$

$$H^+: \qquad 2H_2O + SO_2 \longrightarrow SO_4^{2-} + 4H^+$$

$$e^-: \qquad 2H_2O + SO_2 \longrightarrow SO_4^{2-} + 4H^+ + 2e^-$$

The reduction reaction is multiplied by 2 and the oxidation by 5 to produce 10 electrons for each process, as shown below.

$$2(5e^- + 8H^+ + MnO_4^- \longrightarrow Mn^{2+} + 4H_2O)$$

$$5(2H_2O + SO_2 \longrightarrow SO_4^{2-} + 4H^+ + 2e^-)$$

$$\cancel{10e^-} + 16H^+ + 2MnO_4^- \longrightarrow 2Mn^{2+} + 8H_2O$$

$$\underline{10H_2O + 5SO_2 \longrightarrow 5SO_4^{2-} + 20H^+ + \cancel{10e^-}}$$

$$10H_2O + 16H^+ + 5SO_2 + 2MnO_4^- \longrightarrow 5SO_4^{2-} + 2Mn^{2+} + 8H_2O + 20H^+$$

Note that $H_2O$ and $H^+$ are present on both sides of the equation. Therefore, $8H_2O$ and $16H^+$ can be subtracted from *both sides*, leaving the final balanced net ionic equation as

$$2MnO_4^-(aq) + 5SO_2(g) + 2H_2O(l) \longrightarrow 2Mn^{2+}(aq) + 5SO_4^{2-}(aq) + 4H^+(aq)$$

## SOLUTION (b)

$$\text{Reduction:} \qquad NO_3^- \longrightarrow NO$$

$$H_2O: \qquad NO_3^- \longrightarrow NO + 2H_2O$$

$$H^+: \qquad 4H^+ + NO_3^- \longrightarrow NO + 2H_2O$$

$$e^-: \qquad 3e^- + 4H^+ + NO_3^- \longrightarrow NO + 2H_2O$$

$$\text{Oxidation:} \qquad Cu \longrightarrow Cu^{2+}$$

$$e^-: \qquad Cu \longrightarrow Cu^{2+} + 2e^-$$

Multiply the reduction half-reaction by 2 and the oxidation half-reaction by 3, and then add the two half-reactions.

$$\cancel{6e^-} + 8H^+ + 2NO_3^- \longrightarrow 2NO + 4H_2O$$

$$\underline{3Cu \longrightarrow 3Cu^{2+} + \cancel{6e^-}}$$

$$8H^+(aq) + 2NO_3^-(aq) + 3Cu(s) \longrightarrow 3Cu^{2+}(aq) + 2NO(g) + 4H_2O(l)$$

## ANALYSIS

When checking to see that redox reactions are properly balanced, remember that both the number of atoms and the charge must be the same on both sides. In (a), there are 4 hydrogens, 20 oxygens, 5 sulfurs, and 2 manganese atoms on each side. In addition, the total charge on the left side is $2 \times (-1)$, or $-2$, and on the right side it is $[2 \times (+2)] + [5 \times (-2)] + [4 \times (+1)]$, or $-2$, as well. Both atoms and charges balance. What is the atom and electron inventory for the reaction in (b)? Does it balance?

## SYNTHESIS

In the chapter problems, you will notice that some acids are represented as molecules and others as ions. Thus, nitric acid, $HNO_3$, appears as $H^+ + NO_3^-$ in ionic equations, but sulfurous acid, $H_2SO_3$, appears as $H_2SO_3$. Why is this so? Recall our previous discussion about the difference between strong acids and weak acids. Strong acids (e.g., $HNO_3$) do not exist as molecules in aqueous solution, since they are completely ionized. Weak acids (e.g., $H_2SO_3$), on the other hand, are present mostly as neutral molecules. A weak acid forms very limited amounts of $H^+$ in solution, so we represent it in its more prevalent form as a molecule.

## 14-3.2 Balancing Reactions in Basic Solution

In a basic solution, $OH^-$, rather than $H^+$, is in excess. Perhaps the simplest way to adjust to this condition is to follow the same procedure as in acid solution but change either each half-reaction or the total reaction to basic solution after it is otherwise balanced. We do this by adding one $OH^-$ to *both sides* of the equation for each $H^+$ present in the equation. As we learned in the previous chapter, the $H^+$ ion combines with an $OH^-$ ion to form $H_2O$ [i.e., $H^+(aq) + OH^-(aq) \longrightarrow H_2O(l)$]. In effect, this procedure converts an $H^+$ ion to an $H_2O$ on one side, leaving one $OH^-$ ion on the opposite side of the equation. For example, consider the half-reaction shown below, which has been balanced in acid solution. We will adjust the equation to a basic solution as follows.

1. Reduction half-reaction balanced in acid solution:

$$2e^- + 2H^+ + ClO^- \longrightarrow Cl^- + H_2O$$

2. Add $2OH^-$ to both sides for the two $H^+$'s shown on the left:

$$2e^- + (2H^+ + \mathbf{2OH^-}) + ClO^- \longrightarrow Cl^- + H_2O + \mathbf{2OH^-}$$

3. Convert $2H^+ + 2OH^-$ to $2H_2O$:

$$2e^- + \mathbf{2H_2O} + ClO^- \longrightarrow Cl^- + H_2O + \mathbf{2OH^-}$$

4. Simplify by subtracting the fewer number of $H_2O$'s (1) from both sides of the equation:

$$2e^- + H_2O + ClO^- \longrightarrow Cl^- + 2OH^-$$

Now consider a typical unbalanced equation representing a total redox reaction. The presence of $OH^-$ ion in the equation tells us that this reaction occurs in basic solution.

$$MnO_4^-(aq) + C_2O_4^{2-}(aq) + OH^-(aq) \longrightarrow MnO_2(s) + CO_3^{2-}(aq) + H_2O(l)$$

Because tables of half-reactions are represented as either acidic (with $H^+$ ions) or basic (with $OH^-$ ions), we will change each half-reaction to basic solution. (Alternatively, we could balance the total equation as if in acid solution and then change the final balanced equation to basic solution.)

1. Balance the reduction half-reaction involving $MnO_4^-$ and $MnO_2$ in acid solution.

$$3e^- + 4H^+ + MnO_4^- \longrightarrow MnO_2 + 2H_2O$$

2. Change to basic solution by adding $4OH^-$ to each side.

$$3e^- + (4H^+ + 4OH^-) + MnO_4^- \longrightarrow MnO_2 + 2H_2O + 4OH^-$$

3. Combine $4H^+$ and $4OH^-$ to form $4H_2O$ and then subtract $2H_2O$ from both sides of the equation.

$$3e^- + 2H_2O + MnO_4^- \longrightarrow MnO_2 + 4OH^-$$

4. Balance the oxidation half-reaction involving $C_2O_4^{2-}$ and $CO_3^{2-}$ in acid solution.

$$2H_2O + C_2O_4^{2-} \longrightarrow 2CO_3^{2-} + 4H^+ + 2e^-$$

5. Change to basic solution as before by adding $4OH^-$ to each side and simplify by subtracting out $2H_2O$ from each side.

$$4OH^- + C_2O_4^{2-} \longrightarrow 2CO_3^{2-} + 2H_2O + 2e^-$$

6. Multiply the reduction reaction by 2 and the oxidation half-reaction by 3 and add equations.

$$6e^- + \overset{4}{\cancel{12}}H_2O + \overset{4}{\cancel{12}}OH^- + 3C_2O_4^{2-} + 2MnO_4^- \longrightarrow$$

$$6CO_3^{2-} + \overset{2}{\cancel{6}}H_2O + 2MnO_2 + 8\cancel{OH^-} + \cancel{6e^-}$$

7. Simplify by subtracting out $6e^-$, $4H_2O$, and $8OH^-$.

$$4OH^- + 3C_2O_4{}^{2-} + 2MnO_4{}^- \longrightarrow 6CO_3{}^{2-} + 2H_2O + 2MnO_2$$

## EXAMPLE 14-5   Balancing Redox Equations in Basic Solution

Balance the following equation in basic solution by the ion-electron method.

$$Bi_2O_3(s) + NO_3{}^-(aq) + OH^-(aq) \longrightarrow BiO_3{}^-(aq) + NO_2{}^-(aq) + H_2O(l)$$

**PROCEDURE**

(1) Identify and separate the reduced and oxidized species and their products. (2) Balance in acidic solution. (3) Change from acidic to basic solution. (4) Simplify.

**SOLUTION**

| | |
|---|---|
| Reduction reaction: | $NO_3{}^- \longrightarrow NO_2{}^-$ |
| Balance in acidic: | $2e^- + 2H^+ + NO_3{}^- \longrightarrow NO_2{}^- + H_2O$ |
| Change to basic: | $2e^- + (2H^+ + 2OH^-) + NO_3{}^- \longrightarrow NO_2{}^- + H_2O + 2OH^-$ |
| Simplify $H_2O$: | $2e^- + H_2O + NO_3{}^- \longrightarrow NO_2{}^- + 2OH^-$ |
| Oxidation reaction: | $Bi_2O_3 \longrightarrow 2BiO_3{}^-$ |
| Balance in acidic: | $3H_2O + Bi_2O_3 \longrightarrow 2BiO_3{}^- + 6H^+ + 4e^-$ |
| Change to basic: | $6OH^- + 3H_2O + Bi_2O_3 \longrightarrow 2BiO_3{}^- + (6H^+ + 6OH^-) + 4e^-$ |
| Simplify $H_2O$: | $6OH^- + Bi_2O_3 \longrightarrow 2BiO_3{}^- + 3H_2O + 4e^-$ |

Multiply the reduction reaction by 2 and add to the oxidation half-reaction.

$$4e^- + Bi_2O_3 + 2H_2O + 2NO_3{}^- + 6OH^- \longrightarrow 2BiO_3{}^- + 2NO_2{}^- + 4OH^- + 3H_2O + 4e^-$$

Simplify by subtracting $2H_2O$, $4OH^-$, and $4e^-$ from both sides of the equation.

$$Bi_2O_3(s) + 2NO_3{}^-(aq) + 2OH^-(aq) \longrightarrow 2BiO_3{}^-(aq) + 2NO_2{}^-(aq) + H_2O(l)$$

**ANALYSIS**

Balancing equations in basic solution requires a direct application of the material from the previous chapter. In an aqueous solution, you have at your disposal $H_2O$ and excess $H^+$ or $OH^-$, depending on whether the solution is acidic or basic. By adding an $OH^-$ ion to an $H^+$ ion, you are essentially changing the $H^+$ to an $H_2O$. This is the net ionic equation of a neutralization reaction between a strong acid and a strong base. Remember to add an $OH^-$ to both sides of the equation, however.

**SYNTHESIS**

We make distinctions between acidic and basic solutions because some compounds produce reactions that are different in each case. For example, $MnO_4{}^-$ is reduced to $Mn^{2+}$ in acid solution but to $MnO_2$ in basic solution. In another example, $Fe^{3+}$ is present in acidic solution but forms insoluble $Fe(OH)_3$ in basic solution. Alternately, different forms of the compounds exist in different pH's. $HClO$ is present in acidic solutions and can be reduced to $Cl_2$. $ClO^-$ is present in basic solutions and can be reduced to $Cl^-$. Furthermore, as we'll see in the next section, each one of these reactions has a different potential for occurring, so the amount of energy we can get out of the reaction varies in each case.

▶ **ASSESSING THE OBJECTIVE FOR SECTION 14-3**

**EXERCISE 14-3(a) LEVEL 2:** Balance the following equations by the ion-electron method.

**(a)** $NO_3{}^-(aq) + H_2SO_3(aq) \longrightarrow SO_4{}^{2-}(aq) + NO(g) + H^+(aq) + H_2O(l)$

**(b)** $H_2O(l) + MnO_4{}^-(aq) + S^{2-}(aq) \longrightarrow MnS(s) + S(s) + OH^-(aq)$

(Notice some sulfide ions change and others do not.)

**EXERCISE 14-3(b) LEVEL 3:** When elemental tin is placed in a nitric acid solution, a spontaneous redox reaction occurs, producing solid tin(IV) oxide and nitrogen dioxide gas. Write the equation illustrating this reaction and balance the equation by the ion-electron method. (Water is also a product.)

*For additional practice, work chapter problems 14-18, 14-20, 14-22, and 14-24.*

## PART A SUMMARY

### KEY TERMS

14-1.1 **Half-reactions** indicate either the **oxidation** or **reduction** process. pp. 480–481

14-1.2 An electron exchange reaction is known as an **oxidation-reduction**, or simply **redox**, reaction. p. 481

14-1.2 The species reduced is known as the **oxidizing agent**; the species oxidized is known as the **reducing agent**. p. 481

14-1.3 **Oxidation states** (or **oxidation numbers**) are used to identify the elements that change in redox reactions. p. 482

14-2 The **oxidation state** or **bridge method** balances equations by focusing on the oxidation state changes. p. 486

14-3 The **ion-electron method** is used to balance half-reactions separately before adding to the total reaction. p. 489

### SUMMARY CHART

*Oxidizing and Reducing Agents*

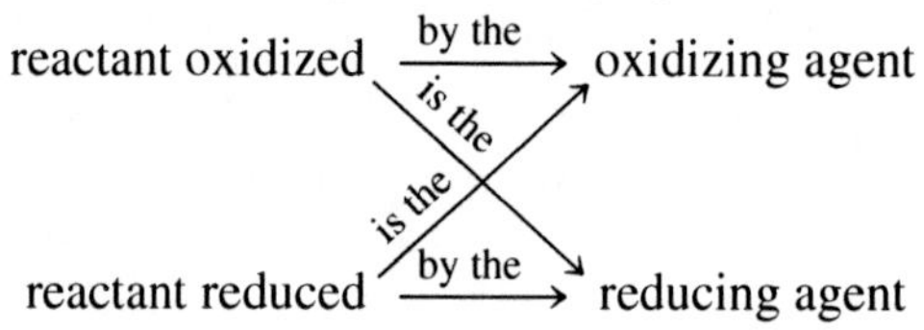

$$\text{reactant oxidized} \xrightarrow{\text{by the}} \text{oxidizing agent}$$

*is the* (crossing arrows) *is the*

$$\text{reactant reduced} \xrightarrow{\text{by the}} \text{reducing agent}$$

***Balancing Redox Reactions in Aqueous Solution***

**Unbalanced core reaction: $X + AO^- \longrightarrow XO_2^- + A$**

**Acidic solution**

Separate into two half-reactions

$$X \longrightarrow XO_2^- \qquad\qquad AO^- \longrightarrow A$$

Add $H_2O$

$$\underline{2H_2O} + X \longrightarrow XO_2^- \qquad\qquad AO^- \longrightarrow A + \underline{H_2O}$$

Add $H^+$

$$2H_2O + X \longrightarrow XO_2^- + \underline{4H^+} \qquad\qquad \underline{2H^+} + AO^- \longrightarrow A + H_2O$$

Add $e^-$

$$2H_2O + X \longrightarrow XO_2^- + 4H^+ + \underline{3e^-} \qquad\qquad \underline{e^-} + 2H^+ + AO^- \longrightarrow A + H_2O$$

Balance electron exchange

$$2H_2O + X \longrightarrow XO_2^- + 4H^+ + 3e^- \qquad\qquad \underline{3}e^- + \underline{6}H^+ + \underline{3}AO^- \longrightarrow \underline{3}A + \underline{3}H_2O$$

Add two reactions and simplify

$$\mathbf{2H^+ + X + 3AO^- \longrightarrow XO_2^- + 3A + H_2O}$$

**To change to a basic solution**

**Add $OH^-$ (on both sides) for each $H^+$**

$$(2H^+ + \underline{2OH^-}) + X + 3AO^- \longrightarrow XO_2^- + 3A + H_2O + \underline{2OH^-}$$

**Combine $H^+$ and $OH^-$ to make $H_2O$ and simplify**

$$H_2O + X + 3AO^- \longrightarrow XO_2^- + 3A + 2OH^-$$

## Part B

## Spontaneous and Nonspontaneous Redox Reactions

**SETTING A GOAL**

■ You will understand the extensive practical applications of redox reactions.

**OBJECTIVES**

14-4 Using a table of relative strengths of oxidizing agents, determine whether a specific redox reaction is spontaneous.

14-5 Describe the structure and electricity-generating ability of voltaic cells and batteries.

14-6 Write the reactions that occur when a salt is electrolyzed.

# 14-4 Predicting Spontaneous Redox Reactions

**► OBJECTIVE FOR SECTION 14-4**
Using a table of relative strengths of oxidizing agents, determine whether a specific redox reaction is spontaneous.

**LOOKING AHEAD!** In the previous chapter, we found that favorable (spontaneous) reactions occur between a stronger acid and a stronger base, forming a weaker acid and a weaker base. Electron exchange reactions between a stronger oxidizing agent and a stronger reducing agent to produce a weaker oxidizing and reducing agent are also spontaneous. In addition, by observing the results of a few reactions, we can rank oxidizing and reducing agents and compile this information into a table. We can then use this table to predict the occurrence of a large number of reactions. ■

We are well aware that gold is not chemically reactive. Why is it so stable? In an earlier chapter, we found that it is hard to remove an electron from a gold atom because of its high ionization energy. Using our current language we would say that gold is very hard to oxidize. It is just the opposite for a metal such as sodium, which is very easily oxidized. In this section, we will compare and rank three metals (zinc, copper, and nickel) as to their ability to be oxidized. This requires that we observe the results of three experiments.

The first experiment involves comparing copper to zinc. We do this by immersing a strip of zinc metal in an aqueous solution containing $Cu^{2+}$ ions. It is obvious that an oxidation–reduction reaction occurs spontaneously, as indicated by the coating of copper that forms on the zinc metal. (In Chapter 6, we referred to this same reaction as a single-replacement reaction.) The zinc metal is oxidized to $Zn^{2+}$ and the $Cu^{2+}$ ion is reduced to copper metal with the transfer of two electrons from the zinc metal to the copper ion. (See Figure 6-5, Section 6-4.) However, if we placed copper metal in a solution of $Zn^{2+}$ ions, we would observe that no reaction occurs. The reverse reaction does not occur spontaneously, since reactions are spontaneous (favorable) in one direction only. (See Figure 6-6, Section 6-4.1.)

The net ionic equation for the spontaneous reaction is

$$Zn(s) + Cu^{2+}(aq) \longrightarrow Zn^{2+}(aq) + Cu(s)$$

*This is a spontaneous reaction because a stronger oxidizing agent and a stronger reducing agent react to form a weaker oxidizing and reducing agent.* Since the spontaneous reaction is from left to right, we can make the following conclusions about the relative strengths of the two oxidizing and reducing agents.

1. $Cu^{2+}$ is a better oxidizing agent than $Zn^{2+}$.
2. Zn metal is a better reducing agent than Cu metal.

In the second experiment, we will compare copper to nickel. As in the first experiment, we find that copper metal also forms a coating on a strip of Ni immersed in a $Cu^{2+}$ solution. This spontaneous reaction is illustrated by the following equation.

$$Ni(s) + Cu^{2+}(aq) \longrightarrow Ni^{2+}(aq) + Cu(s)$$

This result provides similar conclusions as the Zn–Cu experiments.

A coating of copper forms on a strip of zinc in a $Cu^{2+}$ solution.

**3.** $Cu^{2+}$ is a better oxidizing agent than $Ni^{2+}$.

**4.** Ni metal is a better reducing agent than Cu metal.

So far, we know that both zinc and nickel are better reducing agents than copper, but how do they compare to each other? In the third experiment we immerse a strip of zinc in a solution containing $Ni^{2+}$ ions. A coating of nickel eventually appears on the zinc metal. (If we had first tried placing a strip of nickel in a $Zn^{2+}$ solution, we would find that no reaction occurs.) The spontaneous reaction between Zn and $Ni^{2+}$ is represented below.

$$Zn(s) + Ni^{2+}(aq) \longrightarrow Zn^{2+}(aq) + Ni(s)$$

Our conclusions from this experiment are:

**5.** $Ni^{2+}$ is a better oxidizing agent than $Zn^{2+}$.

**6.** Zn metal is a better reducing agent than Ni metal.

We can now rank all three ions as oxidizing agents in order of decreasing strength as follows.

$$Cu^{2+} > Ni^{2+} > Zn^{2+}$$

*Notice that the strength of the metals as reducing agents is inversely related to the strength of their ions as oxidizing agents.* Because of the inverse relationship, the ranking of the three metals as reducing agents is in the reverse order.

$$Zn > Ni > Cu$$

These three metals were included in the *activity series* that was discussed in Chapter 6. In this chapter, we now explain the activity series by comparing the strengths of the metals as reducing agents and of their ions as oxidizing agents.

More experiments can provide additional ions and molecular species for our ranking. Eventually, we can construct a table of oxidizing agents ordered according to strength. Such a ranking is given in Table 14-1 and is an extension of the activity series of metals introduced in Chapter 6. In some cases, instruments are required to give quantitative values, known as *reduction potentials*, which indicate the comparative strength of a given oxidizing agent in relation to a defined standard. The strengths of the oxidizing agents are compared in these measurements at the same concentration for all ions involved (1.00 M) and at the same partial pressure of all gases involved (1.00 atm).

A redox reaction takes place between an oxidizing agent on the left and a reducing agent on the right. *A favorable or spontaneous reaction occurs between an element, ion, or compound on the left (an oxidizing agent) and a species on the right (a reducing agent) that lies below it in the table.* The strongest oxidizing agent ($F_2$) is at the top of Table 14-1, on the left. It will oxidize any reducing agent listed on the right. However, the reducing agents, shown on the right, become stronger *down* the table. Na is the strongest reducing agent listed and so will reduce any oxidizing agent listed on the left. The spontaneous reaction can be visualized as taking place in a clockwise direction, with the oxidizing agent forming a product to the right and the reducing agent below it forming a product in the opposite direction to the left. (See Figure 14-2.)

Table 14-1 is particularly useful in predicting the reactions of certain elements with water. (All the reactions shown in the table are assumed to occur in aqueous solution.) The boxed reaction near the top of the table represents the oxidation of water when read from right to left. Note that the gaseous elements $F_2$ and $Cl_2$ spontaneously oxidize water to produce oxygen gas and an acid. (The reaction of $Cl_2$ with water is quite slow, however.)

$$\text{Cl}_2 + 2e^- \rightleftharpoons 2Cl^-$$

$$O_2 + 4H^+ + 4e^- \rightleftharpoons 2H_2O$$

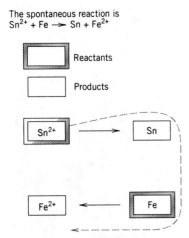

The spontaneous reaction is $Sn^{2+} + Fe \longrightarrow Sn + Fe^{2+}$

**FIGURE 14-2 Spontaneous Reaction** The stronger oxidizing agent reacts with the stronger reducing agent.

TABLE 14-1

**Oxidizing Agents and Reducing Agents**

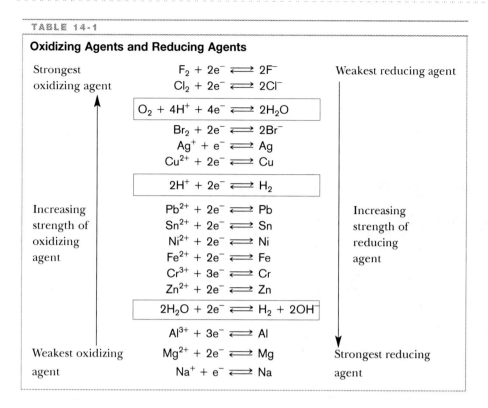

Strongest oxidizing agent → ... Weakest reducing agent

$F_2 + 2e^- \rightleftharpoons 2F^-$
$Cl_2 + 2e^- \rightleftharpoons 2Cl^-$
$O_2 + 4H^+ + 4e^- \rightleftharpoons 2H_2O$
$Br_2 + 2e^- \rightleftharpoons 2Br^-$
$Ag^+ + e^- \rightleftharpoons Ag$
$Cu^{2+} + 2e^- \rightleftharpoons Cu$
$2H^+ + 2e^- \rightleftharpoons H_2$
$Pb^{2+} + 2e^- \rightleftharpoons Pb$
$Sn^{2+} + 2e^- \rightleftharpoons Sn$
$Ni^{2+} + 2e^- \rightleftharpoons Ni$
$Fe^{2+} + 2e^- \rightleftharpoons Fe$
$Cr^{3+} + 3e^- \rightleftharpoons Cr$
$Zn^{2+} + 2e^- \rightleftharpoons Zn$
$2H_2O + 2e^- \rightleftharpoons H_2 + 2OH^-$
$Al^{3+} + 3e^- \rightleftharpoons Al$
$Mg^{2+} + 2e^- \rightleftharpoons Mg$
$Na^+ + e^- \rightleftharpoons Na$

Increasing strength of oxidizing agent

Increasing strength of reducing agent

Weakest oxidizing agent

Strongest reducing agent

The spontaneous reaction is

$$2Cl_2 + 2H_2O \longrightarrow O_2 + 4H^+ + 4Cl^-$$

The boxed reaction near the bottom of the table represents the reduction of water when read from left to right. Note that the metals Al, Mg, and Na spontaneously reduce water to produce hydrogen gas and a base. *(We can say that Na reduces water, or, conversely, we can say that water oxidizes Na.)*

$$2H_2O + 2e^- \rightleftharpoons H_2 + 2OH^-$$
$$Na^+ + e^- \rightleftharpoons Na$$

The spontaneous reaction is

$$2H_2O + 2Na \longrightarrow H_2 + 2Na^+ + 2OH^-$$

These metals are known as *active* metals because of their chemical reactivity with water.

The third boxed reaction, near the middle of the table, represents the reduction of aqueous acid solutions (1.00 M $H^+$) to form hydrogen gas. Note that metals such as Ni and Fe are not oxidized by water but are oxidized by strong acid solutions.

$$2H^+ + 2e^- \rightleftharpoons H_2$$
$$Fe^{2+} + 2e^- \rightleftharpoons Fe$$

The spontaneous reaction is

$$2H^+ + Fe \longrightarrow Fe^{2+} + H_2$$

Acid rain is so named because it contains a considerably higher $H^+$ concentration than ordinary rain. From this discussion, we can understand why metals such as iron and nickel are more likely to be corroded by acid rain.

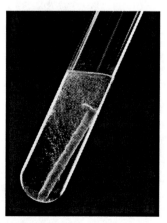

Iron is oxidized by a strong acid solution to form iron(II) ions and hydrogen gas.

227

Two of the metals shown in the table—Cu and Ag—are not oxidized by either water or acid solutions.* Thus, these metals are relatively unreactive and find use in jewelry and coins.

---

*Copper is dissolved by nitric acid solutions, but the copper is oxidized by the nitrate ion, not the hydronium ion. See Example 14-3(b).

## EXAMPLE 14-6 Determining the Direction of a Spontaneous Reaction

A strip of tin is placed in an aqueous solution of $Cr(NO_3)_3$ in one experiment. In another, a strip of chromium is placed in an aqueous solution of $Sn(NO_3)_2$. Write the net ionic equation illustrating the spontaneous reaction that occurs.

### PROCEDURE

In Table 14-1, note that $Sn^{2+}$ is a stronger oxidizing agent than $Cr^{3+}$ and Cr is a stronger reducing agent than Sn. The reactants are, therefore, $Sn^{2+}$ and Cr. A balanced equation is obtained by multiplying the $Sn^{2+}$ half-reaction by 3 and the Cr half-reaction by 2 for an exchange of six electrons.

### SOLUTION

$$3Sn^{2+}(aq) + 2Cr(s) \longrightarrow 3Sn(s) + 2Cr^{3+}(aq)$$

### ANALYSIS

Notice that the spontaneous reaction takes place in a clockwise direction in the table. $Sn^{2+}$ is in the higher position in the table as an oxidizing agent and reacts to the right, forming its product, Sn. Cr is below Sn so is the stronger reducing agent. It reacts to the left, forming its product, $Cr^{3+}$. Six electrons are exchanged to balance the equation. In using the table, remember that one species reacts to the right and one to the left.

### SYNTHESIS

Nonmetal elements tend to be at the upper left of the reduction table and metal elements at the bottom right. These represent the reactive extremes of the table. As you move up the left side and down the right side, the elements become more reactive. It is not surprising that this order is also roughly close to the historical order in which these elements were discovered, isolated, and identified. The more reactive an element is, the harder it becomes to produce it in its elemental state. Metals at the upper right, like copper and silver, have been known since the beginning of civilization. So have iron, lead, mercury, and tin, which require only modest efforts to liberate from their ores. Metal ions of medium reduction potential, such as nickel, cobalt, and manganese, were isolated in the mid-1700s. The most reactive metals were finally isolated after electricity became a viable technique for promoting difficult chemical reactions in the nineteenth century. These include sodium, potassium, lithium, magnesium, and aluminum. Another factor, of course, is the relative abundance of the element, with rarer elements being more difficult to find. A very low reduction potential of the metal ions, though, was the primary roadblock to these elements' discovery.

## EXAMPLE 14-7 Writing a Spontaneous Single-Replacement Reaction

A strip of tin metal is placed in an $AgNO_3$ solution. If a reaction takes place, write the equation illustrating the spontaneous reaction.

### PROCEDURE

In Table 14-1, note that the oxidizing agent $Ag^+$ is above the reducing agent Sn. Therefore, a spontaneous reaction does occur. Write the balanced equation, noticing that two electrons are exchanged.

### SOLUTION

$$2Ag^+(aq) + Sn(s) \longrightarrow Sn^{2+}(aq) + 2Ag(s)$$

ANALYSIS

Again, notice that the spontaneous reaction is in a clockwise direction. The $Ag^+$ reacts to the right and the Sn reacts to the left.

SYNTHESIS

A practical application of this reaction is to "silver coat" tin or some other metal, such as iron or nickel, that lies lower than $Ag^+$ in the table. $Au^{3+}$ also ranks high in the table as an oxidizing agent like $Ag^+$. This means that a cheaper metal can be "gold plated" to give it the outer appearance of gold.

## EXAMPLE 14-8  Writing a Spontaneous Reaction of a Metal with Water

A length of aluminum wire is placed in water. Does the aluminum react with water? What is the spontaneous reaction involving aluminum and water?

PROCEDURE

In Table 14-1, note that aluminum is an active metal and would react with water (as an oxidizing agent). The aluminum is oxidized and the water is reduced.

SOLUTION

$$6H_2O(l) + 2Al(s) \longrightarrow 2Al^{3+}(aq) + 6OH^-(aq) + 3H_2(g)$$

Since $Al(OH)_3$ is insoluble in water, however, the equation should be written as

$$6H_2O(l) + 2Al(s) \longrightarrow 2Al(OH)_3(s) + 3H_2(g)$$

ANALYSIS

How many electrons are being exchanged in this reaction? The oxidation of aluminum to $Al^{3+}$ is a 3-electron half-reaction. In water, hydrogen is reduced from +1 to 0 in $H_2$, but two hydrogen atoms require 2 electrons. The least common multiple of 3 and 2 is 6, so there are 6 electrons exchanging in this reaction.

SYNTHESIS

Theoretically, aluminum should dissolve (i.e., react) in water. How then can we have aluminum boats? Metallic aluminum reacts with oxygen in the air to form a coating of $Al_2O_3$, which protects the metal from coming into contact with water. In other words, it "self-paints." The reaction described above is actually limited to the outermost layer of aluminum. The only thing you would notice is that shiny aluminum forms a gray coating in water.

▶ ASSESSING THE OBJECTIVE FOR SECTION 14-4

EXERCISE 14-4(a) LEVEL 1: Fill in the blanks.
Spontaneous redox reactions occur between the _____ oxidizing and reducing agents to produce _____ oxidizing and reducing agents. In a table, the stronger oxidizing agent is located _____ in the table than the reducing agent.

EXERCISE 14-4(b) LEVEL 2: In which of the following would a spontaneous reaction occur? Write the balanced equation for that reaction.

(a) A strip of Pb is placed in a $Cr^{3+}$ solution.
(b) A strip of Cr is placed in a $Pb^{2+}$ solution.

EXERCISE 14-4(c) LEVEL 2: If zinc and iron were in electrical contact with one another, which would oxidize first?

**EXERCISE 14-4(d) LEVEL 3:** Given the following table of oxidizing and reducing agents, answer the questions below.

strongest ⟶ $I_2 + 2e^- \rightleftharpoons 2I^-$
oxidizing $\quad Cr^{3+} + 3e^- \rightleftharpoons Cr$
agent $\qquad Mn^{2+} + 2e^- \rightleftharpoons Mn \qquad$ strongest
$\qquad\qquad Ca^{2+} + 2e^- \rightleftharpoons Ca \leftarrow$ reducing agent

**(a)** Is the following reaction spontaneous or nonspontaneous?
$$Mn + Ca^{2+} \longrightarrow Ca + Mn^{2+}$$
**(b)** Write a balanced equation representing a spontaneous reaction involving the Cr, $Cr^{3+}$ and the Mn, $Mn^{2+}$ half-reactions.
**(c)** If an aqueous solution of $I_2$ (an antiseptic) is spilled on a chromium-coated automobile bumper, will a reaction occur? If so, write the balanced equation for the reaction.
**(d)** Which substance in the table will react with $Mn^{2+}$?
**(e)** Which substances in the table will not react with any other in the table?

**EXERCISE 14-4(e) LEVEL 3:** Write a balanced equation illustrating how a metal such as iron could be "gold plated" from an $Au^{3+}$ solution.

*For additional practice, work chapter problems 14-20, 14-27, 14-31, and 14-32.*

▶ **OBJECTIVE FOR SECTION 14-5**
Describe the structure and electricity-generating ability of voltaic cells and batteries.

# 14-5 Voltaic Cells

**LOOKING AHEAD!** The electrons exchanged in a spontaneous redox reaction can be detoured through a wire and put to work. This is the principle used in all the different types of batteries that we depend on to run our calculators, remotes, cell phones, and even iPods and MP3 players. How this is accomplished is the topic of this section. ■

Releasing the brake on an automobile parked on the side of a hill brings no surprise. The automobile spontaneously rolls down the hill because the bottom of the hill represents a lower potential energy than the top. Chemical reactions occur spontaneously for the same reason. The products represent a position of lower potential energy than the reactants. In the case of the car, the difference in potential energy is due to position and the attraction of gravity; in the case of a chemical reaction, the difference in potential energy is due to the composition of the reactants and products. (See Figure 14-3.) When the car rolls down the hill, the difference in energy is transformed into the kinetic energy of the moving car and heat from friction. When a

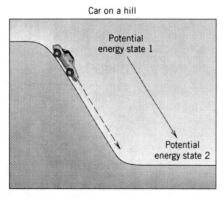
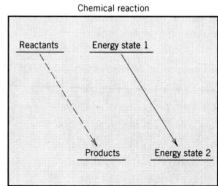

**FIGURE 14-3 Energy States** A chemical reaction proceeds in a certain direction for the same reason that a car rolls down a hill.

chemical reaction proceeds spontaneously from reactants to products, the difference is given off as heat, light, or electrical energy. In this section, we are concerned with the electrical energy provided by spontaneous redox reactions.

## 14-5.1 The Daniell Cell

*A* **voltaic cell** (*also called a galvanic cell*) *uses a favorable or spontaneous redox reaction to generate electrical energy through an external circuit.* One of the earliest voltaic cells put to use the spontaneous reaction discussed in the previous section, which is

$$Zn(s) + Cu^{2+}(aq) \longrightarrow Zn^{2+}(aq) + Cu(s)$$

This voltaic cell is known as the *Daniell cell* and was used to generate electrical current for the new telegraph and doorbells in homes.

In an earlier experiment discussed in the previous section, we found that a strip of zinc placed in a $Cu^{2+}$ solution forms a coating of metallic copper on the zinc strip. To generate electricity, however, the oxidation reaction must be separated from the reduction reaction so that the electrons exchanged can flow in an external wire where they can be put to use. The Daniell cell is illustrated in Figure 14-4. A zinc strip is immersed in a $Zn^{2+}$ solution, and, in a separate compartment, a copper strip is immersed in a $Cu^{2+}$ solution. A wire connects the two metal strips. The two metal strips are called electrodes. *The* **electrodes** *are the surfaces in a cell at which the reactions take place. The electrode at which oxidation takes place is called the* **anode.** *Reduction takes place at the* **cathode.** In the compartment on the left, the strip of Zn serves as the anode, since the following reaction occurs when the circuit is connected.

$$Zn \longrightarrow Zn^{2+} + 2e^-$$

When the circuit is complete, the two electrons travel in the external wire to the Cu electrode, which serves as the cathode. The reduction reaction occurs at the cathode.

$$2e^- + Cu^{2+} \longrightarrow Cu$$

To maintain neutrality in the solution, some means must be provided for the movement of a $SO_4^{2-}$ ion (or some other negative ion) from the right compartment, where a $Cu^{2+}$ has been removed, to the left compartment, where a $Zn^{2+}$ has been produced. The salt bridge is an aqueous gel that allows ions to migrate between compartments but does not allow the mixing of solutions. A porous plate separating the two solutions, as shown in Figure 14-4, also serves this function. (If $Cu^{2+}$ ions mixed into the left compartment, they would form a coating of Cu on the Zn electrode, thus short-circuiting the cell.)

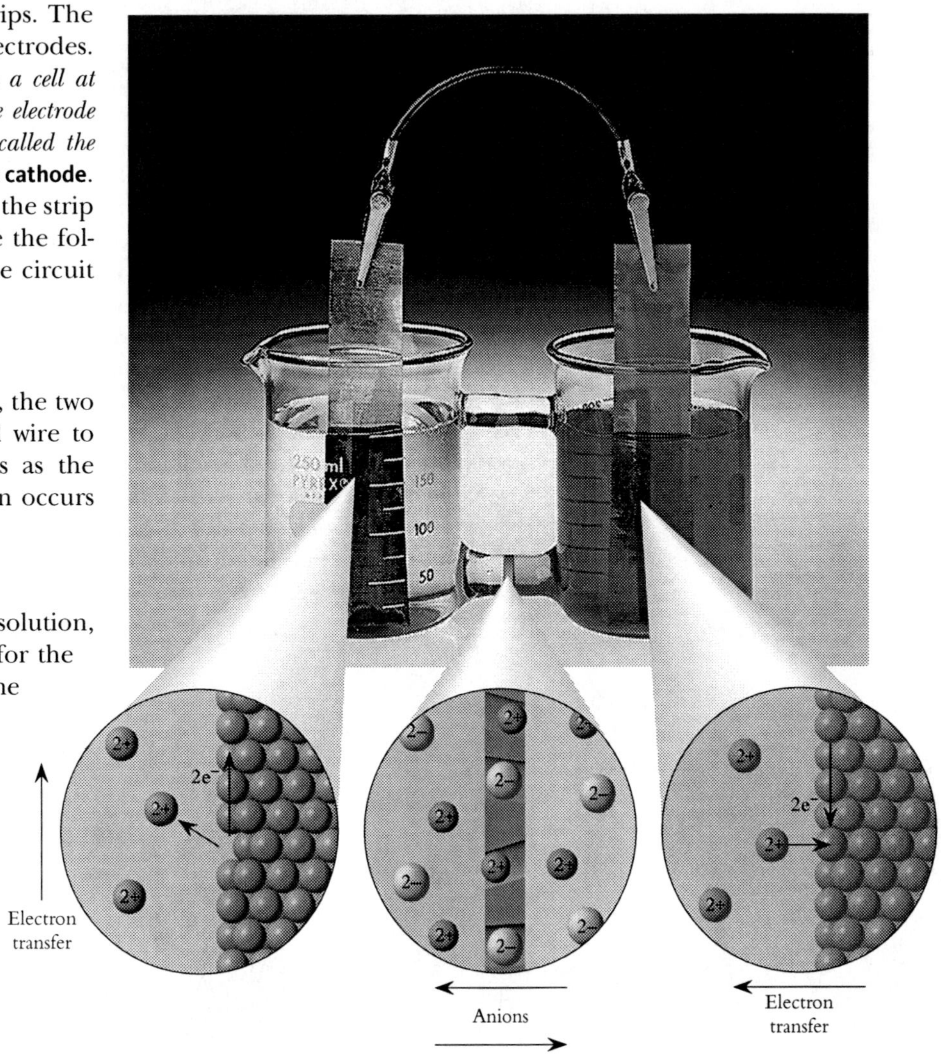

**FIGURE 14-4 The Daniell Cell**
This chemical reaction produced electricity for the first telegraphs.

The electrodes in this cell are called active electrodes because they are involved in the reaction. As the cell discharges (generates electrical energy), the Zn electrode becomes smaller but the Cu electrode becomes larger. The reaction can be stopped by interrupting the external circuit with a switch. If the circuit is open, the electrons can no longer flow, so no further reaction occurs until the switch is again closed. The energy of the cell can thus be stored between uses.

### 14-5.2 Lead-Acid Batteries

Two of the most common voltaic cells in use today are two of the oldest. (Both were invented in the late-nineteenth century.) These are the dry cell (flashlight battery) and the lead-acid cell (car battery). (*A* **battery** *is a collection of one or more separate cells joined together in one unit.*)

We still use good old lead–acid batteries to start our cars. Such a three-cell storage battery is illustrated in Figure 14-5. Each cell is composed of two grids separated by an inert spacer. One grid of a fully charged battery contains metallic lead. The other contains $PbO_2$, which is insoluble in $H_2O$. Both grids are immersed in a sulfuric acid solution (battery acid). When the battery is discharged by connecting the electrodes, the following half-reactions take place spontaneously.

*Anode:* $\quad\quad\quad\quad\quad\quad\quad$ $Pb(s) + H_2SO_4(aq) \longrightarrow PbSO_4(s) + 2H^+(aq) + 2e^-$

*Cathode:* $2e^- + 2H^+(aq) + PbO_2(s) + H_2SO_4(aq) \longrightarrow PbSO_4(s) + 2H_2O(l)$

*Total reaction:* $\quad Pb(s) + PbO_2(s) + 2H_2SO_4(aq) \longrightarrow 2PbSO_4(s) + 2H_2O(l)$

The electrons released at the Pb anode travel through the external circuit to run a car's lights, starter, radio, or whatever is needed. The electrons return to the $PbO_2$ cathode to complete the circuit. As the reaction proceeds, both electrodes are converted to $PbSO_4$, and the $H_2SO_4$ is depleted. Since $PbSO_4$ is also insoluble, it remains attached to the grids as it forms. The degree of discharge of a battery can be determined by the density of the battery acid. Since the density of a fully discharged battery is 1.15 g/mL, the difference in density between this value and the density of a fully charged battery (1.35 g/mL) gives the amount of charge remaining in the battery. As the electrodes convert to $PbSO_4$, the battery loses power and eventually becomes "dead." Most lead batteries sold today are sealed, however, so density cannot be used to determine its condition.

The convenience of a car battery is that it can be recharged. After the engine starts, an alternator or generator is engaged to push electrons back into the cell in the opposite direction from which they came during discharge. This forces the reverse, nonspontaneous reaction to proceed.

$$2PbSO_4(s) + 2H_2O(l) \longrightarrow Pb(s) + PbO_2(s) + 2H_2SO_4(aq)$$

**FIGURE 14-5 Lead Storage Battery** The lead storage battery is rechargeable.

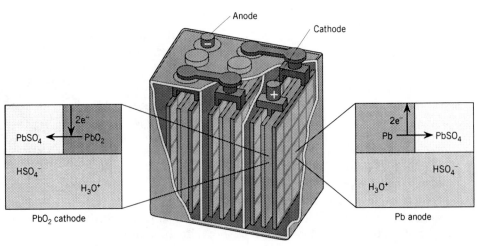

When the battery is fully recharged, the alternator shuts off, the circuit is open, and the battery is ready for the next start.

### 14-5.3 The Dry Cell

The dry cell (invented by Leclanché in 1866) is not rechargeable to any extent but is comparatively inexpensive and easily portable. (In contrast, the lead–acid battery is heavy and expensive and must be kept upright.) The dry cell illustrated in Figure 14-6 consists of a zinc anode, which is the outer rim, and an inert graphite electrode. (An *inert* or *passive* electrode

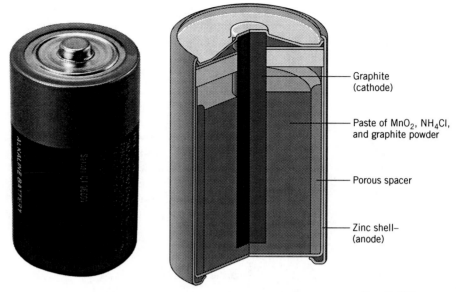

provides a reaction surface but does not itself react.) In between is an aqueous paste containing $NH_4Cl$, $MnO_2$, and carbon. The reactions are as follows.

*Anode:* $Zn(s) \longrightarrow Zn^{2+}(aq) + 2e^-$

*Cathode:* $2NH_4^+(aq) + 2MnO_2(s) + 2e^- \longrightarrow Mn_2O_3(s) + 2NH_3(aq) + H_2O$

A disadvantage of the dry cell is that the $NH_4^+$ ion creates an acidic solution. (In the previous chapter, we discussed how this cation undergoes hydrolysis to form a weakly acidic solution.) The zinc electrode slowly reacts with the weakly acidic solution, so the shelf-life of these batteries is a matter of only a few months. In an *alkaline battery,* NaOH or KOH is substituted for the $NH_4Cl$, so the solution is basic and zinc reacts much more slowly. Alkaline batteries are more expensive, but they have much longer shelf-lives. The anode reaction in the alkaline battery is

$$Zn(s) + 2OH^-(aq) \longrightarrow ZnO(s) + H_2O(l) + 2e^-$$

### 14-5.4 Specialized Batteries

Other types of batteries that have been developed in modern times are more useful for calculators and wristwatches. These batteries are very small and deliver a small amount of current for a long time. Some batteries can produce current for three to five years. One is the *silver battery,* which uses a zinc anode and a silver(I) oxide cathode. Another, known as the *mercury battery,* also uses a zinc anode but a mercury(II) oxide cathode. (See Figure 14-7.) The two reactions in these batteries are

$$Silver\ battery:\ Zn(s) + Ag_2O(s) \longrightarrow ZnO(s) + 2Ag(s)$$

$$Mercury\ battery:\ Zn(s) + HgO(s) \longrightarrow ZnO(s) + Hg(l)$$

**FIGURE 14-6 Dry Cell** The dry cell (left) is comparatively inexpensive, light, and portable. Its contents are depicted on the right.

Graphite (cathode)

Paste of $MnO_2$, $NH_4Cl$, and graphite powder

Porous spacer

Zinc shell (anode)

**FIGURE 14-7 Mercury Battery** These small batteries deliver electrical current for long periods.

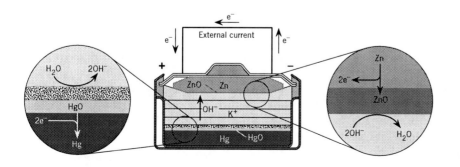

A battery that substitutes for dry cells is known as a *nickel-cadmium battery*. The advantage of this battery is that it is rechargeable. However, it is considerably more expensive initially. The reversible reaction that takes place in this cell is

$$Cd(s) + 2NiO(OH)(s) + 2H_2O(l) \longrightarrow 2Ni(OH)_2(s) + Cd(OH)_2(s)$$

There are many other batteries that have special uses, such as the *lithium battery*, which takes advantage of the light weight and strong reducing ability of lithium. Most laptop computers use what is known as a *lithium ion battery*. It provides a good source of power and is both rechargeable and comparatively light. It actually does not involve a redox reaction, however. Electrical energy is supplied by the movement of lithium ions from one electrode to another while electrons move through an external circuit. Lithium ion batteries are now under development for use in an electrical automobile to be produced by several major manufacturers.

### 14-5.5 Fuel Cells

Space travel requires a tremendous source of electrical energy. The requirements are that the source be continuous (no recharging necessary), lightweight, and dependable. Solar energy directly converts rays from the sun into electricity and is used in the international space station (as well as in an increasing number of homes). It was not practical for shorter runs such as the space shuttle. Although expensive, a source of power that fills the bill nicely is the fuel cell. A **fuel cell** *uses the direct reaction of hydrogen or a hydrogen compound and oxygen to produce electrical energy.* Figure 14-8 is an illustration of a fuel cell. Hydrogen and oxygen gases are fed into the cell, where they form water. As long as the gases enter the cell, power is generated. The water that is formed can be removed and used for other purposes in the spacecraft. Since reactants are supplied from external sources, the electrodes are not consumed, and the cell does not have to be shut down to be regenerated, as a car battery does. The best inert electrode surfaces at which the gases react are made of the extremely expensive metal platinum. The reactions that take place in a basic solution in the fuel cell are

*Anode:* $H_2(g) + 2OH^-(aq) \longrightarrow 2H_2O + 2e^-$

*Cathode:* $O_2(g) + 2H_2O + 4e^- \longrightarrow 4OH^-(aq)$

*Overall:* $2H_2(g) + O_2(g) \longrightarrow 2H_2O$

Fuel cells have had some large-scale application in power generation for commercial purposes. Currently, a great deal of research money and effort is being expended in fuel cell research. See Making It Real, "Fuel Cells—The Future Is (Almost) Here."

More efficient and durable batteries are the focus at the current time. For example, an efficient and relatively inexpensive electric automobile is the object of intensive efforts. A small electric car using lead–acid batteries requires at least 18 batteries. These have to be replaced every year or so, depending on use. Also, much of the power of these batteries must be used just to move the heavy batteries around, not including the car and passengers. There have been some encouraging possibilities for lighter, more durable batteries, and several types of electric automobiles are in the testing phase.

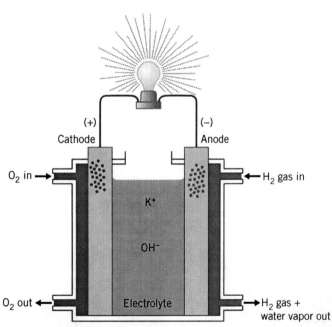

**FIGURE 14-8 Fuel Cell** The fuel cell can generate power without interruption for recharging.

## MAKING IT REAL

### Fuel Cells—The Future Is (Almost) Here

Special vehicles are currently testing fuel cells as a power source.

The simplest combustion reaction, hydrogen plus oxygen to form water, may be the key to the future. On a mass-of-fuel basis, it is by far the most energetic reaction. The combustion of two moles (4 g) of hydrogen produces 570 kJ of energy, much more than any other fuel. Since the combustion of hydrogen is a redox reaction, the energy can be released as electrical energy. This is the principle of the fuel cell, first demonstrated in the nineteenth century. It has long been used in the space program by NASA to continuously generate electricity without releasing toxic products. The two reactions that occur in the fuel cell and a diagram were illustrated in Section 14-5.5 and Figure 14-8.

The use of the fuel cell has been limited by the expense of inert electrodes that have traditionally contained rare platinum and/or palladium, which are more expensive than gold. Also, although hydrogen was previously discussed as the perfect fuel, it is hazardous to handle, it is not cheap in the pure state, and it is not easy to store in large quantities. Another problem involves the high operating temperatures necessary in a fuel cell.

All these problems, however, are being addressed with billions of dollars of investment and research. Much of the hope of making fuel cells practical in the short run rests in using fuels such as methane (natural gas), butane, methanol, ethanol, or even gasoline rather than pure hydrogen. These compounds are readily available and easy to transport. The problem with these fuels is that they tend to gunk up the electrodes and they produce carbon dioxide, which is a greenhouse gas. Still, it would be much easier to dispense natural gas or even butane at a service station rather than pure hydrogen. Hydrogen is ideal for the fuel cell, but its large-scale application may have to wait.

If you have not yet heard much about fuel cells, you will. Experimental cars and buses using fuel cells are already on the road. Reports come in almost daily about advancements in the research on fuel cells. The operating temperatures keep coming down; new and cheaper materials for the electrodes, along with more efficient use of fuels other than hydrogen, are being developed. Eventually, we will even have fuel cells generating electrical power scattered around a city, eliminating the need for extensive overhead transmission lines. Research is in progress to miniaturize the fuel cell so it can be used in cell phones and calculators. It would be smaller, cheaper (eventually), and easily refueled. (Some may even run on the alcohol in wine or beer.) Fuel cells are the power source of the future.

---

▶ **ASSESSING THE OBJECTIVE FOR SECTION 14-5**

**EXERCISE 14-5(a) LEVEL 1:** Fill in the blanks.
A spontaneous chemical reaction is used in a _____ cell. An example is the Daniell cell, where _____ _____ is oxidized at the _____ and _____ _____ is reduced at the _____. An electrolytic balance is maintained by means of a _____ bridge. In the lead–acid battery, _____ _____ is _____ at the anode and _____ is reduced at the _____.

**EXERCISE 14-5(b) LEVEL 1:** Refer to the text to identify the following cells:

**(a)** $2PbSO_4(s) + 2H_2O \longrightarrow Pb(s) + PbO_2(s) + 2H_2SO_4(aq)$

**(b)** $Cd(s) + 2NiO(OH)(s) + 2H_2O(l) \longrightarrow 2Ni(OH)_2(s) + Cd(OH)_2(s)$

**(c)** $Zn(s) + 2NH_4^+(aq) + 2MnO_2(s) \longrightarrow Zn^{2+}(aq) + Mn_2O_3(s) + 2NH_3(aq) + H_2O$

**(d)** $2H_2(g) + O_2(g) \longrightarrow 2H_2O$

**EXERCISE 14-5(c) LEVEL 2:** A cell is constructed of a $Br_2$, $Br^-$ half-cell connected to an $Fe^{2+}$, Fe half-cell. Write a balanced equation representing the spontaneous reaction that occurs.

**EXERCISE 14-5(d) LEVEL 3:** If you were asked to design a battery to replace the lead–acid battery for an automobile, what balanced equation would you propose from the oxidizing and reducing agents listed in Table 14-1? Three things should be considered (in addition to cost, which we will ignore). (1) The mass of the reactants is important. (2) The farther apart the oxidizing and reducing agents are in the table, the more powerful the battery (i.e., the higher voltage). (3) The overall chemical reactivity of the reactants is important. For example, if a reactant explodes in air or water, we would not want to use it.

*For additional practice, work chapter problems 14-36, 14-38, and 14-40.*

▶ OBJECTIVE
FOR SECTION 14-6
Write the reactions that occur when a salt is electrolyzed.

# 14-6 Electrolytic Cells

**LOOKING AHEAD!** Spontaneous reactions are like cars rolling down a hill. They go to lower energy states. Can a car or a chemical reaction go up a hill? Of course—but in order for this to happen, energy in the form of a push for a car or energy for a chemical reaction must be supplied. Nonspontaneous redox reactions can occur if sufficient electrical energy is supplied from an outside source. This is the final topic of this chapter. ■

Back in the good old days before inexpensive but strong plastics, automobiles were equipped with beautiful chrome bumpers and other chromium accessories. Chromium not only looks great but is also resistant to rust, so it protects the underlying iron (which does rust) from exposure to air and water. How is iron metal coated with a layer of chromium? According to Table 14-1, we would *not* predict that a coating of chromium would spontaneously form on iron immersed in a $Cr^{3+}$ solution. But that doesn't mean we can't *make* it happen. Nonspontaneous redox reactions occur if enough electrical energy is supplied from an outside source. *Cells that convert electrical energy into chemical energy are called* **electrolytic cells**. They involve nonspontaneous redox reactions.

An example of an electrolytic cell is shown in Figure 14-9. When sufficient electrical energy is supplied to the electrodes from an outside source, the following non-spontaneous reaction occurs.

$$2H_2O(l) \longrightarrow 2H_2(g) + O_2(g)$$

The electrolysis of water to produce hydrogen using solar energy seems to be a logical solution to the energy crisis. The hydrogen produced could be used in a fuel cell. Unfortunately, the process using solar energy is currently very inefficient and expensive. At this time, the cheapest source of hydrogen is from a hydrocarbon such as methane (natural gas). However, much research is underway to improve the process.

For electrolysis of water to occur, an electrolyte such as $K_2SO_4$ must be present in solution. Pure water alone does not have a sufficient concentration of ions to allow conduction of electricity.

Another example of an electrolytic cell is the recharge cycle of the lead-acid battery described in Section 14-5.2. When energy from gasoline burning in the engine activates the alternator, electrical energy is supplied to the battery, and the nonspontaneous reaction occurs as an electrolysis reaction. This reaction re-forms the original reactants.

Electrolysis has many useful applications. For example, in addition to chromium, silver and gold can be electroplated onto cheaper metals. In

**FIGURE 14-9 An Electrolytic Cell** Electrolysis of a solution of potassium sulfate gives hydrogen gas and oxygen gas as products.

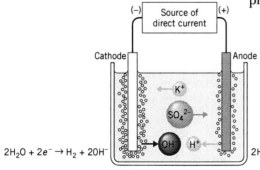

$2H_2O + 2e^- \rightarrow H_2 + 2OH^-$

$2H_2O \rightarrow O_2 + 4H^+ + 4e^-$

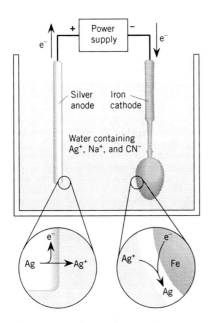

**FIGURE 14-10 Electroplating** With an input of energy, a spoon can be coated with silver. The service has been electroplated with silver.

Figure 14-10 the metal spoon is the cathode and the silver bar serves as the anode. When electricity is supplied, the Ag anode produces $Ag^+$ ions, and the spoon cathode reduces $Ag^+$ ions to form a layer of Ag. The silver-plated spoon can be polished and made to look as good as sterling silver, which is more expensive.

Electrolytic cells are used to free many elements from their compounds. Such cells are especially useful where metals are held in their compounds by strong chemical bonds. Examples are the metals aluminum, sodium, and magnesium. A little over 120 years ago, aluminum was produced through difficult chemical reactions involving elemental sodium as a reducing agent. As a result it was as expensive as gold. Producing molten $Al_2O_3$ (bauxite ore) for electrolysis was not practical because of its very high melting point (2000°C). In 1886, however, it was discovered that when bauxite was mixed with $Na_3AlF_6$ (a mineral called cryolite), the melting point of the mixture was much lower and electrolysis was possible. However, the process does require a large amount of energy. (Recycling requires only about 5% as much energy.) For that reason, recycling aluminum saves money and the environment. Commercial quantities of sodium and chlorine are also produced by electrolysis of molten sodium chloride. An apparatus used for the electrolysis of molten sodium chloride is illustrated in Figure 14-11. At the high temperature required to keep the NaCl in the liquid state, sodium forms as a liquid and is drained from the top of the cell.

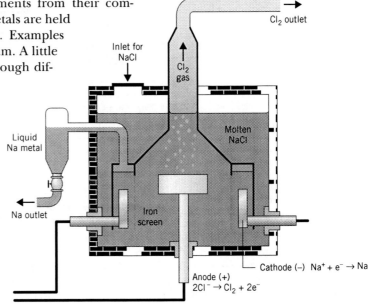

**FIGURE 14-11 Electrolysis of NaCl** Cross section of the Downs cell used for the electrolysis of molten sodium chloride. The cathode is a circular ring that surrounds the anode. The electrodes are separated from each other by an iron screen. During the operation of the cell, molten sodium collects at the top of the cathode compartment, from which it is periodically drained. The chlorine gas bubbles out of the anode compartment and is collected.

▶ **ASSESSING THE OBJECTIVE FOR SECTION 14-6**

**EXERCISE 14-6(a) LEVEL 1:** List four uses for reversing a spontaneous redox reaction.

**EXERCISE 14-6(b) LEVEL 2:** Write the reaction that occurs when molten $MgCl_2$ is electrolyzed.

**EXERCISE 14-6(c) LEVEL 3:** If you want to coat a piece of iron with Cr, it must be electroplated. Is it necessary to electroplate Sn on a piece of iron? If not, why?

**EXERCISE 14-6(d) LEVEL 3:** Aluminum cannot be electroplated from an aqueous solution containing $Al^{3+}$ ions. Why not? Refer to Table 14-1.

*For additional practice, work chapter problem 14-43.*

## PART B SUMMARY

### KEY TERMS

14-5.1  A **voltaic cell** harnesses a spontaneous redox reaction to generate electricity. p. 501

14-5.1  A voltaic cell consists of two **electrodes**, an **anode** for oxidation and a **cathode** for reduction. p. 501

14-5.2  A **battery** consists of one or more voltaic cells arranged in a series. p. 502

14-5.5  A **fuel cell** generates electricity from the reaction of gases at inert electrodes. p. 504

14-6  Electrical energy is supplied to an **electrolytic cell** to cause a nonspontaneous redox reaction. p. 506

### SUMMARY CHART

*Reactions of Elements with Water*

| Elements | Reaction | Products |
|---|---|---|
| Active nonmetals ($F_2$ and $Cl_2$) | Oxidize water | $O_2$ and nonmetal acid (HF, HCl) |
| Other nonmetals | No reaction | |
| Active metals (e.g., K, Ca, Al) | Reduce water | $H_2$ and metal hydroxide [e.g., KOH, $Ca(OH)_2$] |
| Other metals (e.g., Fe, Cu, Au) | No reaction | |

## CHAPTER 14 SYNTHESIS PROBLEM

It was generally accepted just 50 years ago that the noble gases (also called the inert gases) could not form ordinary chemical compounds. A few chemists thought it was possible, however, and the first noble gas compound ($XePtF_6$) was reported in 1962. Very soon after this, xenon was found to form a fluoride [$XeF_2(g)$] by a simple combination reaction catalyzed by sunlight. Prior to the synthesis of $XeF_2$, the perbromate ion ($BrO_4^-$) was unknown although the perchlorate and periodate ions existed. (Chlorine is just above and iodine just below bromine on the periodic table.)

| PROBLEM | SOLUTION |
|---|---|
| **a.** Write the unbalanced core equation illustrating the reaction between $XeF_2$ and bromate ion ($BrO_3^-$) to form Xe and the perbromate ion in aqueous solution. | **a.** $XeF_2(aq) + BrO_3^-(aq) \longrightarrow Xe(g) + BrO_4^-(aq)$ |

| PROBLEM | SOLUTION |
|---|---|
| **b.** What is the substance oxidized and the substance reduced and their oxidation states in the reactants and products? | **b.** $XeF_2$ is reduced to Xe. The oxidation state of Xe in $XeF_2$ is +2 and is reduced to 0 in Xe. The oxidation state of the Br in $BrO_3^-$ is +5 and is oxidized to +7 in $BrO_4^-$. |
| **c.** Balance the reaction in acid solution by the ion-electron method. | **c.** $2e^- + XeF_2 \longrightarrow Xe + 2F^-$<br>$H_2O + BrO_3^- \longrightarrow BrO_4^- + 2H^+ + 2e^-$<br>Add the two half-reactions so that the $2e^-$ cancel.<br>balanced equation: $H_2O(l) + XeF_2(g) + BrO_3^-(aq) \longrightarrow$<br>$Xe(g) + BrO_4^-(aq) + 2HF(aq)$<br>(The HF is written in molecular form since it is a weak acid.) |
| **d.** Write the balanced equation as it would appear in basic solution. | **d.** $2OH^-(aq) + XeF_2(s) + BrO_3^-(aq) \longrightarrow$<br>$Xe(g) + BrO_4^-(aq) + 2F^-(aq) + H_2O(l)$<br>(Add two $OH^-$ to each side. The two $H^+$ in HF neutralize two $OH^-$ on the right to form $2H_2O$. Then cancel one $H_2O$ on each side. |
| **e.** Elemental oxygen is a good oxidizing agent (hence the name) but $XeF_2$ is stronger. Write a balanced equation illustrating a spontaneous reaction involving the $O_2$–$H_2O$ half-reaction and the $XeF_2$–Xe half-reaction. | **e.** $2XeF_2(g) + 2H_2O(l) \longrightarrow 2Xe(g) + O_2(g) + 4HF(aq)$ |

**YOUR TURN**

Bleach (hypochlorous acid, HClO) is a powerful oxidizing agent, which we use around the house to remove stains and to kill germs. We also use it in swimming pools to kill bacteria. We discussed the bromate ion in the problem above. It can be produced from bromide salts such as NaBr by reaction with hypochlorous acid, which forms chlorine gas on reaction.

**a.** Write the unbalanced core equation illustrating the reaction between HOCl and the $Br^-$ ion as described above.

**b.** What is the substance oxidized and the substance reduced and their oxidation states in the reactants and products?

**c.** Balance the reaction in acid solution by the ion-electron method.

**d.** Write the balanced equation as it would appear in basic solution.

**e.** Hypochlorous acid is a good oxidizing agent but hydrogen peroxide is stronger. ($H_2O_2$ is also used as a bleaching agent or antiseptic). Write a balanced equation in acid solution illustrating a spontaneous reaction involving the $H_2O_2$–$H_2O$ half-reaction and the HClO–$Cl_2$ half-reaction.

Answers are on p. xxx.

# CHAPTER SUMMARY

A common characteristic of a large number of chemical reactions is an exchange of electrons between reactants. These reactions are known as **oxidation–reduction reactions**, or simply **redox reactions**. In such reactions, the reactant that gives up or loses the electrons is **oxidized**, and the reactant that gains the electrons is **reduced**. The reactant oxidized is also known as a **reducing agent**, and the reactant reduced is known as an **oxidizing agent**.

To keep track of the electron exchange, we can follow the change in **oxidation states** (or **oxidation numbers**) of the elements in the compounds. The oxidation state increases in the substance oxidized and decreases in the substance reduced. We can use this understanding to balance equations by the **oxidation state (bridge) method**. In another method, a redox reaction can be divided into two **half-reactions**: an oxidation and a reduction. These two processes take place so that all electrons lost in the oxidation process are gained in the reduction process. This fact is useful in balancing oxidation–reduction reactions by the **ion-electron method**. Most of these reactions would, at best, be very difficult to balance by inspection methods, as described in Chapter 6.

Each substance has its own inherent strength as either an oxidizing agent or a reducing agent. A table can be constructed in which oxidizing and reducing agents are ranked by strength as determined by observation or measurements with electrical instruments. From this table, a great many other spontaneous reactions can be predicted. In Table 14-1, stronger oxidizing agents are ranked higher on the left and stronger reducing agents are ranked lower on the right. Reactions can thus be predicted as shown in

Figure 14-2. Also, the reactions (or lack of reactions) of certain elements with water can be predicted.

Spontaneous chemical reactions occur because reactants are higher in chemical (potential) energy than products. We are familiar with many exothermic reactions, where the difference in energy is released as heat. The energy can also be released as electrical energy in a **voltaic cell**. In a voltaic cell, the two half-reactions are physically separated so that electrons travel in an external circuit or wire between **electrodes**. The **anode** is the electrode

at which oxidation takes place, and the **cathode** is the electrode at which reduction takes place. The Daniell cell, the car **battery**, the dry cell, and the **fuel cell** all involve spontaneous chemical reactions in which the chemical energy is converted directly into electrical energy.

Many reactions that are predicted to be unfavorable or nonspontaneous can be made to occur if electrical energy is supplied from an outside source. These are referred to as **electrolytic cells** and are useful in the commercial production of metals and in electroplating.

## OBJECTIVES

| SECTION | YOU SHOULD BE ABLE TO... | EXAMPLES | EXERCISES | CHAPTER PROBLEMS |
|---------|--------------------------|----------|-----------|------------------|
| 14-1 | Using oxidation states, determine the species oxidized, the species reduced, the oxidizing agent, and the reducing agent in an electron exchange reaction. | 14-1, 14-2 | 1a, 1b, 1c, 1d, 1e, 1f, 1g | 1, 2, 6, 8, 9, 11, 12, 14 |
| 14-2 | Balance redox reactions by the oxidation state (bridge) method. | 14-3 | 2a, 2b | 16, 17 |
| 14-3 | Balance redox reactions by the ion-electron (half-reaction) method in both acidic and basic media. | 14-4, 14-5 | 3a, 3b | 19, 21, 23, 25 |
| 14-4 | Using a table or relative strengths of oxidizing agents, determine whether a specific redox reaction is spontaneous. | 14-6, 14-7, 14-8 | 4a, 4b, 4c, 4d, 4e | 27, 28, 30, 32 |
| 14-5 | Describe the structure and electricity-generating ability of voltaic cells and batteries. | | 5a, 5c | 35, 36, 37, 38, 39, 42 |
| 14-6 | Write the reactions that occur when a salt is electrolyzed. | | 6a, 6b, 6c, 6d | 43, 46, 47 |

## ▶ ANSWERS TO ASSESSING THE OBJECTIVES

### Part A
#### EXERCISES

**14-1(a)** If all the atoms in a compound were ions, the charge on the ions would be the same as their <u>oxidation states</u>. For oxygen in compounds, this is usually −2. Hydrogen is usually +1 in compounds. A substance oxidized undergoes a <u>loss</u> of electrons and an <u>increase</u> in oxidation state. This substance is also known as a <u>reducing</u> agent.

**14-1(b)** (a) +3 (b) +2

**14-1(c)** (a) +4 (b) −2 (c) +4 (d) 0

**14-1(d)** $ClO_2 \longrightarrow Cl^-$ $ClO_2$ is reduced and is the oxidizing agent. $H_2O_2 \longrightarrow O_2$ $H_2O_2$ is oxidized and is the reducing agent.

**14-1(e)** Both ions in $CrI_3$ are oxidized. The Cr is oxidized from +3 in $Cr^{3+}$ to +6 in $CrO_4^{2-}$; the I is oxidized from −1 in $I^-$ to 0 in $I_2$. The Cl is reduced from 0 in $Cl_2$ to −1 in $Cl^-$.

**14-1(f)** No, it is not. Reduction is the gain of electrons. They must come from somewhere. Oxidation is the loss of electrons. They must end up somewhere. The two processes always occur together. Certain reactions are referred to as being an oxidation or a reduction, but in these cases, it is because we focus on a molecule of interest. Other, less important molecules in these reactions are always undergoing the complementary process.

**14-1(g)** Mn is +7 (high of state). It would be an oxidizing agent.

**14-2(a)** (a) $2Fe(s) + 6HCl(aq) \longrightarrow 2FeCl_3(aq) + 3H_2(g)$

(b) $2HNO_3(aq) + 2HCl(aq) \longrightarrow 2NO_2(g) + Cl_2(g) + 2H_2O$

**14-2(b)** $2MnO_2(s) + Zn(s) + H_2O(l) \longrightarrow$
$$Mn_2O_3(s) + Zn(OH)_2(s)$$

**14-3(a)** (a) $2NO_3^-(aq) + 3H_2SO_3(aq) \longrightarrow$
$$3SO_4^{2-}(aq) + 2NO(g) + 4H^+(aq) + H_2O$$

(b) $8H_2O(l) + 2MnO_4^-(aq) + 7S^{2-}(aq) \longrightarrow$
$$2MnS(s) + 5S(s) + 16OH^-(aq)$$

**14-3(b)** $Sn(s) + 4HNO_3(aq) \longrightarrow SnO_2(s) + 4NO_2(g) + 2H_2O(l)$

### Part B
#### EXERCISES

**14-4(a)** Spontaneous redox reactions occur between the <u>stronger</u> oxidizing and reducing agents to produce <u>weaker</u> oxidizing and reducing agents. In a table, the stronger oxidizing agent is located <u>higher</u> in the table than the reducing agent.

**14-4(b)** A spontaneous reaction would occur in (b).

$3Pb^{2+}(aq) + 2Cr(s) \longrightarrow 3Pb(s) + 2Cr^{3+}(aq)$

14-4(c) The zinc is the stronger reducing agent. It will be oxidized more easily.

14-4(d) (a) nonspontaneous (b) $2Cr^{3+} + 3Mn \longrightarrow 2Cr + 3Mn^{2+}$ (c) Yes. $3I_2 + 2Cr \longrightarrow 2Cr^{3+} + 6I^-$ (d) Only Ca (e) $Ca^{2+}$ and $I^-$

14-4(e) $2Au^{3+}(aq) + 3Fe(s) \longrightarrow 3Fe^{2+}(aq) + 2Au(s)$

14-5(a) A spontaneous chemical reaction is used in a voltaic cell. An example is the Daniell cell, where zinc metal is oxidized at the anode and copper ion is reduced at the cathode. An electrolytic balance is maintained by means of a salt bridge. In the lead-acid battery, lead–metal is oxidized at the anode and $PbO_2$ is reduced at the cathode.

14-5(b) (a) lead storage battery (b) NiCad battery (c) dry cell (d) fuel cell

14-5(c) $Br_2(l) + Fe(s) \longrightarrow 2Br^-(aq) + Fe^{2+}(aq)$

14-5(d) There actually isn't one correct answer, since the factors involved sometimes conflict, such as mass of the reactants versus the voltage of the cell. The reaction shown above for Exercise 14-5(b) is one possibility because neither reactant reacts directly with water. However, bromine is very corrosive and causes severe burns. Although sodium metal is light and is the most powerful reducing agent, it is very difficult to use because it reacts violently

with water. Likewise, fluorine is almost impossible to use because of its high reactivity. It reacts with almost any container. This leaves magnesium, which is very light and stable, since it reacts with water only at high temperatures, and chlorine gas, which reacts very slowly with water. The reaction is

$$Mg(s) + Cl_2(aq) \longrightarrow Mg^{2+}(aq) + 2Cl^-(aq)$$

In fact, a workable battery has been made using Zn and $Cl_2$.

14-6(a) (1) electroplating metals like silver onto a surface (2) recharging batteries (3) producing fuels like hydrogen (4) producing reactive metals like aluminum and sodium

14-6(b) $MgCl_2(l) \longrightarrow Mg(l) + Cl_2(g)$

14-6(c) The formation of Sn from an $Sn^{2+}$ solution onto a piece of iron is a spontaneous reaction, so energy does not need to be supplied. The spontaneous reaction is

$$Sn^{2+}(aq) + Fe \longrightarrow Sn(s) + Fe^{2+}(aq)$$

14-6(d) Aluminum or any other active metal that reacts with water, such as magnesium or sodium, cannot be electroplated from aqueous solution. All three of these metals are produced from electrolysis of their molten salts. Only metals above water (as a reducing agent) can be electroplated from solutions of their aqueous ions.

## ANSWERS TO CHAPTER SYNTHESIS PROBLEM

**a.** $HClO(aq) + Br^-(aq) \longrightarrow$ $BrO_3^-(aq) + Cl_2(g)$

**b.** HClO is reduced to $Cl_2$. The oxidation state of Cl in HClO is +1 and is reduced to 0 in $Cl_2$. The oxidation state of the Br in $Br^-$ is −1 and is oxidized to +5 in $BrO_3^-$.

**c.** $2e^- + 2H^+ + 2HClO \longrightarrow Cl_2 + 2H_2O$ $3H_2O + Br^- \longrightarrow BrO_3^- + 6H^+ + 6e^-$ Multiply the top reaction by three and add so that $6e^-$ cancel. balanced equation: $6HClO(aq) + Br^- \longrightarrow$ $3Cl_2(g) + BrO_3^-(aq) + 3H_2O(l)$

**d.** $3H_2O + 6ClO^-(aq) + Br^- \longrightarrow$ $3Cl_2(g) + BrO_3^-(aq) + 6OH^-(aq)$

**e.** $H_2O_2(aq) + Cl_2(aq) \longrightarrow 2HClO(aq)$

## CHAPTER PROBLEMS

*Throughout the text, answers to all exercises in color are given in Appendix E. The more difficult exercises are marked with an asterisk.*

### Oxidation States (SECTION 14-1)

14-1. Give the oxidation states of the elements in the following compounds.

(a) $PbO_2$     (c) $C_2H_2$     (e) LiH     (g) $Rb_2Se$

(b) $P_4O_{10}$     (d) $N_2H_4$     (f) $BCl_3$     (h) $Bi_2S_3$

**14-2.** Give the oxidation states of the elements in the following compounds.

(a) $ClO_2$     (c) CO     (e) $Mn_2O_3$

(b) $XeF_2$     (d) $O_2F_2$     (f) $Bi_2O_5$

14-3. Which of the following elements form *only* the +1 oxidation state in compounds?

(a) Li     (c) Ca     (e) K     (g) Rb

(b) H     (d) Cl     (f) Al

**14-4.** Which of the following elements form *only* the +2 oxidation state in compounds?

(a) O     (c) Be     (e) Sc     (g) Ca

(b) B     (d) Sr     (f) Hg

14-5. What is the only oxidation state of Al in its compounds?

14-6. What is the oxidation state of each of the following?

(a) P in $H_3PO_4$     (e) S in $SF_6$

(b) C in $H_2C_2O_4$     (f) N in $CsNO_3$

(c) Cl in $ClO_4^-$     (g) Mn in $KMnO_4$

(d) Cr in $CaCr_2O_7$

14-7. What is the oxidation state of the specified atom?

(a) S in $SO_3$        (b) Co in $Co_2O_3$

(c) U in $UF_6$

(d) N in $HNO_3$

(e) Cr in $K_2CrO_4$

(f) Mn in $CaMnO_4$

(c) $CrI_3 + OH^- + Cl_2 \longrightarrow CrO_4^{2-} + IO_4^- + Cl^- + H_2O$

(d) $I^- + H_2O_2 \longrightarrow I_2 + H_2O + OH^-$

**14-8.** What is the oxidation state of each of the following?

(a) Se in $SeO_3^{2-}$

(b) I in $H_5IO_6$

(c) S in $Al_2(SO_3)_3$

(d) Cl in $HClO_2$

(e) N in $(NH_4)_2S$

**14-15.** Identify the product or products containing the elements oxidized and reduced in problem 14-14.

## Balancing Equations by the Bridge Method (SECTION 14-2)

**14-16.** Balance each of the following equations by the oxidation state method.

(a) $NH_3 + O_2 \longrightarrow NO + H_2O$

(b) $Sn + HNO_3 \longrightarrow SnO_2 + NO_2 + H_2O$

(c) $Cr_2O_3 + Na_2CO_3 + KNO_3 \longrightarrow CO_2 + Na_2CrO_4 + KNO_2$

(d) $Se + BrO_3^- + H_2O \longrightarrow H_2SeO_3 + Br^-$

## Oxidation-Reduction (SECTION 14-1)

**14-9.** Which of the following reactions are oxidation-reduction reactions?

(a) $2H_2 + O_2 \longrightarrow 2H_2O$

(b) $CaCO_3 \longrightarrow CaO + CO_2$

(c) $2Na + 2H_2O \longrightarrow 2NaOH + H_2$

(d) $2HNO_3 + Ca(OH)_2 \longrightarrow Ca(NO_3)_2 + 2H_2O$

(e) $AgNO_3 + KCl \longrightarrow AgCl + KNO_3$

(f) $Zn + CuCl_2 \longrightarrow ZnCl_2 + Cu$

**14-17.** Balance the following equations by the oxidation state method.

(a) $I_2O_5 + CO \longrightarrow I_2 + CO_2$

(b) $Al + H_2O \longrightarrow AlO_2^- + H_2 + H^+$

(c) $HNO_3 + HCl \longrightarrow NO + Cl_2 + H_2O$

(d) $I_2 + Cl_2 + H_2O \longrightarrow HIO_3 + HCl$

**14-10.** Identify each of the following half-reactions as either oxidation or reduction.

(a) $Na \longrightarrow Na^+ + e^-$

(b) $Zn^{2+} + 2e^- \longrightarrow Zn$

(c) $Fe^{2+} \longrightarrow Fe^{3+} + e^-$

(d) $O_2 + 4H^+ + 4e^- \longrightarrow 2H_2O$

(e) $S_2O_8^{2-} + 2e^- \longrightarrow 2SO_4^{2-}$

## Balancing Equations by the Ion-Electron Method (SECTION 14-3)

**14-18.** Balance the following half-reactions in acidic solution.

(a) $Sn^{2+} \longrightarrow SnO_2$

(b) $CH_4 \longrightarrow CO_2$

(c) $Fe^{3+} \longrightarrow Fe^{2+}$

(d) $I_2 \longrightarrow IO_3^-$

(e) $NO_3^- \longrightarrow NO_2$

**14-11.** Identify each of the following changes as either oxidation or reduction.

(a) $P_4 \longrightarrow H_3PO_4$

(b) $NO_3^- \longrightarrow NH_4^+$

(c) $Fe_2O_3 \longrightarrow Fe^{2+}$

(d) $Al \longrightarrow Al(OH)_4^-$

(e) $S^{2-} \longrightarrow SO_4^{2-}$

**14-19.** Balance the following half-reactions in acidic solution.

(a) $P_4 \longrightarrow H_3PO_4$

(b) $ClO_3^- \longrightarrow Cl^-$

(c) $S_2O_3^{2-} \longrightarrow SO_4^{2-}$

(d) $NO_3^- \longrightarrow NH_4^+$

(e) $H_2O_2 \longrightarrow H_2O$

**14-12.** For each of the following unbalanced equations, complete the table below.

(a) $MnO_2 + H^+ + Br^- \longrightarrow Mn^{2+} + Br_2 + H_2O$

(b) $CH_4 + O_2 \longrightarrow CO_2 + H_2O$

(c) $Fe^{2+} + MnO_4^- + H^+ \longrightarrow Fe^{3+} + Mn^{2+} + H_2O$

**14-20.** Balance each of the following by the ion-electron method. All are in acidic solution.

(a) $S^{2-} + NO_3^- + H^+ \longrightarrow S + NO + H_2O$

(b) $I_2 + S_2O_3^{2-} \longrightarrow S_4O_6^{2-} + I^-$

(c) $SO_3^{2-} + ClO_3^- \longrightarrow Cl^- + SO_4^{2-}$

(d) $Fe^{2+} + H_2O_2 + H^+ \longrightarrow Fe^{3+} + H_2O$

(e) $AsO_4^{3-} + I^- + H^+ \longrightarrow I_2 + AsO_3^{3-} + H_2O$

(f) $Zn + H^+ + NO_3^- \longrightarrow Zn^{2+} + NH_4^+ + H_2O$

| Reaction | Reactant Oxidized* | Product of Oxidation | Reactant Reduced | Product of Reduction | Oxidizing Agent | Reducing Agent |
|---|---|---|---|---|---|---|
| (a) | | | | | | |
| (b) | | | | | | |
| (c) | | | | | | |

*Element, molecule, or ion.

**14-13.** For the following two unbalanced equations, construct a table like that in Problem 14-12.

(a) $Al + H_2O \longrightarrow AlO_2^- + H_2 + H^+$

(b) $Mn^{2+} + Cr_2O_7^{2-} + H^+ \longrightarrow MnO_4^- + Cr^{3+} + H_2O$

**14-21.** Balance each of the following by the ion-electron method. All are in acidic solution.

(a) $Mn^{2+} + BiO_3^- + H^+ \longrightarrow MnO_4^- + Bi^{3+} + H_2O$

(b) $IO_3^- + SO_2 + H_2O \longrightarrow I_2 + SO_4^{2-} + H^+$

(c) $Se + BrO_3^- + H_2O \longrightarrow H_2SeO_3 + Br^-$

(d) $P_4 + HClO + H_2O \longrightarrow H_3PO_4 + Cl^- + H^+$

(e) $Al + Cr_2O_7^{2-} + H^+ \longrightarrow Al^{3+} + Cr^{3+} + H_2O$

(f) $ClO_3^- + I^- + H^+ \longrightarrow Cl^- + I_2 + H_2O$

(g) $As_2O_3 + NO_3^- + H_2O \longrightarrow AsO_4^{3-} + NO + H^+$

**14-14.** For the following equations, identify the reactant oxidized, the reactant reduced, the oxidizing agent, and the reducing agent.

(a) $Sn + HNO_3 \longrightarrow SnO_2 + NO_2 + H_2O$

(b) $IO_3^- + SO_2 + H_2O \longrightarrow I_2 + SO_4^{2-} + H^+$

14-22. Balance the following half-reactions in basic solution.

(a) $SnO_2^{2-} \longrightarrow SnO_3^{2-}$    (c) $Si \longrightarrow SiO_3^{2-}$

(b) $ClO_2^- \longrightarrow Cl_2$    (d) $NO_3^- \longrightarrow NH_3$

14-23. Balance the following half-reactions in basic solution.

(a) $Al \longrightarrow Al(OH)_4^-$    (c) $N_2H_4 \longrightarrow NO_3^-$

(b) $S^{2-} \longrightarrow SO_4^{2-}$

14-24. Balance each of the following by the ion-electron method. All are in basic solution.

(a) $S^{2-} + OH^- + I_2 \longrightarrow SO_4^{2-} + I^- + H_2O$

(b) $MnO_4^- + OH^- + I^- \longrightarrow MnO_4^{2-} + IO_4^- + H_2O$

(c) $BiO_3^- + SnO_2^{2-} + H_2O \longrightarrow SnO_3^{2-} + OH^- + Bi(OH)_3$

(d) $CrI_3 + OH^- + Cl_2 \longrightarrow CrO_4^{2-} + IO_4^- + Cl^- + H_2O$

[Hint: In (d), two ions are oxidized; include both in one half-reaction.]

14-25. Balance each of the following by the ion-electron method. All are in basic solution.

(a) $ClO_2 + OH^- \longrightarrow ClO_2^- + ClO_3^- + H_2O$

(b) $OH^- + Cr_2O_3 + NO_3^- \longrightarrow CrO_4^{2-} + NO_2^- + H_2O$

(c) $Cr(OH)_4^- + BrO^- + OH^- \longrightarrow Br^- + CrO_4^{2-} + H_2O$

(d) $Mn^{2+} + H_2O_2 + OH^- \longrightarrow H_2O + MnO_2$

(e) $Ag_2O + Zn + H_2O \longrightarrow Zn(OH)_2 + Ag$

14-26. Balance the following two equations by the ion-electron method, first in acidic solution and then in basic solution.

(a) $H_2 + O_2 \longrightarrow H_2O$    (b) $H_2O_2 \longrightarrow O_2 + H_2O$

## Predicting Redox Reactions (SECTION 14-4)

14-27. Using Table 14-1, predict whether the following reactions occur in aqueous solution. If not, write N.R. (no reaction).

(a) $2Na + 2H_2O \longrightarrow H_2 + 2NaOH$

(b) $Pb + Zn^{2+} \longrightarrow Pb^{2+} + Zn$

(c) $Fe + 2H^+ \longrightarrow Fe^{2+} + H_2$

(d) $Fe + 2H_2O \longrightarrow Fe^{2+} + 2OH^- + H_2$

(e) $Cu + 2Ag^+ \longrightarrow 2Ag + Cu^{2+}$

(f) $2Cl_2 + 2H_2O \longrightarrow 4Cl^- + O_2 + 4H^+$

(g) $3Zn^{2+} + 2Cr \longrightarrow 2Cr^{3+} + 3Zn$

14-28. Using Table 14-1, predict whether the following reactions occur in aqueous solution. If not, write N.R.

(a) $Sn^{2+} + Pb \longrightarrow Pb^{2+} + Sn$

(b) $Ni^{2+} + H_2 \longrightarrow 2H^+ + Ni$

(c) $Cu + F_2 \longrightarrow CuF_2$

(d) $Ni^{2+} + 2Br^- \longrightarrow Ni + Br_2$

(e) $3Ni^{2+} + 2Cr \longrightarrow 2Cr^{3+} + 3Ni$

(f) $2Br_2 + 2H_2O \longrightarrow 4Br^- + O_2 + 4H^+$

14-29. If a reaction occurs, write the balanced molecular equation.

(a) Nickel metal is placed in water.

(b) Bromine is dissolved in water that is in contact with tin metal.

(c) Silver metal is placed in an $HClO_4$ solution.

(d) Oxygen gas is bubbled into an HBr solution.

(e) Liquid bromine is placed on a sheet of aluminum.

14-30. If a reaction occurs, write the balanced molecular equation.

(a) Bromine is added to an HCl solution.

(b) Sodium metal is heated with solid aluminum chloride.

(c) Iron is placed in a $Pb(ClO_4)_2$ solution.

(d) Oxygen gas is bubbled into an HCl solution.

(e) Fluorine gas is added to water.

14-31. Which of the following elements react with water: (a) Pb, (b) Ag, (c) $F_2$, (d) $Br_2$, (e) Mg? Write the balanced equation for any reaction that occurs.

14-32. Which of the following species will be reduced by hydrogen gas in aqueous solution: (a) $Br_2$, (b) Cr, (c) $Ag^+$, (d) $Ni^{2+}$? Write the balanced equation for any reaction that occurs.

14-33. In Chapter 13, we mentioned the corrosiveness of acid rain. Why does rain containing a higher $H^+(aq)$ concentration cause more damage to iron exposed in bridges and buildings than pure $H_2O$? Write the reaction between Fe and $H^+(aq)$

14-34. $Br_2$ can be prepared from the reaction of $Cl_2$ with NaBr dissolved in seawater. Explain. Write the reaction. Can $Cl_2$ be used to prepare $F_2$ from NaF solutions?

## Voltaic Cells (SECTION 14-5)

14-35. What is the function of the salt bridge in the voltaic cell?

14-36. In an alkaline battery, the following two half-reactions occur.

$$Zn(s) + 2OH^-(aq) \longrightarrow Zn(OH)_2(s) + 2e^-$$
$$2MnO_2(s) + 2H_2O(l) + 2e^- \longrightarrow 2MnO(OH)(s) + 2OH^-(aq)$$

Which reaction takes place at the anode and which at the cathode? What is the total reaction?

14-37. The following overall reaction takes place in a silver oxide battery.

$$Ag_2O(s) + H_2O(l) + Zn(s) \longrightarrow Zn(OH)_2(s) + 2Ag(s)$$

The reaction takes place in basic solution. Write the half-reaction that takes place at the anode and the half-reaction that takes place at the cathode.

14-38. The nickel–cadmium (NiCad) battery is used as a replacement for a dry cell because it is rechargeable. The overall reaction that takes place is

$$2NiO(OH)(s) + Cd(s) + 2H_2O(l) \longrightarrow$$
$$2Ni(OH)_2(s) + Cd(OH)_2(s)$$

Write the half-reactions that take place at the anode and the cathode.

14-39. Sketch a galvanic cell in which the following overall reaction occurs.

$$Ni^{2+}(aq) + Fe(s) \longrightarrow Fe^{2+}(aq) + Ni(s)$$

**(a)** What reactions take place at the anode and the cathode?

**(b)** In what direction do the electrons flow in the wire?

**(c)** In what direction do the anions flow in the salt bridge?

14-40. Describe how a voltaic cell could be constructed from a strip of iron, a strip of lead, an $Fe(NO_3)_2$ solution, and a $Pb(NO_3)_2$ solution. Write the anode reaction, the cathode reaction, and the total reaction.

14-41. Judging from the relative difference in the strengths of the oxidizing agents ($Fe^{2+}$ vs. $Pb^{2+}$) and ($Zn^{2+}$ vs. $Cu^{2+}$), which do you think would be the more powerful cell, the one in problem or the Daniell cell? Why?

*14-42. The power of a cell depends on the strength of both the oxidizing and the reducing agents. Write the equation illustrating the most powerful redox reaction possible between an oxidizing agent and a reducing agent *in aqueous solution*. Consider only the species shown in Table 14-1.

## Electrolytic Cells (SECTION 14-6)

14-43. Chrome plating is an electrolytic process. Write the reaction that occurs when an iron bumper is electroplated using a $CrCl_3$ solution. Are there any metals shown in Table 14-1 on which a chromium layer would spontaneously form?

14-44. Why can't elemental sodium be formed in the electrolysis of an aqueous NaCl solution? Write the reaction that does occur at the cathode. How is elemental sodium produced by electrolysis?

14-45. Why can't elemental fluorine be formed by electrolysis of an aqueous NaF solution? Write the reaction that does occur at the anode. How is elemental fluorine produced?

14-46. A "tin can" is made by forming a layer of tin on a sheet of iron. Is electrolysis necessary for such a process or does it occur spontaneously? Write the equation for this reaction. Is electrolysis necessary to form a layer of tin on a sheet of lead? Write the relevant equation.

14-47. Certain metals can be purified by electrolysis. For example, a mixture of Ag, Zn, and Fe can be dissolved so that their metal ions are present in aqueous solution. If a solution containing these ions is electrolyzed, which metal ion would be reduced to the metal first?

## General Problems

14-48. Nitrogen exists in nine oxidation states. Arrange the following compounds in order of increasing oxidation state of N: $K_3N$, $N_2O_4$, $N_2$, $NH_2OH$, $N_2O$, $Ca(NO_3)_2$, $N_2H_4$, $N_2O_3$, NO.

14-49. Given the following information concerning metal strips immersed in certain solutions, write the net ionic equations representing the reactions that occur.

| Metal Strip | Solution | Reaction |
|---|---|---|
| Cd | $NiCl_2$ | Ni coating formed |
| Cd | $FeCl_2$ | no reaction |
| Zn | $CdCl_2$ | Cd coating formed |
| Fe | $CdCl_2$ | no reaction |

Where does $Cd^{2+}$ rank as an oxidizing agent in Table 14-1?

14-50. A hypothetical metal (M) forms a coating of Sn when placed in an $SnCl_2$ solution. However, when a strip of Ni is placed in an $MCl_2$ solution, a coating of the metal M forms on the nickel. Write the net ionic equations representing the reactions that occur. Where does $M^{2+}$ rank as an oxidizing agent in Table 14-1?

14-51. A solution of gold ions ($Au^{3+}$) reacts spontaneously with water to form metallic gold. Metallic gold does not react with chlorine but does react with fluorine. Write the equations representing the two spontaneous reactions, and locate $Au^{3+}$ in Table 14-1 as an oxidizing agent.

14-52. Given the following *unbalanced* equation

$$H^+(aq) + Zn(s) + NO_3^-(aq) \longrightarrow$$
$$Zn^{2+}(aq) + N_2(g) + H_2O(l)$$

what mass of Zn is required to produce 0.658 g of $N_2$?

14-53. Given the following *unbalanced* equation

$$MnO_2(s) + HBr(aq) \longrightarrow MnBr_2(aq) + Br_2(l) + H_2O(l)$$

what mass of $MnO_2$ reacts with 228 mL of 0.560 M HBr?

14-54. Given the following *unbalanced* equation

$$H^+(aq) + NO_3^-(aq) + Cu_2O(s) \longrightarrow$$
$$Cu^{2+}(aq) + NO(g) + H_2O(l)$$

what volume of NO gas measured at STP is produced by the complete reaction of 10.0 g of $Cu_2O$?

*14-55. Given the following *unbalanced* equation in acid solution

$$H_2O(l) + HClO_3(aq) + As(s) \longrightarrow H_3AsO_3(aq) + HClO(aq)$$

If 200 g of As reacts with 200 g of $HClO_3$, what mass of $H_3AsO_3$ is produced? (*Hint:* Calculate the limiting reactant.)

^14-56. Given the following *unbalanced* equation in basic solution

$$Zn(s) + NO_3^-(aq) \longrightarrow NH_3(g) + Zn(OH)_4^{2-}(aq)$$

what volume of $NH_3$ is produced by 6.54 g of Zn? The $NH_3$ is measured at 27.0°C and 1.25 atm pressure.

14-57. Solutions of potassium permanganate are a deep-purple color. Permanganate is a strong oxidizing agent that forms the $Mn^{2+}$ ion in acid solution when it is reduced. When these purple solutions are added to a reducing agent, the purple color disappears until all of the reducing agent reacts. So we have a very convenient way to know when the reducing agent is used up—the solution suddenly turns purple. Balance the following net ionic equations involving permanganate in acidic solution.

**(a)** $MnO_4^-(aq) + Fe^{2+}(aq) \longrightarrow Fe^{3+}(aq) + Mn^{2+}(aq)$

**(b)** $MnO_4^-(aq) + Br^- \longrightarrow Br_2(l) + Mn^{2+}(aq)$

**(c)** $MnO_4^-(aq) + C_2O_4^{2-}(aq) \longrightarrow CO_2(g) + Mn^{2+}(aq)$

14-58. Using the balanced equation from problem 14-57, determine the volume (in mL) of 0.220 M $KMnO_4$ needed to completely react with 25.0 g of $FeCl_2$ dissolved in water.

14-59. Using the balanced equation from problem 14-57, determine the volume (in mL) of 0.450 M KBr needed to completely react with 125 mL of 0.220 M $KMnO_4$.

**14-60.** The active ingredient in household bleach is sodium hypochlorite, which is a strong oxidizing agent. We can tell how much of the active ingredient is present in a two-step analysis. First the hypochlorite oxidizes excess iodide to elemental iodine according to the unbalanced equation that occurs in basic solution.

$$ClO^-(aq) + I^-(aq) \longrightarrow I_2(s) + Cl^-(aq)$$

Next, a solution of sodium thiosulfate ($Na_2S_2O_3$) is added to react with the iodine, as illustrated by the equation

$$I_2(s) + S_2O_3^{2-}(aq) \longrightarrow I^-(aq) + S_4O_6^{2-}(aq)$$

Balance the two equations.

**\*14-61.** Household bleach is 5.00% by weight sodium hypochlorite. Using the balanced equations from problem 14-60, determine the volume (in mL) of 0.358 M $Na_2S_2O_3$ solution needed to react with all the sodium hypochlorite in 100 mL of household bleach. Consider the density of bleach to be the same as water.

## STUDENT WORKSHOP

### Balancing Redox Reactions

**Purpose: To practice balancing a complex redox reaction by the ion-electric method. (Work in groups of three or four. Estimated time: 10 min.)**

This is a challenging problem about balancing redox reactions; it is best done as a group effort to make sure that no atoms or charges are missed. Balance the following reaction in a basic solution, using the ion-electron method:

$$Ce^{4+} + Fe(CN)_6^{4-} \longrightarrow Ce(OH)_3 + Fe(OH)_3 + CO_3^{2-} + NO_3^-$$

Once completed, do an atom and charge inventory to confirm that it is balanced. Then identify the oxidizing and reducing agents for the reaction.

# Foreword to the Appendices

*The successful athlete must be "in shape" physically. The successful chemistry student must be "in shape" mathematically.*

**WHY** do some (one or two, anyway) students seem so self-assured in the study of chemistry and yet others (all the rest) seem so worried? Most likely, it has a lot to do with preparation. Preparation in this case probably does not mean a prior course in chemistry, but it does mean having a solid mathematical background. Most of the students using this text probably are a little rusty on at least some aspects of basic arithmetic, algebra, and scientific notation. There are several reasons for this. Some have not had a good secondary school background in math courses, and others have been away from their high school or college math courses for a number of years. It makes no difference—most students need access to a few reminders, hints, and review exercises to get in shape. The sooner students admit that they have forgotten some math, the faster they do something about it and start to enjoy chemistry. It is really difficult to appreciate the study of this science if math deficiencies get in the way.

**Appendix A** reviews some of the basic arithmetic concepts such as manipulation of fractions, expressing decimal fractions, and, very importantly, the expression and use of percent. **Appendix B** reviews the manipulation and solution of simple algebra equations, which are so important in the quantitative aspects of chemistry. **Appendix C** supplements the discussion of scientific notation in Chapter 1 with more examples and exercises. Also included in this appendix is a discussion of the concept of logarithms, which is a convenient way to express exponential numbers in certain situations. **Appendix D** is a glossary of terms, and **Appendix E** contains answers to more than half of the exercises at the ends of the chapters.

# Basic Mathematics

The following is a very quick refresher of fundamentals of math. This may be sufficient to aid you if you are just a little rusty on some of the basic concepts. For more thorough explanations and practice, however, you are urged to use a more comprehensive math review workbook or consult with your instructor.

One may ask, "Why not just use a calculator?" The answer is that serious science students need a "feeling" for the numbers they use. This can be accomplished only by understanding the calculations involved. Therefore, it is well worth the time to go through this appendix *without a calculator*. Being able to do these calculations on your own will certainly pay off. Someday the battery on the calculator may die during an exam.

## A-1 Addition and Subtraction

Since most calculations in this text use numbers expressed in decimal form, we will emphasize the manipulation of this type of number. In addition and subtraction, it is important to line up the decimal point carefully before doing the math.

Subtraction is simply the addition of a negative number. Remember that subtraction of a negative number changes the sign to a plus (two negatives make a positive). For example, $4 - 7 = -3$, but $4 - (-7) = 4 + 7 = 11$.

---

**EXAMPLE A-1    Addition and Subtraction**

Carry out the following calculations.

**(a)** $16.75 + 13.31 + 175.67$

$$
\begin{array}{r}
16.75 \\
13.31 \\
175.67 \\
\hline
205.73 \\
\hline
\end{array}
$$

**(b)** $11.8 + 13.1 - 6.1$

$$
\begin{array}{r}
11.8 \\
+13.1 \\
\hline
24.9 \\
\end{array}
\qquad
\begin{array}{r}
24.9 \\
-6.1 \\
\hline
18.8 \\
\hline
\end{array}
$$

**(c)** $47.82 - 111.18 - (-12.17)$

This is the same as $47.82 - 111.18 + 12.17$.

$$
\begin{array}{r}
47.82 \\
+12.17 \\
\hline
59.99 \\
\end{array}
\qquad
\begin{array}{r}
-111.18 \\
+59.99 \\
\hline
-51.19 \\
\hline
\end{array}
$$

---

## EXERCISES

**A-1**. Carry out the following calculations.

**(a)** $47 + 1672$

**(e)** $0.897 + 1.310 - 0.063$

**(b)** $11.15 + 190.25$

**(f)** $-0.377 - (-0.101) + 0.975$

**(c)** $114 + 26 - 37$

**(g)** $17.489 - 318.112 - (0.315) + (-3.330)$

**(d)** $-97 + 16 - 118$

*Answers*: **(a)** 1719   **(b)** 201.40   **(c)** 103   **(d)** −199   **(e)** 2.144   **(f)** 0.699
**(g)** −303.638

## A-2 Multiplication

Multiplication is expressed in various ways as follows:

$$13.7 \times 115.35 = 13.7 \cdot 115.35 = (13.7)(115.35) = 13.7(115.35)$$

If it is necessary to carry out the multiplication in longhand, you must be careful to place the decimal point correctly in the answer. Count the *total* number of digits to the right of the decimal point in both multipliers (three in this example). The answer has that number of digits to the right of the decimal point in the answer. Finally, round off to the proper number of significant figures, which is three in this case.

$$13.7 \times 2.15 = 29455 = 29.455 = 29.5^*$$

When a number (called a *base*) is multiplied by itself one or more times, it is said to be raised to a *power*. The power (called the *exponent*) indicates the number of bases multiplied. For example, the exact values of the following numbers raised to a power are

$$4^2 = 4 \times 4 = 16 \text{ (“four squared”)}$$

$$2^2 = 2 \times 2 \times 2 \times 2 = 16 \text{ (“two to the fourth power”)}$$

$$4^3 = 4 \times 4 \times 4 = 64 \text{ (“four cubed”)}$$

$$(14.1)^2 = 14.1 \times 14.1 = 198.81 = 199^*$$

In the calculations used in this book, most numbers have specific units. In multiplication, the units as well as the numbers are multiplied. For example,

$$3.7 \text{ cm} \times 4.61 \text{ cm} = 17 \text{ (cm} \times \text{cm)} = 17 \text{ cm}^2$$

$$(4.5 \text{ in.})^3 = 91 \text{ in.}^3$$

In the multiplication of a series of numbers, grouping is possible.

$$(a \times b) \times c = a \times (b \times c)$$

$$3.0 \text{ cm} \times 148 \text{ cm} \times 3.0 \text{ cm} = (3.0 \times 3.0) \times 148 \times (\text{cm} \times \text{cm} \times \text{cm})$$

$$= \underline{1300 \text{ cm}^3}$$

When multiplying signs, remember:

$$(+) \times (-) = - \qquad (+) \times (+) = + \qquad (-) \times (-) = +$$

For example, $(-3) \times 2 = -6$; $(-9) \times (-8) = +72$.

---

*Rounded off to three significant figures. See Section 1-2.

**EXERCISES**

**A-2.** Carry out the following calculations. For (a) through (d) carry out the multiplications completely. For (e) through (h) round off the answer to the proper number of significant figures and include units.

**(a)** $16.2 \times (-118)$        **(d)** $(-47.8) \times (-9.6)$

**(b)** $(4 \times 2) \times 879$        **(e)** $3.0 \text{ ft} \times 18 \text{ lb}$

**(c)** $(-8) \times (-2) \times (-37)$        **(f)** $17.7 \text{ in.} \times (13.2 \text{ in.} \times 25.0 \text{ in.})$

**(g)** What is the area of a circle where the radius is 2.2 cm? (Area $= \pi r^2$. $\pi = 3.14$.)

**(h)** What is the volume of a cylinder 5.0 in. high with a cross-sectional radius of 0.82 in.? (Volume = area of cross section $\times$ height.)

*Answers:* **(a)** $-1911.6$   **(b)** $7032$   **(c)** $-592$   **(d)** $458.88$   **(e)** $54 \text{ ft} \cdot \text{lb}$
**(f)** $5840 \text{ in.}^3$   **(g)** $15 \text{ cm}^2$   **(h)** $11 \text{ in.}^3$

## A-3 Roots of Numbers

A root of a number is a fractional exponent. It is expressed as

$$\sqrt[x]{a} = a^{1/x}$$

If $x$ is not shown (on the left), it is assumed to be 2 and is known as the *square root*. The square root is the number that when multiplied by itself gives the base $a$. For example,

$$\sqrt{4} = 2 \qquad (2 \times 2 = 4)$$
$$\sqrt{9} = 3 \qquad (3 \times 3 = 9)$$

The square root of a number may have either a positive or a negative sign. Generally, however, we are interested only in the positive root in chemistry calculations.

If the square root of a number is not a whole number, it may be computed on a calculator or found in a table. Without these tools available, an educated approximation can come close to the answer. For example, the square root of 54 lies between 7 ($7^2 = 49$) and 8 ($8^2 = 64$) but closer to 7. An educated guess of 7.3 would be excellent.

The cube root of a number is expressed as

$$\sqrt[3]{b} = b^{1/3}$$

It is the number multiplied by itself two times that gives $b$. For example,

$$\sqrt[3]{27} = 3.0 \qquad (3 \times 3 \times 3 = 27)$$
$$\sqrt[3]{64} = 4.0 \qquad (4 \times 4 \times 4 = 64)$$

A hand calculator is the most convenient source of roots of numbers.

**EXERCISES**

**A-3.** Find the following roots. If necessary, first approximate the answer, then check with a calculator.

**(a)** $\sqrt{25}$    **(b)** $\sqrt{36 \text{ cm}^2}$    **(c)** $\sqrt{144 \text{ ft}^4}$    **(d)** $\sqrt{40}$

**(e)** $\sqrt{7.0}$    **(f)** $110^{1/2}$    **(g)** $100^{1/3}$    **(h)** $\sqrt[3]{50}$

**(i)** What is the radius of a circle that has an area of 150 ft$^2$? (Area $= \pi r^2$)

**(j)** What is the radius of the cross section of a cylinder that has a volume of 320 m$^3$ and a height of 6.0 m? (Volume $= \pi r^2 \times$ height)

*Answers:* **(a)** $5.0$   **(b)** $6.0 \text{ cm}$   **(c)** $12.0 \text{ ft}^2$   **(d)** $6.3$   **(e)** $2.6$   **(f)** $10.5$   **(g)** $4.64$
**(h)** $3.7$   **(i)** $6.91 \text{ ft}$   **(j)** $4.1 \text{ m}$

## A-4 Division, Fractions, and Decimal Numbers

Common fractions express ratios or portions of numbers. A *proper fraction* is less than one so it has a larger denominator than numerator. An *improper fraction* is greater than one so it has a smaller denominator than numerator. In chemistry most fractions are expressed as decimal numbers, which show proper fractions less than 1.0 and improper fractions greater than 1.0. To convert a common fraction to a decimal number, the numerator is divided by the denominator. Consider the two fractions shown below where the decimal is shown to three digits.

proper fraction

improper fraction

$$7/8 = 7 \div 8 = 0.675$$

$$11/9 = 11 \div 9 = 1.22$$

common fraction · decimal fraction

common fraction · decimal fraction

Many divisions can be simplified by cancellation, which is the elimination of common factors in the numerator and denominator. This is possible because a number divided by itself is equal to unity (e.g., $25/25 = 1$). As in multiplication, all units also must be divided. If identical units appear in both numerator and denominator, they also can be canceled. This is the basis of dimensional analysis for problem solving, introduced in Chapter 1.

$$\frac{a \times c}{b \times c} = \frac{a}{b}$$

$$\frac{190 \times 4 \text{ torr}}{190 \text{ torr}} = \frac{4}{}$$

$$\frac{2500 \text{ cm}^3}{150 \text{ cm}} = \frac{50 \times 50 \text{ cm} \times \text{cm} \times \text{cm}}{50 \times 3 \text{ cm}} = \frac{50 \text{ cm}^2}{3} = 17 \text{ cm}^2$$

$$\frac{2800 \text{ mi}}{45 \text{ hr}} = \frac{5 \times 560 \text{ mi}}{5 \times 9 \text{ hr}} = \frac{62 \text{ mi}}{1 \text{ hr}} = 62 \text{ mi/hr}$$

This is read as 62 miles "per" one hour or simply 62 miles per hour. The word per implies a fraction or a ratio with the unit after per in the denominator. If a number is not written or read in the denominator with a unit, it is assumed that the number is unity and is known to as many significant figures as the number in the numerator (i.e., 62 miles per 1.0 hr).

**EXERCISES**

A-4. Express the following in decimal form. Express (a)–(c) to three digits.

(a) 3/7    (d) 892 mi ÷ 41 hr    (g) $\dfrac{67.5 \text{ g}}{15.2 \text{ mL}}$    (j) $\dfrac{0.8772 \text{ ft}^3}{0.0023 \text{ ft}^2}$

(b) 14/19    (e) 982.6 ÷ 0.250    (h) $\dfrac{1890 \text{ cm}^3}{66 \text{ cm}}$    (k) $\dfrac{37.50 \text{ ft}}{0.455 \text{ sec}}$

(c) 19/14    (f) 195 ÷ 2650    (i) $\dfrac{146 \text{ ft} \cdot \text{hr}}{0.68 \text{ ft}}$

*Answers:* (a) 0.429  (b) 0.737  (c) 1.36  (d) 22 mi/hr  (e) 3930  (f) 0.0736
(g) 4.44 g/mL  (h) 29 cm²  (i) 210 hr  (j) 380 ft  (k) 82.4 ft/sec

## A-5 Multiplication and Division of Fractions

When two or more fractions are multiplied, all numbers *and units* in both numerator and denominator can be combined into one fraction.

The division of one fraction by another is the same as the multiplication of the numerator by the *reciprocal* of the denominator. The reciprocal of a fraction is simply the fraction in an inverted form (e.g., 3/5 is the reciprocal of 5/3).

$$\frac{a}{b/c} = a \times \frac{c}{b} \qquad \frac{a/b}{c/d} = \frac{a}{b} \times \frac{d}{c} = \frac{a \times d}{b \times c}$$

### EXAMPLE A-2    Multiplication and Division

Carry out the following calculations. Round off the answer to two digits.

**(a)** $\dfrac{3}{5} \times \dfrac{75}{4} \times \dfrac{16}{7} = \dfrac{3 \times 75 \times 16}{5 \times 4 \times 7} = \dfrac{3 \times \overset{15}{\cancel{75}} \times \overset{4}{\cancel{16}}}{\underset{1}{\cancel{5}} \times \underset{1}{\cancel{4}} \times 7} = \dfrac{180}{7} = \underline{\underline{26}}$

**(b)** $\dfrac{42\ \text{mi}}{\text{hr}} \times \dfrac{3}{7}\ \text{hr} \times \dfrac{5280\ \text{ft}}{\text{mi}} = \dfrac{\overset{6}{\cancel{42}} \times 3 \times 5280\ \cancel{\text{mi}} \times \cancel{\text{hr}} \times \text{ft}}{\underset{1}{\cancel{7}}\ \text{hr} \times \text{mi}} = \underline{\underline{95{,}000\ \text{ft}}}$

**(c)** $\dfrac{3}{4}\ \text{mol} \times \dfrac{0.75\ \text{g}}{\text{mol}} \times \dfrac{1\ \text{mL}}{19.3\ \text{g}} = \dfrac{3 \times 0.75 \times 1 \times \cancel{\text{mol}} \times \cancel{\text{g}} \times \text{mL}}{4 \times 1 \times 19.3 \times \cancel{\text{mol}} \times \cancel{\text{g}}} = \underline{\underline{0.029\ \text{mL}}}$

**(d)** $\dfrac{1650}{3/5} = 1650 \times \dfrac{5}{3} = \underline{\underline{2800}}$

**(e)** $\dfrac{145\ \text{g}}{7.5\ \text{g/mL}} = 145\ \cancel{\text{g}} \times \dfrac{1\ \text{mL}}{7.5\ \cancel{\text{g}}} = \underline{\underline{19\ \text{mL}}}$

### EXERCISES

**A-5.** Express the following answers in decimal form. If units are not used, round off the answer to three digits. If units are included, round off to the proper number of significant figures and include units in the answer.

**(a)** $\dfrac{3}{8} \times \dfrac{4}{7} \times \dfrac{21}{20}$

**(b)** $\dfrac{250}{273} \times \dfrac{175}{300} \times (-6)$

**(c)** $\dfrac{4}{9} \times \left(-\dfrac{5}{8}\right) \times \left(-\dfrac{3}{4}\right)$

**(d)** $195\ \text{g/mL} \times 47.5\ \text{mL}$

**(e)** $0.75\ \text{mol} \times 17.3\ \text{g/mol}$

**(f)** $(3.57\ \text{in.})^2 \times 0.85\ \text{in.} \times \dfrac{16.4\ \text{cm}^3}{\text{in.}^3}$

**(g)** $\dfrac{\dfrac{150}{350}}{\dfrac{25}{42}}$

**(h)** $\dfrac{\left(-\dfrac{3}{7}\right)}{\left(-\dfrac{4}{9}\right)}$

**(i)** $\dfrac{\left(-\dfrac{17}{3}\right)}{\dfrac{8}{9}}$

**(j)** $\dfrac{\dfrac{16}{9} \times \dfrac{10}{14}}{\dfrac{5}{6}}$

**(k)** $\dfrac{75.2 \text{ torr}}{760 \text{ torr/atm}}$

**(m)** $\dfrac{305 \text{ K} \times 62.4 \dfrac{\text{L} \cdot \text{torr}}{\text{K} \cdot \text{torr}} \times 0.25 \text{ mol}}{650 \text{ torr}}$

**(l)** $\dfrac{(55.0 \text{ mi/hr}) \times (5280 \text{ ft/mi}) \times (1 \text{ hr/60 min})}{60 \text{ sec/min}}$

*Answers:* **(a)** 0.225 **(b)** −3.21 **(c)** 0.208 **(d)** 9260 g **(e)** 13 g **(f)** 180 cm$^3$
**(g)** 0.720 **(h)** 0.964 **(i)** −6.38 **(j)** 1.52 **(k)** 0.0989 atm **(l)** 80.7 ft/sec **(m)** 7.3 L

## A-6 Decimal Numbers and Percent

In the examples of fractions thus far, we have seen that the units of the numerator can be profoundly different from those of the denominator (e.g., miles/hr, g/mL, etc.). In other problems in chemistry we use fractions to express a component part in the numerator to the total in the denominator. In most cases such fractions are expressed without units and in decimal form.

---

### EXAMPLE A-3    Decimal Numbers

**(a)** A box of nails contains 985 nails; 415 of these are 6-in. nails, 375 are 3-in. nails, and the rest are roofing nails. What is the fraction of roofing nails in decimal form?

**SOLUTION**

$$\text{Roofing nails} = \text{total} - \text{others} = 985 - (415 + 375) = 195$$

$$\frac{\text{component}}{\text{total}} = \frac{195}{375 + 415 + 195} = \underline{\underline{0.198}}$$

**(b)** A mixture contains 4.25 mol of $N_2$, 2.76 mol of $O_2$, and 1.75 mol of $CO_2$. What is the fraction of moles of $O_2$ present in the mixture? (This fraction is known, not surprisingly, as "the mole fraction." The mole is a unit of quantity, like dozen.)

**SOLUTION**

$$\frac{\text{component}}{\text{total}} = \frac{2.76}{4.25 + 2.76 + 1.75} = \underline{\underline{0.315}}$$

---

**EXERCISES**

**A-6.** A grocer has 195 dozen boxes of fruit; 74 dozen boxes are apples, 62 dozen boxes are peaches, and the rest are oranges. What is the fraction of the boxes that are oranges?

**A-7.** A mixture contains 9.85 mol of gas. A 3.18-mol quantity of the gas is $N_2$, 4.69 mol is $O_2$, and the rest is He. What is the mole fraction of He in the mixture?

**A-8.** The total pressure of a mixture of two gases, $N_2$ and $O_2$, is 0.72 atm. The pressure due to $O_2$ is 0.41 atm. What is the fraction of the pressure due to $O_2$?

*Answers:* **A-6** 0.30    **A-7** 0.201    **A-8** 0.57

The decimal numbers that have just been discussed are frequently expressed as percentages. *Percent simply means parts per 100.* Percent is obtained by multiplying a fraction in decimal form by 100%.

### EXAMPLE A-4   Expressing Percent

If 57 out of 180 people at a party are women, what is the percent women?

**SOLUTION**

The fraction of women in decimal form is

$$\frac{57}{180} = 0.317$$

The percent women is

$$0.317 \times 100\% = \underline{31.7\% \text{ women}}$$

The general method used to obtain percent is

$$\frac{\text{component}}{\text{total}} \times 100\% = \underline{\hspace{2cm}}\% \text{ of component}$$

To change from percent back to a decimal number, divide the percent by 100%, which moves the decimal to the left two places.

$$86.2\% = \frac{86.2\%}{100\%} \times 0.862 \text{(fraction in decimal form)}$$

**EXERCISES**

**A-9.** Express the following fractions or decimal numbers as percents: $\dfrac{1}{4}, \dfrac{3}{8}, \dfrac{9}{8}, \dfrac{55}{25}$, 0.67, 0.13, 1.75, 0.098.

**A-10.** A bushel holds 198 apples, 27 of which are green. What is the percent of green apples?

**A-11.** A basket contains 75 pears, 8 apples, 15 oranges, and 51 grapefruit. What is the percent of each?

*Answers:* **A-9** $\frac{1}{4} = 25\%$, $\frac{3}{8} = 37.5\%$, $\frac{9}{8} = 112.5\%$, $\frac{55}{25} = 220\%$, $0.67 = 67\%$, $0.13 = 13\%$, $1.75 = 175\%$, $0.098 = 9.8\%$   **A-10** 13.6%   **A-11** 50.3% pears, 5.4% apples, 10.1% oranges, 34.2% grapefruit

We have seen how the percent is calculated from the total and the component part. We now consider problems where percent is given and we calculate either the component part as in Example A-5 (a) or the total as in Example A-5 (b). Such problems can be solved in two ways. The method we employ here uses the percent as a conversion factor, and the problems are solved by dimensional analysis. (See Section 1-5.) They also can be solved algebraically as is done in Appendix B.

### EXAMPLE A-5   Using Percent in Calculations

**(a)** A crowd at a rock concert was composed of about 87% teenagers. If the crowd totaled 586 people, how many were teenagers?

**PROCEDURE**

Remember that percent means "per 100." In this case it means 87 teenagers per 100 people or, in fraction form,

$$\frac{87 \text{ teenagers}}{100 \text{ people}}$$

If this fraction is then multiplied by the number of people, the result is the component part or the number of teenagers.

$$586 \text{ people} \times \frac{87 \text{ teenagers}}{100 \text{ people}} = (586 \times 0.87) = \underline{510 \text{ teenagers}}$$

**(b)** A professional baseball player got a hit 28.7% of the times he batted. If he got 246 hits, how many times did he bat?

**PROCEDURE**

The percent can be written in fraction form and then inverted. It thus relates the total at bats to the number of hits:

$$28.7\% = \frac{28.7 \text{ hits}}{100 \text{ at bats}} \quad \text{or} \quad \frac{100 \text{ at bats}}{28.7 \text{ hits}}$$

If this is now multiplied by the number of hits, the result is the total number of at bats.

$$246 \text{ hits} \times \frac{100 \text{ at bats}}{28.7 \text{ hits}} = \frac{246}{0.287} = \underline{857 \text{ at bats}}$$

**EXERCISES**

**A-12.** In a certain audience, 45.9% were men. If there were 196 people in the audience, how many women were present?

**A-13.** In the alcohol molecule, 34.8% of the mass is due to oxygen. What is the mass of oxygen in 497 g of alcohol?

**A-14.** The cost of a hamburger in 2003 is 216% of the cost in 1970. If hamburgers cost $0.75 each in 1970, what do they cost in 2003?

**A-15.** In a certain audience, 46.0% are men. If there are 195 men in the audience, how large is the audience?

**A-16.** If a solution is 23.3% by mass HCl and it contains 14.8 g of HCl, what is the total mass of the solution?

**A-17.** An unstable isotope has a mass of 131 amu. This is 104% of the mass of a stable isotope. What is the mass of the stable isotope?

*Answers:* **A-12** 106 women   **A-13** 173 g   **A-14** $1.62   **A-15** 424 people   **A-16** 63.5 g
**A-17** 126 amu

# Basic Algebra

There are two aspects of the use of algebra that affect chemistry students. First is the actual skill and application of basic concepts and second is the ability to translate words or quantitative concepts into a proper algebraic relationship. In the first section, we will concentrate on the algebra equation itself and how it can be manipulated. In the two sections following this we will concentrate on how we can express quantitative concepts as equations.

## B-1 Operations of Basic Equations

Many of the quantitative problems of chemistry require the use of basic algebra. As an example of a simple algebra equation we use

$$x = y + 8$$

In any algebraic equation the equality remains valid when identical operations are performed on both sides of the equation. The following operations illustrate this principle.

**1.** A quantity may be added to or subtracted from both sides of the equation.

$$\text{(add 8)} \qquad x + \underline{8} = y + 8 + \underline{8} \quad x + 8 = y + 16$$

$$\text{(subtract 8)} \quad x - \underline{8} = y + 8 - \underline{8} \quad x - 8 = y$$

**2.** Both sides of the equation may be multiplied or divided by the same quantity.

$$\text{(multiple by 4)} \quad 4x = 4(y + 8) = 4y + 32$$

$$\text{(divide by 2)} \qquad \frac{x}{2} = \frac{(y + 8)}{2} \quad \frac{x}{2} = \frac{y}{2} + 4$$

**3.** Both sides of the equation may be raised to a power, or a root of both sides of an equation may be taken.

$$\text{(equation squared)} \quad x^2 = (y + 8)^2$$

$$\text{(square root taken)} \quad \sqrt{x} = \sqrt{y + 8}$$

**4.** Both sides of an equation may be inverted.

$$\frac{1}{x} = \frac{1}{y + 8}$$

In addition to operation on both sides of an equation, two other points must be recalled.

**1.** As in any fraction, identical factors in the numerator and the denominator in an algebraic equation may be canceled.

$$\frac{\cancel{4}x}{\cancel{4}} = x = y + 8 \quad \text{or} \quad x = \frac{\cancel{z}(y + 8)}{\cancel{z}} = y + 8$$

**2.** Quantities equal to the same quantity are equal to each other. Thus substitutions for equalities may be made in algebraic equations.

$$x = y + 8$$
$$x = 27$$

Therefore, since $x = x$,

$$y + 8 = 27$$

We can use these basic rules to solve algebraic equations. Usually, we need to isolate one variable on the left-hand side of the equation, with all other numbers and variables on the right-hand side of the equations. The operations previously listed can be simplified for this purpose in two ways.

In practice, a number or a variable may be moved to the other side of an equation with a change of sign. For example, if

$$x + z = y$$

then subtracting $z$ from both sides, in effect, gives us

$$x = y - z$$

Also, the numerator of a fraction on the left becomes the denominator on the right. The denominator of a fraction on the left becomes the numerator on the right. For example, consider the following two cases.

If $xz = y$          If $\dfrac{x}{k + 5} = B,$

then dividing both sides by       then multiplying both sides
$z$, in effect, gives us            by $k + 5$

$$x\textcircled{z} = y \qquad\qquad \dfrac{x}{\textcircled{k + 5}} = B$$

$$x = \dfrac{y}{z} \qquad\qquad x = B(k + 5)$$

The following examples illustrate the isolation of one variable ($x$) on the left-hand side of the equation.

## EXAMPLE B-1   Solving Algebra Equations for a Variable

**(a)** Solve for $x$ in $x + y + 8 = z + 6$.

**SOLUTION**

Move $+y$ and $+8$ to the right by changing signs.

$$x = z + 6 - y - 8$$
$$= z - y + 6 - 8 = \underline{z - y - 2}$$

**(b)** Solve for **x** in

$$\dfrac{x + 8}{y} = z$$

**SOLUTION**

First, move $y$ to the right by multiplying both sides by $y$.

$$y \cdot \dfrac{x + 8}{\cancel{y}} = z \cdot y$$

This leaves

$$x + 8 = zy$$

Subtract 8 from both sides to obtain the final answer.

$$x = \underline{zy - 8}$$

**(c)** Solve for $x$ in

$$\frac{4x + 2}{3 + x} = 7$$

**SOLUTION**

First, multiply both sides by $(3 + x)$ to clear the fraction.

$$\cancel{(3 + x)} \cdot \frac{4x + 2}{\cancel{(3 + x)}} = 7(3 + x)$$

This leaves

$$4x + 2 = 21 + 7x$$

To move integers to the right and the $x$ variable to the left, subtract $7x$ and 2 from both sides of the equation. This leaves

$$-3x = 19$$

Finally, divide both sides by $-3$ to move the $-3$ to the right.

$$x = -\frac{19}{3} = \underline{\underline{-6.33}}$$

**(d)** Solve for $T_2$ in

$$\frac{P_1 V_1}{T_1} = \frac{P_2 V_2}{T_2}$$

**SOLUTION**

To move $T_2$ to the left, multiply both sides by $T_2$.

$$T_2 \cdot \frac{P_1 V_1}{T_1} = \cancel{T_2} \cdot \frac{P_2 V_2}{\cancel{T_2}} = P_2 V_2$$

Move $P_1 V_1$ to the right by dividing by $P_1 V_1$.

$$\frac{T_2}{\cancel{P_1 V_1}} \cdot \frac{\cancel{P_1 V_1}}{T_1} = \frac{P_2 V_2}{P_1 V_1}$$

Finally, move $T_1$ to the right by multiplying both sides by $T_1$.

$$T_2 = \underline{\frac{T_1 P_2 V_2}{P_1 V_1}}$$

**EXERCISES**

**B-1.** Solve for $x$ in $17x = y - 87$.

**B-2.** Solve for $x$ in

$$\frac{y}{x} + 8 = z + 16$$

**B-3.** Solve for $T$ in $PV = (\text{mass}/MM)RT$.

**B-4.** Solve for $x$ in

$$\frac{7x - 3}{6 + 2x} = 3r$$

**B-5.** Solve for $x$ in $18x - 27 = 2x + 4y - 35$. If $y = 3x$, what is the value of $x$?

**B-6.** Solve for $x$ in

$$\frac{x}{4y} + 18 = y + 2$$

**B-7.** Solve for $x$ in $5x^2 + 12 = x^2 + 37$.

**B-8.** Solve for $r$ in

$$\frac{80}{2r} + \frac{y}{r} = 11$$

What is the value of $r$ if $y = 14$?

*Answers:* **B-1** $x = (y - 87)/17$   **B-2** $x = y/(8 + z)$   **B-3** $T = PV \cdot MM/\text{mass} \cdot R$
**B-4** $x = 3(6r + 1)/(7 - 6r)$   **B-5** $x = (y - 2)/4$. When $y = 3x$, $x = -2$.
**B-6** $x = 4y(y - 16)$   **B-7** $x = \pm 2.5$   **B-8** $r = (40 + y)/11$. When $y = 14$, $r = \dfrac{54}{11}$

# B-2 Word Problems and Algebra Equations

Eventually, a necessary skill in chemistry is the ability to translate word problems into algebra equations and then solve. The key is to assign a variable (usually $x$) to be equal to a certain quantity and then to treat the variable consistently throughout the equation. Again, examples are the best way to illustrate the problems.

---

**EXAMPLE B-2   Solving Abstract Word Equations**

Translate each of the following to an equation.

**(a)** A number $x$ is equal to a number that is 4 larger than $y$.

$$x = y + 4$$

**(b)** A number $z$ is equal to three-fourths of $u$.

$$z = \frac{3}{4} u$$

**(c)** The square of a number $r$ is equal to 16.9% of the value of $w$.

$$r^2 = 0.169w \quad \text{(change percent to a decimal number)}$$

**(d)** A number $t$ is equal to 12 plus the square root of $q$.

$$t = 12 + \sqrt{q}$$

---

**EXERCISES**

**B-9.** Write algebraic equations for the following:

**(a)** A number $n$ is equal to a number that is 85 smaller than $m$.

**(b)** A number $y$ is equal to one-fourth of $z$.

**(c)** Fifteen percent of a number $k$ is equal to the square of another number $d$.

**(d)** A number $x$ is equal to 14 more than the square root of $v$.

**(e)** Four times the sum of two numbers, $q$ and $w$, is equal to 68.

**(f)** Five times the product of two variables, $s$ and $t$, is equal to 16 less than the square of $s$.

**(g)** Five-ninths of a number $C$ is equal to 32 less than a number $F$.

*Answers:*   **(a)** $n = m - 85$   **(b)** $y = z/4$   **(c)** $0.15k = d^2$   **(d)** $x = \sqrt{v} + 14$

**(e)** $4(q + w) = 68$   **(f)** $5st = s^2 - 16$   **(g)** $\dfrac{5}{9} C = F - 32$

We now move from the abstract to the real. In the following examples it is necessary to translate the problem into an algebraic expression, as in the previous examples. There are two types of examples that we will use. The first you will certainly recognize, but the second type may be unfamiliar, especially if you have just begun the study of chemistry. However, it is *not* important that you understand the units of chemistry problems at this time. What *is* important is for you to notice that the problems are worked in the same manner regardless of the units.

## EXAMPLE B-3   Solving Concrete Word Equations

**(a)** John is 2 years more than twice as old as Mary. The sum of their ages is 86. How old is each?

**SOLUTION**

Let $x$ = age of Mary. Then $2x + 2$ = age of John.

$$x + (2x + 2) = 86$$
$$3x = 84$$
$$x = \underline{28} \text{ (age of Mary)}$$
$$2(28) + 2 = \underline{58} \text{ (age of John)}$$

**(b)** One mole of $SF_6$ has a mass 30.0 g less than four times the mass of 1 mol of $CO_2$. The mass of 1 mol of $SF_6$ plus the mass of 1 mol of $CO_2$ is equal to 190 g. What is the mass of 1 mol of each?

**SOLUTION**

Let $x$ = mass of 1 mol of $CO_2$. Then $4x - 30$ = mass of 1 mol of $SF_6$.

$$x + (4x - 30) = 190$$
$$x = \underline{44 \text{ g}} \text{ (mass of 1 mol of } CO_2)$$
$$4(44) - 30 = \underline{146 \text{ g}} \text{ (mass of 1 mol of } SF_6)$$

**(c)** Two students took the same test, and their percent scores differed by 10%. If there were 200 points on the test and the total of their point scores was 260 points, what was each student's percent score?

**PROCEDURE**

Set up an equation relating each person's percent scores to their total points (260).

Let $x$ = percent score of higher test.

Then $x - 10$ = percent score of lower test.

The points that each person scores is the percent in fraction form multiplied by the points on the test.

$$\frac{\% \text{ grade}}{100\%} \times (\text{points on test}) = \text{points scored}$$

**SOLUTION**

$$\left[\frac{x}{100}(200 \text{ points})\right] + \left[\frac{x - 10}{100}(200 \text{ points})\right] = 260 \text{ points}$$
$$200x + 200x - 2000 = 26{,}000$$
$$400x = 28{,}000$$
$$x = 70$$

higher score = $\underline{70\%}$ lower score = $70 - 10 = \underline{60\%}$

**(d)** If an 8.75-g quantity of sugar represents 65.7% of a solution, what is the mass of the solution?

**SOLUTION**

Let $x$ = mass of the solution. Then

$$\frac{65.7}{100}x = 0.657x = 8.75$$
$$x = \frac{8.75}{0.657} = \underline{13.3 \text{ g}}$$

**(e)** A used car dealer has Fords, Chevrolets, and Hondas. There are 120 Fords, 152 Chevrolets, and the rest are Hondas. If the fraction of Fords is 0.310, how many Hondas are on the lot?

**SOLUTION**

Let $x$ = number of Hondas.

$$\text{fraction of Fords} = \frac{\text{number of Fords}}{\text{total number of cars}} = 0.310$$

$$\frac{120}{120 + 152 + x} = 0.310$$
$$120 = 0.310(272 + x)$$
$$120 = 84.3 + 0.310x$$
$$x = \underline{115 \text{ Hondas}}$$

In the following exercises, a problem concerning an everyday situation is followed by one or more closely analogous problems concerning a chemistry situation. In both cases the mechanics of the solution are similar. Only the units differ.

**EXERCISES**

**B-10.** The total length of two boards is 18.4 ft. If one board is 4.0 ft longer than the other, what is the length of each board?

**B-11.** An isotope of iodine has a mass 10 amu less than two-thirds the mass of an isotope of thallium. The total mass of the two isotopes is 340 amu. What is the mass of each isotope?

**B-12.** An isotope of gallium has a mass 22 amu more than one-fourth the mass of an isotope of osmium. The difference in the two masses is 122 amu. What is the mass of each?

**B-13.** An oil refinery held 175 barrels of oil. When refined, each barrel yields 24 gallons of gasoline. If 3120 gallons of gasoline were produced, what percentage of the original barrels of oil was refined?

**B-14.** A solution contained 0.856 mol of a substance $A_2X$. In solution some of the $A_2Xs$ break up into As and Xs. (Note that each mole of $A_2X$ yields 2 mol of A.) If 0.224 mol of A is present in the solution, what percentage of the moles of $A_2X$ dissociated (broke apart)?

**B-15.** In Las Vegas, a dealer starts with 264 decks of cards. If 42.8% of the decks were used in an evening, how many jacks (four per deck) were used?

**B-16.** A solution originally contains a 1.45-mol quantity of a compound $A_3X_2$. If 31.5% of the $A_3X_2$ dissociates (three As and two Xs per $A_3X_2$), how many moles of A are formed? How many moles of X? How many moles of undissociated $A_3X_2$ remain? How many moles of particles (As, Xs, and $A_3X_2s$) are present in the solution?

**B-17.** The fraction of kerosene that can be recovered from a barrel of crude oil is 0.200. After a certain amount of oil was refined, 8.90 gal of kerosene, some gasoline, and 18.6 gal of other products were produced. How many gallons of gasoline were produced?

**B-18.** The fraction of moles (mole fraction) of gas A in a mixture is 0.261. If the mixture contains 0.375 mol of gas B and 0.175 mol of gas C as well as gas A, how many moles of gas A are present?

*Answers*: **B-10** 7.2 ft, 11.2 ft  **B-11** thallium, 210 amu; iodine, 130 amu  **B-12** gallium, 70 amu; osmium, 192 amu  **B-13** 74.3%  **B-14** 13.1%  **B-15** 452 jacks  **B-16** 1.37 mol of A, 0.914 mol of X, 0.99 mol of $A_3X_2$, 3.27 mol total  **B-17** 17.0 gal  **B-18** 0.195 mol

# B-3 Direct and Inverse Proportionalities

There is one other point that should be included in a review on algebra—direct and inverse proportionalities. We use these often in chemistry.

When a quantity is directly proportional to another, it means that an increase in one variable will cause a corresponding increase of the same percent in the other variable. A direct proportionality is shown as

$$A \propto B \ ( \propto \text{ is the proportionality symbol})$$

which is read "*A* is directly proportional to *B*." A proportionality can be easily converted to an algebraic equation by the introduction of a constant (in our examples designated $k$), called a constant of proportionality. Thus the proportion becomes

$$A = kB$$

or, rearranging,

$$\frac{A}{B} = k$$

Note that $k$ is not a variable but has a certain numerical value that does not change as do $A$ and $B$ under experimental conditions.

A common, direct proportionality that we will study relates Kelvin temperature $T$ and volume $V$ of a gas at constant pressure. This is written as

$$V \propto T \qquad V = kT \qquad \frac{V}{T} = k$$

(This is known as Charles's law.)

When a quantity is inversely proportional to another quantity, an increase in one brings about a corresponding *decrease* in the other. An inverse proportionality between $A$ and $B$ is written as

$$A \propto \frac{1}{B}$$

As before, the proportionality can be written as an equality by the introduction of a constant (which has a value different from the example above).

$$A = \frac{k}{B} \qquad \text{or} \qquad AB = k$$

A common inverse proportionality that we use relates the volume $V$ of a gas to the pressure $P$ at a constant temperature. This is written as

$$V \propto \frac{1}{P} \qquad V = \frac{k}{P} \qquad PV = k$$

(This is known as Boyle's law.)

When one variable (e.g., $x$) is directly proportional to two other variables (e.g., $y$ and $z$), the proportionality can be written as the product of the two.

$$\text{If } x \propto y \text{ and } x \propto z, \text{ then}$$

$$x \propto yz$$

When one variable (e.g., $a$) is directly proportional to one variable, (e.g., $b$) and inversely proportional to another (e.g., $c$,), the proportionality can be written as the ratio of the two.

$$\text{If } a \propto b \text{ and } a \propto \frac{1}{c}, \text{ then}$$

$$a \propto \frac{b}{c}$$

Quantities can be directly or inversely proportional to the square, square root, or any other function of another variable or number, as illustrated by the examples that follow.

## EXAMPLE B-4   Solving Equations with Proportionalities

**(a)** A quantity $C$ is directly proportional to the square of $D$. Write an equality for this statement and explain how a change in $D$ affects the value of $C$.

**SOLUTION**

The equation is

$$C = kD^2$$

Note that a change in $D$ will have a significant effect on the value of $C$. For example,

$$\text{If } D = 1, \text{ then } C = k$$

$$\text{If } D = 2, \text{ then } C = 4k$$
$$\text{If } D = 3, \text{ then } C = 9k$$

Note that when the value of $D$ is doubled, the value of $C$ is increased *fourfold*.

**(b)** A variable $X$ is directly proportional to the square of the variable $Y$ *and* inversely proportional to the square of another variable $Z$. Write an equality for this statement.

**SOLUTION**

This can be written as two separate equations if it is assumed that $Y$ is constant when $Z$ varies and vice versa.

$$X = k_1 Y^2 \qquad (Z \text{ constant})$$
$$X = k_2/Z^2 \qquad (Y \text{ constant})$$

$k_1$ and $k_2$ are different constants. This relationship can be combined into one equation when both $Y$ and $Z$ are variables.

$$X = \frac{k_3 Y^2}{Z^2}$$

$k_3$ is a third constant that is a combination of $k_1$ and $k_2$.

**EXERCISES**

**B-19.** Write equalities for the following relations.

**(a)** $X$ is inversely proportional to $Y + Z$.

**(b)** $[H_3O^+]$ is inversely proportional to $[OH^-]$.

**(c)** $[H_2]$ is directly proportional to the square root of $r$.

**(d)** $B$ is directly proportional to the square of $y$ and the cube of $z$.

**(e)** The pressure $P$ of a gas is directly proportional to the number of moles $n$ and the temperature $T$, and inversely proportional to the volume $V$.

*Answers:* **(a)** $X = k/(Y + Z)$   **(b)** $[H_3O^+] = k/[OH^-]$   **(c)** $[H_2] = k\sqrt{r}$   **(d)** $B = ky^2 z^3$
**(e)** $P = knT/V$

# Scientific Notation

Although this topic was first introduced in Section 1-3 in this text, we will focus on a review of the mathematical manipulation of numbers expressed in scientific notation in this appendix. Specifically, addition, multiplication, division, and taking the roots of numbers expressed in scientific notation are covered. We conclude this section with how we can simplify the expression of numbers in scientific notation with the use of logarithms. As mentioned in Chapter 1, scientific notation makes use of powers of 10 to express awkward numbers that employ more than two or three zeros that are not significant figures. The exponent of 10 simply indicates how many times we should multiply or divide a number (called the coefficient) by 10 to produce the actual number. For example, $8.9 \times 10^3 = 8.9$ (the coefficient) multiplied by 10 *three* times, or

$$8.9 \times 10 \times 10 \times 10 = 8900$$

Also, $4.7 \times 10^{-3} = 4.7$ (the coefficient) divided by 10 *three* times, or

$$\frac{4.7}{10 \times 10 \times 10} = 0.0047$$

## C-1 Review of Scientific Notation

The method for expressing numbers in scientific notation was explained in Section 1-3. However, to simplify a number or to express it in the standard form with one digit to the left of the decimal point in the coefficient, it is often necessary to change a number already expressed in scientific notation. If this is done in a hurry, errors may result. Thus it is worthwhile to practice moving the decimal point of numbers expressed in scientific notation.

---

**EXAMPLE C-1   Changing Normal Numbers to Scientific Notation**

Change the following numbers to the standard form in scientific notation.

**(a)** $489 \times 10^4$     **(b)** $0.00489 \times 10^8$

**PROCEDURE**

All you need to remember is to raise the power of 10 one unit for each place the decimal point is moved to the left, and lower the power of 10 one unit for each place that the decimal point is moved to the right in the coefficient.

**SOLUTION**

**(a)** $489 \times 10^4 = (4.89) \times 10^4 = 4.89 \times 10^{4+2} = \underline{4.89 \times 10^6}$

**(b)** $0.00489 \times 10^8 = (0.00489) \times 10^8 = 4.89 \times 10^{8-3} = 4.89 \times 10^5$

As an aid to remembering whether you should raise or lower the exponent as you move the decimal point, it is suggested that you write (or at least imagine) the coefficient on a slant. For each place that you move the decimal point *up*, add one to the exponent. For each place that you move the decimal point *down*, subtract one from the exponent. Note that the exponent moves up or down with the decimal point. It may be easier to recall "up or down" rather than "right or left."

---

**EXAMPLE C-2    Changing the Decimal Point in the Coefficient**

Change the following numbers to the standard form in scientific notation.

**(a)** $4223 \times 10^{-7}$    **(b)** $0.00076 \times 10^{18}$

**SOLUTION**

**(a)** $4223 \times 10^{-7} = \begin{bmatrix} 4 \\ 2 & {}^{+3} \\ 2 & {}^{+2} \\ 3 & {}^{+1} \end{bmatrix} \times 10^{-7} = 4.223 \times 10^{-7+3} = \underline{4.223 \times 10^{-4}}$

**(b)** $0.00076 \times 10^{18} = \begin{bmatrix} 0 & {}^{-1} \\ 0 & {}^{-2} \\ 0 & {}^{-3} \\ 0 & {}^{-4} \\ 7 \\ 6 \end{bmatrix} \times 10^{18} = 7.6 \times 10^{18-4} = \underline{7.6 \times 10^{14}}$

---

**EXERCISES**

**C-1.** Change the following numbers to standard scientific notation with one digit to the left of the decimal point in the coefficient.

**(a)** $787 \times 10^{-6}$    **(c)** $0.015 \times 10^{-16}$    **(e)** $49.3 \times 10^{15}$

**(b)** $43.8 \times 10^{-1}$    **(d)** $0.0037 \times 10^{9}$    **(f)** $6678 \times 10^{-16}$

**C-2.** Change the following numbers to a number with two digits to the left of the decimal point in the coefficient.

**(a)** $9554 \times 10^{4}$    **(c)** $1 \times 10^{6}$    **(e)** $0.023 \times 10^{-1}$

**(b)** $1.6 \times 10^{-5}$    **(d)** $116.5 \times 10^{4}$    **(f)** $0.005 \times 10^{23}$

*Answers:* **C-1:** **(a)** $7.87 \times 10^{-4}$    **(b)** $4.38$    **(c)** $1.5 \times 10^{-18}$    **(d)** $3.7 \times 10^{6}$    **(e)** $4.93 \times 10^{16}$    **(f)** $6.678 \times 10^{-13}$    **C-2:** **(a)** $95.54 \times 10^{6}$    **(b)** $16 \times 10^{-6}$    **(c)** $10 \times 10^{5}$    **(d)** $11.65 \times 10^{5}$    **(e)** $23 \times 10^{-4}$    **(f)** $50 \times 10^{19}$

## C-2 Addition and Subtraction

Addition or subtraction of numbers in scientific notation can be accomplished only when all coefficients have the same exponent of 10. When all the exponents are the same, the coefficients are added and then multiplied by the power of 10. The correct number of places to the right of the decimal point, as discussed in Section 1-2, must be shown.

**EXAMPLE C-3   Addition of Numbers in Scientific Notation**

**(a)** Add the following numbers: $3.67 \times 10^{-4}$, $4.879 \times 10^{-4}$, and $18.2 \times 10^{-4}$.

**SOLUTION**

$$
\begin{array}{r}
3.67 \ \times 10^{-4} \\
4.879 \times 10^{-4} \\
\underline{18.2 \ \ \ \times 10^{-4}} \\
26.749 \times 10^{-4} = 26.7 \times 10^{-4} \ = \ 26.7 \times 10^{-3}
\end{array}
$$

**(b)** Add the following numbers: $320.4 \times 10^3$, $1.2 \times 10^5$, and $0.0615 \times 10^7$.

**SOLUTION**

Before adding, change all three numbers to the same exponent of 10.

$$
\begin{array}{rcl}
320.4 \times 10^3 & = & 3.204 \times 10^5 \\
1.2 \times 10^5 & = & 1.2 \ \ \ \times 10^5 \\
0.0615 \times 10^7 & = & \underline{6.15 \ \ \times 10^5} \\
& & 10.554 \times 10^5 = 10.6 \times 10^5 = 1.06 \times 10^6
\end{array}
$$

**EXERCISES**

**C-3.** Add the following numbers. Express the answer to the proper decimal place.

**(a)** $152 + (8.635 \times 10^2) + (0.021 \times 10^3)$

**(b)** $(10.32 \times 10^5) + (1.1 \times 10^5) + (0.4 \times 10^5)$

**(c)** $(1.007 \times 10^{-8}) + (118 \times 10^{-11}) + (0.1141 \times 10^{-6})$

**(d)** $(0.0082) + (2.6 \times 10^{-4}) + (159 \times 10^{-4})$

**C-4.** Carry out the following calculations. Express your answer to the proper decimal place.

**(a)** $(18.75 \times 10^{-6}) - (13.8 \times 10^{-8}) + (1.0 \times 10^{-5})$

**(b)** $(1.52 \times 10^{-11}) + (17.7 \times 10^{-12}) - (7.5 \times 10^{-15})$

**(c)** $(481 \times 10^6) - (0.113 \times 10^9) + (8.5 \times 10^5)$

**(d)** $(0.363 \times 10^{-6}) + (71.2 \times 10^{-9}) + (519 \times 10^{-12})$

*Answers:* **C-3:** **(a)** $1.037 \times 10^3$ **(b)** $1.18 \times 10^6$ **(c)** $1.254 \times 10^{-7}$ **(d)** $2.44 \times 10^{-2}$
**C-4:** **(a)** $2.9 \times 10^{-5}$ **(b)** $3.29 \times 10^{-11}$ **(c)** $3.69 \times 10^8$ **(d)** $4.35 \times 10^{-7}$

## C-3 Multiplication and Division

When numbers expressed in scientific notation are multiplied, the exponents of 10 are *added*. When the numbers are divided, the exponent of 10 in the denominator (the divisor) is subtracted from the exponent of 10 in the numerator (the dividend).

**EXAMPLE C-4   Multiplication and Division**

**(a)** Carry out the following calculation.

$$(4.75 \times 10^6) \times (3.2 \times 10^5)$$

**SOLUTION**

In the first step, group the coefficients and the powers of 10. Carry out each step separately.

$$(4.75 \times 3.2) \times (10^6 \times 10^5) = 15.200 \times 10^{6+5}$$
$$= 15 \times 10^{11} = \underline{1.5 \times 10^{12}}$$

**(b)** Carry out the following calculation.

$$(1.62 \times 10^{-8}) \div (8.55 \times 10^{-3})$$

**SOLUTION**

$$\frac{1.62 \times 10^{-8}}{8.55 \times 10^{-3}} = \frac{1.62}{8.55} \times \frac{10^{-8}}{10^{-3}} = 0.189 \times 10^{-8-(-3)}$$

$$= 0.189 \times 10^{-5} = \underline{\underline{1.89 \times 10^{-6}}}$$

**EXERCISES**

**C-5.** Carry out the following calculations. Express your answer to the proper number of significant figures with one digit to the left of the decimal point.

**(a)** $(7.8 \times 10^{-6}) \times (1.12 \times 10^{-2})$

**(b)** $(0.511 \times 10^{-3}) \times (891 \times 10^{-8})$

**(c)** $(156 \times 10^{-12}) \times (0.010 \times 10^{4})$

**(d)** $(16 \times 10^{9}) \times (0.112 \times 10^{-3})$

**(e)** $(2.35 \times 10^{3}) \times (0.3 \times 10^{5}) \times (3.75 \times 10^{2})$

**(f)** $(6.02 \times 10^{23}) \times (0.0100)$

**C-6.** Follow the instructions in Problem C-5.

**(a)** $(14.6 \times 10^{8}) \div (2.2 \times 10^{8})$

**(b)** $(6.02 \times 10^{23}) \div (3.01 \times 10^{20})$

**(c)** $(0.885 \times 10^{-7}) \div (16.5 \times 10^{3})$

**(d)** $(0.0221 \times 10^{3}) \div (0.57 \times 10^{18})$

**(e)** $238 \div (6.02 \times 10^{23})$

**C-7.** Follow the instructions in Problem C-5.

**(a)** $[(8.70 \times 10^{6}) \times (3.1 \times 10^{8})] \div (5 \times 10^{-3})$

**(b)** $(47.9 \times 10^{-6}) \div [(0.87 \times 10^{6}) \times (1.4 \times 10^{2})]$

**(c)** $1 \div [(3 \times 10^{6}) \times (4 \times 10^{10})]$

**(d)** $1.00 \times 10^{-14} \div [(6.5 \times 10^{5}) \times (0.32 \times 10^{-5})]$

**(e)** $[(147 \times 10^{-6}) \div (154 \times 10^{-6})] \div (3.0 \times 10^{12})$

*Answers:* **C-5:**   **(a)** $8.7 \times 10^{-8}$   **(b)** $4.55 \times 10^{-9}$   **(c)** $1.6 \times 10^{-8}$   **(d)** $1.8 \times 10^{6}$
**(e)** $3 \times 10^{10}$   **(f)** $6.02 \times 10^{21}$   **C-6: (a)** $6.6$   **(b)** $2.00 \times 10^{3}$   **(c)** $5.36 \times 10^{-12}$
**(d)** $3.9 \times 10^{-17}$   **(e)** $3.95 \times 10^{-22}$   **C-7: (a)** $5 \times 10^{17}$   **(b)** $3.9 \times 10^{-13}$   **(c)** $8 \times 10^{-18}$
**(d)** $4.8 \times 10^{-15}$ **(e)** $3.2 \times 10^{-13}$

## C-4 Powers and Roots

When a number expressed in scientific notation is raised to a power, the coefficient is raised to the power and the exponent of 10 is *multiplied* by the power.

For a number expressed in scientific notation, we take the root of the coefficient and *divide* the exponent by the root. (A square root is the same as raising the number to the 1/2 power, a cube root to the 1/3 power, etc.) In the interest of easy viewing in the exercises, we will adjust the number so that division of the exponent by the root produces a whole number. It is not necessary to adjust the number when using a calculator.

## EXAMPLE C-5  Powers and Roots

**(a)** Carry out the following calculation.

$$(3.2 \times 10^3)^2$$

**SOLUTION**

$$(3.2 \times 10^3)^2 = (3.2)^2 \times 10^{3 \times 2}$$
$$= 10.24 \times 10^6 = \underline{1.0 \times 10^7}$$
$$[(10^3)^2 = 10^3 \times 10^3 = 10 \times 10 \times 10 \times 10 \times 10 \times 10 = 10^6]$$

**(b)** Carry out the following calculation.

$$(1.5 \times 10^{-3})^3$$

**SOLUTION**

$$(1.5 \times 10^{-3})^3 = (1.5)^3 \times 10^{-3 \times 3}$$
$$= \underline{3.4 \times 10^{-9}}$$

**(c)** Carry out the following calculation.

$$\sqrt{2.9 \times 10^5}$$

**SOLUTION**

It is easier to see and do (even when using a calculator) if you first adjust the number so that the exponent of 10 is divisible by 2.

$$\sqrt{2.9 \times 10^5} = \sqrt{29 \times 10^4} = \sqrt{29} \times \sqrt{10^4} = \sqrt{29} \times 10^{4/2}$$
$$= \underline{5.4 \times 10^2}$$

**(d)** Carry out the following calculation.

$$\sqrt[3]{6.9 \times 10^{-8}}$$

**SOLUTION**

Adjust the number so that the exponent of 10 is divisible by 3.

$$\sqrt[3]{6.9 \times 10^{-8}} = \sqrt[3]{69 \times 10^{-9}} = \sqrt[3]{69} \times \sqrt[3]{10^{-9}}$$
$$= 4.1 \times 10^{-9/3} = \underline{4.1 \times 10^{-3}}$$

**EXERCISES**

**C-8.** Carry out the following operations.

**(a)** $(6.6 \times 10^4)^2$     **(d)** $(0.035 \times 10^{-3})^3$

**(b)** $(0.7 \times 10^6)^3$     **(e)** $(0.7 \times 10^7)^4$

**(c)** $(1200 \times 10^{-5})^2$

(It will be easier to square if you change the number to $1.2 \times 10^2$ first.)

**C-9.** Take the following roots. Approximate the answer if necessary.

**(a)** $\sqrt{36 \times 10^4}$     **(c)** $\sqrt{64 \times 10^9}$     **(e)** $\sqrt{81 \times 10^{-7}}$

**(b)** $\sqrt[3]{27 \times 10^{12}}$     **(d)** $\sqrt[3]{1.6 \times 10^5}$     **(f)** $\sqrt{180 \times 10^{10}}$

*Answers:* **C-8:** **(a)** $4.4 \times 10^9$  **(b)** $3 \times 10^{17}$  **(c)** $1.4 \times 10^{-4}$  **(d)** $4.3 \times 10^{-14}$  **(e)** $2 \times 10^{27}$
**C-9:** **(a)** $6.0 \times 10^2$  **(b)** $3.0 \times 10^4$  **(c)** $2.5 \times 10^5$  **(d)** $54$  **(e)** $2.8 \times 10^{-3}$  **(f)** $1.3 \times 10^6$

## C-5 Logarithms

Scientific notation is particularly useful in expressing very large or very small numbers. In certain areas of chemistry, however, such as in the expression of $H_3O^+$ concentration, even the repeated use of scientific notation becomes tedious. In this situation, it is convenient to express the concentration as simply the *exponent of 10. The exponent to which 10 must be raised to give a certain number is called its* **common logarithm**. With common logarithms (or just logs) it is possible to express both the coefficient and the exponent of 10 as one number.

Since logarithms are simply exponents of 10, logs of exact multiples of 10 such as 100 can be easily determined. Note that 100 can be expressed as $10^2$, so that the log of 100 is exactly 2. Other examples of simple logs of numbers (that we assume to be exact) are

| | | | |
|---|---|---|---|
| $1 = 10^0$ | $\log 1 = 0$ | $0.1 = 10^{-1}$ | $\log 0.1 = -1$ |
| $10 = 10^1$ | $\log 10 = 1$ | $0.01 = 10^{-2}$ | $\log 0.01 = -2$ |
| $100 = 10^2$ | $\log 100 = 2$ | $0.001 = 10^{-3}$ | $\log 0.001 = -3$ |
| $1000 = 10^3$ | $\log 1000 = 3$ | $0.0001 = 10^{-4}$ | $\log 0.0001 = -4$ |

There are two general rules regarding logarithms.

**1.** $\log (A \times B) = \log A + \log B$

**2.** $\log (A/B) = \log A - \log B$

We can see how these rules apply when we multiply and divide multiples of ten.

| | **Exponents** | **Logarithms** |
|---|---|---|
| multiplication | $10^4 \times 10^3 = 10^{4+3}$ | $\log(10^4 \times 10^3) = \log 10^4 + \log 10^3$ |
| | $= 10^7$ | $= 4 + 3 = 7$ |
| division | $\dfrac{10^{10}}{10^4} = 10^{10-4} = 10^6$ | $\log \dfrac{10^{10}}{10^4} = \log 10^{10} - \log 10^4$ |
| | | $= 10 - 4 = 6$ |

Although we will use the calculator to determine the logs of numbers that are not simple multiples of ten, such as those above, it is helpful to have a sense of how the log of a specific number will appear. The log of a number has two parts. *The number to the left of the decimal is known as the* **characteristic** *and represents the exact exponent of 10 in the exponential number. The number to the right of the decimal is known as the* **mantissa** *and is the log of the coefficient in the exponential number.* For example, consider the log of the following exponential number.

Exponential number   $5.7 \times 10^6$

$$(\log 10^6 = 6) \qquad + \qquad (\log 5.7 = 0.76)$$

$$\log (5.7 \times 10^6) \quad = \quad \boxed{6.\ 76}$$

characteristic                mantissa

*Notice that the mantissa should be expressed with the same number of significant figures as the coefficient of the original exponential number.* In this case, that is two significant figures.

Although the calculator will easily provide logs and antilogs (inverse logs), we should be aware of some of the meanings of these numbers. For example, logs of numbers between one and ten are positive numbers where the characteristic is a zero (i.e., $5.8 = 5.8 \times 10^0$). For example,

$$\log 5.8 = \underline{0.76}$$

Logs of numbers greater than ten have a characteristic greater than zero. For example,

$$\log 4.7 \times 10^3 = \underline{3.67}$$

Logs of numbers that are less than one have a negative value since the exponent is a negative value. For example,

| number | $0.66 = 6.6 \times 10^{-1}$ | $7.3 \times 10^{-4}$ |
|---|---|---|
| | $\log 6.6 + \log 10^{-1}$ | $\log 7.3 + \log 10^{-4}$ |
| | $\log 0.66 = 0.82 + (-1) = \underline{-0.18}$ | $\log (7.3 \times 10^{-4}) = 0.86 - 4 = \underline{-3.14}$ |

Now consider how the *antilog* or *inverse log* of a number will appear. The antilog is the opposite of a logarithm. It is the number whose log has a certain value. For example, consider the antilog ($x$) of 2.

$$\log x = 2 \quad x = \underline{10^2} \text{ since } \log 10^2 = 2$$

Since the log of a number between one and ten is a positive number with zero as the characteristic, then the antilog of a number with zero as a characteristic is between one and ten. If the characteristic of a positive number is greater than zero, that number is the exponent of ten and the antilog of the mantissa is the coefficient. For example,

$$\text{antilog } 0.62 = \underline{4.2} \quad \text{antilog } 6.62 = \underline{4.2 \times 10^6}$$

The antilog of a negative number is somewhat different. In this case, the calculator actually computes the positive value of the characteristic. To change a characteristic with a negative value to one with a positive value requires a mathematical manipulation. The negative number is separated into its two parts, the characteristic and the mantissa. A value of 1 is added to the characteristic (which makes it a positive number) and a value of 1 is subtracted from the mantissa. For example, consider the antilogs of −3.28. This number can be also expressed as $0.74 − 4$. This calculation is shown below.

$$-3.28 = -0.28 - 3$$
$$(-0.28 + 1) - (3 - 1) = 0.72 - 4$$
$$\text{antilog } -3.28 = \text{antilog } 0.72 + \text{antilog } -4 = \underline{5.2 \times 10^{-4}}.$$

---

### EXAMPLE C-6   Logs

Give the logarithms of the following numbers.

| | | |
|---|---|---|
| **(a)** 5.8 | number between one and ten | $\log = \underline{0.76}$ |
| **(b)** $4.7 \times 10^3$ | number greater than ten | $\log = \underline{3.67}$ |
| **(c)** 0.085 | number less than one expressed in scientific notation as $8.5 \times 10^{-2}$ | |
| | $\log 8.5 + \log 10^{-2} = +0.yy - 2 = -1.xx$ | $\log = \underline{-1.07}$ |
| **(d)** $8.7 \times 10^{-7}$ | number less than one | $\log = \underline{-6.06}$ |

---

### EXAMPLE C-7   Antilogs

Give the number whose log is the following.

| | | | |
|---|---|---|---|
| **(a)** 0.84 | antilog between zero and one | exponent = 0 | $6.9 \times 10^0 = \underline{6.9}$ |
| **(b)** 4.65 | antilog greater than one | exponent = 4 | $\underline{4.5 \times 10^{-4}}$ |
| **(c)** −0.020 | antilog less than zero (antilog 0.980 −1) | exponent = −1 | $\underline{0.95}$ |
| **(d)** −4.54 | antilog less than zero (antilog 0.46 −5) | exponent = −5 | $\underline{2.9 \times 10^{-5}}$ |

---

### EXERCISES

**C-10.** Give the value of the logarithm for each of the following numbers.

**(a)** 7.4   **(b)** 0.087   **(c)** 1700   **(d)** $7.3 \times 10^4$   **(e)** $32 \times 10^{-5}$   **(f)** $32 \times 10^5$

**C-11.** Give the number whose log is the following.

**(a)** 0.34   **(b)** −5.48   **(c)** −0.070   **(d)** 8.40   **(e)** 10.94   **(f)** −2.60

*Answers:* **C-10:** **(a)** 0.86   **(b)** −1.06   **(c)** 3.23   **(d)** 4.86   **(e)** −3.49   **(f)** 6.51
**C-11:** **(a)** 2.19   **(b)** $3.3 \times 10^{-6}$   **(c)** 0.85   **(d)** $2.5 \times 10^8$   **(e)** $8.7 \times 10^{10}$   **(f)** $2.5 \times 10^{-3}$

# Glossary

The numbers in parentheses at the end of each entry refer to the chapter in which the entry is first discussed plus any chapter in which the topic is discussed in detail.

## A

**absolute zero.** Theoretically, the lowest possible temperature. The temperature at which translational motion ceases. Defined as zero on the Kelvin scale or $-273°C$. (1, 10)

**accuracy.** How close a measurement is to the true value. (1)

**acid.** A compound that increases the $H^+$ concentration in aqueous solution. In the Brønsted definition, an acid is a proton donor. (4, 6, 13, 15)

**acid anhydride.** A molecular oxide that dissolves in water to form an oxyacid. (13)

**acid ionization constant ($K_a$).** The equilibrium constant specifically for the ionization of a weak acid in water. The magnitude of the constant relates to the strength of the acid. (15)

**acid salt.** An ionic compound containing one or more acidic hydrogens on the anion. (13)

**acidic solution.** A solution with pH $< 7$ or $[H_3O^+] > 10^{-7}$ M. (13)

**actinide.** One of the 14 elements between Ac and Rf. An element whose $5f$ subshell is filling. (4, 8)

**activated complex.** The transition state formed at the instant of maximum impact between reacting molecules. (15)

**activation energy.** The minimum energy needed by reactant molecules to form an activated complex so that a reaction may occur. It is the difference in potential energy between the reactants and the activated complex. (15)

**activity series.** The ability of metals to replace other metal ions in a single-replacement reaction and ranked in a series. (6)

**actual yield.** The experimentally measured amount of product in a chemical reaction. (7)

**alkali metal.** An element in Group IA (1) in the periodic table (except H). Elements with the electron configuration $[NG]ns^1$. (4, 8)

**alkaline earth metal.** An element in Group IIA (2) in the periodic table. Elements with the electron configuration $[NG]ns^2$. (4, 8)

**allotropes.** Different forms of the same element. (9)

**alloy.** A homogeneous mixture of metallic elements in one solid phase. (3)

**alpha ($\alpha$) particle.** A helium nucleus $^4_2He^{2+}$ emitted from a radioactive nucleus. (2, 16)

**amorphous solid.** A solid without a defined shape. The molecules in such a solid do not occupy regular, symmetrical positions. (11)

**amphiprotic.** Refers to a molecule or ion that has both a conjugate acid and a conjugate base. (13)

**anion.** A negatively charged ion. (2)

**anode.** The electrode at which oxidation takes place. (14)

**atmosphere.** The sea of gases above the surface of earth. Also, the average pressure of the atmosphere at sea level, which is defined as the standard pressure and abbreviated atm. (10)

**atom.** The smallest fundamental particle of an element that has the properties of that element. (1, 2)

**atomic mass.** The weighted average of the isotopic masses of all of the naturally occurring isotopes of an element. The mass of an "average" atom of a naturally occurring element compared to $^{12}C$. (1, 2)

**atomic mass unit (amu).** A mass that is exactly one-twelfth of the mass of an atom of $^{12}C$, which is defined as exactly 12 amu. (2)

**atomic number.** The number of protons (positive charge) in the nuclei of the isotopes of a particular element. (2)

**atomic radius.** The distance from the nucleus of an atom to the outermost electron. (8)

**atomic theory.** A theory first proposed by John Dalton in 1803 that holds that the basic components of matter are atoms. (2)

**Aufbau principle.** A rule that states that electrons fill the lowest available energy level first. (8)

**autoionization.** The dissociation of a solvent to produce positive and negative ions. (13)

**Avogadro's law.** A law that states that the volume of a gas is directly proportional to the number of moles of gas present at constant temperature and pressure (i.e., $V = kn$). (10)

**Avogadro's number.** The number of objects or particles in one mole, which is $6.022 \times 10^{23}$. (5)

## B

**balanced equation.** A chemical equation that has the same number and types of atoms on both sides of the equation. (6)

**barometer.** A device that measures the atmospheric pressure. (10)

**base.** A compound that increases the $OH^-$ concentration in aqueous solution. In the Brønsted definition, a base is a proton acceptor. (6, 13)

**base anhydride.** An ionic oxide that dissolves in water to form an ionic hydroxide. (13)

**base ionization constant ($K_b$).** An equilibrium constant specifically for the ionization of a weak base in water. The magnitude of the constant relates to the strength of the base. (15)

**basic solution.** A solution with pH $> 7$ or $[OH^-] > 10^{-7}$ M. (13)

**battery.** One or more voltaic cells joined together as a single unit. (14)

**beta ($\beta$) particle.** A high-energy electron emitted from a radioactive nucleus. (16)

**binary acid.** An acid composed of hydrogen and one other element. (4)

**Bohr model.** A model of the atom in which electrons orbit around a central nucleus in discrete energy levels. (8)

**boiling point.** The temperature at which the vapor pressure of a liquid equals the restraining pressure. (3, 11, 12)

**box diagram.** See *orbital diagram.*

**Boyle's law.** A law that states that the volume of a gas is inversely proportional to the pressure at constant temperature (i.e., $PV = k$). (10)

**Brønsted-Lowry definition.** A definition of acids as proton donors and bases as proton acceptors. (13)

**buffer solution.** A solution that resists changes in pH from the addition of limited amounts of strong acid or base. Made from (a) a solution of a weak acid and a salt containing its conjugate base, or (b) a weak base and a salt containing its conjugate acid. (13, 15)

**C**

**calorie.** The amount of heat required to raise the temperature of one gram of water one degree Celsius. Equal to exactly 4.184 joules. (3)

**catalyst.** A substance that is not consumed in a reaction but whose presence increases the rate of the reaction. A catalyst lowers the activation energy. (15)

**cathode.** The electrode at which reduction takes place. (14)

**cation.** A positively charged ion. (2)

**Celsius.** A temperature scale with 100 equal divisions between the freezing and boiling points of water at average sea level pressure, with exactly zero assigned to the freezing point of water. (1)

**chain reaction.** A self-sustaining reaction. In a nuclear chain reaction, one reacting neutron produces between two and three other neutrons that in turn cause reactions. (16)

**Charles's law.** A law that states that the volume of a gas is directly proportional to the Kelvin temperature at constant pressure (i.e., $V = kT$). (10)

**chemical change.** A change in a substance to another substance or substances. (3)

**chemical equation.** The representation of a chemical reaction using the symbols of the elements and the formulas of compounds. (6)

**chemical property.** The property of a substance relating to its tendency to undergo chemical changes. (3)

**chemical thermodynamics.** The study of heat and its relationship to chemical changes. (7)

**chemistry.** The branch of science dealing with the nature, composition, and structure of matter and the changes it undergoes. (1,3)

**coefficient.** The number in scientific notation that is raised to a power of ten. (1) The number before an element or compound in a balanced chemical equation indicating the number of molecules or moles of that substance. (1, 7)

**colligative property.** A property that depends only on the relative amounts of solute and solvent present, not on their identities. (12)

**collision theory.** A theory that states that chemical reactions are brought about by collisions of molecules. (15)

**combination reaction.** A chemical reaction whereby one compound is formed from two elements and/or compounds. (6)

**combined gas law.** A law that relates the pressure, volume, and temperature of a gas (i.e., $PV = kT$). (10)

**combustion reaction.** A chemical reaction whereby an element or compound reacts with elemental oxygen. (6)

**compound.** A pure substance composed of two or more elements that are chemically combined in fixed proportions. (1, 2)

**concentrated solution.** A solution containing a relatively large amount of a specified solute per unit volume. (12)

**concentration.** The amount of solute present in a specified amount of solvent or solution. (3, 12)

**condensation point.** The temperature at which a pure substance changes from the gas to the liquid or solid state. (3, 11)

**conductor.** A substance that allows a flow of electricity. (12)

**conjugate acid.** An acid formed by addition of one $H^+$ to a base. (13)

**conjugate base.** A base formed by removal of one $H^+$ from an acid. (13)

**conservation of energy.** A law that states that energy is neither created nor destroyed but can be transformed from one form to another. (3)

**conservation of mass.** A law that states that matter is neither created nor destroyed in a chemical reaction. (3)

**continuous spectrum.** A spectrum where one color blends gradually into another. The visible spectrum containing all wavelengths of visible light. (8)

**conversion factor.** A relationship between two units or quantities expressed in fractional form. (1)

**Coulomb's law** A law that states that forces of attraction increase as the charges increase and decrease as the distance between the charges increases. (8)

**covalent bond.** The force that bonds two atoms together by a shared pair or pairs of electrons. (2, 9)

**crystal lattice.** See *lattice*.

**crystalline solid.** A solid with a regular, symmetrical shape where the molecules or ions occupy set positions in the crystal lattice. (11)

**D**

**Dalton's law.** A law that states that the total pressure of a gas in a system is the sum of the partial pressures of all component gases. (10)

**Daniell cell.** A voltaic cell made up of zinc and copper electrodes immersed in solutions of their respective ions that are connected by a salt bridge. (14)

**decomposition reaction.** A chemical reaction whereby one compound decomposes to two or more elements and/or compounds. (6)

**density.** The ratio of the mass (usually in grams) to the volume (usually in milliliters or liters) of a substance. (3, 10)

**diffusion.** The mixing of one gas or liquid into others. (10)

**dilute solution.** A solution containing a relatively small amount of a specified solute per unit volume. (12)

**dilution.** The preparation of a dilute solution from a concentrated solution by the addition of more solvent. (12)

**dimensional analysis.** A problem-solving technique that converts from one unit to another by use of conversion factors. (1)

**dipole.** Two poles—one positive and one negative—that may exist in a bond or molecule. (9)

**dipole–dipole attractions.** The force of attraction between a dipole on one polar molecule and a dipole on another polar molecule. (11)

**diprotic acid.** An acid that can produce two $H^+$ ions per molecule. (13)

**discrete spectrum.** A spectrum containing specific wavelengths of light originating from the hot gaseous atoms of an element. (8)

**distillation.** A laboratory procedure where a solution is separated into its components by boiling the mixture and condensing the vapor to form a liquid. (3)

**double bond.** The sharing of two pairs of electrons between two atoms. (9)

**double-replacement reaction.** A chemical reaction whereby the cations and anions in two compounds exchange, leading to formation of either a precipitate or a molecular compound such as water. (6)

**dry cell.** A voltaic cell composed of zinc and graphite electrodes immersed in an aqueous paste of $NH_4Cl$ and $MnO_2$. (14)

**dynamic equilibrium.** See *point of equilibrium*.

**E**

**effusion.** The movement of gases through an opening or hole. (10)

**electricity.** A flow of electrons through a conductor. (14)

**electrode.** A surface in a cell where the oxidation or reduction reaction takes place. (14)

**electrolysis.** The process of forcing electrical energy through an electrolytic cell, thereby causing a chemical reaction. (14)

**electrolyte.** A solute whose aqueous solution or molten state conducts electricity. (12)

**electrolytic cell.** A voltaic cell that converts electrical energy into chemical energy by means of a nonspontaneous reaction. (14)

**electron.** A negatively charged particle in an atom, with a comparatively very small mass. (2)

**electron capture.** The capture of an orbital electron by the nucleus of a radioactive isotope. (16)

**electron configuration.** The designation of all of the electrons in an atom into specific shells and subshells. (8)

**electronegativity.** The ability of the atoms of an element to attract electrons in a covalent bond. (7)

**electrostatic forces.** The forces of attraction between unlike charges and of repulsion by like charges. (2)

**element.** A pure substance that cannot be broken down into simpler substances. The most basic form of matter existing under ordinary conditions. (1, 2)

**empirical formula.** The simplest whole-number ratio of atoms in a compound. (5)

**endothermic reaction.** A chemical reaction that absorbs heat from the surroundings. (3, 7, 15)

**energy.** The capacity or the ability to do work. It has several different forms (e.g., light and heat) and two types (kinetic and potential). (3)

**equilibrium.** See *point of equilibrium*.

**equilibrium constant.** A number that defines the position of equilibrium for a particular reaction at a specified temperature. (15)

**equilibrium constant expression.** The ratio of the concentrations of products to reactants, each raised to the power corresponding to its coefficient in the balanced equation. (15)

**equilibrium vapor pressure.** The pressure exerted by a vapor above a liquid at a certain temperature. (11)

**evaporation.** The vaporization of a liquid below its boiling point. (11)

**exact number.** A number that results from a definition or an actual count. (1)

**excited state.** Occupation by an electron of higher energy level than the lowest available energy level. (8)

**exothermic reaction.** A chemical reaction that occurs with the evolution of heat to the surroundings. (3, 7, 15)

**exponent.** In scientific notation, it is the power to which ten is raised. (1)

**F**

**Fahrenheit.** A temperature scale with 180 divisions between the freezing and boiling points of water, with exactly 32 assigned to the freezing point of water. (1)

**family.** See *group*.

**filtration.** A laboratory procedure where solids are removed from liquids by passing the heterogeneous mixture through a filter. (3)

**fission.** The splitting of a large, unstable nucleus into two smaller nuclei of similar size, resulting in the production of energy. (16)

**formula.** The symbols of the elements and the number of atoms of each element that make up a compound. (2)

**formula unit.** The simplest whole-number ratio of ions in an ionic compound. (2)

**formula weight.** The mass of a compound (in amu), which is determined from the number of atoms and the atomic masses of the elements indicated by the formula. (5)

**freezing point.** The temperature at which a pure substance changes from the liquid to the solid state. (3, 12)

**fuel cell.** A voltaic cell that can generate a continuous flow of electricity from the reaction of hydrogen and oxygen to produce water. (14)

**fusion (nuclear).** The combination of two small nuclei to form a larger nucleus, resulting in the production of energy. (16)

**G**

**gamma ($\gamma$) ray.** A high-energy form of light emitted from a radioactive nucleus. (16)

**gas.** A physical state that has neither a definite volume nor a definite shape and fills a container uniformly. (3, 10)

**gas constant.** The constant of proportionality ($R$) in the ideal gas law. (10)

**gas law.** A law governing the behavior of gases that is consistent with the kinetic molecular theory as applied to gases. (10)

**Gay-Lussac's law.** A law that states that the pressure of a gas is directly proportional to the Kelvin temperature at constant volume (i.e., $P = kT$). (10)

**Graham's law.** A law that states that the rates of diffusion of gases are inversely proportional to the square root of their molar masses. (10)

**ground state.** Occupation of an electron of the lowest available energy level in an atom. (8)

**group.** A vertical column of elements in the periodic table. (4)

**H**

**half-life.** The time required for one-half of a given sample of an isotope to undergo radioactive decay. (16)

**half-reaction.** The oxidation or reduction process in a redox reaction written separately. (14)

**halogen.** An element in Group VIIA (17) in the periodic table. Elements with the electron configuration [NG] $ns^2np^5$. (4, 8)

**heat of fusion.** The amount of heat in calories or joules required to melt one gram of a substance. (11)

**heat of reaction.** The amount of heat energy absorbed or evolved in a specified chemical reaction. (7)

**heat of vaporization.** The amount of heat in calories or joules required to vaporize one gram of the substance. (11)

**heating curve.** The graphical representation of the temperature as a solid is heated through two phase changes, plotted as a function of the time of heating. (11)

**Henderson-Hasselbalch equation.** Equations that are used to calculate the pH of buffer solutions. (13)

$$\text{pH} = \text{p}K_a + \log \frac{[\text{base}]}{[\text{acid}]} \qquad \text{pOH} = \text{p}K_b + \log \frac{[\text{acid}]}{[\text{base}]}$$

**heterogeneous mixture.** A nonuniform mixture containing two or more phases with definite boundaries between phases. (3)

**homogeneous mixture.** A mixture that is the same throughout and contains only one phase. (3)

**Hund's rule.** A rule that states that electrons occupy separate orbitals of the same energy with parallel spins if possible. (8)

**hydrogen bonding.** A force of attraction between a lone pair of electrons on an N, O, or F atom on one molecule and a hydrogen bonded to an N, O, or F atom on another. (11)

**hydrolysis reaction.** The reaction of an anion as a base or a cation as an acid with water. (13)

**hydronium ion.** A representation of the hydrogen ion in aqueous solution ($H_3O^+$). (13)

**hypothesis.** A tentative explanation of related data. It can be used to predict results of more experiments. (Prologue)

**I**

**ideal gas.** A hypothetical gas whose molecules are considered to have no volume or interactions with each other. An ideal gas would obey the ideal gas law under all conditions. (10)

**ideal gas law.** A relationship between the pressure, volume, temperature, and number of moles of gas (i.e., $PV = nRT$) (10)

**immiscible liquids.** Two liquids that do not mix and thus form a heterogeneous mixture. (12)

**improper fraction.** A fraction whose numerator is larger than the denominator and thus has a value greater than one. (Appendix A)

**infrared light.** Light with wavelengths somewhat longer than those of red light in the visible spectrum. (8)

**inner transition element.** Either a lanthanide, where the $4f$ subshell is filling, or an actinide, where the $5f$ subshell is filling. (4, 8)

**insoluble compound.** A compound that does not dissolve to any appreciable extent in a solvent. (6, 15)

**insulator.** See *nonconductor*.

**intermolecular forces.** The attractive forces between molecules. (11)

**ion.** An atom or group of covalently bonded atoms that has a net electrical charge. (2)

**ion product ($K_w$).** The equilibrium expression of the anion and the cation of water (i.e., $[H_3O^+][OH^-] = K_w$). (13)

**ion–dipole force.** The force between an ion and the dipoles of a polar molecule. (12)

**ion-electron method.** A method of balancing oxidation–reduction reactions where two half-reactions are balanced separately and then added so that electrons gained equal electrons lost. (14)

**ionic bond.** The electrostatic force holding the positive and negative ions together in an ionic compound. (2, 9)

**ionic compound.** Compounds containing positive and negative ions. (2, 9)

**ionic solid.** A solid where the crystal lattice positions are occupied by ions. (11)

**ionization.** The process of forming an ion or ions from a molecule or atom. (8, 12, 13, 16)

**ionization energy.** The energy required to remove an electron from a gaseous atom or ion. (8)

**isoelectronic** Two species having the same number of electrons and having the same electron configuration. (8)

**isotopes.** Atoms of the same element but having different numbers of neutrons. (2)

**isotopic mass.** The mass of an isotope compared to $^{12}C$, which is defined as having a mass of exactly 12 amu. (2)

**J**

**Joule.** The SI unit for measurement of heat energy. (3)

**K**

**Kelvin scale.** A temperature scale in which 0 K is the lowest possible temperature. $T(K) = T(°C) + 273$. (1, 10)

**kinetic energy.** Energy as a result of motion; equal to $\frac{1}{2}mv^2$ (3, 11)

**kinetic molecular theory.** A theory advanced in the late 1800s to explain the nature of gases. (10)

**L**

**lanthanide.** One of 14 elements between La and Hf. Elements whose $4f$ subshell is filling. (4, 8)

**lattice.** A three-dimensional array of ions or molecules in a solid crystal. (9)

**law.** A concise statement or mathematical relationship that describes some behavior of matter. (Prologue)

**law of conservation of energy.** A law that states that energy cannot be created or destroyed but only transformed from one form to another. (3)

**law of conservation of mass.** A law that states that matter is neither created nor destroyed in a chemical reaction. (3)

**lead–acid battery.** A rechargeable voltaic battery composed of lead and lead dioxide electrodes in a sulfuric acid solution. (14)

**Le Châtelier's principle.** A principle that states that when stress is applied to a system at equilibrium, the system reacts in such a way as to counteract the stress. (15)

**Lewis dot symbols.** The representation of an element by its symbol with its valence electrons as dots. (9)

**Lewis structure.** The representation of a molecule or ion showing the order and arrangement of the atoms as well as the bonded pairs and unshared electrons of all the atoms. (9)

**limiting reactant.** The reactant that produces the least amount of product when that reactant is completely consumed. (7)

**liquid.** A physical state that has a definite volume but not a definite shape. Liquids take the shape of the lower part of the container. (3, 11)

**London forces.** The instantaneous dipole–induced dipole forces between molecules caused by an instantaneous imbalance of electrical charge in a molecule. The force is roughly dependent on the size of the molecule. (11)

**M**

**main group element.** See *representative element.*

**mass.** The quantity of matter (usually in grams or kilograms) in a sample. (1)

**mass number.** The number of nucleons (neutrons and protons) in a nucleus. (2)

**matter.** Anything that has mass and occupies space. (2)

**measurement.** The quantity, dimensions, or extent of something, usually in comparison to a specific unit. (1)

**melting point.** The temperature at which a pure substance changes from the solid to the liquid state. (3, 11)

**metal.** An element with a comparatively low ionization energy that forms positive ions in compounds. Generally, metals are hard, lustrous elements that are ductile and malleable. (4, 8)

**metallic solid.** A solid made of metals where positive metal ions occupy regular positions in the crystal lattice with the valence electrons moving freely among these positive ions. (11)

**metalloid.** Elements with properties intermediate between metals and nonmetals. Many of the elements on the metal–nonmetal borderline in the periodic table. (4)

**metallurgy.** The conversion of metal ores into metals. (Prologue)

**metric system.** A system of measurement based on multiples of 10. (1)

**miscible liquids.** Two liquids that mix or dissolve in each other to form a solution. (12)

**model.** A description or analogy used to help visualize a phenomenon. (8)

**molality.** A temperature-independent unit of concentration that relates the moles of solute to the mass (kg) of solvent. (12)

**molar mass.** The atomic mass of an element or the formula weight of a compound expressed in grams. (5)

**molar volume.** The volume of one mole of a gas at STP, which is 22.4 L. (10)

**molarity.** A unit of concentration that relates moles of solute to volume (in liters) of solution. (12)

**mole.** A unit of $6.022 \times 10^{23}$ atoms, molecules, or formula units. It is the same number of particles as there are atoms in exactly 12 grams of $^{12}C$. It also represents the atomic mass of an element or the formula weight of a compound expressed in grams. (5)

**mole ratio.** The ratios of moles from a balanced equation that serve as conversion factors in stoichiometric calculations. (7)

**molecular compound.** A compound composed of discrete molecules. (2)

**molecular dipole.** The combined or net effect of all of the bond dipoles in a molecule as determined by the molecular geometry. (9)

**molecular equation.** A chemical equation showing all reactants and products as neutral compounds. (6)

**molecular formula.** See *formula*.

**molecular geometry.** The geometry of a molecule or ion described by the bonded atoms. It does not include the unshared pairs of electrons. (9)

**molecular solid.** A solid where the individual molecules in the crystal lattice are held together by London forces, dipole–dipole attractions, or hydrogen bonding. (11)

**molecular weight.** The formula weight of a molecular compound. (8)

**molecule.** The basic unit of a molecular compound, which is two or more atoms held together by covalent bonds. (1, 2)

**monoprotic acid.** An acid that can produce one $H^+$ ion per molecule. (13)

**N**

**net ionic equation.** A chemical equation shown in ionic form with spectator ions eliminated. (6)

**network solid.** A solid where the atoms are covalently bonded to each other throughout the entire crystal. (11)

**neutral.** Pure water or a solution with pH = 7. (13)

**neutralization reaction.** A reaction whereby an acid reacts with a base to form a salt and water. The reaction of $H^+(aq)$ with $OH^-(aq)$. (6, 13)

**neutron.** A particle in the nucleus with a mass of about 1 amu and no charge. (2)

**noble gas.** An element with a full outer $s$ and $p$ subshell. Group VIIIA (17) in the periodic table. (2, 4, 8)

**nonconductor.** A substance that does not conduct electricity. (12)

**nonelectrolyte.** A solute whose aqueous solution or molten state does not conduct electricity. (12)

**nonmetal.** Elements to the right in the periodic table. These elements generally lack metallic properties. They have relatively high ionization energies. (4, 8, 9)

**nonpolar bond.** A covalent bond in which electrons are shared equally. (9)

**normal boiling point.** The temperature at which the vapor pressure of a liquid is equal to exactly one atmosphere pressure. (11)

**nuclear equation.** A symbolic representation of the changes of a nucleus or nuclei into other nuclei and particles. (16)

**nuclear reactor.** A device that can maintain a controlled nuclear fission reaction. Used either for research or generation of electrical power. (16)

**nucleons.** The protons and neutrons that make up the nucleus of the atom. (2, 16)

**nucleus.** The core of the atom containing neutrons, protons, and most of the mass. (2, 16)

**O**

**octet rule.** A rule that states that atoms of representative elements form bonds so as to have access to eight electrons either through bonds or unshared pairs of electrons. (9)

**orbital.** A region of space where there is the highest probability of finding a particular electron. There are four types of orbitals; each has a characteristic shape. (8)

**orbital diagram.** The representation of specific orbitals of a subshell as boxes and the electrons as arrows in the boxes. (8)

**osmosis.** The tendency of a solvent to move through a semipermeable membrane from a region of low concentration to a region of high concentration of solute. (12)

**osmotic pressure.** The pressure needed to counteract the movement of solvent through a semipermeable membrane from a region of low concentration of solute to a region of high concentration. (12)

**oxidation.** The loss of electrons as indicated by an increase in oxidation state. (14)

**oxidation–reduction reaction.** A chemical reaction involving an exchange of electrons. (14)

**oxidation state (number).** The charge on an atom in a compound if all atoms were present as monatomic ions. The electrons in bonds are assigned to the more electronegative atom. (14)

**oxidation state method.** A method of balancing oxidation–reduction reactions that focuses on the atoms of the elements undergoing a change in oxidation state. (14)

**oxidizing agent.** The element, compound, or ion that oxidizes another reactant. It is reduced. (14)

**oxyacid.** An acid composed of hydrogen and an oxyanion. (4)

**oxyanion.** An anion composed of oxygen and one other element. (4)

**P**

**partial pressure.** The pressure of one component in a mixture of gases. (10)

**parts per billion (ppb).** A unit of concentration obtained by multiplying the ratio of the mass of solute to the mass of solution by $10^9$ ppb. (12)

**parts per million (ppm).** A unit of concentration obtained by multiplying the ratio of the mass of solute to the mass of solution by $10^6$ ppm. (12)

**Pauli exclusion principle.** A rule that states that no two electrons can have the same spin in the same orbital. (8)

**percent by mass.** The mass of solute expressed as a percent of the mass of solution. (3, 12)

**percent composition.** The mass of each element expressed per 100 mass units of the compound. (5)

**percent yield.** The actual yield in grams or moles divided by the theoretical yield in grams or moles and multiplied by 100%. (7)

**period.** A horizontal row of elements between noble gases in the periodic table. (4)

**periodic law.** A law that states that the properties of elements are periodic functions of their atomic numbers. (4)

**periodic table.** An arrangement of elements in order of increasing atomic number. Elements with the same number of outer electrons are arranged in vertical columns. (4, 8)

**pH.** The negative of the common logarithm of the $H_3O^+$ concentration. (13)

**phase.** A homogeneous state (solid, liquid, or gas) with distinct boundaries and uniform properties. (3)

**physical change.** A change in physical state or dimensions of a substance that does not involve a change in composition. (3)

**physical properties.** Properties that can be observed without changing the composition of a substance. (3)

**physical states.** The physical condition of matter—solid, liquid, or gas. (3)

**pOH.** The negative of the common logarithm of the $OH^-$ concentration. (13)

**point of equilibrium.** The point at which the forward and reverse processes in a reversible process occur at the same rate so that the concentrations of all species remain constant. (11, 13, 15)

**polar covalent bond.** A covalent bond that has a partial separation of charge due to the unequal sharing of electrons. (9)

**polyatomic ion.** A group of atoms covalently bonded to each other that have a net electrical charge. (2, 4)

**polyprotic acid.** An acid that can produce more than one $H^+$ ion per molecule. (13)

**positron.** An antimatter particle with the same mass as an electron but positively charged. Emitted from certain radioactive isotopes. (16)

**potential energy.** Energy as a result of position or composition. (3, 15)

**precipitate.** A solid compound formed in a solution. (6)

**precipitation reaction.** A type of double-replacement reaction in which an insoluble ionic compound is formed by an exchange of ions in the reactants. (6)

**precision.** The reproducibility of a measurement as indicated by the number of significant figures expressed. (1)

**pressure.** The force per unit area. (10)

**principal quantum number (*n*).** A number that corresponds to a particular shell occupied by the electrons in an atom. (8)

**product.** An element or compound in an equation that is formed as a result of a chemical reaction. (6)

**proper fraction.** A fraction whose numerator is smaller than the denominator and thus has a value less than one. (Appendix A)

**property.** A particular characteristic or trait of a substance. (2, 3)

**proton.** A particle in the nucleus with a mass of about 1 amu and a charge of +1. (2)

**pure substance.** A substance that has a definite composition with definite and unchanging properties (i.e., elements and compounds). (3)

**Q**

**quantized energy level.** An energy level with a definite and measurable energy. (8)

**R**

**radiation.** Particles or high-energy light rays that are emitted by an atom or a nucleus of an atom. (8, 16)

**radioactive decay series.** A series of elements formed from the successive emission of alpha and beta particles starting from a long-lived isotope and ending with a stable isotope. (16)

**radioactivity.** The emission of energy or particles from an unstable nucleus. (16)

**rate of reaction.** A measure of the increase in concentration of a product or the decrease in concentration of a reactant per unit time. (15)

**reactant.** An element or compound in an equation that undergoes a chemical reaction. (6)

**recrystallization.** A laboratory procedure whereby a solid compound is purified by saturating a solution at a high temperature and then forming a precipitate at a lower temperature. (12)

**redox reaction.** See *oxidation-reduction reaction.*

**reducing agent.** An element, compound, or ion that reduces another reactant. It is oxidized. (14)

**reduction.** The gain of electrons as indicated by a decrease in the oxidation state. (14)

**representative element.** Elements whose outer *s* and *p* subshells are filling. The A Group elements (i.e., groups 1, 2, 13–17) in the periodic table [except for VIIIA (18)]. (4, 8)

**resonance hybrid.** The actual structure of the molecule as implied by the separate resonance structures. (9)

**resonance structure.** A Lewis structure showing one of two or more possible Lewis structures. (9)

**reversible reaction.** A reaction where both a forward reaction (forming products) and a reverse reaction (reforming reactants) can occur. (15)

**room temperature.** The standard reference temperature for physical state, which is usually defined as 25°C. (4)

**S**

**salt.** An ionic compound formed by the combination of most cations and anions. Also, the compound that forms from the cation of a base and the anion of an acid. (4, 6, 13)

**salt bridge.** An aqueous gel that allows anions to migrate between compartments in a voltaic cell. (14)

**saturated solution.** A solution containing the maximum amount of dissolved solute at a specific temperature. (12)

**scientific method.** The method whereby modern scientists explain the behavior of nature with hypotheses and theories, or describe the behavior of nature with laws. (Prologue)

**scientific notation.** A number expressed with one nonzero digit to the left of the decimal point multiplied by 10 raised to a given power. (1, Appendix C)

**semimetal.** See *metalloid*.

**shell.** The principal energy level that contains one or more subshells. (8)

**SI units.** An international system of units of measurement. (1)

**significant figure.** A digit or number in a measurement that either is reliably known or is estimated. (1)

**single-replacement reaction.** A chemical reaction whereby a free element substitutes for another element in a compound. (6)

**solid.** A physical state with both a definite shape and a definite volume. (3, 11)

**solubility.** The maximum amount of a solute that dissolves in a specific amount of solvent at a certain temperature. (6, 12)

**solubility product constant ($K_{sp}$).** The equilibrium constant associated with the solution of ionic compounds. (15)

**soluble compound.** A compound that dissolves to an appreciable extent in a solvent. (6)

**solute.** A substance that dissolves in a solvent. (6, 12)

**solution.** A homogeneous mixture with one phase. It is composed of a solute dissolved in a solvent. (3, 6, 12)

**solvent.** A medium, usually a liquid, that disperses a solute to form a solution. (6, 12)

**specific gravity.** The ratio of the mass of a substance to the mass of an equal volume of water at the same temperature. (3)

**specific heat.** The amount of heat required to raise the temperature of one gram of a substance one degree Celsius. (3)

**spectator ion.** An ion that is in an identical state on both sides of an equation and not specifically involved in a reaction. (6)

**spectrum.** The separate color components of a beam of light. (8)

**standard temperature and pressure (STP).** The defined standard conditions for a gas, which are exactly 0°C and one atmosphere pressure. (10)

**Stock method.** A method used to name metal–nonmetal or metal–polyatomic ion compounds where the charge on the metal is indicated by Roman numerals enclosed in parentheses. (4)

**stoichiometry.** The quantitative relationship among reactants and products. (7)

**strong acid (base).** An acid (or base) that is completely ionized in aqueous solution. (6, 13)

**structural formula.** Formulas written so that the order and arrangement of specific atoms are shown. (2, 9)

**sublimation.** The vaporization of a solid. (11)

**subshell.** The orbitals of the same type within a shell. The subshells are named for the types of orbitals, that is, *s, p, d,* or *f.* (8)

**substance.** A form of matter. Usually thought of as either an element or a compound. (3)

**supersaturated solution.** A solution containing more than the maximum amount of solute indicated by the compound's solubility at that temperature. (12)

**surface tension.** The forces of attraction between molecules that cause a liquid surface to contract. (11)

**symbol.** One or two letters from an element's English or, in some cases, Latin name. (2)

**T**

**temperature.** A measure of the intensity of heat of a substance. It relates to the average kinetic energy of the substance. (1, 10)

**theoretical yield.** The calculated amount of product that would be obtained if all of a reactant were converted to a certain product. (7)

**theory.** A hypothesis that withstands the test of time and experiments designed to test the hypothesis. (Prologue)

**thermochemical equation.** A balanced equation that includes the amount of heat energy. (7)

**thermometer.** A device that measures temperature. (1)

**torr.** A unit of gas pressure equivalent to the height of one millimeter of mercury. (10)

**total ionic equation.** A chemical equation showing all soluble compounds that exist primarily as ions in aqueous solution as separate ions. (6)

**transition element.** Elements whose outer *s* and *d* subshells are filling. The B Group elements (i.e., groups 3–12) in the periodic table. (4, 8)

**transmutation.** The changing of one element into another by a nuclear reaction. (16)

**triple bond.** The sharing of three pairs of electrons in a bond between two atoms. (7)

**triprotic acid.** An acid that can produce three $H^+$ ions per molecule. (13)

**U**

**ultraviolet light.** Light with wavelengths somewhat shorter than those of violet light. (8)

**unit.** A definite quantity adapted as a standard of measurement. (1)

**unit factor.** A fractional expression that relates a quantity in a certain unit to "one" of another unit. (1)

**unit map.** A shorthand representation of the procedure for solving a problem that indicates the conversion of units in one or more steps. (1, 5, 7)

**unsaturated solution.** A solution that contains less than the maximum amount of solute indicated by the compound's solubility at that temperature. (12)

**V**

**valence electron.** An outer $s$ or $p$ electron in the atom of a representative element. (8)

**valence shell electron-pair repulsion theory (VSEPR).** A theory that predicts that electron pairs either unshared or in a bond repel each other to the maximum extent. (7)

**vapor pressure.** See *equilibrium vapor pressure*.

**viscosity.** A measure of the resistance of a liquid to flow. (11)

**volatile.** Refers to a liquid or solid with a significant vapor pressure. (11)

**voltaic cell.** A spontaneous oxidation–reduction reaction that can be used to produce electrical energy. (14)

**volume.** The space that a certain quantity of matter occupies. (1)

**W**

**wavelength ($\lambda$).** The distance between two adjacent peaks in a wave. (8)

**wave mechanics.** A complex mathematical approach to the electrons in an atom that considers the electron as having both a particle and a wave nature. (8)

**weak acid (base).** An acid (or base) that is only partially ionized in aqueous solution. (13)

**weak electrolyte.** A solute whose aqueous solution allows only a limited amount of electrical conduction. (12)

**weight.** A measure of the attraction of gravity for a sample of matter. (1)

# Answers to Chapter Problems

## CHAPTER 1

**1-1. (b)** 74.212 gal (the most significant figures)

**1-2.** A device used to produce a measurement may provide a reproducible answer to several significant figures, but if the device itself is inaccurate (such as a ruler with the tip broken off) the measurement is inaccurate.

**1-4. (a)** three   **(b)** two   **(c)** three   **(d)** one   **(e)** four
**f)** two   **(g)** two   **(h)** three

**1-6. (a)** $\pm 10$   **(b)** $\pm 0.1$   **(c)** $\pm 0.01$   **(d)** $\pm 0.01$
**(e)** $\pm 1$   **(f)** $\pm 0.001$   **(g)** $\pm 100$   **(h)** $\pm 0.00001$

**1-8. (a)** 16.0   **(b)** 1.01   **(c)** 0.665   **(d)** 489
**(e)** 87,600   **(f)** 0.0272   **(g)** 301

**1-10. (a)** 0.250   **(b)** 0.800   **(c)** 1.67   **(d)** 1.17

**1-12. (a)** $\pm 0.1$   **(b)** $\pm 1000$   **(c)** $\pm 1$   **(d)** $\pm 0.01$

**1-14. (a)** 188   **(b)** 12.90   **(c)** 2300   **(d)** 48   **(e)** 0.84

**1-16.** 37.9 qt

**1-18. (a)** 7.0   **(b)** 137   **(c)** 192   **(d)** 0.445   **(e)** 3.20   **(f)** 2.9

**1-20. (a)** two   **(b)** three   **(c)** two   **(d)** one

**1-23. (a)** 6.07   **(b)** 0.08   **(c)** 8.624   **(d)** 24   **(e)** 0.220
**(f)** 0.52

**1-26. (a)** $(63) + 75.0 = \underline{138}$
     **(b)** $(45) \times 25.6 = \underline{1200}$
     **(c)** $(2.7) \times (10.52) = \underline{28}$

**1-28.** 13%

**1-30.** 0.11%

**1-32.(a)** $1.57 \times 10^2$   **(b)** $1.57 \times 10^{-1}$ **(c)** $3.00 \times 10^{-2}$
**(d)** $4.0 \times 10^7$   **(e)** $3.49 \times 10^{-2}$   **(f)** $3.2 \times 10^4$
**(g)** $3.2 \times 10^{10}$   **(h)** $7.71 \times 10^{-4}$   **(i)** $2.34 \times 10^3$

**1-34.(a)** $9 \times 10^7$   **(b)** $8.7 \times 10^7$   **(c)** $8.70 \times 10^7$

**1-36. (a)** 0.000476   **(b)** 6550   **(c)** 0.0078   **(d)** 48,900
**(e)** 4.75   **(f)** 0.0000034

**1-38. (a)** $4.89 \times 10^{-4}$   **(b)** $4.56 \times 10^{-5}$   **(c)** $7.8 \times 10^3$
**(d)** $5.71 \times 10^{-2}$   **(e)** $4.975 \times 10^8$   **(f)** $3.0 \times 10^{-4}$

**1-40. (b)** $<$ **(f)** $<$ **(g)** $<$ **(d)** $<$ **(a)** $<$ **(e)** $<$ **(c)**

**1-42. (a)** $1.597 \times 10^{-3}$   **(b)** $2.30 \times 10^7$   **(c)** $3.5 \times 10^{-5}$
**(d)** $2.0 \times 10^{14}$

**1-44. (a)** $10^7$   **(b)** $10^0 = 1$   **(c)** $10^{29}$   **(d)** $10^9$

**1-46. (a)** $3.1 \times 10^{10}$ **(b)** $2 \times 10^9$   **(c)** $4 \times 10^{13}$   **(d)** 14
**(e)** $2.56 \times 10^{-14}$

**1-48. (a)** $2.0 \times 10^{12}$   **(b)** $3.7 \times 10^{16}$   **(c)** $6.0 \times 10^2$
**(d)** $2 \times 10^{-12}$   **(e)** $1.9 \times 10^8$

**1-49. (a)** $1.225 \times 10^7$   **(b)** $9.00 \times 10^{-12}$   **(c)** $3.0 \times 10^{-24}$
**(d)** $9 \times 10^4$   **(e)** $1 \times 10^{10}$

**1-51. (a)** milliliter (mL)   **(b)** hectogram (hg)
**(c)** nanojoule (nJ)   **(d)** centimeter (cm)
**(e)** microgram ($\mu$g)   **(f)** decipascal (dPa)

**1-53. (a)** 720 cm, 7.2 m, $7.2 \times 10^{-3}$ km
     **(b)** $5.64 \times 10^4$ mm, 5640 cm, 0.0564 km
     **(c)** $2.50 \times 10^5$ mm, $2.50 \times 10^4$ cm, 250 m

**1-54. (a)** 8.9 g, $8.9 \times 10^{-3}$ kg
     **(b)** $2.57 \times 10^4$ mg, 0.0257 kg
     **(c)** $1.25 \times 10^6$ mg, 1250 g

**1-56. (a)** 12 = 1 doz   **(c)** 3 ft = 1 yd   **(e)** $10^3$ m = 1 km

**1-58. (a)** $\dfrac{1\,\text{g}}{10^3\,\text{mg}}$   **(b)** $\dfrac{1\,\text{km}}{10^3\,\text{m}}$   **(c)** $\dfrac{1\,\text{L}}{100\,\text{cL}}$
     **(d)** $\dfrac{1\,\text{m}}{10^3\,\text{mm}}, \dfrac{1\,\text{km}}{10^3\,\text{m}}$

**1-60. (a)** $\dfrac{1\,\text{ft}}{12\,\text{in.}}$   **(b)** $\dfrac{2.54\,\text{cm}}{\text{in.}}$   **(c)** $\dfrac{5280\,\text{ft}}{\text{mi}}$
     **(d)** $\dfrac{1.057\,\text{qt}}{\text{L}}$   **(e)** $\dfrac{1\,\text{qt}}{2\,\text{pt}}, \dfrac{1\,\text{L}}{1.057\,\text{qt}}$

**1-62. (a)** 47 L   **(b)** 98 cm   **(c)** 1.85 mi   **(d)** 51.56 yd
**(e)** 92 m   **(f)** 10.27 bbl   **(g)** 32 Gg

**1-64. (a)** 7.8 km, 4.8 mi, $2.5 \times 10^4$ ft
     **(b)** 2380 ft, 0.724 km, 724 m
     **(c)** 1.70 mi, 2.74 km, 2740 m
     **(d)** 4.21 mi, $2.22 \times 10^4$ ft, 6780 m

**1-65. (a)** 25.7 L, 27.2 qt   **(b)** 630 L, 170 gal
**(c)** $8.12 \times 10^3$ qt, $2.03 \times 10^3$ gal

**1-67.** 55.3 kg

**1-69.** $28.0\,\text{m} \times \dfrac{10^2\,\text{cm}}{\text{m}} \times \dfrac{1\,\text{in.}}{2.54\,\text{cm}} \times \dfrac{1\,\text{ft}}{12\,\text{in.}} \times \dfrac{1\,\text{yd}}{3\,\text{ft}}$
$= \underline{30.6\,\text{yd}}$ (New punter is needed.)

**1-71.** 0.355 L

**1-73.** 6 ft 10 1/2 in. = 82.5 in.
$82.5\,\text{in.} \times \dfrac{2.54\,\text{cm}}{\text{in.}} \times \dfrac{1\,\text{m}}{10^2\,\text{cm}} = \underline{2.10\,\text{m}}$

$$212 \text{ lb} \times \frac{1 \text{ kg}}{2.205 \text{ lb}} = \underline{96.1 \text{ kg}}$$

**1-74.** 14.5 gal

**1-76.** $0.200 \text{ gal} \times \dfrac{4 \text{ qt}}{\text{gal}} = 0.800 \text{ qt}$

$$0.800 \text{ qt} \times \frac{1 \text{ L}}{1.057 \text{ qt}} \times \frac{1 \text{ mL}}{10^{-3} \text{ L}} = \underline{757 \text{ mL}}$$

There is slightly more in a "fifth" than in 750 mL.

**1-78.** 105 km/hr

**1-82.** $\dfrac{\$0.899}{\text{gal}} \times \dfrac{1 \text{ gal}}{4 \text{ qt}} \times \dfrac{1.057 \text{ qt}}{\text{L}} = \$0.238/\text{L}$

$19.04 (2001), $58.31 (2010)

**1-83.** $72.39 (551 mi), $39.36 (482 km)

**1-84.** 674 km

**1-88.** $28.20

**1-89.** $38.21 (the hybrid); $79.53 (the SUV)

**1-92.** 3.31 hr

**1-93.** (a) 7.28 euro   (b) $11.29   (c) $19.79

**1-94.** 0.824 pound/euro, 21,100 pound

**1-97.** 2100 s, 0.58 hr

**1-98.** 572°F

**1-99.** 24°C

**1-101.** −38°F

**1-103.** 95.0°F

**1-104.** (a) −98°C   (b) 22°C   (c) 27°C   (d) −48°C   (e) 600°C

**1-105.** (a) 320 K   (b) 296 K   (c) 200 K   (d) 261 K
(e) 291 K   (f) 244 K

**1-107.** Since $T\,(°C) = T\,(°F)$ substitute $T\,(°C)$ for $T\,(°F)$ and set the two equations equal.

$$[T\,(°C) \times 1.8] + 32 = \frac{T\,(°C) - 32}{1.8}$$

$$(1.8)^2 T\,(°C) - T\,(°C) = -32 - 32(1.8)$$

$$T\,(°C) = -40°C$$

**1-108.** (a) $3 \times 10^2$   (b) $8.26 \text{ g} \cdot \text{cm}$   (c) 5.24 g/mL
(d) 19.1

**1-109.** (a) $\dfrac{1 \text{ g}}{10^3 \text{ mg}}, \dfrac{1 \text{ lb}}{453.6 \text{ g}}$   (b) $\dfrac{1.057 \text{ qt}}{\text{L}}, \dfrac{2 \text{ pt}}{\text{qt}}$

(c) $\dfrac{1 \text{ km}}{10 \text{ hm}}, \dfrac{1 \text{ mi}}{1.609 \text{ km}}$   (d) $\dfrac{1 \text{ in.}}{2.54 \text{ cm}}, \dfrac{1 \text{ ft}}{12 \text{ in.}}$

**1-110.** $5.34 \times 10^{10} \text{ ng} \times \dfrac{10^{-9} \text{ g}}{\text{ng}} \times \dfrac{1 \text{ lb}}{453.6 \text{ g}} = \underline{0.118 \text{ lb}}$

**1-112.** $40,182

**1-113.** $\dfrac{247 \text{ lb}}{82.3 \text{ doz}} = \underline{3.00 \text{ lb/doz}}$   $\dfrac{82.3 \text{ doz}}{247 \text{ lb}} = \underline{0.333 \text{ doz/lb}}$

**1-114.** $12.0 \text{ fur} \times \dfrac{1 \text{ mi}}{8 \text{ fur}} \times \dfrac{5280 \text{ ft}}{\text{mi}} \times \dfrac{12 \text{ in.}}{\text{ft}} \times \dfrac{1 \text{ hand}}{4 \text{ in.}}$

$$= \underline{2.38 \times 10^4 \text{ hands}}$$

**1-116.** 1030 pkgs, 1.41 years

**1-117.** 5.02 L

**1-119.** $5.4 \times 10^7$°F   $3.0 \times 10^7$°C + 273 = $3.0 \times 10^7$ K

**1-121.** 9,300 lb, 4.65 ton,

## CHAPTER 2

**2-2.** cadmium-Cd, calcium-Ca, californium-Cf, carbon-C, cerium-Ce, cesium-Cs, chlorine-Cl, chromium-Cr, cobalt-Co, copper-Cu, curium-Cm

**2-5.** (a) Ba   (b) Ne   (c) Cs   (d) Pt   (e) Mn   (f) W

**2-7.** (a) boron   (b) bismuth   (c) germanium
(d) uranium   (e) cobalt   (f) mercury   (g) beryllium
(h) arsenic

**2-8.** (b) and (e)

**2-9.** (c)

**2-12.** (a) 21 p, 21 e, 24 n   (b) 90 p, 90 e, 142 n   (c) 87 p, 87 e, 136 n   (d) 38 p, 38 e, 52 n

**2-14.**

| Isotope Name | Isotope Notation | Atomic Number | Mass Number | p | n | e |
|---|---|---|---|---|---|---|
| **(a)** silver-108 | $^{108}_{47}\text{Ag}$ | 47 | 108 | 47 | 61 | 47 |
| **(b)** silicon-28 | $^{28}_{14}\text{Si}$ | 14 | 28 | 14 | 14 | 14 |
| **(c)** potassium-39 | $^{39}_{19}\text{K}$ | 19 | 39 | 19 | 20 | 19 |
| **(d)** cerium-140 | $^{140}_{58}\text{Ce}$ | 58 | 140 | 58 | 82 | 58 |
| **(e)** iron-56 | $^{56}_{26}\text{Fe}$ | 26 | 56 | 26 | 30 | 26 |
| **(f)** tin-110 | $^{110}_{50}\text{Sn}$ | 50 | 110 | 50 | 60 | 50 |
| **(g)** iodine-118 | $^{118}_{53}\text{I}$ | 53 | 118 | 53 | 65 | 53 |
| **(h)** mercury-196 | $^{196}_{80}\text{Hg}$ | 80 | 196 | 80 | 116 | 80 |

**2-16.** $^{59}\text{Co}$

**2-18.** (a) The identity of a specific element is determined by its atomic number. An element is a basic form of matter and its atomic number relates to the number of protons in the nuclei of its atoms.

(b) Both relate to the particles in the nucleus of the atoms of an element. The atomic mass is the mass of an average atom since elements are usually composed of more than one isotope. The atomic number is the number of protons.

(c) Both relate to the number of particles in a nucleus. The mass number relates to the total number of protons and neutrons in an isotope of an element while the atomic number is the number of protons in the atoms of a specific element.

**(d)** All isotopes of an element have the same atomic number.

**(e)** Different isotopes of a specific element have the same number of protons but different numbers of neutrons or mass numbers.

**2-19. (a)** Re: at. no. 75, at. wt. 186.2 **(b)** Co: at. no. 27, at. wt. 58.9332 **(c)** Br: at. no. 35, at. wt. 79.904 **(d)** Si: at. no. 14, at. wt. 28.086

**2-20.** copper (Cu)

**2-22.** O: at. no. 8, mass no. 16

N: at. no. 7, mass no. 14

Si: at. no. 14, mass no. 28

Ca: at. no. 20, mass no. 40

**2-24.** $5.81 \times 12.00 = 69.7$ amu. The element is Ga.

**2-26.** 79.9 amu

**2-27.** $^{28}$Si: $0.9221 \times 27.98 = 25.80$

$^{29}$Si: $0.0470 \times 28.98 = 1.362$

$^{30}$Si: $0.0309 \times 29.97 = \underline{0.926}$

$$28.088 \quad = \quad \underline{28.09 \text{ amu}}$$

**2-29.** Let $x$ = decimal fraction of $^{35}$Cl and $y$ = decimal fraction of $^{37}$Cl. Since there are two isotopes present, $x + y = 1$, $y = 1 - x$.

$(x \times 35) + (y \times 37) = 35.5$

$(x \times 35) + [(1 - x) \times 37] = 35.5$

$x = 0.75$ ($\underline{75\%}$ $^{35}$Cl) $\quad y = 0.25$ ($\underline{25\%}$ $^{37}$Cl)

**2-31. (a)** They are both basic units of matter. Most elements are composed of individual atoms and many compounds are composed of individual molecules. Molecules are composed of atoms chemically bonded together.

**(b)** A compound is a pure form of matter. It is composed of individual units called molecules.

**(c)** They are both pure forms of matter. Compounds, however, are composed of two or more elements chemically combined.

**(d)** Most elements are composed of individual atoms. Some elements, however, are composed of molecules, which in most cases, contain two atoms.

**2-32. (b)** $Br_2$ **(d)** $S_8$ **(f)** $P_4$

**2-33.** P, phosphorus O, oxygen Br, bromine F, fluorine S, sulfur Mg, magnesium

**2-34.** Hf is the symbol of the element hafnium. HF is the formula of a compound composed of one atom of hydrogen and one atom of fluorine.

**2-36. (b)** CO, diatomic compound **(e)** $N_2$, diatomic element

**2-39. (a)** six carbons, four hydrogens, two chlorines

**(b)** two carbons, six hydrogens, one oxygen

**(c)** one copper, one sulfur, 18 hydrogens, 13 oxygens

**(d)** nine carbons, eight hydrogens, four oxygens

**(e)** two aluminums, three sulfurs, 12 oxygens

**(f)** two nitrogens, eight hydrogens, one carbon, three oxygens

**2-40. (a)** 12 **(b)** 9 **(c)** 33 **(d)** 21 **(e)** 17 **(f)** 14

**2-41. (a)** 8 **(b)** 7 **(c)** 4 **(d)** 3

**2-42. (a)** $SO_2$ **(b)** $CO_2$ **(c)** $H_2SO_4$ **(d)** $C_2H_2$

**2-44. (a)** They are both basic forms of matter. Atoms are neutral but ions are atoms that have acquired an electrical charge. Positive and negative ions are always found together.

**(b)** They are both basic forms of matter containing more than one atom. Molecules are neutral but polyatomic ions have acquired an electrical charge.

**(c)** Both have an electrical charge. Cations have a positive charge and anions have a negative charge.

**(d)** Both are classified as compounds, which are composed of the atoms of two or more elements. The basic unit of a molecular compound is a neutral molecule but the basic units of ionic compounds are cations and anions.

**(e)** Both are the basic units of compounds. Molecules are the basic entities of molecular compounds, and an ionic formula unit represents the smallest whole number of cations and anions representing a net charge of zero.

**2-46. (a)** $Ca(ClO_4)_2$ **(b)** $(NH_4)_3PO_4$ **(c)** $FeSO_4$

**2-47. (a)** one calcium, two chlorines, and eight oxygens **(b)** three nitrogens, 12 hydrogens, one phosphorus, and four oxygens **(c)** one iron, one sulfur, and four oxygens

**2-50. (c)** $S^{2-}$

**2-52. (d)** $Li^+$

**2-54.** FeS, $Li_2SO_3$

**2-56.** $SO_3$ represents the formula of a compound. It could be a gas. $SO_3^{2-}$ is an anion and does not exist independently. It is part of an ionic compound with the other part being a cation.

**2-57. (a)** $K^+$: 19 p, 18 e **(b)** $Br^-$: 35 p, 36 e **(c)** $S^{2-}$: 16 p, 18 e **(d)** $NO_2^-$: $7 + 16 = 23$ p, 24 e **(e)** $Al^{3+}$: 13 p, 10 e **(f)** $NH_4^+$: $7 + 4 = 11$ p, 10 e

**2-59. (a)** $Ca^{2+}$ **(b)** $Te^{2-}$ **(c)** $PO_3^{3-}$ **(d)** $NO_2^+$

**2-61.** This is the $Br^-$ ion. It is part of an ionic compound.

**2-64. (a)** $^{90}_{38}Sr^{2+}$ **(b)** $^{52}_{24}Cr^{3+}$ **(c)** $^{79}_{34}Se^{2-}$ **(d)** $^{14}_{7}N^{3-}$ **(e)** $^{139}_{57}La^{3+}$

**2-66. (a)** Na: 11 p, 12 n, and 11 e; $Na^+$ has 10 electrons.

**(b)** Ca: 20 p, 20 n, and 20 e; $Ca^{2+}$ has 18 electrons.

**(c)** F: 9 p, 10 n, and 9 e; $F^-$ has 10 electrons.

**(d)** Sc: 21 p, 24 n, and 21 e; $Sc^{3+}$ has 18 electrons.

**2-68.** Let $x$ = mass no. of I and $y$ = mass no. of Tl Then (1) $x + y = 340$ or $x = 340 - y$

$(2) x = \dfrac{2}{3}y - 10$

Substituting for $x$ from (1) and solving for $y$

$y = 210$ amu (Tl) and $x = 340 - 210 = 130$ amu (I)

**2-70.** 121.8 (Sb) $Sb^{3+}$ has $51 - 3 = 48$ electrons. $^{121}$Sb has $121 - 51 = 70$ neutrons. $^{123}$Sb has $123 - 51 = 72$ neutrons. $^{121}$Sb, 57.9% due to neutrons; $^{121}$Sb, 58.5% due to neutrons

**2-71.** 118 neutrons and 78 protons [platinum (Pt)]

$78 - 2 = 76$ electrons for $Pt^{2+}$

**2-73.** Mass of other atom = 16 (oxygen)
$NO^+ = (7 + 8) - 1 = 14$ electrons

**2-75. (a)** H: $\dfrac{1.008}{12.00} \times 8.000 = 0.672$

 **(b)** N: $\dfrac{14.01}{12.00} \times 8.000 = 9.34$

 **(c)** Na: $\dfrac{22.99}{12.00} \times 8.000 = 15.3$

 **(d)** Ca: $\dfrac{40.08}{12.00} \times 8.000 = 26.7$

**2-76.** $\dfrac{43.3}{10.0} = 4.33$ times as heavy as $^{12}C$

 $4.33 \times 12.0$ amu = 52.0 amu. The element is Cr.

**CHAPTER 3**

**3-1. (c)** It has a definite volume but not a definite shape.

**3-2.** The gaseous state is compressible because the basic particles are very far apart and thus the volume of a gas is mostly empty space.

**3-4. (a)** physical  **(b)** chemical  **(c)** physical  **(d)** chemical
**(e)** chemical  **(f)** physical  **(g)** physical  **(h)** chemical
**(i)** physical

**3-6. (a)** chemical  **(b)** physical  **(c)** physical  **(d)** chemical
**(e)** physical

**3-9.** Physical property: melts at 660°C; Physical change: melting; Chemical property: burns in oxygen; Chemical change: formation of aluminum oxide from aluminum and oxygen.

**3-10.** Original substance: green, solid (physical); can be decomposed (chemical). Substance is a compound. Gas: gas, colorless (physical); can be decomposed (chemical). Substance is a compound since it can be decomposed. Solid: shiny, solid (physical); cannot be decomposed (chemical). Substance is an element since it cannot be decomposed.

**3-12.** 2.60 g/mL

**3-14.** 1064 g/657 mL = 1.62 g/mL (carbon tetrachloride)

**3-17.** 1450 g

**3-18.** 670 g

**3-19.** 5.6 lb

**3-21.** 625 mL

**3-22.** 1.74 g/mL (magnesium)

**3-23.** 0.476 g/mL; Yes, it floats.

**3-24.** 0.951 g/mL, 4790 mL

 Pumice floats in water but sinks in alcohol.

**3-27.** 2080 g

**3-28.** 111.0 g/125 mL = 0.888 g/mL

**3-30.** Water: 1000 g; Gasoline: 670 g
One liter of water has a greater mass.

**3-31.** 160 g/8.3 mL = 19 g/mL. It's gold.

**3-34.** One needs a conversion factor between mL ($cm^3$) and $ft^3$.

$$\left(\dfrac{2.54\ cm}{in.}\right)^3 = \dfrac{16.4\ cm^3}{in.^3} = \dfrac{16.4\ mL}{in.^3} \quad \left(\dfrac{12\ in.}{ft}\right)^3 = \dfrac{1728\ in.^3}{ft^3}$$

$$\dfrac{1.00\ g}{mL} \times \dfrac{1\ lb}{453.6\ g} \times \dfrac{16.4\ mL}{in.^3} \times \dfrac{1728\ in.^3}{ft^3} = \underline{62.5\ lb/ft^3}$$

**3-35.** $2.0 \times 10^5$ lb (100 tons)

**3-36.** Carbon dioxide is a compound composed of carbon and oxygen. It can be prepared from a mixture of carbon and oxygen, but the compound is no longer a mixture of the two elements.

**3-38.** Ocean water is the least pure because it contains a large amount of dissolved compounds. That is why it is not drinkable and cannot be used for crop irrigation. Drinking water also contains chlorine and some dissolved compounds but not nearly as much as ocean water. Rainwater is most pure but still contains some dissolved gases from the air.

**3-40. (a)** liquid only

**3-41. (a)** homogeneous   **(b)** heterogeneous
 **(c)** heterogeneous   **(d)** homogeneous
 **(e)** homogeneous   **(f)** homogeneous solution
 **(g)** heterogeneous   **(h)** homogeneous

**3-43. (a)** liquid  **(b)** various solid phases  **(c)** gas and liquid  **(d)** liquid  **(e)** solid  **(f)** liquid  **(g)** liquid and gas  **(h)** gas

**3-45.** A mixture of all three would have carbon tetrachloride on the bottom, water in the middle, and kerosene on top. Water and kerosene float on carbon tetrachloride; kerosene floats on water.

**3-47.** Ice is less dense than water. An ice–water mixture is pure but heterogeneous.

**3-48. (a)** solution (a solid dissolved in a liquid)
**(b)** heterogeneous mixture (probably a solid suspended in a liquid such as dirty water)  **(c)** element  **(d)** compound
**(e)** solution (two liquids)

**3-50.** Mass of mixture = 22.6 + 855 = 878 g

$$\dfrac{22.6}{878} \times 100\% = \underline{2.57\%}\ NaCl\ (100\% - 2.57 = \underline{97.4\%}\ water)$$

**3-52.** $255\ \cancel{kg\ solution} \times \dfrac{25\ g\ solute}{100\ \cancel{kg\ solution}} = \underline{64\ kg\ solute}$

**3-54.** $122\ \cancel{lb\ iron} \times \dfrac{100\ lb\ duriron}{86\ \cancel{lb\ iron}} = \underline{140\ lb\ duriron}$

**3-56. (a)** exothermic  **(b)** endothermic  **(c)** endothermic
**(d)** exothermic  **(e)** exothermic

**3-57.** Gasoline is converted into heat energy when it burns. The heat energy causes the pistons to move, which is mechanical energy. The mechanical energy turns the alternator, which generates electrical energy. The electrical energy is converted into chemical energy in the battery.

**3-59. (a)** potential  **(b)** kinetic  **(c)** potential (It is stored because of its composition.)  **(d)** kinetic  **(e)** kinetic

**3-62.** Kinetic energy is at a maximum nearest the ground when the swing is moving the fastest. Potential energy is at a maximum when the swing has momentarily stopped at the highest point. Assuming no gain or loss of energy, the total of the two energies is constant.

**3-63.** $0.853 \, J/(g \cdot {}^\circ C)$

**3-64.** $\dfrac{56.6 \text{ cal}}{365 \text{ g} \cdot 5.0\,{}^\circ C} = 0.031 \text{ cal}/(g \cdot {}^\circ C) \text{ (gold)}$

**3-66.**

$${}^\circ C = \frac{\text{cal}}{\text{sp. heat} \times \text{g}} = \frac{150 \text{ cal}}{0.092 \dfrac{\text{cal}}{\text{g} \cdot {}^\circ C} \times 50.0 \text{ g}} = 33{}^\circ C \text{ rise}$$

$T\,{}^\circ C = 25 + 33 = \underline{58{}^\circ C}$

This compares to a 3.0°C rise in temperature for 50.0 g of water.

**3-68.** 506 J

**3-69.** $58 - 25 = 33{}^\circ C$ rise in temperature

$$\text{g} = \frac{\text{cal}}{\text{sp. heat} \cdot {}^\circ C} = \frac{16.0 \text{ cal}}{0.106 \dfrac{\text{cal}}{\text{g} \cdot {}^\circ C} \cdot 33{}^\circ C} = \underline{4.6 \text{ g}}$$

**3-70.** The copper skillet, because it has a lower specific heat. The same amount of applied heat will heat the copper skillet more than the iron.

**3-72.** Iron: 9.38°C rise  Gold: 32°C rise  Water: 0.997°C rise

**3-74.** 45°C

**3-76.** 2910 J

**3-80.** 860 g

**3-81.** heat lost by metal = heat gained by water
$100.0 \text{ g} \times 68.7{}^\circ C \times \text{specific heat} = 100.0 \text{ g} \times 6.3{}^\circ C \times 4.184 \, J/g \cdot {}^\circ C$

Specific heat = $0.38 \, J/g \cdot {}^\circ C$. The metal is copper.

**3-82.** Density of A = 0.86 g/mL; density of B = 0.89 g/mL Liquid A floats on liquid B.

**3-84.** 15 g of sugar

**3-85.** 9.27 g/mL

**3-87.** 3.17% salt

**3-89.** $50.0 \text{ mL gold} \times \dfrac{19.3 \text{ g}}{\text{mL gold}} = 965 \text{ g gold}$

$50.0 \text{ mL alum.} \times \dfrac{2.70 \text{ g}}{\text{mL alum.}} = 135 \text{ g alum.}$

$\dfrac{965 \text{ g gold}}{(965 + 135) \text{ g alloy}} \times 100\% = \underline{87.7\% \text{ gold}}$

**3-91.** specific heat = $0.13 \dfrac{J}{g \cdot {}^\circ C}$ (gold)

$25.0 \text{ g gold} \times \dfrac{1 \text{ mL}}{19.3 \text{ g gold}} = \underline{1.30 \text{ mL}}$

**3-94.** When a log burns, most of the compounds formed in the combustion are gases and dissipate into the atmosphere. Only some solid residue (ashes) is left. When zinc and sulfur (both solids) combine, the only product is a solid so there is no weight change. When iron burns, however, its only product is a solid. It weighs more than the original iron because the iron has combined with the oxygen gas from the air.

**CHAPTER 4**

**4-1.** An active metal reacts with water and air. A noble metal is not affected by air, water, or most acids.

**4-2.** 32

**4-3. (c)** $I_2$, and **(g)** $Br_2$

**4-5. (a)** Fe, and  **(d)** La—transition elements  **(b)** Te, **(f)** H, and  **(g)** In—representative elements  **(e)** Xe— noble gas **(c)** Pm—inner transition element

**4-7. (b)** Ti,  **(e)** Pd, and  **(g)** Ag

**4-8.** The most common physical state is a solid, and metals are more common than nonmetals.

**4-10. (a)** Ne,  **(d)** Cl, and  **(f)** N

**4-12. (a)** Ru,  **(b)** Sn,  **(c)** Hf, and  **(h)** W

**4-13. (d)** Te and  **(f)** B

**4-14. (a)** Ar  **(b)** Hg  **(c)** $N_2$  **(d)** Be  **(e)** Po

**4-16.** Element 118 is in Group VIIIA. It should be a noble gas. In fact, it should be the last nonmetal on the periodic table.

**4-18. (a)** lithium fluoride  **(b)** barium telluride
**(c)** strontium nitride  **(d)** barium hydride
**(e)** aluminum chloride

**4-20. (a)** $Rb_2Se$  **(b)** $SrH_2$  **(c)** $RaO$  **(d)** $Al_2Te_3$  **(e)** $BeF_2$

**4-22. (a)** bismuth (V) oxide  **(b)** tin (II) sulfide
**(c)** tin (IV) sulfide  **(d)** copper(I) telluride
**(e)** titanium(IV) oxide

**4-24. (a)** $Cu_2S$  **(b)** $V_2O_3$  **(c)** $AuBr$  **(d)** $Ni_3P_2$  **(e)** $CrO_3$

**4-26.** In 4-22:  **(a)** $Bi_2O_5$,  **(c)** $SnS_2$, and  **(e)** $TiO_2$; In 4-24: **(e)** $CrO_3$

**4-28. (c)** $ClO_3^-$

**4-30.** ammonium, $NH_4^+$

**4-31. (b)** permanganate ($MnO_4^-$),  **(c)** perchlorate ($ClO_4^-$), **(e)** phosphate ($PO_4^{3-}$), and  **(f)** oxalate ($C_2O_4^{2-}$)

**4-32. (a)** chromium(II) sulfate  **(b)** aluminum sulfite
**(c)** iron(II) cyanide  **(d)** rubidium hydrogen carbonate
**(e)** ammonium carbonate  **(f)** ammonium nitrate
**(g)** bismuth(III) hydroxide

**4-34. (a)** $Mg(MnO_4)_2$  **(b)** $Co(CN)_2$  **(c)** $Sr(OH)_2$
**(d)** $Tl_2SO_3$  **(e)** $Fe_2(C_2O_4)_3$  **(f)** $(NH_4)_2Cr_2O_7$
**(g)** $Hg_2(C_2H_3O_2)_2$

**4-36.**

| | $HSO_3^-$ | $Te^{2-}$ | $PO_4^{3-}$ |
|---|---|---|---|
| $NH_4^+$ | $NH_4HSO_3$ ammonium bisulfite | $(NH_4)_2Te$ ammonium telluride | $(NH_4)_3PO_4$ ammonium phosphate |
| $Co^{2+}$ | $Co(HSO_3)_2$ cobalt(ll) bisulfite | *CoTe* cobalt(ll) telluride | $Co_3(PO_4)_2$ cobalt(ll) phosphate |
| $Al^{3+}$ | $Al(HSO_3)_3$ aluminum bisulfite | $Al_2Te_3$ aluminum telluride | $AlPO_4$ *aluminum phosphate* |

**4-38.** (a) sodium chloride  (b) sodium hydrogen carbonate  (c) calcium carbonate  (d) sodium hydroxide  (e) sodium nitrate  (f) ammonium chloride  (g) aluminum oxide  (h) calcium hydroxide  (i) potassium hydroxide

**4-39.** (a) $Ca_2XeO_6$  (b) $K_4XeO_6$ (c) $Al_4(XeO_6)_3$

**4-40.** (a) phosphonium fluoride  (b) potassium hypobromite  (c) cobalt(III) iodate  (d) calcium silicate (actual name is calcium metasilicate)  (e) aluminum phosphite  (f) chromium(II) molybdate

**4-41.** (a) Si  (b) I  (c) H  (d) Kr  (e) H  (f) As

**4-43.** (a) carbon disulfide  (b) boron trifluoride  (c) tetraphosphorus decoxide  (d) dibromine trioxide  (e) methane  (f) dichlorine oxide or dichlorine monoxide  (g) phosphorus pentachloride  (h) sulfur hexafluoride

**4-45.** (a) $P_4O_6$  (b) $CCl_4$  (c) $IF_3$  (d) $C_6H_{14}$  (e) $SF_6$  (f) $XeO_2$

**4-47.** (a) hydrochloric acid  (b) nitric acid  (c) hypochlorous acid  (d) permanganic acid  (e) periodic acid  (f) hydrobromic acid

**4-48.** (a) HCN  (b) $H_2Se$  (c) $HClO_2$  (d) $H_2CO_3$  (e) HI  (f) $HC_2H_3O_2$

**4-50.** (a) hypobromous acid  (b) iodic acid  (c) phosphorous acid  (d) molybdic acid  (e) perxenic acid

**4-52.** $ClO_2$ chlorine dioxide

**4-53.** A = F  X = Br  $BrF_5$ (Br is more metallic.) bromine pentafluoride

**4-55.** Gas = $N_2$; Al forms only +3. Thus the formula is AlN ($N^{3-}$), for aluminum nitride. $Ti_3N_2$, titanium(II) nitride

**4-57.** $Co^{2+}$ and $Br^-$: $CoBr_2$ cobalt(II) bromide

**4-58.** Metal = Mg, nonmetal = S: $MgH_2$, magnesium hydride; $H_2S$, hydrogen sulfide or hydrosulfuric acid

**4-60.** $NiI_2$, nickel(II) iodide; $H_3PO_4$, phosphoric acid; $Sr(ClO_3)_2$, strontium chlorate; $H_2Te$, hydrogen telluride or hydrotelluric acid; $As_2O_3$, diarsenic trioxide; $Sb_2O_3$, antimony(III) oxide; $SnC_2O_4$, tin(II) oxalate

**4-62.** tin(II) hypochlorite, $Sn(ClO)_2$; chromic acid, $H_2CrO_4$; xenon hexafluoride, $XeF_6$; barium nitride, $Ba_3N_2$; hydrofluoric acid, HF; iron(III) telluride, $Fe_2Te_3$; lithium phosphate, $Li_3PO_4$

**4-63.** (e) $Rb_2C_2O_4$

**4-65.** $Rb_2O_2$, $MgO_2$, $Al_2(O_2)_3$, $Ti(O_2)_2$. $H_2O_2$, hydrogen peroxide, hydroperoxic acid

**4-67.** (a) $Na_2CO_3$  (b) $CaCl_2$  (c) $KClO_4$  (d) $Al(NO_3)_3$  (e) $Ca(OH)_2$  (f) $NH_4Cl$

**4-69.** $N^{3-}$, nitride; $NO_2^-$, nitrite; $NO_3^-$, nitrate; $NH_4^+$, ammonium; $CN^-$, cyanide

**4-71.** (e) chromium(III) carbonate

**4-73.** (c) barium chlorite

**CHAPTER 5**

**5-1.** 6.09 lb of pennies

**5-3.** $145 \; \text{g Au} \times \dfrac{108 \text{ g Ag}}{197.0 \text{ g Au}} = \underline{79.5 \text{ g Ag}}$

**5-4.** 94.4 lb C

**5-6.** 71.5 g Cu

**5-8.** $25.0 \; \text{g C} \times \dfrac{x \text{ g}}{12.01 \text{ g C}} = 33.3 \text{ g}$   $x = 16.0 \text{ g(O)}$

The compound is CO.

**5-10.** 40.1 lb S

**5-11.** $\dfrac{9.548 \times 10^{15}}{6.8 \times 10^9} = \underline{1.4 \times 10^6 \text{ years (1.4 million)}}$

**5-13.** $6.022 \times 10^{26}$ (if mass in kg); $6.022 \times 10^{20}$ (if mass in mg)

**5-14.** (a) 0.468 mol P, $2.82 \times 10^{23}$ atoms P

(b) 150 g Rb, $1.05 \times 10^{24}$ atoms

(c) Al: 27.0 g, 1.00 mol,

(d) 5.00 mol X element is Ge

(e) $1.66 \times 10^{-24}$ mol, $7.95 \times 10^{-23}$ g

**5-16.** (a) 63.5 g Cu  (b) 16 g S  (c) 40.1 g Ca

**5-18.** (a) $1.93 \times 10^{25}$ atoms  (b) $6.03 \times 10^{23}$ atoms

(c) $1.20 \times 10^{24}$ atoms

**5-20.** $50.0 \; \text{g Al} \times \dfrac{1 \text{ mol Al}}{26.98 \text{ g Al}} = 1.85 \text{ mol Al}$

$= 0.895 \text{ mol Fe}$

There are more moles of atoms (more atoms) in 50.0 g of Al.

**5-21.** $20.0 \; \text{g Ni} \times \dfrac{1 \text{ mol Ni}}{58.69 \text{ g Ni}} = 0.341 \text{ mol Ni}$

$2.85 \times 10^{23} \; \text{atoms} \times \dfrac{1 \text{ mol Ni}}{6.022 \times 10^{23} \text{ atoms}}$

$= 0.473 \text{ mol Ni}$

The $2.85 \times 10^{23}$ atoms of Ni contain more atoms than 20.0 g.

**5-23.** $1.40 \times 10^{21}$ atoms $= 2.32 \times 10^{-3}$ mol

$0.251 \text{ g}/(2.32 \times 10^{-3} \text{ mol}) = 108 \text{ g/mol (silver)}$

**5-25.** (a) 106.6 amu  (b) 80.07 amu  (c) 108.0 amu  (d) 98.09 amu  (e) 106.0 amu  (f) 60.05 amu  (g) 459.7 amu

**5-27.** $Cr_2(SO_4)_3$ $(2 \times 52.00) + (3 \times 32.07) + (12 \times 16.00)$
$$= \underline{392.2 \text{ amu}}$$

**5-29. (a)** 189 g $H_2O$, $6.32 \times 10^{24}$ molecules

**(b)** $5.00 \times 10^{-3}$ mol $BF_3$, 0.339 g $BF_3$

**(c)** 0.219 mol $SO_2$, $1.32 \times 10^{23}$ molecules

**(d)** 0.0209 g $K_2SO_4$, $7.23 \times 10^{19}$ formula units

**(e)** 7.47 mol $SO_3$, 598 g $SO_3$

**(f)** $7.61 \times 10^{-3}$ mol, $4.58 \times 10^{21}$ molecules

**5-31.** 21.5 g/0.0684 mol $= \underline{314 \text{ g/mol}}$

**5-33.** 161 g/mol

**5-35.** 5.10 mol C, 15.3 mol H, 2.55 mol O: Total $= 23.0$ mol of atoms; 61.3 g C, 15.4 g H, 40.8 g O: Total mass $= \underline{117.5 \text{ g}}$

**5-36.** 0.135 mol $Ca(ClO_3)_2$, 0.135 mol Ca, 0.270 mol Cl, 0.810 mol O Total $= \underline{1.215 \text{ mol of atoms}}$

**5-38.** $1.50 \text{ mol } H_2SO_3 \times \dfrac{2 \text{ mol H}}{\text{mol } H_2SO_4} \times \dfrac{1.008 \text{ g H}}{\text{mol H}}$
$$= \underline{3.02 \text{ g H}}$$

48.1 g S, 72.0 g O

**5-40.** $1.20 \times 10^{22} \text{ molecules} \times \dfrac{1 \text{ mol } O_2}{6.022 \times 10^{23} \text{ molecules}}$
$$= \underline{0.0199 \text{ mol } O_2}$$

$0.0199 \text{ mol } O_2 \times \dfrac{2 \text{ mol O atoms}}{\text{mol } O_2}$
$$= 0.0398 \text{ mol O atoms}$$

$0.0199 \text{ mol } O_2 \times \dfrac{32.00 \text{ g } O_2}{\text{mol } O_2}$
$$= 0.637 \text{ g } O_2 \text{ The mass is the same.}$$

**5-42.** Total mass of compound $= 1.375 + 3.935 = 5.310$ g, 25.89% N, 74.11% O

**5-43.** 46.7% Si, 53.3% O

**5-45. (a)** $C_2H_6O$ 52.14% C, 13.13% H, 34.73% O

**(b)** $C_3H_6$ 85.62% C, 14.38% H

**(c)** $C_9H_{18}$ 85.66% C, 14.34% H

**(b)** and **(c)** are actually the same. The difference comes from rounding off.

**(d)** $Na_2SO_4$ 32.36% Na, 22.57% S, 45.07% O

**(e)** $(NH_4)_2CO_3$ 29.16% N, 8.392% H, 12.50% C, 49.95% O

**5-47.** 12.06% Na, 11.34% B, 71.31% O, 5.286% H

**5-49.** $C_7H_5SNO_3$. Formula weight $= (7 \times 12.01) + (5 \times 1.008) + 32.07 + 14.01 + (3 \times 16.00) = 183.2$ amu

C: $\dfrac{84.07 \text{ amu}}{183.2 \text{ amu}} \times 100\% = \underline{45.89\% \text{ C}}$

H: $\dfrac{5.040 \text{ amu}}{183.2 \text{ amu}} \times 100\% = \underline{2.751\% \text{ H}}$

S: $\dfrac{32.07 \text{ amu}}{183.2 \text{ amu}} \times 100\% = \underline{17.51\% \text{ S}}$

N: $\dfrac{14.01 \text{ amu}}{183.2 \text{ amu}} \times 100\% = \underline{7.647\% \text{ C}}$

O: $100\% - (45.89 + 2.751 + 17.51 + 7.647)$
$$= \underline{26.20\% \text{ O}}$$

**5-51.** $Na_2C_2O_4$ Formula weight $= (2 \times 22.99) + (2 \times 12.01) + (4 \times 16.00) = 134.0$ amu

There is 24.02 g $(2 \times 12.01)$ of C in 134.0 g of compound.

$125 \text{ g } Na_2C_2O_4 \times \dfrac{24.02 \text{ g C}}{134.0 \text{ g } Na_2C_2O_4} = \underline{22.4 \text{ g C}}$

**5-52.** 4.72 lb P

**5-54.** $1.40 \times 10^3$ lb Fe

**5-55. (a)** $N_2O_4$ and **(d)** $H_2C_2O_4$

**5-56. (a)** FeS   **(b)** $SrI_2$   **(c)** $KClO_3$   **(d)** $I_2O_5$

**(e)** $Fe_2O_{2.66} = Fe_3O_4$   **(f)** $C_3H_5Cl_3$

**5-58.** $N_2O_3$

**5-60.** $KO_2$

**5-62.** $MgC_2O_4$

**5-63.** $CH_2Cl$

**5-65.** $N_2H_8SO_3$

**5-66.** $C_{8/3}H_{8/3}O = C_8H_8O_3$

**5-68.** $C_3H_4Cl_4$ (empirical formula) $C_9H_{12}Cl_{12}$ (molecular formula)

**5-70.** $B_2C_2H_6O_4$ (molecular formula)

**5-71.** Empirical formula $= KC_2NH_3O_2$ Empirical mass $= 112.2$ g/emp. unit

$\dfrac{224 \text{ g/mol}}{112.2 \text{ g/emp. unit}} = 2$ emp. units/mol

$K_2C_4N_2H_6O_4$ (molecular formula)

**5-73.** $I_6C_6$

**5-75.** $7.5 \times 10^{-10}$ mol pennies

**5-76.** $0.443 \text{ g N} \times \dfrac{1 \text{ mol N}}{14.01 \text{ g N}} = 0.0316$ mol N

Thus 1.420 g of M also equals 0.0316 mol M since M and N are present in equimolar amounts.

$1.420 \text{ g}/0.0316 \text{ mol} = \underline{44.9 \text{ g/mol [scandium (Sc)]}}$

**5-79.** $2.78 \times 10^{-3}$ mol $P_4$

$2.78 \times 10^{-3} \text{ mol } P_4 \times \dfrac{4 \text{ mol P}}{\text{mol } P_4}$

$\times \dfrac{6.022 \times 10^{23} \text{ atoms P}}{\text{mol P}} = \underline{6.70 \times 10^{21} \text{ atoms P}}$

**5-80.** 100 mol $H_2 = 202$ g $H_2$ therefore

100 H atoms $<$ 100 $H_2$ molecules $<$ 100 g $H_2$
$$< 100 \text{ mol } H_2$$

**5-82.** 120 g/mol of compound $120 - 55.8 = 64$ g of S

$\dfrac{64 \text{ g S}}{32.07 \text{ g S /mol}} = 2$ mol S

Formula $= FeS_2$

**5-83.** (a) $2Na^+$ and $S_4O_6^{2-}$   (b) 27.9 g S   (c) $NaS_2O_3$
(d) 270.3 g/mol   (e) 0.0925 mol $Na_2S_4O_6$, $5.57 \times 10^{22}$
formula units   (f) 35.5% oxygen

**5-85.** $\dfrac{2N}{2N + xO} = 0.368$   $\dfrac{28.02}{28.05 + 16.00x} = 0.368$

$x = 3$ $N_2O_3$ dinitrogen trioxide

**5-87.** $C_{12}H_4Cl_4O_2$ (molecular formula)

**5-89.** Empirical formula $CrCl_3O_{12}$ Actual formula =
$Cr(ClO_4)_3$ chromium(III) perchlorate

**5-90.** Assume exactly 100 g of compound. There is then
51.1 g $H_2O$ and 48.9 g $MgSO_4$.

$MgSO_4$:48.9 g $\overline{MgSO_4} \times \dfrac{1\ mol}{120.4\ g\ \overline{MgSO_4}}$

$= 0.406\ mol\ MgSO_4$

2.94 mol $H_2O$/0.406 mol $MgSO_4$

$= 7.0\ mol\ H_2O/mol\ MgSO_4$

The formula is $MgSO_4 \cdot 7H_2O$

**5-93.** $1.20\ \overline{g\ CO_2} \times \dfrac{1\ \overline{mol\ CO_2}}{44.01\ \overline{g\ CO_2}} \times \dfrac{1\ mol\ C}{\overline{mol\ CO_2}}$

$= 0.0273\ mol\ C$

$0.489\ \overline{g\ H_2O} \times \dfrac{1\ \overline{mol\ H_2O}}{18.02\ \overline{g\ H_2O}} \times \dfrac{2\ mol\ H}{\overline{mol\ H_2O}}$

$= 0.0543\ mol\ H$

C: $\dfrac{0.0273}{0.0273} = 1.0$   H: $\dfrac{0.0543}{0.0273} = 2.0$   $CH_2$

## CHAPTER 6

**6-1.** (a) $Cl_2(g)$   (b) $C(s)$   (c) $K_2SO_4(s)$   (d) $H_2O(l)$
(e) $P_4(s)$   (f) $H_2(g)$   (g) $Br_2(l)$   (h) $NaBr(s)$
(i) $S_8(s)$   (j) $Na(s)$   (k) $Hg(l)$   (l) $CO_2(g)$

**6-2.** (a) $CaCO_3 \longrightarrow CaO + CO_2$

(b) $4\,Na + O_2 \longrightarrow 2Na_2O$

(c) $H_2SO_4 + 2NaOH \longrightarrow Na_2SO_4 + 2H_2O$

(d) $2H_2O_2 \longrightarrow 2H_2O + O_2$

**6-4.** (a) $2Al + 2H_3PO_4 \longrightarrow 2AlPO_4 + 3H_2$

(b) $Ca(OH)_2 + 2HCl \longrightarrow CaCl_2 + 2H_2O$

(c) $3Mg + N_2 \longrightarrow Mg_3N_2$

(d) $2C_2H_6 + 7O_2 \longrightarrow 4CO_2 + 6H_2O$

**6-6.** (a) $Mg_3N_2 + 6H_2O \longrightarrow 3Mg(OH)_2 + 2NH_3$

(b) $2H_2S + O_2 \longrightarrow 2S + 2H_2O$

(c) $Si_2H_6 + 8H_2O \longrightarrow 2Si(OH)_4 + 7H_2$

(d) $C_2H_6 + 5Cl_2 \longrightarrow C_2HCl_5 + 5HCl$

**6-8.** (a) $2B_4H_{10} + 11O_2 \longrightarrow 4B_2O_3 + 10H_2O$

(b) $SF_6 + 2SO_3 \longrightarrow 3O_2SF_2$

(c) $CS_2 + 3O_2 \longrightarrow CO_2 + 2SO_2$

(d) $2BF_3 + 6NaH \longrightarrow B_2H_6 + 6NaF$

**6-10.** (a) $2Na(s) + 2H_2O(l) \longrightarrow H_2(g) + 2NaOH(aq)$

(b) $2KClO_3(s) \longrightarrow 2KCl(s) + 3O_2(g)$

(c) $NaCl(aq) + AgNO_3(aq) \longrightarrow AgCl(s) + NaNO_3(aq)$

(d) $2H_3PO_4(aq) + 3Ca(OH)_2(aq) \longrightarrow$
$\qquad\qquad\qquad\qquad Ca_3(PO_4)_2(s) + 6H_2O(l)$

**6-12.** $Ni(s) + 2N_2O_4(l) \longrightarrow Ni(NO_3)_2(s) + 2NO(g)$

**6-14.** In exercise 6-2, (a) and (d) are decomposition reactions and (b) is a combination and combustion reaction. In exercise 6-4, (c) is a combination reaction and (d) is a combustion reaction.

**6-16.** (a) $2C_7H_{14}(l) + 21O_2(g) \longrightarrow 14CO_2(g) + 14H_2O(l)$

(b) $2LiCH_3(s) + 4O_2(g) \longrightarrow$
$\qquad\qquad\qquad Li_2O(s) + 2CO_2(g) + 3H_2O(l)$

(c) $C_4H_{10}O(l) + 6O_2(g) \longrightarrow 4CO_2(g) + 5H_2O(l)$

(d) $2C_2H_5SH(g) + 9O_2(g) \longrightarrow$
$\qquad\qquad\qquad 2SO_2(g) + 4CO_2(g) + 6H_2O(l)$

**6-18.** (a) $Ba(s) + H_2(g) \longrightarrow BaH_2(s)$

(b) $8Ba(s) + S_8(s) \longrightarrow 8BaS(s)$

(c) $Ba(s) + Br_2(l) \longrightarrow BaBr_2(s)$

(d) $3Ba(s) + N_2(g) \longrightarrow Ba_3N_2(s)$

**6-20.** (a) $Ca(HCO_3)_2(s) \longrightarrow CaO(s) + 2CO_2(g) + H_2O(l)$

(b) $2Ag_2O(s) \longrightarrow 4Ag(s) + O_2(g)$

(c) $N_2O_3(g) \longrightarrow NO_2(g) + NO(g)$

**6-22.** (a) $2K(s) + Cl_2(g) \longrightarrow 2KCl(s)$

(b) $2C_6H_6(l) + 15O_2(g) \longrightarrow 12CO_2(g) + 6H_2O(l)$

(c) $2Au_2O_3(s) \longrightarrow 4Au(s) + 3O_2(g)$

(d) $2C_3H_8O(l) + 9O_2(g) \longrightarrow 6CO_2(g) + 8H_2O(l)$

(e) $P_4(s) + 10F_2(g) \longrightarrow 4PF_5(s)$

**6-24.** (a) $Na_2S \longrightarrow 2Na^+(aq) + S^{2-}(aq)$

(b) $Li_2SO_4 \longrightarrow 2Li^+(aq) + SO_4^{2-}(aq)$

(c) $K_2Cr_2O_7 \longrightarrow 2K^+(aq) + Cr_2O_7^{2-}(aq)$

(d) $CaS \longrightarrow Ca^{2+}(aq) + S^{2-}(aq)$

(e) $(NH_4)_2S \longrightarrow 2NH_4^+(aq) + S^{2-}(aq)$

(f) $Ba(OH)_2 \longrightarrow Ba^{2+}(aq) + 2OH^-(aq)$

**6-26.** (a) $HNO_3(aq) \longrightarrow H^+(aq) + NO_3^-(aq)$

(b) $Sr(OH)_2(s) \longrightarrow Sr^{2+}(aq) + 2OH^-(aq)$

**6-28.** (a) no reaction

(b) $Fe + 2H^+ \longrightarrow Fe^{2+} + H_2$

(c) $Cu + 2Ag^+ \longrightarrow Cu^{2+} + 2Ag$

(d) no reaction

**6-30.** (a) $CuCl_2(aq) + Fe(s) \longrightarrow FeCl_2(aq) + Cu(s)$

$Cu^{2+}(aq) + 2Cl^-(aq) + Fe(s) \longrightarrow$
$\qquad\qquad\qquad Fe^{2+}(aq) + 2Cl^-(aq) + Cu(s)$

$Cu^{2+}(aq) + Fe(s) \longrightarrow Fe^{2+}(aq) + Cu(s)$

**(b)** and **(c)** no reaction

**(d)** $3Zn(s) + 2Cr(NO_3)_3(aq) \longrightarrow$
$$3Zn(NO_3)_2(aq) + 2Cr(s)$$

$3Zn(s) + 2Cr^{3+}(aq) + 6NO_3^-(aq) \longrightarrow$
$$3Zn^{2+}(aq) + 6NO_3^-(aq) + 2Cr(s)$$

$3Zn(s) + 2Cr^{3+}(aq) \longrightarrow 3Zn^{2+}(aq) + 2Cr(s)$

**6-32.** $6Na(l) + Cr_2O_3(s) \longrightarrow 2Cr(s) + 3Na_2O(s)$

$3Na + Cr^{3+} \longrightarrow Cr + 3Na^+$

**6-34.** Insoluble compounds are **(b)** $PbSO_4$, and **(d)** $Ag_2S$

**6-36. (a)** $AgBr$   **(b)** $Ag_2CO_3$   **(c)** $Ag_3PO_4$

**6-38. (a)** $CuCO_3$   **(b)** $CdCO_3$   **(c)** $Cr_2(CO_3)_3$

**6-40.** $Hg_2Cl_2$

**6-42. (b)** $Ca_3(PO_4)_2$

**6-44. (a)** $2KI(aq) + Pb(C_2H_3O_2)_2(aq) \longrightarrow$
$$PbI_2(s) + 2KC_2H_3O_2(aq)$$

**(b)** and **(c)** no reaction occurs

**(d)** $BaS(aq) + Hg_2(NO_3)_2(aq) \longrightarrow$
$$Hg_2S(s) + Ba(NO_3)_2(aq)$$

**(e)** $FeCl_3(aq) + 3KOH(aq) \longrightarrow$
$$Fe(OH)_3(s) + 3KCl(aq)$$

**6-46. (a)** $2K^+(aq) + 2I^-(aq) + Pb^{2+}(aq) + 2C_2H_3O_2^-(aq)$
$$\longrightarrow PbI_2(s) + 2K^+(aq) + 2C_2H_3O_2^-(aq)$$
$Pb^{2+}(aq) + 2I^-(aq) \longrightarrow PbI_2(s)$

**(d)** $Ba^{2+}(aq) + S^{2-}(aq) + Hg_2^{2+}(aq) + 2NO_3^-(aq) \longrightarrow$
$$Hg_2S(s) + Ba^{2+}(aq) + 2NO_3^-(aq)$$
$Hg_2^{2+}(aq) + S^{2-}(aq) \longrightarrow Hg_2S(s)$

**(e)** $Fe^{3+}(aq) + 3Cl^-(aq) + 3K^+(aq) + 3OH^-(aq)$
$$\longrightarrow Fe(OH)_3(s) + 3K^+(aq) + 3Cl^-(aq)$$
$Fe^{3+}(aq) + 3OH^-(aq) \longrightarrow Fe(OH)_3(s)$

**6-48. (a)** $2K^+(aq) + S^{2-}(aq) + Pb^{2+}(aq) + 2NO_3^-(aq)$
$$\longrightarrow PbS(s) + 2K^+(aq) + 2NO_3^-(aq)$$
$S^{2-}(aq) + Pb^{2+}(aq) \longrightarrow PbS(s)$

**(b)** $2NH_4^+(aq) + CO_3^{2-}(aq) + Ca^{2+}(aq) + 2Cl^-(aq)$
$$\longrightarrow CaCO_3(s) + 2NH_4^+(aq) + 2Cl^-(aq)$$
$CO_3^{2-}(aq) + Ca^{2+}(aq) \longrightarrow CaCO_3(s)$

**(c)** $2Ag^+(aq) + 2ClO_4^-(aq) + 2Na^+(aq) + CrO_4^{2-}(aq)$
$$\longrightarrow Ag_2CrO_4(s) + 2Na^+(aq) + 2ClO_4^-(aq)$$
$2Ag^+(aq) + CrO_4^{2-}(aq) \longrightarrow Ag_2CrO_4(s)$

**6-50. (a)** $CuCl_2(aq) + Na_2CO_3(aq) \longrightarrow$
$$CuCO_3(s) + 2NaCl(aq)$$

Filter the solid $CuCO_3$.

**(b)** $(NH_4)_2SO_4(aq) + Pb(NO_3)_2(aq) \longrightarrow$
$$PbSO_4(s) + 2NH_4NO_3(aq)$$

Filter the solid $PbSO_4$.

**(c)** $2KI(aq) + Hg_2(NO_3)_2(aq) \longrightarrow$
$$Hg_2I_2(s) + 2KNO_3(aq)$$

Filter the solid $Hg_2I_2$.

**(d)** $NH_4Cl(aq) + AgNO_3(aq) \longrightarrow$
$$AgCl(s) + NH_4NO_3(aq)$$

Filter the solid AgCl; the desired product remains after water is removed by boiling.

**(e)** $Ca(C_2H_3O_2)_2(aq) + K_2CO_3(aq) \longrightarrow$
$$CaCO_3(s) + 2KC_2H_3O_2(aq)$$

Filter the solid $CaCO_3$; the desired product remains after the water is removed by boiling.

**6-51. (b)** HF

**6-53. (c)** $Al(OH)_3$

**6-55. (a)** $HI(aq) + CsOH(aq) \longrightarrow CsI(aq) + H_2O(l)$

**(b)** $2HNO_3(aq) + Ca(OH)_2(aq) \longrightarrow$
$$Ca(NO_3)_2(aq) + 2H_2O(l)$$

**(c)** $H_2SO_4(aq) + Sr(OH)_2(aq) \longrightarrow$
$$SrSO_4(s) + 2H_2O(l)$$

**(d)** $HNO_3(aq) + NaHCO_3(s) \longrightarrow$
$$NaNO_3(aq) + CO_2(g) + H_2O(l)$$

**6-57. (a)** $H^+(aq) + I^-(aq) + Cs^+(aq) + OH^-(aq) \longrightarrow$
$$Cs^+(aq) + I^-(aq) + H_2O(l)$$
$H^+(aq) + OH^-(aq) \longrightarrow H_2O(l)$

**(b)** $2H^+(aq) + 2NO_3^-(aq) + Ca^{2+}(aq) + 2OH^-(aq) \longrightarrow$
$$Ca^{2+}(aq) + 2NO_3^-(aq) + 2H_2O(l)$$
$H^+(aq) + OH^-(aq) \longrightarrow H_2O(l)$

**(c)** $2H^+(aq) + SO_4^{2-}(aq) + Sr^{2+}(aq) + 2OH^-(aq) \longrightarrow$
$$SrSO_4(s) + 2H_2O(l)$$
$H^+(aq) + OH^-(aq) \longrightarrow H_2O(l)$

**(d)** $H^+(aq) + NO_3^-(aq) + Na^+(aq) + HCO_3^-(s) \longrightarrow$
$$Na^+(aq) + NO_3^-(aq) + CO_2(g) + H_2O(l)$$
$H^+(aq) + HCO_3^-(s) \longrightarrow CO_2(g) + H_2O(l)$

Net ionic equation is the same as the total ionic equation since $SrSO_4$ precipitates.

**6-59.** $Mg(OH)_2(s) + 2HCl(aq) \longrightarrow MgCl_2(aq) + 2H_2O(l)$

$Mg(OH)_2(s) + 2H^+(aq) + 2Cl^-(aq) \longrightarrow$
$$Mg^{2+}(aq) + 2Cl^-(aq) + 2H_2O(l)$$
$Mg(OH)_2(s) + 2H^+(aq) \longrightarrow Mg^{2+}(aq) + 2H_2O(l)$

**6-61.** $C_3H_8(g) + 5O_2(g) \longrightarrow 3CO_2(g) + 4H_2O(l)$
$2C_4H_{10}(g) + 13O_2(g) \longrightarrow 8CO_2(g) + 10H_2O(l)$
$2C_8H_{18}(l) + 25O_2(g) \longrightarrow 16CO_2(g) + 18H_2O(l)$
$C_2H_5OH(l) + 3O_2(g) \longrightarrow 2CO_2(g) + 3H_2O(l)$

**6-62.** In both of these reactions, the reactants change from neutral atoms to cations and anions in the products. Ions are formed from neutral atoms from the loss or gain of electrons.

**6-64. (a)** $Ba(s) + I_2(s) \longrightarrow BaI_2(s)$

**(b)** $HBr(aq) + RbOH(aq) \longrightarrow RbBr(aq) + H_2O(l)$

**(c)** $Ca(s) + 2HNO_3(aq) \longrightarrow Ca(NO_3)_2(aq) + H_2(g)$

**(d)** $C_{10}H_8(s) + 12O_2(g) \longrightarrow 10CO_2(g) + 4H_2O(l)$

**(e)** $(NH_4)_2CrO_4(aq) + BaBr_2(aq) \longrightarrow$
$$BaCrO_4(s) + 2NH_4Br(aq)$$

**(f)** $2Al(OH)_3(s) \longrightarrow Al_2O_3(s) + 3H_2O(g)$

**6-65. (b)** $H^+(aq) + Br^-(aq) + Rb^+(aq) + OH^-(aq) \longrightarrow$
$$Rb^+(aq) + Br^-(aq) + H_2O(l)$$
$$H^+(aq) + OH^-(aq) \longrightarrow H_2O(l)$$

**(c)** $Ca(s) + 2H^+(aq) + 2NO_3^-(aq) \longrightarrow$
$$Ca^{2+}(aq) + 2NO_3^-(aq) + H_2(g)$$
$$Ca(s) + 2H^+(aq) \longrightarrow Ca^{2+}(aq) + H_2(g)$$

**(e)** $2NH_4^+(aq) + CrO_4^{2-}(aq) + Ba^{2+}(aq) + 2Br^-(aq)$
$$\longrightarrow BaCrO_4(s) + 2NH_4^+ + 2Br^-(aq)$$
$$CrO_4^{2-}(aq) + Ba^{2+}(aq) \longrightarrow BaCrO_4(s)$$

**6-68.** $H^+(aq) + OH^-(aq) \longrightarrow H_2O(l)$
$$Ba^{2+}(aq) + SO_4^{2-}(aq) \longrightarrow BaSO_4(s)$$

**6-70.** $Fe^{3+}(aq) + PO_4^{3-}(aq) \longrightarrow FePO_4(s)$
$$2Fe^{3+}(aq) + 3S^{2-}(aq) \longrightarrow Fe_2S_3(s)$$
$$Pb^{2+}(aq) + 2I^-(aq) \longrightarrow PbI_2(s)$$
$$3Pb^{2+}(aq) + 2PO_4^{3-}(aq) \longrightarrow Pb_3(PO_4)_2(s)$$
$$Pb^{2+}(aq) + S^{2-}(aq) \longrightarrow PbS(s)$$

## CHAPTER 7

**7-1. (a)** $\dfrac{1 \text{ mol } H_2}{1 \text{ mol } Mg}$ **(b)** $\dfrac{2 \text{ mol } HCl}{1 \text{ mol } Mg}$ **(c)** $\dfrac{1 \text{ mol } H_2}{2 \text{ mol } HCl}$

**(d)** $\dfrac{2 \text{ mol } HCl}{1 \text{ mol } MgCl_2}$

**7-2. (a)** $\dfrac{2 \text{ mol } C_4H_{10}}{8 \text{ mol } CO_2}$ **(b)** $\dfrac{2 \text{ mol } C_4H_{10}}{13 \text{ mol } O_2}$

**(c)** $\dfrac{13 \text{ mol } O_2}{8 \text{ mol } CO_2}$ **(d)** $\dfrac{10 \text{ mol } H_2O}{13 \text{ mol } O_2}$

**7-4. (a)** 3.33 mol $Al_2O_3$, 3.33 mol $AlCl_3$, 10.0 mol NO, 20.0 mol $H_2O$ **(b)** 1.00 mol $Al_2O_3$, 1.00 mol $AlCl_3$, 3.00 mol NO, 6.00 mol $H_2O$

**7-6. (a)** 15.0 mol $O_2$ and 10.0 mol $CH_4$ react

**(b)** 6.67 mol HCN and 20.0 mol $H_2O$ produced

**7-8. (a)** 126 g $SiF_4$ and **(b)** 43.8 g $H_2O$ produced

**(c)** 73.0 g $SiO_2$ reacts

**7-9. (a)** mol $H_2O \longrightarrow$ mol $H_2$

$$0.400 \text{ mol } H_2O \times \frac{2 \text{ mol } H_2}{2 \text{ mol } H_2O} = \underline{0.400 \text{ mol } H2}$$

**(b)** g $O_2 \longrightarrow$ mol $O_2 \longrightarrow$ mol $H_2O \longrightarrow$ g $H_2O$

$$0.640 \text{ g } O_2 \times \frac{1 \text{ mol } O_2}{32.00 \text{ g } O_2} \times \frac{2 \text{ mol } H_2O}{1 \text{ mol } O_2} \times \frac{18.02 \text{ g } H_2O}{\text{mol } H_2O}$$
$$= \underline{0.721 \text{ g } H_2O}$$

**(c)** g $O_2 \longrightarrow$ mol $O_2 \longrightarrow$ mol $H_2 \longrightarrow$ g $H_2$

$$0.032 \text{ g } O_2 \times \frac{1 \text{ mol } O_2}{32.00 \text{ g } O_2} \times \frac{2 \text{ mol } H_2}{1 \text{ mol } O_2} \times \frac{2.016 \text{ g } H_2}{\text{mol } H_2}$$
$$= \underline{0.0040 \text{ g } H_2}$$

**(d)** g $H_2 \longrightarrow$ mol $H_2 \longrightarrow$ mol $H_2O \longrightarrow$ g $H_2O$

$$0.400 \text{ g } H_2 \times \frac{1 \text{ mol } H_2}{2.016 \text{ g } H_2} \times \frac{2 \text{ mol } H_2O}{2 \text{ mol } H_2} \times \frac{18.02 \text{ g } H_2O}{\text{mol } H_2O}$$
$$= \underline{3.58 \text{ g } H_2O}$$

**7-10. (a)** 1.35 mol $CO_2$, 1.80 mol $H_2O$, 2.25 mol $O_2$

**(b)** 4.81 g $H_2O$ **(c)** 1.10 g $C_3H_8$ **(d)** 44.1 g $C_3H_8$

**(e)** 5.26 g $CO_2$ **(f)** 0.0996 mol $H_2O$

**7-12.** 47.2 g $N_2$

**7-14.** 0.728 g HCl

**7-16.** mol $FeS_2 \longrightarrow$ mol $H_2S \longrightarrow$ molecules $H_2S$

$$0.520 \text{ mol } FeS_2 \times \frac{1 \text{ mol } H_2S}{1 \text{ mol } FeS_2}$$
$$\times \frac{6.022 \times 10^{23} \text{ molecules}}{\text{mol } H_2S} = \underline{3.13 \times 10^{23} \text{ molecules}}$$

**7-17.** 16,900 g (16.9 kg) $HNO_3$

**7-19.** $2.30 \times 10^3$ g (2.30 kg) $C_2H_5OH$

**7-20.** 8140 g (8.14 kg) CO

**7-21. (a)** CuO limiting reactant producing 1.00 mol $N_2$

**(b)** stoichiometric mixture producing 1.00 mol $N_2$

**(c)** $NH_3$ limiting reactant producing 0.500 mol $N_2$

**(d)** CuO limiting reactant producing 0.209 mol $N_2$

**(e)** $NH_3$ limiting reactant producing 1.75 mol $N_2$

**7-22. (a)** $3.00 \text{ mol } CuO \times \dfrac{2 \text{ mol } NH_3}{3 \text{ mol } CuO}$
$$= 2.00 \text{ mol } NH_3 \text{ used}$$
$$3.00 - 2.00 = 1.00 \text{ mol } NH_3 \text{ in excess}$$

**(c)** 1.50 mol CuO in excess

**7-25.** $H_2SO_4$ is the limiting reactant and the yield of $H_2$ is 1.00 mole.

$$1.00 \text{ mol } H_2SO_4 \times \frac{2 \text{ mol } Al}{3 \text{ mol } H_2SO_4}$$
$$= 0.667 \text{ mol of Al used}$$
$$0.800 - 0.667 = \underline{0.133 \text{ mol Al remaining}}$$

**7-26.** $3.44 \text{ mol } C_5H_6 \times \dfrac{10 \text{ mol } CO_2}{2 \text{ mol } C_5H_6} = 17.2 \text{ mol } CO_2$

$$20.6 \text{ mol } O_2 \times \frac{10 \text{ mol } CO_2}{13 \text{ mol } O_2} = 15.8 \text{ mol } CO_2$$

Since $O_2$ is the limiting reactant:

$$15.8 \text{ mol } CO_2 \times \frac{44.01 \text{ g } CO_2}{\text{mol } CO_2} = \underline{695 \text{ g } CO_2}$$

**7-28.** Since $NH_3$ produces the least $N_2$, it is the limiting reactant and the yield of $N_2$ is $\underline{0.750 \text{ mol.}}$

**7-29.** $20.0 \text{ g } AgNO_3 \times \dfrac{1 \text{ mol } AgNO_3}{169.9 \text{ g } AgNO_3} \times \dfrac{2 \text{ mol } AgCl}{2 \text{ mol } AgNO_3}$
$$= 0.118 \text{ mol AgCl}$$

$$10.0 \text{ g } CaCl_2 \times \frac{1 \text{ mol } CaCl_2}{111.0 \text{ g } CaCl_2} \times \frac{2 \text{ mol } AgCl}{1 \text{ mol } CaCl_2}$$
$$= 0.180 \text{ mol AgCl}$$

Since $AgNO_3$ produces the least AgCl, it is the limiting reactant.

$$0.118 \text{ mol } AgCl \times \frac{143.4 \text{ g } AgCl}{\text{mol } AgCl} = \underline{16.9 \text{ g } AgCl}$$

Convert moles of AgCl (the limiting reactant) to grams of $CaCl_2$ used.

$$0.118 \text{ mol } AgCl \times \frac{1 \text{ mol } CaCl_2}{2 \text{ mol } AgCl} \times \frac{111.0 \text{ g } CaCl_2}{\text{mol } CaCl_2}$$
$$= \underline{6.55 \text{ g } CaCl_2 \text{ used}}$$

$$10.0 \text{ g} - 6.55 \text{ g} = \underline{3.5 \text{ g } CaCl_2 \text{ remaining}}$$

**7-31.** Products: 3.53 g $H_2O$, 4.71 g S, 2.94 g NO
Reactants remaining: remaining: 3.8 g $HNO_3$ remaining

**7-32.** 30.0 g $SO_3$ (theoretical yield) and 70.7% yield

**7-35.** <u>86.4%</u>

**7-36.** If 86.4% is converted to $CO_2$, the remainder (13.6%) is converted to CO. Thus, $0.136 \times 57.0$ g $= 7.75$ g of $C_8H_{18}$ is converted to CO. Notice that 1 mole of $C_8H_{18}$ forms 8 moles of CO (because of the eight carbons in $C_8H_{18}$). Thus

$$7.75 \ \overline{\text{g} \ C_8H_{18}} \times \frac{1 \ \overline{\text{mol} \ C_8H_{18}}}{114.2 \ \overline{\text{g} \ C_8H_{18}}} \times \frac{8 \ \overline{\text{mol} \ CO}}{1 \ \overline{\text{mol} \ C_8H_{18}}}$$
$$\times \frac{28.01 \ \text{g CO}}{\overline{\text{mol} \ CO}} = \underline{15.2 \ \text{g CO}}$$

**7-37.** Theoretical yield $\times 0.700 = 250$ g (actual yield)
Theoretical yield $= 250$ g$/0.700 = 357$ g $N_2$

**g $N_2$ $\longrightarrow$ mol $N_2$ $\longrightarrow$ mol $H_2$ $\longrightarrow$ g $H_2$**

$$357 \ \overline{\text{g} \ Na_2} \times \frac{1 \ \overline{\text{mol} \ N_2}}{28.02 \ \overline{\text{g} \ N_2}} \times \frac{4 \ \overline{\text{mol} \ H_2}}{1 \ \overline{\text{mol} \ N_2}} \times \frac{2.016 \ \text{g} \ H_2}{\overline{\text{mol} \ H_2}}$$
$$= \underline{103 \ \text{g} \ H_2}$$

**7-40.** $2Mg(s) + O_2 \longrightarrow 2MgO(s) + 1204$ kJ
$2Mg(s) + O_2(g) \longrightarrow 2MgO(s) \quad \Delta H = -1204$ kJ

**7-42.** $CaCO_3(s) + 176$ kJ $\longrightarrow CaO(s) + CO_2(g)$
$CaCO_3(s) \longrightarrow CaO(s) + CO_2(g) \quad \Delta H = 176$ kJ

**7-43.** $1.00 \ \overline{\text{g} \ C_8H_{18}} \times \frac{1 \ \overline{\text{mol} \ C_8H_{18}}}{114.2 \ \overline{\text{g} \ C_8H_{18}}} \times \frac{5840 \ \text{kJ}}{\overline{\text{mol} \ C_8H_{18}}}$
$$= \underline{48.0 \ \text{kJ}}$$

$1.00 \ \overline{\text{g} \ CH_4} \times \frac{1 \ \overline{\text{mol} \ CH_4}}{16.04 \ \overline{\text{g} \ CH_4}} \times \frac{890 \ \text{kJ}}{\overline{\text{mol} \ CH_4}} = \underline{55.6 \ \text{kJ}}$

**7-45.** **kJ $\longrightarrow$ mol Al $\longrightarrow$ g Al**

$$35.8 \ \overline{\text{kJ}} \times \frac{2 \ \overline{\text{mol} \ Al}}{850 \ \overline{\text{kJ}}} \times \frac{26.98 \ \text{g Al}}{\overline{\text{mol} \ Al}} = \underline{2.27 \ \text{g Al}}$$

**7-46.** 69.7 g $C_6H_{12}O_6$

**7-48.** $125 \ \overline{\text{g} \ Fe_2O_3} \times \frac{1 \ \overline{\text{mol} \ Fe_2O_3}}{159.7 \ \overline{\text{g} \ Fe_2O_3}} \times \frac{2 \ \overline{\text{mol} \ Fe_3O_4}}{3 \ \overline{\text{mol} \ Fe_2O_3}}$
$$\times \frac{3 \ \overline{\text{mol} \ FeO}}{1 \ \overline{\text{mol} \ Fe_3O_4}} \times \frac{1 \ \overline{\text{mol} \ Fe}}{1 \ \overline{\text{mol} \ FeO}} \times \frac{55.85 \ \text{g Fe}}{\overline{\text{mol} \ Fe}}$$
$$= \underline{87.4 \ \text{g Fe}}$$

**7-49.** $2KClO_3 \longrightarrow 2KCl + 3O_2$
Find the mass of $KClO_3$ needed to produce 12.0 g $O_2$.

**g $O_2$ $\longrightarrow$ mol $O_2$ $\longrightarrow$ mol $KClO_3$ $\longrightarrow$ g $KClO_3$**

$$12.0 \ \overline{\text{g} \ O_2} \times \frac{1 \ \overline{\text{mol} \ O_2}}{32.00 \ \overline{\text{g} \ O_2}} \times \frac{2 \ \overline{\text{mol} \ KClO_3}}{3 \ \overline{\text{mol} \ O_2}} \times \frac{122.6 \ \text{g} \ KClO_3}{\overline{\text{mol} \ KClO_3}}$$
$$= 30.7 \ \text{g} \ KClO_3$$
$$\text{percent purity} = \frac{30.7 \ \text{g}}{50.0 \ \text{g}} \times 100\% = \underline{61.4\%}$$

**7-50.** <u>4.49% $FeS_2$</u>

**7-52.** (1) $NH_3$ is the limiting reactant.
(2) 141 g NO (theoretical yield), <u>28.4% yield</u>

**7-54.** $H_2O$ is the limiting reactant producing 11.0 g $CaCl_2 \cdot 6H_2O$

**7-55.** Molecular formula $= CH_2Cl_2$
$CH_4(g) + 2Cl_2(g) \longrightarrow CH_2Cl_2(l) + 2HCl(g)$
$Cl_2$ is the limiting reactant producing 9.00 g $CH_2Cl_2$

**CHAPTER 8**

**8-1.** Ultraviolet light has shorter wavelengths but higher energy than visible light. Because of this high energy, ultraviolet light can damage living cells in tissues, thus causing a burn.

**8-2.** Since these two shells are close in energy, transitions of electrons from these two levels to the $n = 1$ shell have similar energy. Thus, the wavelengths of light from the two transitions are very close together.

**8-3.** Since these two shells are comparatively far apart in energy, transitions from these two levels to the $n = 1$ shell have comparatively different energies. Thus, the wavelengths of light from the two transitions are quite different. (The $n = 3$ to $n = 1$ transition has a shorter wavelength and higher energy than the $n = 2$ to $n = 1$ transition.)

**8-5.** $1p$ and $3f$

**8-8.** A $4p$ orbital is shaped roughly like a two-sided baseball bat with two "lobes" lying along one of the three axes. This shape represents the region of highest probability of finding the $4p$ electrons.

**8-9.** The $3s$ orbital is spherical in shape. There is an equal probability of finding the electron regardless of the orientation from the nucleus. (In fact, the probability lies in three concentric spheres with the highest probability in the sphere farthest from the nucleus.) The highest probability of finding the electron lies farther from the nucleus in the $3s$ than in the $2s$.

**8-11.** One $3s$, three $3p$, and five $3d$, for a total of nine.

**8-13.** (a) $3p$, three     (b) $4d$, five     (c) $6s$, one

**8-15.** $2n^2$: $2(3)^2 = 18$ and $2(2)^2 = 8$

**8-18.** $2(5)^2 = 50$

**8-19.** The first four subshells in the fifth shell ($s$, $p$, $d$, and $f$) hold 32 electrons. The $g$ subshell holds $50 - 32 = 18$ electrons.

**8-20.** Since each orbital holds two electrons, there are nine orbitals in this subshell.

**8-21.** The $1s$ subshell always fills first.

**8-24.** (a) $6s$  (b) $5p$  (c) $4p$  (d) $4d$

**8-26.** $4s$, $4p$, $5s$, $4d$, $5p$, $6s$, $4f$

**8-27.** (a) Mg: $1s^2 2s^2 2p^6 3s^2$
(b) Ge: $1s^2 2s^2 2p^6 3s^2 3p^6 4s^2 3d^{10} 4p^2$
(c) Cd: $1s^2 2s^2 2p^6 3s^2 3p^6 4s^2 3d^{10} 4p^6 5s^2 4d^{10}$
(d) Si: $1s^2 2s^2 2p^6 3s^2 3p^2$

**8-29.** $1s^2 2s^2 2p^6 3s^2 3p^6$

**8-31.** (a) S: $[Ne]3s^2 3p^4$     (b) Zn: $[Ar]4s^2 3d^{10}$
(c) Hf: $[Xe]6s^2 5d^2 4f^1$  (d) I: $[Kr]5s^2 4d^{10} 5p^5$

**8-33. (a)** In  **(b)** Y  **(c)** Ce  **(d)** Ar

**8-35. (a)** $3p$  **(b)** $5p$  **(c)** $5d$  **(d)** $5s$

**8-37.** Both have three valence electrons. The outer electron in IIIA is in a $p$ subshell; in IIIB it is in a $d$ subshell.

**8-39. (a)** F  **(b)** Ga  **(c)** Ba  **(d)** Gd  **(e)** Cu

**8-41. (a)** VIIA  **(b)** IIIA  **(c)** IIA  **(e)** IB

**8-42.** VA: [NG] $ns^2np^3$  VB: [NG] $ns^2(n-1)d^3$

**8-44. (b)** and **(e)** belong to Group IVA

**8-46. (a)** IVA  **(b)** VIIIA  **(c)** IB  **(d)** Pr and Pa

**8-47. (a)** [NG] $ns^2$  **(b)** [NG] $ns^2 (n-1)d^{10}$

    **(c)** [NG] $ns^2 np^4$ or [NG] $ns^2 (n-1)d^{10}np^4$

    **(d)** [NG] $ns^2 (n-1)d^2$

**8-48.** Helium does not have a filled $p$ subshell. (There is no $1p$ subshell.)

**8-50.** [Ne] $3s^2 3p^6$

**8-52.** The theoretical order of filling is $6d$, $7p$, $8s$, $5g$. The $6d$ is completed at element number 112. The $7p$ fills at element number 118, and the $8s$ fills at element number 120. Thus element number 121 would theoretically begin the filling of the $5g$ subshell. This assumes the normal order of filling.

**8-54.** $7s^2 6d^{10} 5f^{14} 7p^6$ Total 32

**8-55.** $8s^2 5g^{18} 7d^{10} 6f^{14} 8p^6$ Total 50

**8-56. (a)** transition  **(b)** representative  **(c)** noble gas  **(d)** inner transition

**8-58.** element number 118 (under Rn)

**8-60. (a)** This is excluded by Hund's rule since electrons are not shown in separate orbitals of the same subshell with parallel spins,  **(b)** This is correct,  **(c)** This is excluded by the Aufbau principle because the $2s$ subshell fills before the $2p$. **(d)** This is excluded by the Pauli exclusion principle since the two electrons in the 2s orbital cannot have the same spin.

**8-61.**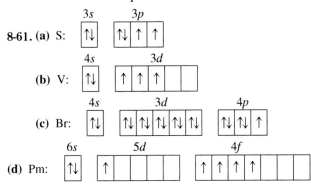

**8-63.** IIB, none; VB, three; VIA, two; VIIA, one; $[ns^1(n-1)d^5]$, six; Pm, five

**8-65.** IVA and VIA

**8-67. (a)** As  **(b)** Ru  **(c)** Ba  **(d)** I

**8-69.** Cr, 117 pm; Nb, 134 pm

**8-71. (a)** V  **(b)** Cl  **(c)** Mg  **(d)** Fe  **(e)** B

**8-72.** In, 558 kJ/mol; Ge, 762 kJ/mol

**8-73.** Te, 869 kJ/mol; Br, 1140 kJ/mol

**8-75. (a)** Cs$^+$ easiest, **(b)** Rb$^{2+}$ hardest

**8-77. (d)** I

**8-79. (a)** Rb

**8-81. (a)** Mg$^{2+}$  **(b)** K$^+$  **(c)** S  **(d)** Mg  **(e)** S$^{2-}$  **(f)** Se$^{2-}$

**8-83.** The outer electron in Hf is in a shell higher in energy than that in Zr. This alone would make Hf a larger atom. However, in between Zr and Hf lie several subshells including the long $4f$ subshell (Ce through Lu). The filling of these subshells, especially the $4f$, causes a gradual contraction that offsets the higher shell for Hf.

**8-84.** C$^+$ (1086 kJ/mol), C$^{2+}$ (3439 kJ/mol), C$^{3+}$ (8059 kJ/mol), C$^{4+}$ (14,282 kJ/mol), C$^{5+}$ (52,112 kJ/mol). Notice that the energy required to form C$^+$ (1086 kj) is about twice the energy required to form Ga$^+$ (579 kJ), which is a metal. Thus it is apparent that metal cations form more easily than nonmetal cations.

**8-85. (a)** B  **(b)** Kr  **(c)** K, Cr, and Cu  **(d)** Ga  **(e)** Hf

**8-87. (a)** B  **(b)** Br  **(c)** Sb  **(d)** Si

**8-89. (a)** Sr, metal, representative element, IIA

    **(b)** Pt, metal, transition metal, VIIIB

    **(c)** Br, nonmetal, representative element, VIIA

**8-91.** P

**8-93.** Z = Sn, X = Zr

**8-97. (a)** Ca  **(b)** Br$^-$  **(c)** S  **(d)** S$^{2-}$  **(e)** Na$^+$

**8-99.**

| $s^1$ | | | | | | | | | | | | | | | | $p^4$ |
|---|---|---|---|---|---|---|---|---|---|---|---|---|---|---|---|---|
| 1 | $s^2$ | | | | | | | | | | | $p^1$ | $p^2$ | $p^3$ | | 2 |
| 3 | 4 | | | | | | | | | | | 5 | 6 | 7 | | 8 |
| 9 | 10 | $d^1$ | $d^2$ | $d^3$ | $d^4$ | $d^5$ | $d^6$ | $d^7$ | $d^8$ | | | 11 | 12 | 13 | | 14 |
| 15 | 16 | 17 | 18 | 19 | 20 | 21 | 22 | 23 | 24 | | | 25 | 26 | 27 | | 28 |
| 29 | 30 | 31 | 32 | 33 | 34 | 35 | 36 | 37 | 38 | | | 39 | 40 | 41 | | 42 |
| 43 | 44 | 45* | | | | | | | | | | | | | | |

*46–50 would be in a $4f$ subshell

**(a)** six in second period, 14 in fourth

**(b)** third period, #14; fourth period, #28

**(c)** first inner transition element is #46 (assuming an order of filling like that on Earth)

**(d)** Elements #11 and #17 are most likely to be metals.

**(e)** Element #12 would have the larger radius in both cases.

**(f)** Element #7 would have the higher ionization energy in all three cases.

**(g)** The ions that would be reasonable are 16$^{2+}$ (metal cation), 13$^-$ (nonmetal anion), 15$^+$ (metal cation), and 1$^-$ (nonmetal anion). The 9$^{2+}$ ion is not likely because the second electron would come from a filled inner subshell. The 7$^+$ ion is not likely because it would be a nonmetal cation. The 17$^{4+}$ ion is not likely because #17 has only three electrons in the outer shell.

## CHAPTER 9

**9-1. (a)** $Ca\cdot$   **(b)** $\cdot \ddot{S}b\cdot$   **(c)** $\cdot \ddot{S}n\cdot$   **(d)** $\cdot \ddot{\underset{\cdot\cdot}{I}} :$

**(e)** $:\ddot{\underset{\cdot\cdot}{Ne}}:$   **(f)** $\cdot \ddot{B}i\cdot$   **(g)** $\cdot$ VIA$:$

**9-2. (a)** Group IIIA   **(b)** Group VA   **(c)** Group IIA

**9-4.** The electrons from filled inner subshells are not involved in bonding.

**9-6. (b)** Sr and S   **(c)** H and K   **(d)** Al and F

**9-8. (b)** $S^-$   **(c)** $Cr^{2+}$   **(e)** $In^+$   **(f)** $Pb^{2+}$   **(h)** $Tl^{3+}$

**9-10.** They have the noble gas configuration of He, which requires only two electrons.

**9-11. (a)** $K^+$   **(b)** $\cdot \ddot{\underset{\cdot\cdot}{O}} :^-$   **(c)** $:\ddot{\underset{\cdot\cdot}{I}} :^-$   **(d)** $:\ddot{\underset{\cdot\cdot}{P}} :^{3-}$   **(e)** $Ba^+$

**(f)** $\cdot \ddot{\underset{\cdot\cdot}{Xe}} :^+$   **(g)** $Sc^{3+}$

**9-13. (b)** $O^-$   **(e)** $Ba^+$   **(f)** $Xe^+$

**9-14. (a)** $Mg^{2+}$   **(b)** $Ga^{3+}$ (pseudo-noble gas configuration.)
**(c)** $Br^-$   **(d)** $S^{2-}$   **(e)** $P^{3-}$

**9-17.** $Se^{2-}$, $Br^-$, $Rb^+$, $Sr^{2+}$, $Y^{3+}$

**9-18.** $Tl^{3+}$ has a full $5d$ subshell. This is a pseudo-noble gas configuration.

**9-19.** $Cs_2S$, $Cs_3N$, $BaBr_2$, $BaS$, $Ba_3N_2$, $InBr_3$, $In_2S_3$, $InN$

**9-21. (a)** $CaI_2$   **(b)** $CaO$   **(c)** $Ca_3N_2$   **(d)** $CaTe$   **(e)** $CaF_2$

**9-23. (a)** $Cr^{3+}$   **(b)** $Fe^{3+}$   **(c)** $Mn^{2+}$   **(d)** $Co^{2+}$   **(e)** $Ni^{2+}$
**(f)** $V^{3+}$

**9-26. (a)** $H_2Se$   **(b)** $GeH_4$   **(c)** $ClF$   **(d)** $Cl_2O$   **(e)** $NCl_3$
**(f)** $CBr_4$

**9-28. (b)** $Cl_3$   **(d)** $NBr_4$   **(e)** $H_3O$

**9-30. (a)** $SO_4^{2-}$   **(b)** $IO_3^-$   **(c)** $SeO_4^{2-}$   **(d)** $H_2PO_3^-$
**(e)** $S_2O_3^{2-}$

**9-32.**

**9-34. (a)** $:C\equiv O:$   **(b)** (S trigonal with two O and one O below)   **(c)** $K^+[:C\equiv N:]^-$

**(d)** (H—O—S—O—H structure)

**9-36. (a)** $\ddot{N}=N=\ddot{O}$   **(b)** $Ca^{2+}\left[\begin{array}{c} N \\ O \quad O \end{array}\right]^-$

**(c)** $:\ddot{C}l—\underset{:\ddot{C}l:}{\overset{}{As}}—\ddot{C}l:$   **(d)** $\underset{H \quad\quad H}{\overset{\ddot{S}}{}}$

**(e)** $:\ddot{C}l—\underset{H}{\overset{H}{C}}—\ddot{C}l:$   **(f)** $\left[H—\underset{H}{\overset{H}{N}}—H\right]^+$

**9-37. (a)** $:\ddot{C}l—\ddot{O}—\ddot{C}l:$   **(b)** $\left[:\ddot{O}—\underset{:\ddot{O}:}{\overset{}{S}}—\ddot{O}:\right]^{2-}$

**(c)** $\underset{H \quad\quad H}{\overset{H \quad\quad H}{C=C}}$   **(d)** $\underset{H}{\overset{H}{C}}=\ddot{O}$

**(e)** $\underset{:\ddot{F} \quad \ddot{F}:}{\overset{:\ddot{F}:}{B}}$   **(f)** $[:N\equiv O:]^+$

**9-40.**

**(a)** (three resonance structures of $SO_3$)

**(b)** (two resonance structures of $NO_2^-$)   **(c)** $\left[:\ddot{O}—\underset{:\ddot{O}:}{\overset{}{S}}—\ddot{O}:\right]^{2-}$
(only one structure)

**9-42.** (two resonance structures with $BH_2CO_2^{2-}$)

**9-43.** A resonance hybrid is the actual structure of a molecule or ion that is implied by the various resonance structures. Each resonance structure contributes a portion of the actual structure. For example, the two structures shown in problem 9–42 imply that both carbon-oxygen bonds have properties that are halfway between those of a single and a double bond.

**9-45.** $\overset{-1}{:\ddot{O}}—\overset{+1}{\ddot{N}}=\ddot{O}$.   $:\ddot{O}=\ddot{N}—\ddot{O}:$

**9-47. (a)** $C=-1$, $O=+1$   **(b)** $S=+2$, single bonded O's $=-1$
**(c)** $K=+1$; $C=-1$; $N=0$

**(d)** H's $=0$; $S=+1$; O in H—O—S $=0$, other O $=-1$

**9-49.** $\underset{:\ddot{O}:^{-1}}{\overset{-1}{:\ddot{O}}—\overset{+2}{\ddot{C}l}—\overset{-1}{\ddot{O}:}}$   $\underset{:\ddot{O}:^{-1}}{\overset{}{:\ddot{O}=\ddot{C}l—\ddot{O}:^-}}$

**9-51.** $\overset{-1}{:N}=\overset{+1}{N}=\ddot{O}.$ $\longleftrightarrow$ $\overset{+1}{:N}\equiv\overset{-1}{N}—\ddot{O}:$   $\overset{-1}{:N}=\overset{+2}{O}=\overset{-1}{N}:$

Both resonance structures for NNO have much less formal charge than the NON structure.

**9-52.** Cs, Ba, Be, B, C, Cl, O, F

**9-53. (a)** $\overset{\delta-}{N} \rightleftharpoons \overset{\delta+}{H}$ **(b)** $\overset{\delta+}{B} \rightleftharpoons \overset{\delta-}{H}$ **(c)** $\overset{\delta+}{Li} \rightleftharpoons \overset{\delta-}{H}$
**(d)** $\overset{\delta-}{F} \rightleftharpoons \overset{\delta+}{O}$ **(e)** $\overset{\delta-}{O} \rightleftharpoons \overset{\delta+}{Cl}$ **(f)** $\overset{\delta-}{S} \rightleftharpoons \overset{\delta+}{Se}$
**(g)** $\overset{\delta-}{C} \rightleftharpoons \overset{\delta+}{B}$ **(h)** $\overset{\delta+}{Cs} \rightleftharpoons \overset{\delta-}{N}$

(i) C—S (very low polarity)

**9-54. (i)** nonpolar, **(b)** = **(f)**, **(d)** = **(e)** = **(g)**, **(a)**, **(c)**, **(h)**

**9-55. (a)** CF polar covalent **(b)** AIF ionic **(c)** FF nonpolar

**9-56.** Only **(d)** Al — F is predicted to be ionic on this basis since the electronegativity difference is 2.5.

**9-58. (b)** I—I nonpolar, **(c)** C—H (nearly nonpolar)

**9-59.** If the molecule has a symmetrical geometry and all bonds are the same, the bond dipoles cancel and the molecule is nonpolar.

**9-60. (a)** is V-shaped **(b)** $\ddot{S}=C=\ddot{S}$ is linear

**(c)** is tetrahedral **(d)** is V-shaped

**(e)** is V-shaped

**9-62. (a)** No angle between two points **(b)** 180° **(c)** 120°

**9-64. (a)** N–trigonal pyramid, O–V-shaped

**(b)** H—$\ddot{O}$—C≡N : O–V-shaped, C–linear

**(c)** H—C—C≡N : C–tetrahedral, C–linear

**(d)** See problem 9-42. B– tetrahedral, C– trigonal planar

**9-66.** If the molecule has a symmetrical geometry and all bonds are the same, the bond dipoles cancel and the molecule is nonpolar.

**9-67. (a)** polar **(b)** nonpolar **(c)** polar **(d)** polar **(e)** polar

**9-69.** The molecule is polar.

**9-70.** Since the H — S bond is much less polar than the H — O bond, the resultant molecular dipole is much less. The $H_2S$ molecule is less polar than the $H_2O$ molecule.

**9-72.** The $CHF_3$ molecule is more polar than the $CHCl_3$ molecule. The C — F bond is more polar than the C — Cl bond, which means that the resultant molecular dipole is larger for $CHF_3$.

**9-74.** All bond dipoles in $SO_3$ cancel.

Bond dipoles in $SO_2$ do not cancel.

**9-76. (a)** e.g., RbCl **(b)** e.g., SrO **(c)** e.g., AlN

**9-77.** is trigonal pyramid; the molecule is polar.

**9-79.** No resonance structures. Geometry around B is tetrahedral. Geometry around C is linear.

**9-81.** Geometry is V-shaped around N's.

Other resonance structures:

$:\ddot{O}—N≡N—\ddot{O}: \longleftrightarrow :O≡N—\dot{N}—\ddot{O}: \longleftrightarrow :\ddot{O}—\dot{N}—N≡O:$

**9-84.** Valence electrons for neutral $PO_3 = 5(P) + (3 \times 6)$ (O's) = 23. Since the species has 26 electrons it must be an anion with a – 3 charge (i.e., $PO_3{}^{3-}$)

The geometry of the anion is trigonal pyramid with a O—P—O angle of about 109°.

**9-85.** Valence electrons for neutral $ClI_2 = 3 \times 7 = 21$. Since the species has 20 valence electrons it must be a cation with a + 1 charge (i.e. $ClI_2{}^+$).

The geometry of the cation is V-shaped with an angle of about 109°.

**9-87.** $K_3N$, potassium nitride $KN_3 = K^+N_3^-$ Resonance structures:

$\dot{N}=N=\dot{N} \longleftrightarrow :\ddot{N}—N≡N: \longleftrightarrow :N≡N—\ddot{N}:$

In all resonance structures, the geometry around N is linear.

**9-90.** H—$\ddot{O}$—C≡N :

The angle of 105° indicates that the H—O—C angle is V-shaped with an angle of about 109°. This would involve two bonds and two pairs of electrons on the O. The geometry around the C is linear.

**9-91.** H—$\ddot{S}$=C=$\ddot{N}$.

The angle of 116° indicates that the H—S—C angle is V-shaped with an angle of about 120°. This would involve three bonds and one pair of electrons on the S. The geometry around the C is linear.

**9-92.** $:\ddot{F}—\ddot{N}=\ddot{N}—\ddot{F}:$

**9-94.** Oxygen difluoride, $OF_2$. Lewis structure: $:\ddot{F}:$  $:\ddot{F}:$

Dioxygen difluoride, $O_2F_2$. Lewis structure: $:\ddot{F}:$  $:\ddot{F}:$

Oxygen is less electronegative (more metallic) than fluorine and so is named first. Both molecules are angular; thus they are polar.

**9-96.** Formula = $NaHCO_3 = Na^+HCO_3^-$

$$H—\ddot{O}—C\underset{\displaystyle\ddot{O}:}{\overset{\displaystyle\ddot{O}:^-}{}}$$

The geometry around the C is trigonal planar with the approximate H—O—C angle of 120°.

**9-96.** Formula = $CaH_2S_2O_6 = Ca(HSO_3)_2$ calcium bisulfite or calcium hydrogen sulfite

$$H—\ddot{O}—\underset{\displaystyle:\ddot{O}:}{\overset{\displaystyle}{\ddot{S}}}—\ddot{O}:^-$$

The geometry around the S is trigonal pyramid. The H—O—S angle is about 109°.

**9-99.** (1) **(a)** 17 **(b)** 31 **(c)** $51_3$ **(d)** 97 **(e)** 7(13)

**(f)** $10(13)_2$ **(g)** $67_2$ **(h)** $3_26$

**(2)** On Zerk, six electrons fill the outer *s* and *p* orbitals to make a noble gas configuration. Therefore, we have a "sextet" rule on Zerk.

**(a)** $1—\ddot{7}:$ **(b)** $3^+1:^-$ (ionic) **(c)** $1—5—1$
$\qquad\qquad\qquad\qquad\qquad\qquad\qquad\underset{\displaystyle 1}{|}$

**(d)** $9^+\ :\ddot{7}:^-$ (ionic) **(e)** $:\ddot{7}—\ddot{13}:$ **(f)** $10^{2+}(:\ddot{13}:^-)_2$ (ionic)

**(g)** $:7—6—7:$ **(h)** $(3^+)_2\ \dot{6}:^{2-}$ (ionic)

### CHAPTER 10

**10-1.** The molecules of water are closely packed together and thus offer much more resistance. The molecules in a gas are dispersed into what is mostly empty space.

**10-3.** Since a gas is mostly empty space, more molecules can be added. In a liquid, the space is mostly occupied by the molecules so no more can be added.

**10-5.** Gas molecules are in rapid but random motion. When gas molecules collide with a light dust particle suspended in the air, they impart a random motion to the particle.

**10-6.** 1260 mi/hr

**10-7.** The molecule with the largest formula weight travels the slowest. $SF_6$( 146.1 amu) $< SO_2$ (64.07 amu) $< N_2O$(44.02 amu) $< CO_2$(44.01 amu) $< N_2$(28.02 amu) $< H_2$(2.016 amu)

**10-9.** When the pressure is high, the gas molecules are forced close together. In a highly compressed gas the molecules can occupy an appreciable part of the total volume. When the temperature is low, molecules have a lower average velocity. If there is some attraction, they can momentarily stick together when moving slowly.

**10-10.** **(a)** 2.17 atm **(b)** 0.0266 torr **(c)** 9560 torr **(d)** 0.0558 atm **(e)** 3.68 lb/in.² **(f)** 11 kPa

**10-11.** **(a)** 768 torr **(b)** $2.54 \times 10^4$ atm **(c)** 8.40 lb/in.² **(d)** 19 torr

**10-13.** 0.0102 atm

**10-15.** Assume a column of Hg has a cross-section of 1 cm² and is 76.0 cm high. Weight of Hg = 76.0 cm $\times$ 1cm² $\times$ 13.6 g/cm² = 1030 g. If water is substituted, 1030 g of water in the column is required. Height $\times$ 1 cm² $\times$ 1.00 g/cm³ = 1030 g height = 1030 cm

$$1030\ \text{cm} \times \frac{1\ \text{in.}}{2.54\ \text{cm}} \times \frac{1\ \text{ft}}{12\ \text{in.}} = \underline{\underline{33.8\ \text{ft}}}$$

If a well is 40 ft deep, the water cannot be raised in one stage by suction since 33.8 ft is the theoretical maximum height that is supported by the atmosphere.

**10-16.** 10.2 L

**10-18.** 978 mL

**10-19.** 67.9 torr

**10-22.** $V_{final}\ (V_f) = 15$   $V_{initial}\ (V_i)\ \dfrac{V_f}{V_i} = \dfrac{P_i}{P_f};$

$$\frac{15\ V_i}{V_i} = \frac{0.950\ \text{atm}}{P_f}\quad P_f = 0.950\ \text{atm} \times 15 = 14.3\ \text{atm}$$

**10-23.**

No, the graph is not linear.

**10-24.** 1.94 L

**10-26.** 77°C

**10-28.** $2.60 \times 10^4$ L

**10-29.** 341 K (68°C)

**10-31.** 2.94 atm

**10-32.** 191 K − 273 = −82°C

**10-34.** 596 K (323°C)

**10-35.** 30.2 lb/in.$^2$

**10-38.** (a) and (d)

**10-40.** Exp. 1, $T$ increases; Exp. 2, $V$ decreases; Exp. 3, $P$ increases; Exp. 4, $T$ increases

**10-42.** 1.24 atm

**10-43.** 76.8 L

**10-45.** 88.5 K = −185°C

**10-48.** 258 K(−15°C)

**10-49.** 409 mL

**10-50.** 1.70 L

**10-51.** Let $x$ = total moles needed in the expanded balloon.

$$188 \text{ L} \times \frac{x}{8.40 \text{ mol}} = 275 \text{ L} \quad x = 12.3 \text{ mol}$$

12.3 − 8.4 = 3.9 mol must be added.

**10-53.**

$$n_2 = 2.50 \times 10^{-3} \text{mol} \times \frac{164 \text{ mL}}{75.0 \text{ mL}} = 5.47 \times 10^{-3} \text{mol}$$

$$(5.47 \times 10^{-3}) - (2.50 \times 10^{-3}) = 2.97 \times 10^{-3} \text{ mol}$$

$$2.97 \times 10^{-3} \text{ mol N}_2 \times \frac{28.02 \text{ g N}_2}{\text{mol N}_2} = 0.0832 \text{ g N}_2$$

**10-55.** 98°C

**10-57.** 13.0 g

**10-58.** 589 torr

**10-60.** 3.35 g

**10-62.** $n = 1.0 \times 10^6$ mol of gas in the balloon. 8800 lb He or 64,000 lb air

Lifting power with He = 64,000 − 8800 = 55,000 lb

Lifting power with H$_2$ = 64,000 − 4000 = 60,000 lb

Helium is a noncombustible gas whereas hydrogen forms an explosive mixture with O$_2$.

**10-64.** 762 torr

**10-66.** 6.8 torr

**10-69.** $P_{\text{N}_2} = 756$ torr; $P_{\text{O}_2} = 84.0$ torr; $P_{\text{SO}_2} = 210$ torr

**10-70.** 731 torr

**10-72.** $P_{\text{N}_2} = 300$ torr; $P_{\text{O}_2} = 85$ torr $\times \dfrac{4.00 \text{ L}}{2.00 \text{ L}} = 170$ torr;

$P_{\text{CO}_2} = 225$ torr; $P_{\text{tot}} = 695$ torr;

**10-73.** $P_A = 0.550$ atm; $P_B = 0.300$ atm;

**10-75.** 7.63 L

**10-77.** 112 L

**10-79.** $1.39 \times 10^{-3}$ g

**10-80.** 1.24 g/L

**10-82.** 34.0 g/mol

**10-84.** $1.00 \text{ L} \times \dfrac{273 \text{ K}}{298 \text{ K}} \times \dfrac{1.20 \text{ atm}}{1.00 \text{ atm}} = 1.10 \text{ L (STP)}$

$$\frac{3.60 \text{ g}}{1.10 \text{ L}} = 3.27 \text{ g/L (STP)}$$

**10-85.** Find moles of N$_2$ in 1 L at 500 torr and 22°C using the ideal gas law. $n = 0.272$ mol N$_2$, mass = 0.762 g N$_2$ Density = 0.762 g/L (500 torr and 22°C)

**10-87.** 25.7 L CO$_2$ (STP)

**10-88.** Vol. O$_2 \longrightarrow$ mol O$_2 \longrightarrow$ mol Mg $\longrightarrow$ g Mg

$$5.80 \text{ L O}_2 \times \frac{1 \text{ mol O}_2}{22.4 \text{ L O}_2} \times \frac{2 \text{ mol Mg}}{1 \text{ mol O}_2} \times \frac{24.31 \text{ g Mg}}{\text{mol Mg}}$$

$$= 12.6 \text{ g Mg}$$

**10-90.** 3.47 L

**10-92.** (a) g C$_4$H$_{10} \longrightarrow$ mol C$_4$H$_{10} \longrightarrow$ mol CO$_2 \longrightarrow$ Vol CO$_2$

$$85.0 \text{ g C}_4\text{H}_{10} \times \frac{1 \text{ mol C}_4\text{H}_{10}}{58.12 \text{ g C}_4\text{H}_{10}} \times \frac{8 \text{ mol CO}_2}{2 \text{ mol C}_4\text{H}_{10}} \times$$

$$\frac{22.4 \text{ L}}{\text{mol CO}_2} = 131 \text{ L}$$

(b) 96.1 L O$_2$ (c) 124 L CO$_2$

**10-93.** 2080 kg Zr (2.29 tons)

**10-95.** $n_{\text{O}_2} = 1.46$ mol O$_2$ $\quad 1.46 \text{ mol O}_2 \times \dfrac{1 \text{ mol CO}_2}{2 \text{ mol O}_2} =$

0.730 mol CO$_2$ $V = 12.0$ L CO$_2$

**10-96.** Force = $12.0 \text{ cm}^2 \times 15.0 \text{ cm} \times \dfrac{13.6 \text{ g}}{\text{cm}^3} = 2450$ g

$$P = \frac{2450 \text{ g}}{12.0 \text{ cm}^2} = 204 \text{ g/cm}^2$$

$$1 \text{ atm} = 76.0 \text{ cm} \times \frac{13.6 \text{ g}}{\text{cm}^3} = 1030 \text{ g/cm}^2$$

$$204 \text{ g/cm}^2 \times \frac{1 \text{ atm}}{1030 \text{ g/cm}^2} = 0.198 \text{ atm}$$

**10-98.** $n = 0.0573$ mol $\quad \dfrac{8.37 \text{ g}}{0.0573 \text{ mol}} = 146 \text{ g/mol}$

**10-99.** Empirical formula = CH$_2$ molar mass = 41.9 g/mol

molecular formula = C$_3$H$_6$

**10-101.** $n_{\text{tot}} = 0.265$ mol O$_2$ + 0.353 mol N$_2$ +

0.160 mol CO$_2$ = 0.778 mol of gas

$V = 6.92$ L

$$P_{\text{O}_2} = \frac{0.265}{0.778} \times 2.86 \text{ atm} = 0.974 \text{ atm}$$

$P_{\text{N}_2} = 1.30$ atm $\qquad P_{\text{CO}_2} = 0.59$ atm

**10-102.** $n = 5 \times 10^{-20}$ mol $\quad P = 4 \times 10^{-17}$ atm

**10-103.** 19.6 L/mol density of CO$_2$ = 2.25 g/L

**10-104.** Density $= \dfrac{\text{mass}}{\text{V}} = \dfrac{P \times MM}{RT} = 0.525$ g/L (hot air)

density at STP = 1.29 g/L

0.525/1.29 = 0.41 (Hot air is less than half as dense as air at STP.)

**10-106.** 0.0103 mol of H$_3$BCO produces 0.0412 mol of gaseous products; $V = 1.12$ L (products at 25°C and 0.900 atm)

**10-108.** $2Al(s) + 3F_2(g) \longrightarrow 2AlF_3(s)$

original $\underline{F_2 = 0.310 \text{ mol } F_2}$

leftover $F_2 = 0.0921$ mol

$0.310 - 0.092 = 0.218$ mol $F_2$ reacts forming $\underline{12.2 \text{ g AlF}_3}$

**10-110.** 135 L

**10-112.** 0.763 mol $H_2O$ in the ice. V (of vapor) = $\underline{645 \text{ L}}$

**10-113.** $9.81 \times 10^{-4}$ mol $NH_3$ produces 11.0 mL $N_2H_4$

**10-115.** Empirical formula = $NO_2$

**(2)** Find molar mass of product compound.

$$n = \frac{PV}{RT} = \frac{\dfrac{715 \text{ torr}}{760 \text{ torr/atm}} \times 1.05 \text{ L}}{0.0821 \dfrac{\text{L} \cdot \text{atm}}{\text{K} \cdot \text{mol}} \times 273 \text{ K}} = 0.0441 \text{ mol}$$

$$\text{Molar mass} = \frac{2.03 \text{ g}}{0.0441 \text{ mol}} = 46.0 \text{ g/mol}$$

**(3)** Since one compound decomposes to one other compound, the reactant compound must have the same empirical formula as the product compound. Since the empirical mass of $NO_2$ = 46.01 g/emp unit, then the product must be $NO_2$(MM = 46.0 g/mol). Since 0.0220 mol of reactant form 0.0441 mol of product (1:2 ratio), the reaction must be

$$N_2O_4(l) \longrightarrow 2NO_2(g)$$

**10-117.** $6Li(s) + N_2(g) \longrightarrow 2Li_3N(s)$

$3Mg(s) + N_2(g) \longrightarrow Mg_3N_2(s)$

10.8 mol $N_2$ reacts with $\underline{450 \text{ g Li}}$ or $\underline{788 \text{ g Mg}}$

**CHAPTER 11**

**11-1.** Since gas molecules are far apart, they travel a comparatively large distance between collisions. Liquid molecules, on the other hand, are close together so do not travel far between collisions. The farther molecules travel, the faster they mix.

**11-3.** Both the liquid molecules and food coloring molecules are in motion. Through constant motion and collisions the food coloring molecules eventually become dispersed.

**11-5.** Generally, solids have greater densities than liquids. (Ice and water are notable exceptions.) Since the molecules of a solid are held in fixed positions, more of them usually fit into the same volume compared to the liquid state. This is similar to being able to get more people into a room if they are standing still than if they are moving around.

**11-6.** $CH_4 < CCl_4 < GeCl_4$

**11-8.** All are nonpolar molecules with only London forces between molecules. The higher the molar mass, the greater the London forces and the more likely that the compound is a solid. $I_2$ is the heaviest and is a solid; $Cl_2$ is the lightest and is a gas.

**11-10.** If $H_2O$ were linear, the two equal bond dipoles would be exactly opposite and would therefore cancel. Hydrogen bonding can occur only when the molecule is polar.

**11-12.**

$NH_3$ molecules interact by hydrogen bonding.

**11-14.** (a) HBr  (b) $SO_2$  (f) CO

**11-17.** (a) HF  (c) $H_2NCl$  (d) $H_2O$  (f) HCOOH

**11-19.** (a) ion–ion  (b) hydrogen bonding plus London  (c) dipole–dipole plus London  (d) London only

**11-20.** $F_2 < HCl < HF < KF$

**11-23.** $CO_2$ is a nonpolar molecular compound. $SiO_2$ is a network solid.

**11-25.** $PbCl_2$ is most likely ionic ($Pb^{2+}$, $2Cl^-$), while the melting point of $PbCl_4$ indicates that it is a molecular compound.

**11-26.** Motor oil is composed of large molecules that increase viscosity. Motor oil also has a higher surface tension.

**11-28.** Water evaporates quickly on a hot day and thus lowers the air temperature.

**11-30.** The comparatively low boiling point of ethyl chloride indicates that it has a high vapor pressure at room temperature (25°C). In fact, it boils rapidly, cooling the skin to below the freezing point of water.

**11-32.** The ethyl ether. The higher the vapor pressure, the faster the liquid evaporates and the liquid cools.

**11-33.** Equilibrium refers to a state where opposing forces are balanced. In the case of a liquid in equilibrium with its vapor, it means that a molecule escaping to the vapor is replaced by one condensing to the liquid.

**11-35.** The substance is a gas at 1 atm and 75°C. It would boil at a temperature below 75 °C.

**11-38.** Ethyl alcohol boils at about 52°C at that altitude. At 10°C ethyl ether is a gas at that altitude.

**11-39.** Death Valley is below sea level. The atmospheric pressure is more than 1 atm so water boils above its normal boiling point.

**11-41.** Both exist as atoms with only London forces, but the higher atomic mass of argon accounts for its higher boiling point.

**11-43.** Figure 11-15 is not very precise; at 10°C the actual vapor pressure of water is 9.2 torr. Liquid water could theoretically exist but it would rapidly evaporate and be changed to ice by the cooling effect.

**11-44.** The hexane (75 torr) has the lower boiling point. It also probably has the lower heat of vaporization.

**11-46.** Molecular $O_2$ is heavier than Ne atoms and so has stronger intermolecular forces (London). $CH_3OH$ has hydrogen bonding, which would indicate a much higher heat of vaporization than the other two.

**11-47.** This is a comparatively high heat of fusion, so the melting point is probably also comparatively high.

**11-49.** This is a comparatively high boiling point, so the compound probably also has a high melting point.

**11-50.**

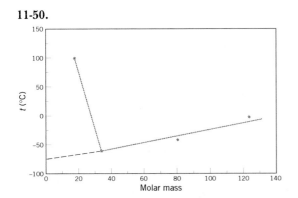

The boiling point of $H_2O$ would be about $-75°C$ without hydrogen bonding.

**11-53.** $7.07 \times 10^3$ J

**11-55.** 2.54 g $H_2O$, 1.64 g NaCl, 6.69 g benzene

**11-57.** 555 cal (ether), 2000 cal ($H_2O$) Water would be more effective. $1.30 \times 10^4$ J (13.0 kJ)

**11-59.** $NH_3$: $6.12 \times 10^5$ J  Freon: $7.25 \times 10^4$ J

On the basis of mass, ammonia is the more effective refrigerant.

**11-61.** Condensation: $62.2 \times 10^4$ J  Cooling: $8.63 \times 10^4$ J

Total $= \underline{7.08 \times 10^5 \text{ J}}$ (708 kJ)

**11-63.** $2.83 \times 10^4$ cal

**11-65.** heat ice: $132 \text{ g} \times 20.0°C \times \dfrac{0.492 \text{ cal}}{\text{g} \cdot °C} = 1300 \text{ cal}$

melt ice: $132 \text{ g} \times \dfrac{79.8 \text{ cal}}{\text{g}} = 10{,}500 \text{ cal}$

heat $H_2O$: $132 \text{ g} \times 100°C \times \dfrac{1.00 \text{ cal}}{\text{g} \cdot °C} = 13{,}200 \text{ cal}$

vap. $H_2O$: $132 \text{ g} \times \dfrac{540 \text{ cal}}{\text{g}} = 71{,}300 \text{ cal}$

Total $= \underline{96{,}300 \text{ cal} \text{ (96.3 kcal)}}$

**11-67.** Let $Y =$ the mass of the sample in grams. Then

$$\left(\frac{2260 \text{ J}}{\text{g}} \times Y\right) + \left(25.0°C \times Y \times \frac{4.18 \text{ J}}{\text{g} \cdot °C}\right) = 28{,}400 \text{ J}$$

$Y = \underline{12.0 \text{ g}}$

**11-69.** 18°C

**11-70. (b)** melting  **(c)** boiling

**11-71.** The average kinetic energy of all molecules of water at the same temperature is the same regardless of the physical state.

**11-73.** Because $H_2O$ molecules have an attraction for each other, moving them apart increases the potential energy. Since the molecules in a gas at 100°C are farther apart than in a liquid at the same temperature, the potential energy of the gas molecules is greater.

**11-74.** The water does not become hotter, but it will boil faster.

**11-76.**

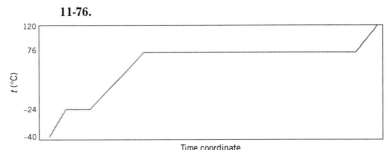

Time coordinate
The time of boiling is over ten times longer than the time of melting

**11-78.** $C_2H_5NH_2$: 17°C, hydrogen bonding

$CH_3OCH_3$: $-25°C$, dipole–dipole (polar)

$CO_2$: $-78°C$, London forces only (nonpolar)

**11-79.** $SF_6$ is a molecular compound and SnO is an ionic compound (i.e., $Sn^{2+}$, $O^{2-}$). All ionic compounds are found as solids at room temperature because of the strong ion–ion forces.

**11-81.** There is hydrogen bonding in $CH_3OH$. Hydrogen bonding is a considerably stronger attraction than ordinary dipole–dipole forces. The stronger the attractions the higher the boiling point.

**11-83.** $SiH_4$ is nonpolar. $PH_3$ and $H_2S$ are both polar but $H_2S$ is more polar with more and stronger dipole–dipole attractions.

**11-85.** Carbon monoxide is polar, whereas nitrogen is not. The added dipole–dipole attraction in CO may account for the slightly higher boiling point.

**11-87.** $2000 \text{ lb} \times \dfrac{453.6 \text{ g}}{\text{lb}} \times \dfrac{266 \text{ J}}{\text{g}} = 2.41 \times 10^8 \text{ J}$

Heating 1 g of $H_2O$ from 25.0°C to 100.0°C and the vaporizing the water requires

$(75.0°C \times 4.184 \text{ J/}°C) + 2260 \text{ J} = 2.57 \times 10^3 \text{ J/g } H_2O$

$\dfrac{2.41 \times 10^8 \text{ J}}{2.57 \times 10^3 \text{ J/g } H_2O} = 9.38 \times 10^4 \text{ g } H_2O = \underline{93.8 \text{ kg } H_2O}$

$= 9.38 \times 10^4 \text{ g } H_2O = \underline{93.8 \text{ kg } H_2O}$

**11-88.** V = 100 L, T = 34 + 273 = 307 K,

$P(H_2O) = 0.700 \times 39.0 \text{ torr} = 27.3 \text{ torr}$

Use the ideal gas law to find moles of water.

$$n = \frac{PV}{RT} = \frac{\dfrac{27.3 \text{ torr}}{760 \text{ torr/atm}} \times 100 \text{ L}}{0.0821 \dfrac{\text{L} \cdot \text{atm}}{\text{K} \cdot \text{mol}} \times 307 \text{ K}} = 0.143 \text{ mol}$$

$0.143 \text{ mol } H_2O \times \dfrac{18.02 \text{ g } H_2O}{\text{mol } H_2O} = \underline{2.58 \text{ g } H_2O}$

**11-90.** Calculate the heat required first to heat the water from 25°C to 100°C then to vaporize the water.

$3.10 \times 10^5$ J (to heat water), $2.260 \times 10^6$ J (to vaporize water) = 2570 kJ total

Cr: $\dfrac{2570 \text{ kJ}}{21.0 \text{ kJ/mol}} \times \dfrac{52.00 \text{ g Cr}}{\text{mol Cr}} \times \dfrac{1 \text{ kg}}{10^3 \text{ g}} = \underline{6.36 \text{ kg Cr}}$,

$\underline{8.81 \text{ kg Mo}}$, $\underline{13.5 \text{ kg W}}$

**11-91.** The element must be mercury (Hg) since it is a liquid at room temperature and must be a metal since it forms a +2 ion.

The 15.0 kJ represents the heat required to melt $X$ g of Hg, heat $X$ g from $-39°C$ to $357°C$ (i.e., $396°C$), and vaporize $X$ g of Hg.

$$(11.5 \text{ J/g} \times X) + \left[ 396°C \times 0.139 \frac{J}{g \, °C} \times X \right]$$

$$+ (29.5 \text{ J/g} \times X) = 15.00 \text{ kJ} \times \frac{10^3 \text{ J}}{\text{kJ}}$$

$$11.5 \text{ J/g } X + 55.0 \text{ J/g } X + 29.5 \text{ J/g } X = 15,000 \text{ J}$$

$$X = \underline{156 \text{ g Hg}}$$

**11-93.** Calculate the mass of water in the vapor state in the room at $-5°C$ (268 K) using the ideal gas law. 2.99 mol $H_2O$ (in vapor) = 53.9 g $H_2O$ (capacity of the room) Eventually, all of the 50.0 g should sublime since it is less than the room could contain.

**CHAPTER 12**

**12-1.** The ion–ion forces in the crystal hold the crystal together and resist the ion–dipole forces between water and the ions in the crystal. The ion–dipole forces remove the ions from the crystal.

**12-3.** Calcium bromide is soluble, lead (II) bromide is insoluble, benzene and water are immiscible, and alcohol and water are miscible.

**12-4.** (a) $LiF \longrightarrow Li^+(aq) + F^-(aq)$

(b) $(NH_4)_3PO_4 \longrightarrow 3NH_4^+(aq) + PO_4^{3-}(aq)$

(c) $Na_2CO_3 \longrightarrow 2Na^+(aq) + CO_3^{2-}(aq)$

(d) $Ca(C_2H_3O_2)_2 \longrightarrow Ca^{2+}(aq) + 2C_2H_3O_2^-(aq)$

**12-6.**

There is hydrogen bonding between solute and solvent.

**12-8.** At $10°C$, $Li_2SO_4$ is the most soluble; at $70°C$, KCl is the most soluble.

**12-10.** (a) unsaturated    (b) supersaturated

(c) saturated    (d) unsaturated

**12-12.** A specific amount of $Li_2SO_4$ will precipitate unless the solution becomes supersaturated.

$$\left[ 500 \text{ g } H_2O \times \frac{35 \text{ g}}{100 \text{ g } H_2O} \right] - \left( 500 \text{ g } H_2O \times \frac{28 \text{ g}}{100 \text{ g } H_2O} \right)$$

$$= \underline{35 \text{ g } Li_2SO_4 \text{ (precipitate)}}$$

**12-13.** 1.49%

**12-15.** 0.375 mol NaOH

**12-17.** 30 g $KNO_3$

**12-18.** 8.81% NaOH

**12-19.** 100 ppm

**12-21.** $8.3 \times 10^7$ L

**12-23.** 0.542 M

**12-24.** (a) 0.873 M    (b) 1.40 M    (c) 12.4 L    (d) 41.4 g
(e) 0.294 M    (f) 0.024 mol    (g) 307 mL    (h) 49.1 g
(i) 2.00 mL

**12-28.** $1.17 \times 10^{-3}$ M

**12-29.** $Ba^{2+}$: 0.166 M    $OH^-$: 0.332 M

**12-31.** 1.84 M

**12-33.** 1.32 g/mL

**12-34.** 0.833 L

**12-36.** Slowly add 313 mL of the 0.800 M NaOH to about 500 mL of water in a 1-L volumetric flask. Dilute to the 1-L mark with water.

**12-38.** 0.140 M

**12-39.** 720 mL

**12-41.** 2.86 mL

**12-42.** Find the total moles and the total volume.

$n = V \times M = 0.150 \, L \times 0.250 \text{ mol/}L = 0.0375 \text{ mol}$ (solution 1)

$n = V \times M = 0.450 \, L \times 0.375 \text{ mol/}L = 0.169 \text{ mol}$ (solution 2)

$n_{tot} = 0.206 \text{ mol} \qquad V_{tot} = 0.600 \text{ L}$

$\dfrac{n}{V} = \dfrac{0.206 \text{ mol}}{0.600 \text{ L}} = \underline{0.343 \text{ M}}$

**12-43.** $0.500 \, L \times \dfrac{0.250 \text{ mol KOH}}{L} \times \dfrac{1 \text{ mol Cr(OH)}_3^-}{3 \text{ mol KOH}} \times$

$\dfrac{103.0 \text{ g Cr(OH)}_3}{\text{mol Cr(OH)}_3^-} = \underline{4.29 \text{ g Cr(OH)}_3}$

**12-45.** 146 g $BaSO_4$

**12-46.** 4.08 L

**12-48.** 0.653 L

**12-50.** 0.864 M

**12-52.** 0.994 M

**12-54.** NaOH is the limiting reactant, producing 1.75 g of $Mg(OH)_2$.

**12-56.** An aqueous solution of AB is a good conductor of electricity. AB is dissociated into ions such as $A^+$ and $B^-$. A solution of AC is a weak conductor of electricity, which means that AC is only partially dissociated into ions: i.e., $AC \rightleftharpoons A^+ + C^-$. A solution of AD is a nonconductor of electricity because it is present as undissociated molecules in solution.

**12-58.** 1 mole of NaBr has a mass of 102.9 g, 1 molar NaBr is a solution containing 102.9 g of NaBr per liter of solution, and 1 molal NaBr is a solution containing 102.9 g of NaBr per kilogram of solvent.

**12-59.** 2.50 $m$ (The molality is the same in both solvents since the mass of solvent is the same.)

**12-61.** 15.8 g NaOH

**12-63.** $-0.37°C$

**12-65.** The salty water removes water from the cells of the skin by osmosis. After a prolonged period, a person would dehydrate and become thirsty.

**12-68.** We can concentrate a dilute solution by boiling away some solvent if the solute is not volatile. Reverse osmosis can also be used to concentrate a solution if pressure greater than the osmotic pressure is applied on a concentrated solution separated from the solvent by a semipermeable membrane. As the solution becomes more concentrated, the osmotic pressure becomes greater, and the corresponding pressure that is applied must be increased.

**12-69.** 1.00 $m$

**12-71.** 870 g glycol

**12-72.** 101.4°C

**12-74.** 2.9 $m$

**12-77.** $-14.5°C$

**12-79.** HCl is a strong electrolyte that produces two particles (ions) for each mole of HCl that dissolves. HF is a weak electrolyte that is essentially present as nonionized molecules in solution.

**12-82. (a)** $-5.8°C$   **(b)** $-6.4°C$   **(c)** $-5.0°C$

**12-83.** Dissolve the mixture in 100 g of $H_2O$ and heat to over 45°C. Cool to 0°C where the solution is saturated with about 10 g of $KNO_3$ and about 25 g of KCl. $50 - 25 = 25$ g of KCl precipitates.

**12-85.** 90.9% $H_2O$; 3.03% salt; 6.06% sugar

**12-87.** 0.10 mol of $Ag^+$ reacts with 0.10 mol of $Cl^-$, leaving 0.05 mol of $Cl^-$ in 1.0 L of solution. $[Cl^-] = 0.05$ M

**12-89.** $0.225 \, \cancel{L} \times \dfrac{0.196 \, \cancel{\text{mol HCl}}}{\cancel{L}} \times \dfrac{1 \, \text{mol M}}{2 \, \cancel{\text{mol HCl}}}$
$$= 0.0221 \, \text{mol M}$$

$$\dfrac{1.44 \, \text{g}}{0.0221 \, \text{mol}} = \underline{65.2 \, \text{g/mol (Zn)}}$$

**12-91.** molality $= 0.426 \, m$   molar mass $= 60.1$ g/mol
empirical formula $= CH_4N$   molecular formula $= C_2H_8N_2$

**12-93.** 0.30 $m$ sugar $< 0.12 \, m$ KCl (0.24 $m$ ions) $< 0.05 \, m$ CrCl$_3$ (0.20 $m$ ions) $< 0.05 \, m$ K$_2$CO$_3$ (0.15 $m$ ions) $<$ pure water.

**12-95.** n(hydroxide) $= 0.0584$ mol

n($H_2$) $= 0.0292$ mol $H_2$

$$\dfrac{0.0584}{0.0292} = 2(2 \, \text{mol hydroxide: 1 mol } H_2)$$

Balanced Equations:

$$2Na(s) + 2H_2O(l) \longrightarrow 2NaOH(aq) + H_2(g)$$
$$(2 \, \text{mol sodium:1 mol } H_2)$$

$$Ca(s) + 2H_2O(l) \longrightarrow Ca(OH)_2(aq) + H_2(g)$$
$$(1 \, \text{mol calcium:1 mol } H_2)$$

The answer is sodium since it produces the correct ratio of hydrogen.

**12-96.** 2.91 L

**12-98.** 8.60 L

**12-100.** The formula must be $PCl_3$. The Lewis structure shows the structure to be trigonal pyramidal.

The reaction is $PCl_3(g) + 3H_2O \longrightarrow H_3PO_3(aq) + 3HCl(aq)$

$\underline{0.404 \, \text{M HCl}}$

**12-102.** $(2Na^+S^{2-})$ $10.0 \, \cancel{\text{g Na}_2\text{S}} \times \dfrac{1 \, \text{mol Na}_2\text{S}}{78.05 \, \cancel{\text{g Na}_2\text{S}}}$
$$= 0.128 \, \text{mol Na}_2\text{S}$$

$$\Delta T = 1.86 \times \dfrac{\dfrac{0.128 \, \text{mol}}{100 \, \text{g}}}{1000 \, \text{g/kg}} \times 3 \, \text{mol ions/mol Na}_2\text{S}$$
$$= 7.14°C \, \text{change}$$

The answer is $Na_2S$ since it would have a freezing point of $-7.14°C$.

**12-104.** $\Delta T = K_f m$   $1.15°C = 1.86 \times \dfrac{0.806}{1.00 + X}$

Solving for $X$, $X = 0.30$ kg $0.30$ kg $= 300$ g $=$
$$\underline{300 \, \text{mL of water added.}}$$

CHAPTER 13

**13-1. (a)** $HNO_3$, nitric acid   **(b)** $HNO_2$, nitrous acid
   **(c)** $HClO_3$, chloric acid   **(d)** $H_2SO_3$, sulfurous acid

**13-3. (a)** CsOH, cesium hydroxide   **(b)** $Sr(OH)_2$, strontium hydroxide   **(c)** $Al(OH)_3$, aluminum hydroxide
   **(d)** $Mn(OH)_3$, manganese(III) hydroxide

**13-5. (a)** $HNO_3 + H_2O \longrightarrow H_3O^+ + NO_3^-$
   **(b)** $CsOH \longrightarrow Cs^+ + OH^-$
   **(c)** $Ba(OH)_2 \longrightarrow Ba^{2+} + 2OH^-$
   **(d)** $HBr + H_2O \longrightarrow H_3O^+ + Br^-$

**13-7.**

| Acid | Conjugate base | | Acid | Conjugate base |
|------|------|------|------|------|
| **(a)** $HNO_3$ | $NO_3^-$ | | **(d)** $CH_4$ | $CH_3^-$ |
| **(b)** $H_2SO_4$ | $HSO_4^-$ | | **(e)** $H_2O$ | $OH^-$ |
| **(c)** $HPO_4^{2-}$ | $PO_4^{3-}$ | | **(f)** $NH_3$ | $NH_2^-$ |

**13-9. (a)** $HClO_4$, $ClO_4^-$ and $H_2O$, $OH^-$
   **(b)** $HSO_4^-$, $SO_4^{2-}$ and $HClO$ and $ClO^-$
   **(c)** $H_2O$, $OH^-$ and $NH_3$, $NH_2^-$
   **(d)** $NH_4^+$, $NH_3$ and $H_3O^+$, $H_2O$

**13-12. (a)** $NH_3 + H_2O \longrightarrow NH_4^+ + OH^-$
   $B_1$ $A_1$ $A_2$ $B_2$

   **(b)** $N_2H_4 + H_2O \longrightarrow N_2H_5^+ + OH^-$
   $B_1$ $A_1$ $A_2$ $B_2$

   **(c)** $HS^- + H_2O \longrightarrow H_2S + OH^-$
   $B_1$ $A_1$ $A_2$ $B_2$

**(d)** $H^- + H_2O \longrightarrow H_2 + OH^-$

$\underset{B_1}{\phantom{H^-}} \quad \underset{A_1}{\phantom{H_2O}}$

$\underset{A_2}{\phantom{H^-}} \qquad \underset{B_2}{\phantom{H_2O}}$

**(e)** $F^- + H_2O \longrightarrow HF + OH^-$

$\underset{B_1}{\phantom{F^-}} \quad \underset{A_1}{\phantom{H_2O}}$

$\underset{A_2}{\phantom{F^-}} \qquad \underset{B_2}{\phantom{H_2O}}$

**13-13.** base: $HS^- + H_3O^+ \Longrightarrow H_2S + H_2O$

acid: $HS^- + OH^- \Longrightarrow S^{2-} + H_2O$

**13-16.** The information indicates that HBr is a strong acid. The $Br^-$ ion, however, would be a very weak base in water.

**13-18. (a)** $HNO_3 + H_2O \longrightarrow H_3O^+ + NO_3^-$

**(b)** $HNO_2 + H_2O \Longrightarrow H_3O^+ + NO_2^-$

**(c)** $HClO_3 + H_2O \Longrightarrow H_3O^+ + ClO_3^-$

**(d)** $H_2SO_3 + H_2O \Longrightarrow H_3O^+ + HSO_3^-$

**13-20.** $(CH_3)_2NH + H_2O \Longrightarrow (CH_3)_2NH_2^+ + OH^-$

**13-22.** HX is a weak acid. The concentration of $H_3O^+$ must equal the concentration of the HX that ionized.

$$\frac{0.010}{0.100} \times 100\% = \underline{10\% \text{ ionized}}$$

**13-24.** $[H_3O^+] = 0.55 \text{ M}$

**13-25.** $[H_3O^+] = 0.030 \times 0.55 = 0.017 \text{ M}$

**13-27.** From the first ionization: $[H_3O^+] = 0.354$ M Of that, 25% undergoes further ionization.

$0.25 \times 0.354 = 0.089$ M $[H_3O^+]$

from the second ionization.

The total $[H_3O^+] = 0.354 + 0.089 = \underline{0.443 \text{ M}}$

**13-28.** $\dfrac{0.050}{1.0} \times 100\% = \underline{5.0\% \text{ ionized}}$

**13-30.** The conjugate acid of $HSO_4^-$ is $H_2SO_4$. This is a strong acid so it completely ionizes in water. Thus it cannot exist in the molecular form in water.

**13-31. (a)** acid **(b)** salt **(c)** acid **(d)** acid salt **(e)** salt **(f)** base

**13-33. (a)** $HNO_3 + NaOH \longrightarrow NaNO_3 + H_2O$

**(b)** $2HI + Ca(OH)_2 \longrightarrow CaI_2 + 2H_2O$

**(c)** $HClO_2 + KOH \longrightarrow KClO_2 + H_2O$

**13-35. (a)** $H^+(aq) + NO_3^-(aq) + Na^+(aq) + OH^-(aq) \longrightarrow$
$Na^+(aq) + NO_3^-(aq) + H_2O(l)$

$H^+(aq) + OH^-(aq) \longrightarrow H_2O(l)$ (net ionic)

**(b)** $2H^+(aq) + 2I^-(aq) + Ca^{2+}(aq) + 2OH^-(aq) \longrightarrow$
$Ca^{2+}(aq) + 2I^-(aq) + 2H_2O(l)$

$H^+(aq) + OH^-(aq) \longrightarrow H_2O(l)$ (net ionic)

**(c)** $HClO_2(aq) + K^+(aq) + OH^-(aq) \longrightarrow$
$K^+(aq) + ClO_2^-(aq) + H_2O(l)$

$HClO_2(aq) + OH^-(aq) \longrightarrow ClO_2^-(aq) + H_2O(l)$
(net ionic)

**13-37.** $H_2C_2O_4(aq) + 2NH_3(aq) \longrightarrow (NH_4)_2C_2O_4(aq)$

$H_2C_2O_4(aq) + 2NH_3(aq) \longrightarrow 2NH_4^+(aq) +$
$C_2O_4^{2-}(aq)$

Net ionic equation is the same as the total ionic equation.

**13-39. (a)** KOH and $HClO_3$ **(b)** $Al(OH)_3$ and $H_2SO_3$

**(c)** $Ba(OH)_2$ and $HNO_2$ **(d)** $NH_3$ and $HNO_3$

**13-41. (a)** $2HBr + Ca(OH)_2 \longrightarrow CaBr_2 + 2H_2O$

**(b)** $2HClO_2 + Sr(OH)_2 \longrightarrow Sr(ClO_2)_2 + 2H_2O$

**(c)** $2H_2S + Ba(OH)_2 \longrightarrow Ba(HS)_2 + 2H_2O$

**(d)** $H_2S + 2LiOH \longrightarrow Li_2S + 2H_2O$

**13-43.** $LiOH + H_2S \longrightarrow LiHS + H_2O$

$LiOH + LiHS \longrightarrow Li_2S + H_2O$

**13-44.** $H_2S(aq) + OH^-(aq) \longrightarrow HS^-(aq) + H_2O(l)$

$HS^-(aq) + OH^-(aq) \longrightarrow S^{2-}(aq) + H_2O(l)$

**13-47.** $H_2S + NaOH \longrightarrow NaHS + H_2O$

**13-50.** The system would not be at equilibrium if $[H_3O^+]$ $= [OH^-] = 10^{-2}$M. Therefore, $H_3O^+$ reacts with $OH^-$ until the concentration of each is reduced to $10^{-7}$ M. This is a neutralization reaction,

i.e., $H_3O^+ + OH^- \longrightarrow 2H_2O$

**13-51. (a)** $[H_3O^+] = \dfrac{K_w}{[OH^-]} = \dfrac{10^{-14}}{10^{-12}} = 10^{-2} \text{ M}$

**(b)** $[H_3O^+] = 10^{-15} \text{ M}$

**(c)** $[OH^-] = 5.0 \times 10^{-10} \text{ M}$

**13-53.** $[H_3O^+] = 0.0250$ M, $[OH^-] = 4.00 \times 10^{-13}$ M

**13-55. (a)** acidic **(b)** basic **(c)** acidic

**13-57. (a)** acidic **(b)** basic **(c)** acidic **(d)** basic

**13-59. (a)** 6.00 **(b)** 9.00 **(c)** 12.00 **(d)** 9.40 **(e)** 10.19

**13-61. (a)** pH = 4.0, pOH = 10.0 **(b)** pOH = 5.0, pH = 9.0

**(c)** pH = 1.70, pOH = 12.30 **(d)** pOH = 3.495, pH = 10.505

**13-63. (a)** $1.0 \times 10^{-3}$ M **(b)** $2.9 \times 10^{-4}$ M

**(c)** $1.0 \times 10^{-6}$ M **(d)** $2.4 \times 10^{-8}$ M

**(e)** $2.0 \times 10^{-13}$ M

**13-65.** For exercise **13-59: (a)** acidic **(b)** basic **(c)** basic **(d)** basic **(e)** basic

For exercise **13-63: (a)** acidic **(b)** acidic **(c)** acidic **(d)** basic **(e)** basic

**13-67.** pH = 5.0 (less acidic), pH = 2.0 (more acidic)

**13-69.** pH = 1.12

**13-71.** pH = 12.56

**13-72.** $[H_3O^+] = 0.100 \times 0.10 = 0.010 = 1.0 \times 10^{-2}$ M

pH = $\underline{2.00}$

**13-74. (a)** strongly acidic **(b)** strongly acidic **(c)** weakly acidic **(d)** strongly basic **(e)** neutral **(f)** weakly basic **(g)** weakly acidic **(h)** strongly acidic

**13-75.** Ammonia (pH $= 11.4$), eggs (pH $= 7.8$), rainwater ($[H_3O^+] = 2.0 \times 10^{-6}$ M, pH $= 5.70$), grape juice ($[OH^-] = 1.0 \times 10^{-10}$ M, pH $= 4.0$), vinegar ($[H_3O^+] = 2.5 \times 10^{-3}$ M, pH $= 2.60$), sulfuric acid (pOH $= 13.6$, pH $= 0.4$)

**13-78.** (b) $C_2H_3O_2^- + H_2O \rightleftharpoons HC_2H_3O_2 + OH^-$

    (c) $NH_3 + H_2O \rightleftharpoons NH_4^+ + OH^-$

**13-80.** (a) $K^+$ The cation of the strong base KOH.

    (d) $NO_3^-$ The conjugate base of the strong acid $HNO_3$.

    (e) $O_2$ dissolves in water without formation of ions.

**13-81.** (a) $HS^-$  (b) $H_3O^+$  (c) $OH^-$  (d) $(CH_3)_2NH$

**13-83.** (a) $F^- + H_2O \rightleftharpoons HF + OH^-$

    (b) $SO_3^{2-} + H_2O \rightleftharpoons HSO_3^- + OH^-$

    (c) $(CH_3)_2NH_2^+ + H_2O \rightleftharpoons (CH_3)_2NH + H_3O^+$

    (d) $HPO_4^{2-} + H_2O \rightleftharpoons H_2PO_4^- + OH^-$

    (e) $CN^- + H_2O \rightleftharpoons HCN + OH^-$

    (f) no hydrolysis (cation of a strong base)

**13-85.** $Ca(ClO)_2 \longrightarrow Ca^{2+}(aq) + 2ClO^-(aq)$

$ClO^-(aq) + H_2O \rightleftharpoons HClO(aq) + OH^-(aq)$

**13-87.** (a) neutral (neither ion hydrolyzes)

    (b) acidic (cation hydrolysis)

    (c) basic (anion hydrolysis)

    (d) neutral (neither ion hydrolyzes)

    (e) acidic (cation hydrolysis)

    (f) basic (anion hydrolysis)

**13-89.** $CaC_2(s) + 2H_2O(l) \longrightarrow$
$$C_2H_2(g) + Ca^{2+}(aq) + 2OH^-(aq)$$

**13-90.** cation: $NH_4^+ + H_2O \rightleftharpoons NH_3 + H_3O^+$

anion: $CN^- + H_2O \rightleftharpoons HCN + OH^-$

Since the solution is basic, the anion hydrolysis reaction must take place to a greater extent than the cation hydrolysis.

**13-92.** (a), (b), (e), (h), and (i) are buffer solutions.

**13-93.** There is no equilibrium when HCl dissolves in water. A reservoir of nonionized acid must be present to react with any strong base that is added. Likewise, the $Cl^-$ ion does not exhibit base behavior in water, so it cannot react with any $H_3O^+$ added to the solution.

**13-94.** $N_2H_4(aq) + H_2O \rightleftharpoons N_2H_5^+(aq) + OH^-(aq)$

    added $H_3O^+$: $H_3O^+ + N_2H_4 \longrightarrow N_2H_5^+ + H_2O$

    added $OH^-$: $OH^- + N_2H_5^+ \longrightarrow N_2H_4 + H_2O$

**13-96.** $HPO_4^{2-}(aq) + H_2O(l) \rightleftharpoons PO_4^{3-}(aq) + H_3O^+(aq)$

    added $H_3O^+$: $H_3O^+ + PO_4^{3-} \longrightarrow HPO_4^{2-} + H_2O$

    added $OH^-$: $OH^- + HPO_4^{2-} \longrightarrow PO_4^{3-} + H_2O$

**13-99.** (a) $Sr(OH)_2$  (b) $H_2SeO_4$  (c) $H_3PO_4$

    (d) $CsOH$  (e) $HNO_2$  (f) $HClO_3$

**13-101.** $CO_2(g) + LiOH(aq) \longrightarrow LiHCO_3(aq)$

**13-102.** $2LiNO_3(s)$

**13-103.** $Fe(s) + 2HI \longrightarrow FeI_2(aq) + H_2(g)$

**13-105.** $2HNO_3(aq) + Na_2SO_3(aq) \longrightarrow$
$$2NaNO_3(aq) + SO_2(g) + H_2O(l)$$

**13-107.** (a) $HCN + NH_3 \longrightarrow NH_4^+ + CN^-$

    (b) $NH_3 + H^- \longrightarrow H_2 + NH_2^-$

    (c) $HCO_3^- + NH_3 \longrightarrow NH_4^+ + CO_3^{2-}$

    (d) $NH_4^+Cl^- + Na^+NH_2^- \longrightarrow Na^+Cl^- + 2NH_3$

**13-108.** (a) $HCl + CH_3OH \longrightarrow CH_3OH_2^+ + Cl^-$

    (b) $CH_3OH + NH_2^- \longrightarrow NH_3 + CH_3O^-$

**13-110.** (a) acidic: $H_2S + H_2O \rightleftharpoons H_3O^+ + HS^-$

    (b) basic: $ClO^- + H_2O \rightleftharpoons HClO + OH^-$

    (c) neutral

    (d) basic: $NH_3 + H_2O \rightleftharpoons NH_4^+ + OH^-$

    (e) acidic: $N_2H_5^+ + H_2O \rightleftharpoons N_2H_4 + H_3O^+$

    (f) basic: $Ba(OH)_2 \longrightarrow Ba^{2+} + 2OH^-$

    (g) neutral

    (h) basic: $NO_2^- + H_2O \rightleftharpoons HNO_2 + OH^-$

    (i) acidic: $H_2SO_3 + H_2O \rightleftharpoons H_3O^+ + HSO_3^-$

    (j) acidic: $Cl_2O_3 + H_2O \longrightarrow 2HClO_2$;
$$HClO_2 + H_2O \rightleftharpoons H_3O^+ + ClO_2^-$$

**13-112.** LiOH, strongly basic, pH $= 13.0$; $SrBr_2$, neutral, pH $= 7.0$; KClO, weakly basic, pH $= 10.2$; $NH_4Cl$, weakly acidic, pH $= 5.2$; HI, strongly acidic, pH $= 1.0$

When pH $= 1.0$, $[H_3O^+] = 0.10$ M. If HI is completely ionized, its initial concentration must be 0.10 M.

**13-114.** 8.2 kg of $H_2SO_4$

**13-115.** pH $= 0.553$ (con) pH $= 1.113$ (dilute)

**13-117.** 0.024 mol of HCl remains after neutralization pH $= 1.62$

**13-119.** 0.025 mol $Ca(OH)_2$ remaining in 1.00 L

$$[OH^-] = 0.025 \; \overline{mol \; Ca(OH)_2} \times \frac{2 \; mol \; OH^-}{\overline{mol \; Ca(OH)_2}}$$

$$= 0.050 \; mol/L \quad pOH = 1.30 \quad \underline{pH = 12.70}$$

**CHAPTER 14**

**14-1.** (a) Pb $+4$, O $-2$  (b) P $+5$, O $-2$  (c) C $-1$, H $+1$
    (d) N $-2$, H $+1$  (e) Li $+1$, H $-1$  (f) B $+3$, Cl $-1$
    (g) Rb $+1$, Se $-2$  (h) Bi $+3$, S $-2$

**14-3.** (a) Li,  (e) K, and  (g) Rb

**14-5.** $+3$

**14-6.** (a) P $= +5$  (b) C $= +3$  (c) Cl $= +7$  (d) Cr $= +6$
    (e) S $= +6$  (f) N $= +5$  (g) Mn $= +7$

**14-7.** (a) S $= +6$  (b) Co $= +3$  (c) U $= +6$  (d) N $= +5$
    (e) Cr $= +6$  (f) Mn $= +6$

**14-9.** (a), (c), and (f)

**14-10.** (a) oxidation  (b) reduction  (c) oxidation
    (d) reduction  (e) reduction

**14-12.**

| Reactant Oxidized | Product of Oxidation | Reactant Reduced | Product of Reduction | Oxidizing Agent | Reducing Agent |
|---|---|---|---|---|---|
| $Br^-$ | $Br_2$ | $MnO_2$ | $Mn^{2+}$ | $MnO_2$ | $Br^-$ |
| $CH_4$ | $CO_2$ | $O_2$ | $CO_2$, $H_2O$ | $O_2$ | $CH_4$ |
| $Fe^{2+}$ | $Fe^{3+}$ | $MnO_4^-$ | $Mn^{2+}$ | $MnO_4^-$ | $Fe^{2+}$ |

**14-13.**

| Reactant Oxidized | Product of Oxidation | Reactant Reduced | Product of Reduction | Oxidizing Agent | Reducing Agent |
|---|---|---|---|---|---|
| $Al$ | $AlO_2^-$ | $H_2O$ | $H_2$ | $H_2O$ | $Al$ |
| $Mn^{2+}$ | $MnO_4^-$ | $Cr_2O_7^{2-}$ | $Cr^{3+}$ | $Cr_2O_7^{2-}$ | $Mn^{2+}$ |

**14-16.**

(a) $\overset{-3}{N}H_3 + 5O_2 \longrightarrow 4\overset{+2}{N}O + 6H_2O$    $-5e^- \times 4 = -20e^-$

$\overset{0}{O}_2 \cdots \overset{-2}{} \quad +4e^- \times 5 = +20e^-$

(b) $Sn + 4HNO_3 \longrightarrow SnO_2 + 4NO_2 + 2H_2O$

$-4e^- \times 1 = -4e^-$   $\overset{0}{Sn} \longrightarrow \overset{+4}{}$

$+5 \quad +4 \quad +1e^- \times 4 = +4e^-$

(c) Before the number of electrons lost is calculated, notice that a temporary coefficient of "2" is needed for the $Na_2CrO_4$ in the products since there are 2 Cr's in $Cr_2O_3$ in the reactants.

$+2e^- \times 3 = +6e^-$

$Cr_2O_3 + 2Na_2CO_3 + 3KNO_3 \longrightarrow 2CO_2 + 2Na_2CrO_4 + 3KNO_2$

$\overset{+5}{} \quad \overset{+3}{}$

$\overset{+6}{} \quad \overset{+12}{} \quad -6e^- \times 1 = -6e^-$

$-4e^- \times 3 = -12e^-$

(d) $3Se + 2BrO_3^- + 3H_2O \longrightarrow 3H_2SeO_3 + 2Br^-$

$\overset{0}{} \quad \overset{+4}{}$

$\overset{+5}{} \quad \overset{-1}{} \quad +6e^- \times 2 = +12e^-$

**14-18.** (a) $2H_2O + Sn^{2+} \longrightarrow SnO_2 + 4H^+ + 2e^-$

(b) $2H_2O + CH_4 \longrightarrow CO_2 + 8H^+ + 8e^-$

(c) $e^- + Fe^{3+} \longrightarrow Fe^{2+}$

(d) $6H_2O + I_2 \longrightarrow 2IO_3^- + 12H^+ + 10e^-$

(e) $e^- + 2H^+ + NO_3^- \longrightarrow NO_2 + H_2O$

**14-20.** (a)

$$S^{2-} \longrightarrow S + 2e^- \quad \times 3$$
$$3e^- + 4H^+ + NO_3^- \longrightarrow NO + 2H_2O \quad \times 2$$
$$\overline{3S^{2-} + 8H^+ + 2NO_3^- \longrightarrow 3S + 2NO + 4H_2O}$$

(b) $2S_2O_3^{2-} + I_2 \longrightarrow S_4O_6^{2-} + 2I^-$

(c)
$$H_2O + SO_3^{2-} \longrightarrow SO_4^{2-} + 2H^+ + 2e^- \quad \times 3$$
$$6e^- + 6H^+ + ClO_3^- \longrightarrow Cl^- + 3H_2O \quad \times 1$$
$$\overline{3SO_3^{2-} + ClO_3^- \longrightarrow Cl^- + 3SO_4^{2-}}$$

(d) $2H^+ + 2Fe^{3+} + H_2O_2 \longrightarrow 2Fe^{3+} + 2H_2O$

(e) $AsO_4^{3-} + 2I^- + 2H^+ \longrightarrow I_2 + AsO_3^{3-} + H_2O$

(f) $4Zn + NO_3^- + 10H^+ \longrightarrow 4Zn^{2+} + NH_4^+ + 3H_2O$

**14-22.** (a) $2OH^- + SnO_2^{2-} \longrightarrow SnO_3^{2-} + H_2O + 2e^-$

(b) $6e^- + 4H_2O + 2ClO_2^- \longrightarrow Cl_2 + 8OH^-$

(c) $6OH^- + Si \longrightarrow SiO_3^{2-} + 3H_2O + 4e^-$

(d) $8e^- + 6H_2O + NO_3^- \longrightarrow NH_3 + 9OH^-$

**14-24.** (a) In acid solution:

$$4H_2O + S^{2-} + 4I_2 \longrightarrow SO_4^{2-} + 8I^- + 8H^+$$

Add $8OH^-$ to both sides and simplify.

$$8OH^- + S^{2-} + 4I_2 \longrightarrow SO_4^{2-} + 8I^- + 4H_2O$$

(b) $8OH^- + I^- + 8MnO_4^- \longrightarrow$
$$8MnO_4^{2-} + IO_4^- + 4H_2O$$

(c) $2H_2O + SnO_2^{2-} + BiO_3^- \longrightarrow$
$$SnO_3^{2-} + Bi(OH)_3 + OH^-$$

(d) $32OH^- + CrI_3 \longrightarrow$
$$CrO_4^{2-} + 3IO_4^- + 16H_2O + 27e^- \quad \times 2$$
$$2e^- + Cl_2 \longrightarrow 2Cl^- \quad \times 27$$
$$\overline{2CrI_3 + 64OH^- + 27Cl_2 \longrightarrow}$$
$$2CrO_4^{2-} + 6IO_4^- + 32H_2O + 54Cl^-$$

**14-26.** (a) $2H_2 + O_2 \longrightarrow 2H_2O$

(b)
$$H_2O_2 \longrightarrow O_2 + 2H^+ + 2e^-$$
$$2e^- + 2H^+ + H_2O_2 \longrightarrow 2H_2O$$
$$\overline{2H_2O_2 \longrightarrow O_2 + 2H_2O}$$

$$2OH^- + H_2O_2 \longrightarrow O_2 + 2H_2O + 2e^-$$
$$2e^- + H_2O_2 \longrightarrow 2OH^-$$
$$\overline{2H_2O_2 \longrightarrow O_2 + 2H_2O}$$

**14-27.** Reactions (a), (c), (e), and (f) are predicted to be favorable.

**14-29.** (a) no reaction

(b) $Br_2(aq) + Sn(s) \longrightarrow SnBr_2(aq)$

(c) no reaction

(d) $O_2(g) + 4H^+(aq) + 4Br^-(aq) \longrightarrow$
$$2Br_2(l) + 2H_2O(l)$$

(e) $3Br_2(l) + 2Al(s) \longrightarrow 2AlBr_3(s)$

**14-31.** (c) $2F_2(g) + 2H_2O(l) \longrightarrow 4HF(aq) + O_2(g)$

(e) $Mg(s) + 2H_2O(l) \longrightarrow Mg(OH)_2(s) + H_2(g)$

**14-33.** From Table 14-1:

$$Fe + 2H_2O \longrightarrow \text{no reaction}$$
$$Fe + 2H^+ \longrightarrow Fe^{2+} + H_2$$

Acid rain has a higher $H^+(aq)$ concentration, thus making the second reaction more likely.

**14-36.** $Zn(s)$ reacts at the anode and $MnO_2(s)$ reacts at the cathode. The total reaction is

$$Zn(s) + 2MnO_2(s) + 2H_2O(l) \longrightarrow$$
$$Zn(OH)_2(s) + 2MnO(OH)(s)$$

**14-38.** anode: $Cd(s) + 2OH^-(aq) \longrightarrow Cd(OH)_2(s) + 2e^-$

cathode: $NiO(OH)(s) + 2H_2O(l) + e^- \longrightarrow$
$$Ni(OH)_2(s) + OH^-(aq)$$

**14-40.** The spontaneous reaction is

$$Pb(NO_3)_2(aq) + Fe(s) \longrightarrow Fe(NO_3)_2(aq) + Pb(s)$$

anode: $Fe \longrightarrow Fe^2 + 2e^-$

cathode: $Pb^{2+} + 2e^- \longrightarrow Pb$

**14-41.** The Daniell cell is more powerful. The greater the separation between oxidizing and reducing agents as shown in Table 14-1, the more powerful is the cell.

**14-43.** $3Fe(s) + 2Cr^{3+}(aq) \longrightarrow 3Fe^{2+}(aq) + 2Cr(s)$

Zinc would spontaneously form a chromium coating as illustrated by the equation:

$$3Zn(s) + 2Cr^{3+}(aq) \longrightarrow 3Zn^{2+}(aq) + 2Cr(s)$$

**14-44.** Sodium reacts spontaneously with water since it is an active metal. The actual cathode reaction is

$$2H_2O + 2e^- \longrightarrow H_2 + 2OH^-$$

Elemental sodium is produced by electrolysis of the molten salt, NaCl.

**14-47.** The strongest oxidizing agent is reduced the easiest. Thus the reduction of $Ag^+$ to Ag occurs first. This procedure can be used to purify silver.

**14-48.** $K_3N$ (–3), $N_2H_4$ (–2), $NH_2OH$, (–1), $N_2$ (0), $N_2O$ (+1), NO (+2), $N_2O_3$ (+ 3), $N_2O_4$ (+4), $Ca(NO_3)_2$ (+5)

**14-49.** $Cd(s) + NiCl_2(aq) \longrightarrow Ni(s) + CdCl_2(aq)$

$Zn(s) + CdCl_2(aq) \longrightarrow Cd(s) + ZnCl_2(aq)$

These reactions indicate that $Cd^{2+}$ is a stronger oxidizing agent than $Zn^{2+}$ but weaker than $Ni^{2+}$. It appears about the same as $Fe^{2+}$.

**14-51.** The reactions that occur are

$$4Au^{3+} + 6H_2O \longrightarrow 4Au + 12H^+ + 3O_2$$

$$2Au + 3F_2 \longrightarrow 2AuF_3$$

These reactions and the fact that Au does not react with $Cl_2$ rank $Au^{3+}$ above $H^+$ and $Cl_2$ but below $F_2$.

**14-52.** $12H^+(aq) + 5Zn(s) + 2NO_3^-(aq) \longrightarrow$
$$5Zn^{2+}(aq) + N_2(g) + 6H_2O(l)$$

0.658 g $N_2$ requires <u>7.68 g Zn.</u>

**14-54.** $14H^+(aq) + 2NO_3^-(aq) + 3Cu_2O(s) \longrightarrow$
$$6Cu^{2+}(aq) + 2NO(g) + 7H_2O(l)$$

10.0 g of $Cu_2O$ produces <u>1.04 L of NO</u> measured at STP.

**14-56.** $7OH^-(aq) + 4Zn(s) + 6H_2O(l) + NO_3^-(aq) \longrightarrow$
$$NH_3(g) + 4Zn(OH)_4^{2-}(aq)$$

6.54 g of Zn produces <u>0.493 L of $NH_3$</u> at 27.0°C and 1.25 atm pressure.

**14-57.** (a) $MnO_4^- + 8H^+ + 5Fe^{2+} \longrightarrow$
$$5Fe^{3+} + Mn^{2+} + 4H_2O$$

(b) $2MnO_4^- + 16H^+ + 10Br^- \longrightarrow$
$$5Br_2 + 2Mn^{2+} + 8H_2O$$

(c) $2MnO_4^- + 16H^+ + 5C_2O_4^{2-} \longrightarrow$
$$10CO_2 + 2Mn^{2+} + 8H_2O$$

**14-58.** 179 mL

**14-59.** 306 mL

**CHAPTER 15**

**15-1.** Colliding molecules must have the proper orientation relative to each other at the time of the collision, and the colliding molecules must have the minimum kinetic energy for the particular reaction.

**15-3. (a)** As the temperature increases, the frequency of collisions between molecules increases, as does the average energy of the collisions. Both contribute to the increased rate of reaction.

**(b)** The cooking of eggs initiates a chemical reaction that occurs more slowly at lower temperatures.

**(c)** The average energy of colliding molecules at room temperature is not sufficient to initiate a reaction between $H_2$ and $O_2$.

**(d)** A higher concentration of oxygen increases the rate of combustion.

**(e)** When a solid is finely divided, a greater surface area is available for collisions with oxygen molecules. Thus it burns faster.

**(f)** The souring of milk is a chemical reaction that slows as the temperature drops. It takes several days in a refrigerator.

**(g)** The platinum is a catalyst. Since the activation energy in the presence of a catalyst is lower, the reaction can occur at a lower temperature.

**15-6.** The rate of the forward reaction was at a maximum at the beginning of the reaction; the rate of the reverse reaction was at a maximum at the point of equilibrium.

**15-7.** In many cases, reactions do not proceed directly to the right because other products are formed between the same reactants. For example, combustion may produce carbon monoxide as well as carbon dioxide.

**15-8.** Products are easier to form because the activation energy for the forward reaction is less than for the reverse reaction. This is true of all exothermic reactions. The system should come to equilibrium faster starting with pure reactants.

**15-10. (a)** right **(b)** left **(c)** left **(d)** right
**(e)** right **(f)** has no effect **(g)** yield decreases
**(h)** yield increases but rate of formation decreases

**15-12. (a)** increase **(b)** increase **(c)** decrease
**(d)** decrease **(e)** decrease **(f)** no effect

**15-14. (a)** Since there are the same number of moles of gas on both sides of the equation, pressure (or volume) has no effect on the point of equilibrium.

**(b)** decrease the amount of NO

**(c)** decrease the amount of NO

**15-15. (a)** $K_{eq} = \dfrac{[COCl_2]}{[CO][Cl_2]}$  **(b)** $K_{eq} = \dfrac{[CO_2][H_2]^4}{[CH_4][H_2O]^2}$

**(c)** $K_{eq} = \dfrac{[Cl_2]^2[H_2O]^2}{[HCl]^4[O_2]}$  **(d)** $K_{eq} = \dfrac{[CH_3Cl][HCl]}{[CH_4][Cl_2]}$

**15-17.** products

**15-19.** There will be an appreciable concentration of both reactants and products at equilibrium.

**15-20.** $K_{eq} = 0.34$

**15-21.** $K_{eq} = 49.2$

**15-23.**
$$K_{eq} = \frac{[CO_2][H_2]^4}{[CH_4][H_2O]^2} = \frac{(2.20/30.0)(4.00/30.0)^4}{(6.20/30.0)(3.00/30.0)^2} = 0.0112$$

**15-25.** (a) $[H_2] = [I_2] = 0.30$ mol/L

(b) $[H_2] = 0.30$ mol/L; $[I_2] = 0.50$ mol/L

(c) $[HI] = 0.40$ mol/L; $[I_2] = [H_2] = 0.10$ mol/L

(d) $K_{eq} = 0.063$ (e) $K_r = 16$.

This is a smaller value than that used in Table 15-1. This indicates that the equilibrium in this problem was established at a different temperature than that of Table 15-1.

**15-27.** (a) $[N_2]_{reacts} = 0.50 - 0.40 = 0.10$ mol/L

$$0.10 \text{ mol } N_2 \times \frac{3 \text{ mol } H_2}{1 \text{ mol } N_2} = 0.30 \text{ mol/L } H_2 \text{ (reacts)}$$

$[H_2]_{eq} = 0.50 - 0.30 = \underline{0.20 \text{ mol/L}}$

$$0.10 \text{ mol } N_2 \times \frac{2 \text{ mol } NH_3}{1 \text{ mol } N_2} = 0.20 \text{ mol/L } NH_3 \text{ formed}$$

$[NH_3]_{eq} = 0.50 + 0.20 = \underline{0.70 \text{ mol/L}}$

(b) $K_{eq} = \dfrac{(0.70)^2}{(0.20)^3(0.40)} = \underline{150}$

**15-28.** (a) The concentration of $O_2$ that reacts is

$$0.25 \text{ mol } NH_3 \times \frac{5 \text{ mol } O_2}{4 \text{ mol } NH_3} = 0.31 \text{ mol/L } O_2$$

(b) $[NH_3] = 0.75$ mol/L; $[O_2] = 0.69$ mol/L $O_2$;

$[NO] = 0.25$ mol/L NO (formed)

$[H_2O] = 0.38$ mol/L $H_2O$

(c) $K_{eq} = \dfrac{[NO]^4[H_2O]^6}{[NH_3]^4[O_2]^5} = \dfrac{(0.25)^4(0.38)^6}{(0.75)^4(0.69)^5}$

**15-30.** $[PCl_5] = 0.28$ mol/L

**15-32.** $[H_2O] = 0.26$ mol/L

**15-33.** Let $x = [HCl] = [CH_3Cl]$

$$K_{eq} = \frac{[HCl][CH_3Cl]}{[CH_4][Cl_2]} = \frac{x^2}{(0.20)(0.40)} = 56$$

$x^2 = 4.5 \qquad x = 2.1$ mol/L

**15-35.** (a) $K_a = \dfrac{[H_3O^+][BrO^-]}{[HBrO]}$

(b) $K_b = \dfrac{[NH_4^+][OH^-]}{[NH_3]}$ (c) $K_a = \dfrac{[H_3O^+][HSO_3^-]}{[H_2SO_3]}$

(d) $K_a = \dfrac{[H_3O^+][SO_3^{2-}]}{[HSO_3^-]}$ (e) $K_a = \dfrac{[H_3O^+][H_2PO_4^-]}{[H_3PO_4]}$

(f) $K_b = \dfrac{[(CH_3)_2NH_2^+][OH^-]}{[(CH_3)_2NH]}$

**15-37.** The acid HB is weaker because it produces a smaller hydronium ion concentration (higher pH) at the same initial concentration of acid. The stronger acid HX has the larger value of $K_a$.

**15-39.** (a) $[HOCN]_{eq} = 0.20 - 0.0062 = 0.19$

(b) $K_a = \dfrac{[H_3O^+][OCN^-]}{[HOCN]} = \dfrac{(6.2 \times 10^{-3})(6.2 \times 10^{-3})}{0.19} = 2.0 \times 10^{-4}$

(c) pH = 2.21

**15-40.** (a) $HX + H_2O \rightleftharpoons H_3O^+ + X^- \quad K_a = \dfrac{[H_3O^+][X^-]}{[HX]}$

(b) From the equation $[H_3O^+] = [X^-] = 0.100 \times 0.58 = 0.058$ $[HX] = 0.58 - 0.058 = 0.52$

(c) $K_a = 6.5 \times 10^{-3}$ (d) pH = 1.24

**15-43.** $Nv + H_2O \rightleftharpoons NvH^+ + OH^- \quad K_b = 6.6 \times 10^{-6}$

**15-44.** $[H_3O^+] = 0.300 - 0.277 = 0.023$

pH = 1.64 $\quad K_a = 1.9 \times 10^{-3}$

**15-45.** pH = 4.43

**15-47.** $[OH^-] = 3.2 \times 10^{-3}$

**15-49.** pH = 12.43

**15-51.** pH = 9.40

**15-53.** $pK_a = 8.68 \quad$ pH $= 8.68 + \log \dfrac{0.20/0.850}{0.60/0.850} = 8.68 - 0.48 = \underline{8.20}$

**15-56.** $pK_b = 6.01 \quad$ pOH $= 6.01 + \log \dfrac{0.0288 \text{ mol acid}}{0.0469 \text{ mol base}}$

pOH $= 6.01 - 0.21 = 5.80 \qquad$ pH $= \underline{8.20}$

**15-58.** When the concentrations of acid and base species are equal, pH $= pK_a$ and pOH $= pK_b$. If a buffer of pH $= 7.50$ is required, then we look for an acid with $K_a = [H_3O^+] = 3.2 \times 10^{-8}$ or a base with $K_b = [OH^-] = 3.2 \times 10^{-7}$. Since $K_a = 3.2 \times 10^{-8}$ for HClO, an equimolar mixture of HClO and KClO produces the required buffer.

**15-60.** (a) $FeS(s) \rightleftharpoons Fe^{2+}(aq) + S^{2-}(aq)$

$K_{sp} = [Fe^{2+}][S^{2-}]$

(b) $Ag_2S(s) \rightleftharpoons 2Ag^+(aq) + S^{2-}(aq)$

$K_{sp} = [Ag^+]^2[S^{2-}]$

(c) $Zn(OH)_2(s) \rightleftharpoons Zn^{2+}(aq) + 2OH^-(aq)$

$K_{sp} = [Zn^{2+}][OH^-]^2$

**15-62.** $K_{sp} = 4.8 \times 10^{-12}$

**15-64.** $Ca(OH)_2(s) \longrightarrow Ca^{2+}(aq) + 2OH^-(aq)$

$K_{sp} = [Ca^{2+}][OH^-]^2$

At equilibrium $[Ca^{2+}] = 1.3 \times 10^{-2}$ mol/L; $[OH^-]$ $= 2 \times (1.3 \times 10^{-2})$ mol/L $= 2.6 \times 10^{-2}$ mol/L

$K_{sp} = [1.3 \times 10^{-2}][2.6 \times 10^{-2}]^2 = 8.8 \times 10^{-6}$

**15-66.** $9.1 \times 10^{-9}$ mol/L

**15-68.** $AgBr(s) \longrightarrow Ag^+(aq) + Br^-(aq)$

$K_{sp} = [Ag^+][Br^-] = 7.7 \times 10^{-13}$

$[7 \times 10^{-6}][8 \times 10^{-7}] = 6 \times 10^{-12}$

This is a larger number than $K_{sp}$, so a precipitate of AgBr does form.

**15-70.** (a) $3Cl_2(g) + NH_3(g) \rightleftharpoons NCl_3(g) + 3HCl(g)$

(b) $K_{eq} = \dfrac{[NCl_3][HCl]^3}{[NH_3][Cl_2]^3}$

(c) no effect

(d) decreases $[NH_3]$   (e) reactants

(f) $[NH_3] = 0.083$ mol/L

**15-72.** (a) $2N_2O(g) \rightleftharpoons 2N_2(g) + O_2(g)$

(b) $K_{eq} = \dfrac{[N_2]^2[O_2]}{[N_2O]^2}$

(c) decreases $[N_2]$

(d) decreases $[N_2O]$

(e) $[N_2O]_{eq} = 0.10 - (0.015 \times 0.10) = 0.10$ mol/L;

$[N_2] = 0.015 \times 0.10 = 1.5 \times 10^{-3}$ mol/L;

$[O_2] = \dfrac{1.5 \times 10^{-3}}{2} = 7.5 \times 10^{-4}$ mol/L

$K_{eq} = \underline{1.7 \times 10^{-7}}$

**15-74.** (a) A solution of $NaHCO_3$ is slightly basic because the hydrolysis reaction occurs to a greater extent than the acid ionization reaction. That is, $K_b$ is larger than $K_a$.

(b) It is used as an antacid to counteract excess stomach acidity.

(c) $HCl + H_2O \longrightarrow H_3O^+ + Cl^-$ (HCl is a strong acid.)

$H_3O^+(aq) + HCO_3^-(aq) \longrightarrow H_2CO_3(aq) + H_2O(l)$

$H_2CO_3(aq) \longrightarrow H_2O(l) + CO_2(g)$

(d) No. The $HSO_4^-$ does not react with $H_3O^+$ because it would form $H_2SO_4$, which is a strong acid. The molecular form of a strong acid does not exist in water.

**15-76.** $0.265 \, L \times 0.22 \, \text{mol}/L = 0.058$ mol $HC_2H_3O_2$

$0.375 \, L \times \dfrac{0.12 \, \text{mol Ba}(C_2H_3O_2)_2}{L} \times$

$\dfrac{2 \, \text{mol} \, C_2H_3O_2^-}{\text{mol Ba}(C_2H_3O_2)_2} = 0.090$ mol $C_2H_3O_2^-$   $\underline{pH = 4.93}$

**15-77.** The addition of the NaOH neutralizes part of the acetic acid to produce sodium acetate.

$HC_2H_3O_2 + NaOH \longrightarrow NaC_2H_3O_2 + H_2O$

$1.00 - 0.20 = 0.80$ mol of $HC_2H_3O_2$ remains, and 0.20 mol of $C_2H_3O_2^-$ is formed after 0.20 mol of $OH^-$ is added.

$\underline{pH = 4.14}$

**15-78.** $[OH^-] = 3.2 \times 10^{-4}$; $[Mg^{2+}] = [OH^-]/2 = 1.6 \times 10^{-4}$

$K_{sp} = [1.6 \times 10^{-4}][3.2 \times 10^{-4}]^2 = 1.6 \times 10^{-11}$

**15-80.** $1.0 \times 10^{-5}$ mol/L, 0.023 g $BaSO_4$/L

## CHAPTER 16

**16-1.** (a) $^{210}_{84}Po$   (b) $^{84}_{38}Sr$   (c) $^{257}_{100}Fm$   (d) $^{206}_{82}Pb$   (e) $^{233}_{92}U$

**16-3.** (a) $^4_2He$   (b) $^0_{-1}e$   (c) $^1_0n$

**16-4.** $^2_1H$

**16-6.** (a) $^{206}_{82}Pb$   (b) $^{148}_{62}Sm$   (c) $^{248}_{98}Cf$   (d) $^{262}_{107}Bh$

**16-8.** (a) $^3_2He$   (b) $^{153}_{65}Tb$   (c) $^{59}_{27}Co$   (d) $^{24}_{12}Mg$

**16-11.** $^{51}_{25}Mn \rightarrow {}^{51}_{24}Cr + {}^0_{+1}e$

**16-14.** $^{68}_{32}Ge + {}^0_{-1}e \rightarrow {}^{68}_{31}Ga$

**16-16.** (a) $^0_{-1}e$   (b) $^{90}_{38}Sr$   (c) $^{26}_{13}Al$   (d) $^{231}_{90}Th$

(e) $^{179}_{72}Hf$   (f) $^{41}_{20}Ca$   (g) $^{210}_{81}Tl$

**16-18.** (a) $^{230}_{90}Th \longrightarrow {}^{226}_{88}Ra + {}^4_2He$

(b) $^{214}_{84}Po \longrightarrow {}^{210}_{82}Pb + {}^4_2He$

(c) $^{210}_{84}Po \longrightarrow {}^{210}_{85}At + {}^0_{-1}e$

(d) $^{218}_{84}Po \longrightarrow {}^{214}_{82}Pb + {}^4_2He$

(e) $^{14}_6C \longrightarrow {}^{14}_7N + {}^0_{-1}e$

(f) $^{50}_{25}Mn \longrightarrow {}^{50}_{24}Cr + {}^0_{+1}e$

(g) $^{37}_{18}Ar + {}^0_{-1}e \longrightarrow {}^{37}_{17}Cl$

**16-19.** $^{234}_{90}Th$, $^{234}_{91}Pa$, $^{234}_{92}U$, $^{230}_{90}Th$, $^{226}_{88}Ra$, $^{222}_{86}Rn$, $^{218}_{84}Po$, $^{214}_{82}Pb$, $^{214}_{83}Bi$, $^{210}_{81}Tl$, $^{210}_{82}Pb$, $^{210}_{83}Bi$, $^{210}_{84}Po$, $^{206}_{82}Pb$

**16-20.** $\dfrac{1}{16}$

**16-22.** (a) 5 mg   (b) 1.25 mg   (c) 1.25 mg

**16-23.** 2.50 g

**16-25.** about 11,500 years old

**16-27.** The energy from the radiation causes an electron in an atom or a molecule to be expelled, leaving behind a positive ion. When a molecule in a cell is ionized, it is damaged and may die or mutate.

**16-29.** Radiation entering a chamber causes ionization. The electrons formed migrate to the central electrode (positive) and cause a burst of current that can be detected and amplified. In a scintillation counter, the radiation is detected by phosphors that glow when radiation is absorbed.

**16-30.** (a) $^{35}_{16}S$   (b) $^2_1H$   (c) $^{30}_{15}P$   (d) $8 \, {}^0_{-1}e$   (e) $^{254}_{102}No$

(f) $^{237}_{92}U$   (g) $4 \, {}^1_0n$

**16-32.** one neutron

**16-34.** $^{208}_{82}Pb$

**16-35.** $^{262}_{107}Bh$

**16-36.** (a) $^{87}_{34}Se$   (b) $^{97}_{38}Sr$

**16-38.** $^2_1H + {}^2_1H \Big\langle \begin{array}{l} \nearrow \, {}^3_2He + {}^1_0n \\ \searrow \, {}^3_1H + {}^1_1H \end{array}$

**16-39.** (a) $^{106}_{46}Pd + {}^4_2He \longrightarrow {}^{109}_{47}Ag + {}^1_1H$

(b) $^{266}_{109}Mt \longrightarrow {}^{262}_{107}Bh + {}^4_2He$

$^{262}_{107}Bh \longrightarrow {}^{258}_{105}Db + {}^4_2He$

(c) $^{212}_{83}Bi \longrightarrow {}^{212}_{84}Po + {}^0_{-1}e$

(d) $^{60}_{30}Zn \longrightarrow {}^{60}_{29}Cu + {}^0_{+1}e$

(e) $^{239}_{94}Pu + {}^1_0n \longrightarrow {}^{140}_{55}Cs + {}^{97}_{39}Y + 3\, {}^1_0n$

(f) $^{206}_{82}Pb + {}^{54}_{24}Cr \longrightarrow {}^{257}_{106}Sg + 3\, {}^1_0n$

(g) $^{93}_{42}Mo + {}^0_{-1}e \longrightarrow {}^{93}_{41}Nb$

**16-41.** (a) $^{90}_{39}Y$   (b) 50 years

**16-44.** 60 years is five half-lives. $0.42 \, \mu g \times 2^5 = \underline{13.4 \, \mu g}$

**16-46.** $^{272}_{111}Rg$

**16-48.** $^{70}Zn$

# Index

317

# Atomic Masses of the Elements

This table is based on the 2007 table at *Pure Appl. Chem.*, **81**, 2131–2156 (2009) with changes to the values for lutetium, molybdenum, nickel, ytterbium and zinc from the 2005 table. Mass number of the longest-lived isotope of hassium from *Phys. Rev. Lett.*, **97** 242501 (2006). For the name of element 112 see *Pure Appl. Chem.* 2010, **82**, 753–755. http://www.chem.qmul.ac.uk/iupac/AtWt/. The number in parentheses following the atomic mass is the estimated uncertainty in the last digit.

| At No | Symbol | Name | Atomic Mass | At No | Symbol | Name | Atomic Mass |
|---|---|---|---|---|---|---|---|
| 89 | Ac | Actinium* | [227] | 42 | Mo | Molybdenum | 95.96(2) |
| 13 | Al | Aluminium | 26.9815386(8) | 60 | Nd | Neodymium | 144.242(3) |
| 95 | Am | Americium* | [243] | 10 | Ne | Neon | 20.1797(6) |
| 51 | Sb | Antimony | 121.760(1) | 93 | Np | Neptunium* | [237] |
| 18 | Ar | Argon | 39.948(1) | 28 | Ni | Nickel | 58.6934(4) |
| 33 | As | Arsenic | 74.92160(2) | 41 | Nb | Niobium | 92.90638(2) |
| 85 | At | Astatine* | [210] | 7 | N | Nitrogen | 14.0067(2) |
| 56 | Ba | Barium | 137.327(7) | 102 | No | Nobelium* | [259] |
| 97 | Bk | Berkelium* | [247] | 76 | Os | Osmium | 190.23(3) |
| 4 | Be | Beryllium | 9.012182(3) | 8 | O | Oxygen | 15.9994(3) |
| 83 | Bi | Bismuth | 208.98040(1) | 46 | Pd | Palladium | 106.42(1) |
| 107 | Bh | Bohrium* | [272] | 15 | P | Phosphorus | 30.973762(2) |
| 5 | B | Boron | 10.811(7) | 78 | Pt | Platinum | 195.084(9) |
| 35 | Br | Bromine | 79.904(1) | 94 | Pu | Plutonium* | [244] |
| 48 | Cd | Cadmium | 112.411(8) | 84 | Po | Polonium* | [209] |
| 55 | Cs | Cesium | 132.9054519(2) | 19 | K | Potassium | 39.0983(1) |
| 20 | Ca | Calcium | 40.078(4) | 59 | Pr | Praseodymium | 140.90765(2) |
| 98 | Cf | Californium* | [251] | 61 | Pm | Promethium* | [145] |
| 6 | C | Carbon | 12.0107(8) | 91 | Pa | Protactinium* | 231.03588(2) |
| 58 | Ce | Cerium | 140.116(1) | 88 | Ra | Radium* | [226] |
| 17 | Cl | Chlorine | 35.453(2) | 86 | Rn | Radon* | [222] |
| 24 | Cr | Chromium | 51.9961(6) | 75 | Re | Rhenium | 186.207(1) |
| 27 | Co | Cobalt | 58.933195(5) | 45 | Rh | Rhodium | 102.90550(2) |
| 112 | Cn | Copernicium* | [285] | 111 | Rg | Roentgenium* | [280] |
| 29 | Cu | Copper | 63.546(3) | 37 | Rb | Rubidium | 85.4678(3) |
| 96 | Cm | Curium* | [247] | 44 | Ru | Ruthenium | 101.07(2) |
| 110 | Ds | Darmstadtium* | [281] | 104 | Rf | Rutherfordium* | [265] |
| 105 | Db | Dubnium* | [268] | 62 | Sm | Samarium | 150.36(2) |
| 66 | Dy | Dysprosium | 162.500(1) | 21 | Sc | Scandium | 44.955912(6) |
| 99 | Es | Einsteinium* | [252] | 106 | Sg | Seaborgium* | [271] |
| 68 | Er | Erbium | 167.259(3) | 34 | Se | Selenium | 78.96(3) |
| 63 | Eu | Europium | 151.964(1) | 14 | Si | Silicon | 28.0855(3) |
| 100 | Fm | Fermium* | [257] | 47 | Ag | Silver | 107.8682(2) |
| 9 | F | Fluorine | 18.9984032(5) | 11 | Na | Sodium | 22.98976928(2) |
| 87 | Fr | Francium* | [223] | 38 | Sr | Strontium | 87.62(1) |
| 64 | Gd | Gadolinium | 157.25(3) | 16 | S | Sulfur | 32.065(5) |
| 31 | Ga | Gallium | 69.723(1) | 73 | Ta | Tantalum | 180.94788(2) |
| 32 | Ge | Germanium | 72.64(1) | 43 | Tc | Technetium* | [98] |
| 79 | Au | Gold | 196.966569(4) | 52 | Te | Tellurium | 127.60(3) |
| 72 | Hf | Hafnium | 178.49(2) | 65 | Tb | Terbium | 158.92535(2) |
| 108 | Hs | Hassium* | [270] | 81 | Tl | Thallium | 204.3833(2) |
| 2 | He | Helium | 4.002602(2) | 90 | Th | Thorium | 232.03806(2) |
| 67 | Ho | Holmium | 164.93032(2) | 69 | Tm | Thulium | 168.93421(2) |
| 1 | H | Hydrogen | 1.00794(7) | 50 | Sn | Tin | 118.710(7) |
| 49 | In | Indium | 114.818(3) | 22 | Ti | Titanium | 47.867(1) |
| 53 | I | Iodine | 126.90447(3) | 74 | W | Tungsten | 183.84(1) |
| 77 | Ir | Iridium | 192.217(3) | 116 | Uuh | Ununhexium* | [293] |
| 26 | Fe | Iron | 55.845(2) | 118 | Uuo | Ununoctium* | [294] |
| 36 | Kr | Krypton | 83.798(2) | 117 | Uus | Ununseptium* | [294] |
| 57 | La | Lanthanum | 138.90547(7) | 115 | Uup | Ununpentium* | [288] |
| 103 | Lr | Lawrencium* | [262] | 114 | Uuq | Ununquadium* | [289] |
| 82 | Pb | Lead | 207.2(1) | 113 | Uut | Ununtrium* | [284] |
| 3 | Li | Lithium | 6.941(2) | 92 | U | Uranium | 238.02891(3) |
| 71 | Lu | Lutetium | 174.9668(1) | 23 | V | Vanadium | 50.9415(1) |
| 12 | Mg | Magnesium | 24.3050(6) | 54 | Xe | Xenon | 131.293(6) |
| 25 | Mn | Manganese | 54.938045(5) | 70 | Yb | Ytterbium | 173.054(5) |
| 109 | Mt | Meitnerium* | [276] | 39 | Y | Yttrium | 88.90585(2) |
| 101 | Md | Mendelevium* | [258] | 30 | Zn | Zinc | 65.38(2) |
| 80 | Hg | Mercury | 200.59(2) | 40 | Zr | Zirconium | 91.224(2) |

* This element has no stable isotopes. The atomic mass given is that of the isotope with the longest known half-life.

# Names, Formulas, and Charges of Common Ions

| Positive Ions (Cations) | | | Negative Ions (Anions) | | |
|---|---|---|---|---|---|
| | Ammonium | $NH_4^+$ | | Acetate | $C_2H_3O_2^-$ |
| | Copper(I) | $Cu^+$ | | Bromate | $BrO_3^-$ |
| **1+** | Potassium | $K^+$ | | Bromide | $Br^-$ |
| | Silver | $Ag^+$ | | Chlorate | $ClO_3^-$ |
| | Sodium | $Na^+$ | | Chloride | $Cl^-$ |
| | Barium | $Ba^{2+}$ | | Chlorite | $ClO_2^-$ |
| | Cadmium | $Cd^{2+}$ | | Cyanide | $CN^-$ |
| | Calcium | $Ca^{2+}$ | | Fluoride | $F^-$ |
| | Cobalt(II) | $Co^{2+}$ | | Hydride | $H^-$ |
| | Copper(II) | $Cu^{2+}$ | | Hydrogen carbonate (Bicarbonate) | $HCO_3^-$ |
| | Iron(II) | $Fe^{2+}$ | | Hydrogen sulfate (Bisulfate) | $HSO_4^-$ |
| **2+** | Lead(II) | $Pb^{2+}$ | | Hydrogen sulfite (Bisulfite) | $HSO_3^-$ |
| | Magnesium | $Mg^{2+}$ | **1-** | Hydroxide | $OH^-$ |
| | Manganese(II) | $Mn^{2+}$ | | Hypochlorite | $ClO^-$ |
| | Mercury(II) | $Hg^{2+}$ | | Iodate | $IO_3^-$ |
| | Nickel(II) | $Ni^{2+}$ | | Iodide | $I^-$ |
| | Tin(II) | $Sn^{2+}$ | | Nitrate | $NO_3^-$ |
| | Zinc | $Zn^{2+}$ | | Nitrite | $NO_2^-$ |
| | | | | Perchlorate | $ClO_4^-$ |
| | | | | Permanganate | $MnO_4^-$ |
| | | | | Thiocyanate | $SCN^-$ |
| | Aluminum | $Al^{3+}$ | | Carbonate | $CO_3^{2-}$ |
| | Antimony(III) | $Sb^{3+}$ | | Chromate | $CrO_4^{2-}$ |
| | Arsenic(III) | $As^{3+}$ | | Dichromate | $Cr_2O_7^{2-}$ |
| **3+** | Bismuth(III) | $Bi^{3+}$ | | Oxalate | $C_2O_4^{2-}$ |
| | Chromium(III) | $Cr^{3+}$ | | Oxide | $O^{2-}$ |
| | Iron(III) | $Fe^{3+}$ | **2-** | Peroxide | $O_2^{2-}$ |
| | Titanium(III) | $Ti^{3+}$ | | Silicate | $SiO_3^{2-}$ |
| | Manganese (IV) | $Mn^{4+}$ | | Sulfate | $SO_4^{2-}$ |
| **4+** | Tin(IV) | $Sn^{4+}$ | | Sulfide | $S^{2-}$ |
| | Titanium(IV) | $Ti^{4+}$ | | Sulfite | $SO_3^{2-}$ |
| **5+** | Antimony(V) | $Sb^{5+}$ | | Arsenate | $AsO_4^{3-}$ |
| | Arsenic(V) | $As^{5+}$ | | Borate | $BO_3^{3-}$ |
| | | | **3-** | Phosphate | $PO_4^{3-}$ |
| | | | | Phosphide | $P^{3-}$ |
| | | | | Phosphite | $PO_3^{3-}$ |

# Prefixes and Numerical Values for SI Units

| Prefix | Symbol | Numerical value | Power of 10 equivalent |
|--------|--------|-----------------|------------------------|
| exa | E | 1,000,000,000,000,000,000 | $10^{18}$ |
| peta | P | 1,000,000,000,000,000 | $10^{15}$ |
| tera | T | 1,000,000,000,000 | $10^{12}$ |
| giga | G | 1,000,000,000 | $10^{9}$ |
| mega | M | 1,000,000 | $10^{6}$ |
| kilo | k | 1,000 | $10^{3}$ |
| hecto | h | 100 | $10^{2}$ |
| deka | da | 10 | $10^{1}$ |
| — | — | 1 | $10^{0}$ |
| deci | d | 0.1 | $10^{-1}$ |
| centi | c | 0.01 | $10^{-2}$ |
| milli | m | 0.001 | $10^{-3}$ |
| micro | μ | 0.000001 | $10^{-6}$ |
| nano | n | 0.000000001 | $10^{-9}$ |
| pico | p | 0.000000000001 | $10^{-12}$ |
| femto | f | 0.000000000000001 | $10^{-15}$ |
| atto | a | 0.000000000000000001 | $10^{-18}$ |

# SI Units and Conversion Factors

## Length

**SI unit: meter (m)**

| | | |
|---|---|---|
| 1 meter | = | 1000 millimeters |
| | = | 1.0936 yards |
| 1 centimeter | = | 0.3937 inch |
| 1 inch | = | 2.54 centimeters (exactly) |
| 1 kilometer | = | 0.62137 mile |
| 1 mile | = | 5280 feet |
| | = | 1.609 kilometers |
| 1 angstrom | = | $10^{-10}$ meter |

## Mass

**SI unit: kilogram (kg)**

| | | |
|---|---|---|
| 1 kilogram | = | 1000 grams |
| | = | 2.20 pounds |
| 1 gram | = | 1000 milligrams |
| 1 pound | = | 453.59 grams |
| | = | 0.45359 kilogram |
| | = | 16 ounces |
| 1 ton | = | 2000 pounds |
| | = | 907.185 kilograms |
| 1 ounce | = | 28.3 grams |
| 1 atomic mass unit | = | $1.6606 \times 10^{-27}$ kilograms |

## Volume

**SI unit: cubic meter ($m^3$)**

| | | |
|---|---|---|
| 1 liter | = | 1000 milliliters |
| | = | $10^{-3} m^3$ |
| | = | 1 $dm^3$ |
| | = | 1.0567 quarts |
| 1 gallon | = | 4 quarts |
| | = | 8 pints |
| | = | 3.785 liters |
| 1 quart | = | 32 fluid ounces |
| | = | 0.946 liter |
| | = | 4 cups |
| 1 fluid ounce | = | 29.6 mL |

## Temperature

**SI unit: kelvin (K)**

| | | |
|---|---|---|
| 0 K | = | $-273.15°C$ |
| | = | $-459.67°F$ |
| K | − | $°C + 273.15$ |
| °C | = | $\dfrac{(°F - 32)}{1.8}$ |
| °F | − | $1.8(°C) + 32$ |

## Energy

**SI unit: joule (J)**

| | | |
|---|---|---|
| 1 joule | = | 1 kg $m^2/s^2$ |
| | = | 0.23901 calorie |
| 1 calorie | = | 4.184 joules |

## Pressure

**SI unit: pascal (Pa)**

| | | |
|---|---|---|
| 1 pascal | = | 1 kg/($ms^2$) |
| 1 atmosphere | = | 101.325 kilopascals |
| | = | 760 torr |
| | = | 760 mm Hg |
| | = | 14.70 pounds per square inch (psi) |

# The Modern Periodic Table of the Elements

Periodic table of the elements showing atomic number, symbol, and atomic mass for each element, organized by periods (rows 1–7) and groups (columns). Includes legend indicating metal, metalloid, and nonmetal categories, and a separate block for the lanthanide (*) and actinide (†) series.

Atomic number

Atomic mass

| | | 1 H 1.00794 | | |
|---|---|---|---|---|

metal

metalloid

nonmetal

Noble gases

1 ve⁻  2 ve⁻  3

1 ve⁻  2 ve⁻  3 ve⁻  8 ve⁻

O

**Legend values (main table):**

IA (1): 1 H 1.00794; 3 Li 6.941; 11 Na 22.98977; 19 K 39.0983; 37 Rb 85.4678; 55 Cs 132.90543; 87 Fr 223.0197

IIA (2): 4 Be 9.01218; 12 Mg 24.3050; 20 Ca 40.078; 38 Sr 87.62; 56 Ba 137.327; 88 Ra 226.0254

IIIB (3): 21 Sc 44.95591; 39 Y 88.90585; 57 *La 138.9055; 89 †Ac (227)

IVB (4): 22 Ti 47.88; 40 Zr 91.224; 72 Hf 178.49; 104 Rf (267)

VB (5): 23 V 50.9415; 41 Nb 92.90638; 73 Ta 180.9479; 105 Db (268)

VIB (6): 24 Cr 51.9961; 42 Mo 95.94; 74 W 183.85; 106 Sg (271)

VIIB (7): 25 Mn 54.9380; 43 Tc 98.9072; 75 Re 186.207; 107 Bh (272)

VIIIB (8): 26 Fe 55.847; 44 Ru 101.07; 76 Os 190.2; 108 Hs (270)

VIIIB (9): 27 Co 58.93320; 45 Rh 102.90550; 77 Ir 192.22; 109 Mt (276)

VIIIB (10): 28 Ni 58.69; 46 Pd 106.42; 78 Pt 195.08; 110 Ds (281)

IB (11): 29 Cu 63.546; 47 Ag 107.8682; 79 Au 196.96654; 111 Rg (280)

IIB (12): 30 Zn 65.39; 48 Cd 112.411; 80 Hg 200.59; 112 Cn (285)

IIIA (13): 5 B 10.811; 13 Al 26.98154; 31 Ga 69.723; 49 In 114.82; 81 Tl 204.3833; 113 Uut (284)

IVA (14): 6 C 12.011; 14 Si 28.0855; 32 Ge 72.61; 50 Sn 118.710; 82 Pb 207.2; 114 Uuq (289)

VA (15): 7 N 14.00674; 15 P 30.97376; 33 As 74.92159; 51 Sb 121.75; 83 Bi 208.98037; 115 Uup (288)

VIA (16): 8 O 15.9994; 16 S 32.066; 34 Se 78.96; 52 Te 127.60; 84 Po 208.9824; 116 Uuh (293)

VIIA (17): 9 F 18.99840; 17 Cl 35.4527; 35 Br 79.904; 53 I 126.90447; 85 At 209.9871; 117 Uus (294)

VIIIA (18): 2 He 4.00260; 10 Ne 20.1797; 18 Ar 39.948; 36 Kr 83.80; 54 Xe 131.29; 86 Rn 222.0176; 118 Uuo (294)

**Lanthanides (*):** 58 Ce 140.115; 59 Pr 140.90765; 60 Nd 144.24; 61 Pm 144.9127; 62 Sm 150.36; 63 Eu 151.965; 64 Gd 157.25; 65 Tb 158.92534; 66 Dy 162.50; 67 Ho 164.93032; 68 Er 167.26; 69 Tm 168.93421; 70 Yb 173.04; 71 Lu 174.967

**Actinides (†):** 90 Th 232.0381; 91 Pa 231.0359; 92 U 238.0289; 93 Np 237.0482; 94 Pu 244.0642; 95 Am 243.0614; 96 Cm 247.0703; 97 Bk 247.0703; 98 Cf 242.0587; 99 Es 252.083; 100 Fm 257.0951; 101 Md 258.10; 102 No 259.1009; 103 Lr 260.105

# Textbook and Laboratory Manual
# SCI 102: Electricity
# Chemistry Portion

Laboratory Manual by

James S. Falcone, Maurine E. V. Falcone, and John R. Townsend

With Contributions from Other Members of the

Department of Chemistry

West Chester University

Laboratory Manual

SCI 102: Electricity

Chemistry Portion

# Final Exam Study Guide

**By the end of the chemistry portion of this course, you should be able to:**

1. Construct classification schemes.
2. Distinguish between elements, compounds, and mixtures.
3. State the names of groups 1, 2, 17, and 18 on the periodic table.
4. Define atomic number, identify the atomic number of an element on the periodic table, and note that elements are arranged in order of increasing atomic number.
5. Determine if an element is a metal or nonmetal based on its location on the periodic table.
6. State some of the usual characteristics of metals and nonmetals.
7. Determine if a change is a chemical or physical change.
8. Identify that a solution that conducts electricity contains ions.
9. Identify the smallest particles of an element as being atoms.
10. State the key points of Dalton's atomic theory and Rutherford's nuclear atom.
11. List the location and relative charge of a proton, neutron, and electron.
12. State the number of protons and electrons in a neutral atom or ion of any element.
13. Predict the number of electrons in the outermost shell (number of valence electrons) of any main group element.
14. Define and use the terms electrolyte, non-electrolyte, strong electrolyte, weak electrolyte, ion, cation, anion, and dissociation.
15. Predict whether a compound is an ionic compound or a molecular compound.
16. Predict whether a compound that dissolves in water is an electrolyte or a non-electrolyte.
17. Write chemical equations to represent the dissociation of ionic compounds in water.
18. Use the octet rule to predict the charges of ions, particularly those in the groups previously emphasized.
19. Predict the formulas of ionic binary compounds.
20. Draw Lewis symbols for the main group elements.
21. Use the octet rule to draw Lewis structures for molecular compounds.
22. Predict the acidity or basicity of everyday products.
23. If given whether a material is a strong or weak electrolyte and whether it is an acid or base, write an equation for its ionization or dissociation and indicate whether it ionizes completely or only partially.
24. Predict whether a solute will be present as ions, molecules or both in aqueous solutions.
25. State that acids produce $H^+$ ions in aqueous solutions and that bases produce $OH^-$ ions in aqueous solutions.
26. Know how the strength of an acid or of a base is related to its dissociation.
27. Identify whether a strong or weak acid solution will have a lower pH if their concentrations are equal.
28. Identify a solution as being acidic, basic, or neutral on the basis of pH.
29. Explain the relationship between the concentrations of $H^+$ ions and $OH^-$ ions in aqueous solutions.
30. Explain the relationship between concentration of $H^+$ and pH and between $OH^-$ and pH.
31. Define and use the terms exothermic and endothermic.
32. State whether acid/base reactions are exothermic or endothermic.
33. Explain neutralization in terms of activity.

34. State that more reactive things react to form less reactive things.
35. Write the overall and net ionic equation for the neutralization of an acid with a base.
36. Predict the products of an acid-base reaction both for any given specific example and also in general terms.
37. Determine an activity series from experimental data.
38. Define and use the terms oxidation, reduction, and half-reaction.
39. Describe oxidation-reduction reactions by writing simple chemical equations and half-reactions.
40. Write Lewis dot structures of atoms and ions and write chemical equations using these.
41. Write half-reactions for the formation of the proper ions for main group elements.
42. Identify a half-reaction as being either an oxidation half-reaction or a reduction half-reaction.
43. Balance simple oxidation-reduction equations.
44. Use an activity series to predict whether a reaction would occur or not.
45. Predict the direction of a reaction given an activity or electrochemical series.
46. Describe the chemistry of voltaic cells by writing half-reactions.
47. Construct an electrochemical series from experimental data.
48. Define and use the terms cathode and anode.
49. Understand the purpose of a salt bridge in a voltaic cell.
50. Appreciate that a battery is a voltaic cell.
51. Recognize that in a voltaic cell, the half-reactions are separated and that we are making the electrons travel through a wire.
52. Properly place in order an electrochemical series given an activity series and vice versa.
53. Use a table of standard reduction potentials.
54. Identify and write the half-cell reactions for the electrolysis products at the anode and cathode.
55. State that in a voltaic cell, chemistry is used to create electricity, whereas in an electrolytic cell, electricity is used to do chemistry.
56. Compare commercial batteries to the voltaic cells we have built.
57. Compare and contrast voltaic and electrolytic cells.
58. Recognize that in an electrolytic cell, a non-spontaneous reaction is forced to occur. In other words, it is made to go in the opposite direction to that predicted using the activity series.
59. Calculate the E° for a voltaic cell.
60. State that the volume of a gas is proportional to the number of molecules of gas.
61. Explain why a salt must be added to distilled water in order to carry out the electrolysis of water.
62. Identify the anode and cathode of an electrolytic cell.
63. Write a cell reaction given an activity or electrochemical series.
64. Know the function each component in voltaic cells and electrolysis cells.
65. Understand that in a rechargeable battery, when the battery is being used, it is operating as a voltaic cell, whereas when it is being charged, it is operating as an electrolytic cell.
66. Discuss the energy transformations that occur in the hydrogen fuel set-up we used in class and relate these to voltaic cells, electrolytic cells, and acid-base chemistry.
67. Understand that energy can be stored and transferred in many ways.

# Day 1.  OBSERVING CHANGES

## Overview:
You will:
1. Observe a variety of demonstrations and classify them as being physical or chemical changes
2. Learn the terminology used in classifying different samples of matter.

## Objectives:
**By the end of this lesson you should be able to:**
- **Construct classification schemes.**
- **Distinguish between elements, compounds, and mixtures.**
- **State the names of groups 1, 2, 16, 17, and 18 on the periodic table.**
- **Identify the atomic number of an element on the periodic table and note that elements are arranged in order of increasing atomic number.**
- **Determine if an element is a metal or nonmetal based on its location on the periodic table.**
- **State some of the usual characteristics of metals and nonmetals.**
- **Determine if a change is a chemical or physical change.**
- **State that more reactive things react to form less reactive things.**

## Definitions:
Chemical Change: A chemical change is a change in which the chemical identities of the materials change.

Physical Change: A physical change is a change in which the chemical identities of the materials do not change.

## Procedure:
The instructor will demonstrate a series of changes. After each demonstration, the class will discuss that change.  The discussion should focus on what changes were observed and whether a new material was formed.

# DAY 2: Determination of Conductance

**Overview:**
You will:
1. Learn about the subatomic particles present in atoms (protons, neutrons, and electrons).
2. Construct a conductance tester and use it to determine the presence of ions in various solutions by checking their conductance.
3. Learn how to predict the charges of common monatomic ions.

**Objectives:**
**By the end of today's class, you should be able to:**
- **Identify the smallest particles of an element as being atoms.**
- **State the key points of Dalton's atomic theory and Rutherford's nuclear atom.**
- **List the location and relative charge of a proton, neutron, and electron.**
- **Define atomic number.**
- **State the number of protons and electrons in a neutral atom of any element.**
- **Predict the number of electrons in the outermost shell (number of valence electrons) of any main group element.**
- **Define and use the terms electrolyte, nonelectrolyte, ion, cation, anion, and dissociation.**
- **Predict whether a compound is an ionic compound or a molecular compound.**
- **Predict whether a compound that dissolves in water is a strong electrolyte.**
- **Write chemical equations to represent the dissociation of ionic compounds in water.**
- **Use the octet rule to predict the charges of ions, particularly those in the groups previously emphasized.**

**Purpose**
You will use a conductivity tester with circuit components used in the physics section of the SCI 102. It will be used to check the conductance of a series of solutions as a rough estimation of the ion concentration. This information can be related to the structure of the substances making up the solutions.

**Definitions:**
Ion: a charged atom or group of atoms.
Dissociate: break apart

## Introduction

As was learned in the physics portion of this course, resistance limits the current in a circuit (figure 1 below). If we increase the circuit resistance, then the current decreases. If a solution is added to the circuit (figure 2 below), an additional resistance is added to the circuit resistance. This additional resistance depends on the ion concentration because ions carry the current in a solution. So, as the ion concentration increases, the solution resistance decreases (we call this an inverse relationship). Because of this, the current flow through the solution increases, and the conductivity increases. Adding substances to water can change the resulting solution's conductance because the contribution to ion concentration for a substance added to water depends on its ability to dissociate or "break apart" into ions. Some substances dissociate, some do not, and some dissociate to an intermediate extent.

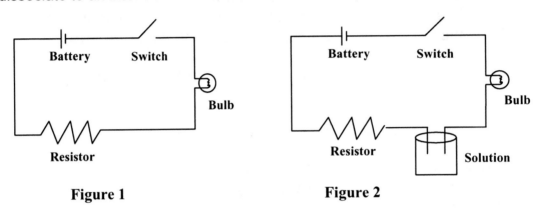

**Figure 1**                    **Figure 2**

## Safety

Wear your safety glasses at all times in the laboratory unless otherwise directed.

## Materials

| Solutions | Apparatus |
|---|---|
| table salt, NaCl | 9V battery |
| calcium chloride, $CaCl_2$ | LED, light emitting diode |
| potassium iodide, KI | 300 or 1000 ohm resistor |
| sodium sulfide, $Na_2S$ | 6 x 6 well plate |
| sugar, $C_{12}H_{22}O_{11}$ | |
| ethanol, $C_2H_5OH$ | |
| deionized water, $H_2O$ | |
| tap water | |

**Procedure**

1.      The conductivity tester we will use can be represented on paper as in the following figure. You will only need to connect wires 1) from the negative side of the battery to the LED, 2) from the resistor to a paperclip and 3) from the positive end of the battery to another paperclip. Make sure that you connect the short leg of the LED to the negative cell of the battery.   If you reverse the polarity, the LED will burn out.

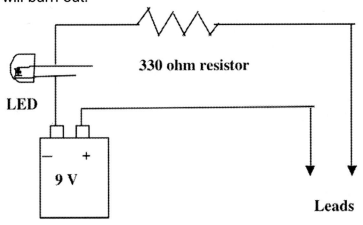

2.      Ask your instructor to check your conductivity tester before proceeding to the next step.

3.      Look at the LED with the circuit open.  Assign a brightness level of "O" to it in the data table.

4.      Short the leads and check the brightness of the LED.  Assign a brightness level of "5" to it in the data table.

5.      Rinse a well plate thoroughly with distilled water and dry with a paper towel.  Fill the cells half full with each of your assigned solutions starting with deionized water.  Be sure that you can identify the contents of each cell.

6.      Immerse the two conductivity cell leads in the cell containing the deionized water.   Make sure that the two leads do not touch each other.  Assign an estimated brightness level to the LED based on your observations from steps 3 and 4 and record it in the data table.

7.      Check and record the LED brightness level for each of the remaining solutions.  Wash the conductivity cell leads in distilled water after immersion in each well.

8.      Take apart your conductivity cell and return the components to their original storage area.  Rinse out the well plate.

# Guided Inquiry Activity About Ion Formation

1. Obtain a metal board showing a model of an atom and the magnets used to represent its protons and electrons.

2. Construct a model of a hydrogen (H) atom by placing one proton in the nucleus of the atom and one electron in the first energy level outside the nucleus. Fill in Table 1 with the information about the hydrogen atom.

3. Construct a model of a helium (He) atom and then fill in the appropriate information in Table 1.

4. Construct a model of a lithium (Li) atom and fill in the appropriate information in Table 1.

5. Now, construct a lithium ion by removing or adding electrons so as to obtain whichever of the following states is closest: either zero electrons in the original outermost shell or eight electrons in the outermost shell. Fill in Table 2 with the information about the lithium ion.

6. In a similar fashion, construct the other atoms and ions indicated in Tables 1 and 2 and fill in the tables about each.

7. Finally, construct a lithium ion on one board and a fluorine atom on another. Sketch these atoms on the answer sheet. Next, transfer one electron from the lithium atom to the fluorine atom forming a lithium ion and a fluoride ion. Sketch these ions on the answer sheet.

HELPFUL DEFINITIONS: A positive ion is called a <u>cation</u>, and a negative ion is called an <u>anion</u>.

<u>Valence electrons</u> are the electrons in the outermost energy level.

# DAY 3: Formulas of Ionic Compounds

# Acids and Bases

## Overview:
You will:
1. Learn how to write the formulas for binary ionic compounds.
2. Understand that in molecular compounds, electrons are shared between atoms.
3. Gain an understanding of sources of $H^+$ and $OH^-$, strong and weak acids and bases, and pH value.

## Objectives:
**By the end of today's class, you should be able to**
- **Predict the formulas of ionic binary compounds.**
- **Draw Lewis symbols for the main groups elements.**
- **Use the octet rule to draw Lewis structures for some molecular compounds.**
- **Write Lewis dot structures of atoms and ions and write chemical equations using these.**
- **State that acids produce $H^+$ ions in aqueous solutions and that bases produce $OH^-$ ions in aqueous solutions.**
- **Know how the strength of an acid or of a base is related to its extent of ionization.**
- **If given whether a material is a strong or weak electrolyte and whether it is an acid or base, write an equation for its ionization or dissociation and indicate whether it ionizes completely or only partially.**
- **Predict whether a solute will be present as ions, molecules or both in aqueous solutions.**

# Guided Inquiry: Formulas of Ionic Compounds

## Purpose
In this activity, you will learn how to write the formulas for simple binary ionic compounds.

## Introduction:
When we form ions, the electrons do not go off into nothingness or come from out of the blue. When an atom gains an electron, it gets that electron from another atom – this other atom loses it. When something loses an electron, the electron goes to another atom – this other atom gains it.

To form an ionic compound from the elements, the metal atoms lose electrons to form their ions, and the nonmetal atoms gain electrons to form their ions. The metal gives electrons to the nonmetal, and the nonmetal thus gains electrons from the metal.

**Materials:**
Plates with attached cups
Ping-Pong balls
Magnetic formulas of ions

**Procedure**
**A. Lithium Fluoride**
1. Obtain a set of plates with attached cups and ping-pong balls. The plate represents an atom and the core electrons. The cups represent the spaces for the possible valence electrons in the atom. The ping-pong balls represent valence electrons.

2. Make a model of a lithium atom by placing one ping-pong ball in one of the cups. Similarly, make a model of a fluorine atom by placing seven ping-pong balls in the cups of another plate.

3. Form the ionic compound lithium fluoride by forming the ions that these elements normally form. Remember that in these ions, the outer shell will either have zero electrons or eight electrons. We want there to be no electrons left over without a home.

4. Fill in your data sheet with the requested information about lithium fluoride.
**B. Magnesium Fluoride**
Now, make models showing the formation of the compound formed between Mg and F. Remember that we cannot have any electrons that do not have a home. Fill in the requested information on the data sheet.

**C. Magnesium Oxide**
Make models showing the formation of the compound formed between Mg and O. Remember that we cannot have any electrons that do not have a home. Fill in the requested information on the data sheet.

**D. Aluminum Oxide**
Now, make models showing the formation of the compound formed between Al and O. Remember that we cannot have any electrons that do not have a home. Fill in the requested information on the data sheet.

**E. Other Ionic Compounds**
Now that you are comfortable using the plates and Lewis structures, use the magnetic formulas of ions to come up with the formulas of three other binary ionic compounds. Fill in the requested information on the data sheet.

# Acids and Bases

**Purpose**
In this lab you will study acids and bases. You will use your conductivity tester to investigate the presence of ions in solutions of acids and bases.

**Definitions:**
Acid: a substance the produces hydrogen ($H^+$) ions in aqueous solutions.
Base: a substance that produces hydroxide ($OH^-$) ions in aqueous solutions.

**Introduction**
Acids and bases are very important classes of chemicals. On a list of the top twenty chemicals produced in the United States, sulfuric acid is number one, and it has held this position for a very long time. In 1993, 80.3 billion tons of it were produced. Phosphoric acid and nitric acid were tenth and fourteenth on this list. The bases ammonia and sodium hydroxide were numbers 6 and 7. Their production and use generally grows with the gross national product (GNP) of a country. This is big business. They are produced in these quantities because there are many uses for them. In today's lab, we will begin our study of acids and bases.

Acids and bases are generally very reactive. Throughout this course, we shall examine what we mean by activity/reactivity. You may be familiar with the way that the reactivity of acids is portrayed in television and movies: that acids will cause awful burns that cause someone to become the Phantom of the Opera or that acids will eat away anything in their path. This popular view of acids has some basis in reality, but it is exaggerated. Concentrated solutions of acids are very reactive; they will cause nasty burns and will react with many metals causing the metals to appear to dissolve. These acids must be handled with great care. They will not, however, eat through everything. Strongly basic solutions do not get nearly as much press, but they too are very corrosive, having an ability to react with many things, an ability to cause nasty burns, and an ability to denature proteins.

In addition to these extreme examples, however, there are many acids and bases in the things we use and even eat everyday.

What makes something an acid? Various models for acids have been developed. The one we shall use is that proposed by Svante Arrhenius. An acid is something that produces hydrogen ions ($H^+$) in aqueous solutions, whereas a base is something that produces hydroxide ions ($OH^-$) in aqueous solutions.

Recall from the conductance lab that you found pure water not to be a conductor of electricity. As it turns out, both $H^+$ and $OH^-$ ions are present in pure water, but at very low concentrations; too low for your conductivity tester to register. They get there by the water itself breaking apart.

$$H_2O \rightleftarrows H^+ + OH^-$$

This naturally occurring breaking apart of water molecules is called "autoionization". The amounts of $H^+$ and $OH^-$ ions formed are extremely low.

Let's talk a little bit more about concentration. The concentration of a solution refers to how much of a material is dissolved in a given amount of solution. The most common unit of concentration used in chemistry is molarity, abbreviated M. The molarity of a solution is how many moles of the dissolved material are present in 1 liter of solution. We're not going to deal with moles very much in this course; all you need to know is that the number of moles is directly proportional to how many molecules or formula units of the material are present. Thus, a 2 M solution of ethanol contains twice as many molecules of ethanol per liter than does a 1 M solution of ethanol.

Let's now return to our acid/base discussion. The concentration of $H^+$ ions in neutral water is 0.0000001 M (=$10^{-7}$ M, a lot easier to write). This is a tiny concentration. It is roughly one thousand to ten thousand times less than that found in a soft drink or fruit juice, for example.

In pure water, the concentrations of $H^+$ and $OH^-$ are equal, and so we say the water is neutral. This designation simply means that the water is neither acidic nor basic. When the amount of $H^+$ is made to be greater than the amount of $OH^-$ in water, the solution becomes acidic. Conversely, if the amount of $OH^-$ is greater than the amount of $H^+$ in solution, the solution is basic. The amounts of $H^+$ and $OH^-$ complement each other in that if the concentration of $H^+$ increases by some factor, the concentration of $OH^-$ will <u>decrease</u> by the exact same factor. The opposite is also true.

### Safety
- Always wear safety glasses in the laboratory.
- Do not attempt to identify the acids in natural or commercial products by tasting or smelling directly.

### Materials:

| | |
|---|---|
| HCl solutions | one 4x6 wellplate |
| 0.1 M NaOH | 0.1 M HCl |
| 0.1 M $HC_2H_3O_2$ (dilute vinegar) | 0.1 M $NH_3$ |
| deionized water | conductivity apparatus (disk, resistor, LED, |
| tap water | electrical leads, paperclips, battery) |

### Procedure
### A.    Conductivity of Acid and Base Solutions
1.    Obtain the materials to build the same conductivity tester you made in the conductivity lab (shown on next page). Connect the short leg of the LED to the negative cell of the battery. If you reverse the polarity, the LED will burn out.

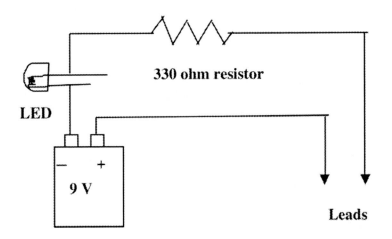

330 ohm resistor

LED

9 V

Leads

2. Ask your instructor to check your conductivity tester before proceeding to the next step.

3. Look at the LED with the circuit open. Assign a brightness level of "O" to it in the data table.

4. Short the leads and check the brightness of the LED. Assign a brightness level of "5" to it in the data table.

5. Rinse a well plate thoroughly with distilled water and dry it with a paper towel. Fill the cells half full with each of your assigned solutions. Be sure that you can identify the contents of each cell.

6. Immerse the two conductivity cell leads into each solution as you did in the previous experiment. For each solution, assign an estimated brightness level to the LED based on your observations from steps 3 and 4 and record it in the data table. Wash the conductivity cell leads in distilled water after each test.

7. In an empty well on your well plate, add 10 drops of 0.1 M $NH_3$. Insert your conductivity leads into this solution. With the leads still inserted, add 10 drops of 0.1 M $HC_2H_3O_2$ drop by drop and observe what occurs.

8. Take apart your conductivity cell and return the components to their original storage area. Rinse out the well plate.

# Day 4: Determination of pH and Reactions of Acids and Bases

## Overview
You will
1. Examine the pH scale.
2. Carry out an acid/base titration (an incremental combination of acids and bases).
3. Determine whether acid/base reactions are exothermic or endothermic.
4. Examine a key pattern of reactivity: more reactive things react with each other to form less reactive things.

## Objectives
**By the end of today's class, you should be able to:**
- **Explain the relationship between the concentrations of $H^+$ ions and $OH^-$ ions in aqueous solutions.**
- **Identify a solution as being acidic, basic, or neutral on the basis of pH.**
- **Explain the relationship between concentration of $H^+$ and pH and between $OH^-$ and pH.**
- **Identify whether a strong or weak acid solution will have a lower pH if their concentrations are equal.**
- **Write the overall and net ionic equation for the neutralization of an acid with a base.**
- **Explain neutralization in terms of activity.**
- **State that more reactive things react to form less reactive things.**
- **Predict the products of an acid-base reaction both for any given specific example and also in general terms.**
- **Define and use the terms exothermic and endothermic.**
- **State whether acid-base reactions are exothermic or endothermic.**

## Purpose:
In this lab, you will measure the pH of various solutions and investigate the reactions of acids with bases.

## Definitions:
pH: a concentration scale used to describe acidic and basic solutions. The pH of a solution is equal to $-\log[H_3O^+]$.
Exothermic: energy is released as heat
Endothermic: energy is absorbed as heat

## Introduction
### pH
In the last lab, you learned about acids and bases. Acids produce $H^+$ ions in

aqueous solutions.  Bases produce OH⁻ ions in aqueous solutions.

In a neutral solution at 25°C, the concentration of $H^+$ in an aqueous solution is 0.0000001 M (= $10^{-7}$ M), and the concentration of OH⁻ is also 0.0000001 M (= $10^{-7}$ M).

The pH scale was designed to measure the acidity or basicity of a solution. The pH of a solution is defined as follows:

$$pH = - \log [H^+]$$

where $[H^+]$ is the concentration of $H^+$ given in units of molarity (M). This also corresponds to the following being true

$$[H^+] = 10^{-pH}$$

We can see that in a neutral solution, the pH value is equal to 7.  (pH = 7).
     In an acidic solution, the pH value is less than 7.  (pH < 7)
     In a basic solution, the pH value is greater than 7. (pH > 7)

The pH scale is based on powers of ten.  When the pH value changes to 6:
- $H^+$ concentration has increased by 10X and
- OH⁻ concentration has decreased by 10X.

The concentration of $H^+$ in a pH 5 solution is **10X** more concentrated than that of a pH 6 solution and **100X** more than pH 7. What about a pH 8 solution?

**Reactions of Acids and Bases**

Acids react with bases.

Let's consider what a hydrogen ion is in a bit more detail.  Think about a hydrogen atom.  The most common form has one proton, one electron, and no neutrons.  To form a hydrogen ion, we must lose the electron.  This leaves behind just the proton.  For this reason, an $H^+$ ion is sometimes simply referred to as a proton.  When an acid reacts with something, it is usually the hydrogen ions that react.  They end up attached to something else.  For this reason, acid/base reactions are sometimes referred to as proton transfer reactions.  The proton is transferred from the acid to something else.

A process that gives off energy to the surroundings is said to be exothermic.  An exothermic process will feel warm to the touch because it is giving off or transferring energy to you.  A process that absorbs energy from the surroundings is said to be endothermic.  An endothermic process will feel cold to the touch because it is absorbing energy from you.

In today's lab, we are going to study reactions of acids and bases.  We are reacting something very active (an acid) with something else that is very active (a base).  What happens to the pH? What do we form?  Is there an energy change that occurs?

**Materials**

| | |
|---|---|
| 0.10 M HCl | Well plate |
| 0.10 M NaOH | pH paper |
| 2 M HCl | 2 - 50 mL graduated cylinders |
| 2 M NaOH | 250 mL beaker |
| 0.10 M $HC_2H_3O_2$ | thermometer |

**Safety**

You will be working with concentrated solutions of strong acids and bases today. You must wear your safety glasses! If any of the solutions should spill on you, rinse the solution off with plenty of water and notify your instructor immediately.

**Procedure**

**Part I: An Investigation of pH.**

You will be starting with a 0.1 M solution of HCl(aq) and a 0.1 M solution of NaOH(aq) [0.1 mol of the substance in 1 liter of solution]. To demonstrate the relationship between concentration and pH value of an acid or base we will employ a method called successive dilutions. Each dilution will result in a new solution with a concentration that is $1/10^{th}$ the value of the solution being diluted.

1) Place 10 drops of 0.1 M HCl (aq) in a well on your well plate. Record the concentration. Use a piece of pH paper to determine the pH of this solution. To do this, dip a glass rod in the well and then touch the glass rod to a small piece of pH paper that is sitting on a watch glass. Immediately compare the color of the pH paper where the glass rod touched it to the color code on the container of pH paper. Record the indicated pH value on your data sheet.

2) Transfer 1 drop of this 0.1 M HCl (aq) solution to a second well and dilute it with 9 drops of DI water. Mix thoroughly; this solution will have $1/10^{th}$ of the original concentration. It will be 0.1/10 or 0.01 M HCl (aq). Record this new concentration and determine the pH value using the pH paper.

3) Transfer 1 drop of this 0.01 M HCl (aq) solution to a third well and dilute it with 9 drops of DI water. Mix thoroughly; this solution will have $1/10^{th}$ of the concentration of the solution in well 2 and $1/10^{th}$ of $1/10^{th}$ or $1/100^{th}$ ($1/10^2$) of the original concentration. It will be 0.001 M HCl (aq). Record the concentration and pH value as before.

4) Transfer 1 drop of this 0.001 M HCl (aq) solution to a fourth well and dilute it with 9 drops of DI water. Mix thoroughly; this solution will have $1/10^{th}$ of the concentration of the solution in well 3 and $1/10^{th}$ of $1/10^{th}$ of $1/10^{th}$ or $1/1000^{th}$ ($1/10^3$) the original concentration. It will be 0.0001 M HCl (aq). Record the concentration and pH value as before.

5) Add a few drops of an acid-base indicator to each of your solutions and record the color of each solution.

6) Repeat steps 1 through 5, but use 0.1 M NaOH(aq) instead of 0.1 M HCl.

7) Place ten drops of 0.1 M $HC_2H_3O_2$ (acetic acid) in a well plate and

determine its pH value using pH paper.

## Part II: Acid-Base Titration

1. **Wash your well plate with deionized water and dry it with a paper towel. It does need to be completely dry.**
2. Use a paper towel to identify 10 wells in your well plate with the number of drops of 0.10 M HCl and 0.10 M NaOH indicated in the Acid-Base Titration table shown below. Place your well plate on the paper towel.
3. Use the 0.10 M HCl and 0.10 M NaOH dropper bottles to add the indicated number of drops of each to the appropriate well.

| Well # | 1 | 2 | 3 | 4 | 5 | 6 | 7 | 8 | 9 | 10 |
|--------|---|---|---|---|---|---|---|---|---|----|
| **Drops HCl** | 0 | 1 | 2 | 3 | 4 | 5 | 6 | 7 | 8 | 9 |
| **Drops NaOH** | 9 | 8 | 7 | 6 | 5 | 4 | 3 | 2 | 1 | 0 |

4. Using pH paper determine the pH value of each mixture. Record these values on your data sheet.

From these data determine what happens as you add acid to base. In this experiment you are adding a strong acid to a strong base. The concentration of the strong acid we are using is the same as the concentration of the strong base that we are using. Each drop of the base solution contains a certain number of $OH^-$ ions. Each drop of the acid solution contains this same number of $H^+$ ions.

## Part III: Heat of Reaction

When acids and bases are mixed, an energy change also occurs. In the last part, we did not use a sufficient quantity in order to tell this. We will once again mix hydrochloric acid and sodium hydroxide but use a much greater volume and a greater concentration of each.

1. Measure out in a 50 mL graduated cylinder 50 mL of 2 M HCl. Pour this solution into a 250 mL beaker.

2. In another 50 mL graduated cylinder measure out 50 mL of 2 M NaOH.

3. Record the temperature of the acid solution in the beaker.

4. Carefully pour the contents of the base solution into the beaker containing the acid solution. Gently stir the contents of the beaker with a glass stirring rod, not the thermometer.

5. Touch the outside of the beaker with your hand. Does it feel warm or cold?

6. Record the temperature that the solution goes up to or goes down to before it starts to return to room temperature.

# DAY 5: DETERMINATION OF AN ACTIVITY SERIES

**Overview:**
You will:
1. Learn about the processes of oxidation and reduction.
2. Construct an activity series.

**Objectives**
**By the end of this class, you should be able to**
- **Determine an activity series from experimental data.**
- **Define and use the terms oxidation, reduction, and half-reaction.**
- **Describe oxidation-reduction reactions by writing simple chemical equations and half-reactions.**
- **Write half-reactions for the formation of the proper ions for main group elements.**
- **Identify a half-reaction as being either an oxidation half-reaction or a reduction half-reaction.**
- **Balance simple oxidation-reduction equations.**
- **Use an activity series to predict whether a reaction would occur or not.**
- **State that more reactive things react to form less reactive things.**

**Purpose:**
In this lab you will carry out a series of reactions in which electrons are gained and lost between metals and metal ions and construct an activity series listing the metals and the metal ions in order of reactivity.

**Definitions:**
Oxidation: loss of electrons
Reduction: gain of electrons
Activity series: a listing of chemical species in order of reactivity

**Introduction**
In this lab you will carry out a series of reactions in which electrons are gained and lost between metals and metal ions. The experiments are organized so that metals actually compete for each other's electrons. You will observe which metals lose electrons (oxidation) more readily and which metal ions gain electrons (reduction) more readily. The relative tendencies of metals to gain or lose electrons can be compared by counting the number of reactions each metal and each metal ion undergoes. The metal involved in the most reactions is the one that loses electrons (is oxidized) the most readily. The metal involved in the least number of reactions loses electrons the least readily. Similarly, the metal ion that is involved in the most reactions is the one that gains electrons (is reduced) the most readily. The metal ion involved in the least number of reactions gains electrons the least readily. A list of metals ranging from the one

most easily oxidized to the one least easily oxidized or a list of metal ions ranging from the one most easily reduced to the one least easily reduced is called an activity series. From your data you should be able develop activity series for common metals and metal ions.

## Demonstrations

Your laboratory instructor will perform a series of demonstrations involving reactions of magnesium, zinc, and copper with hydrochloric acid, HCl(aq), which you will remember is a source of hydrogen ions, $H^+$. You should observe that magnesium reacts with HCl much more vigorously than does zinc while copper appears not to react at all with HCl. The implication is that magnesium loses electrons more readily than zinc or copper and that zinc loses electrons more readily than copper. The half-reactions that describe these processes reveal that electrons are lost by the metals and gained by the hydrogen ions. For example, the half-reactions for the reaction of magnesium with hydrochloric acid are:

$$2H^+ + 2e^- \rightarrow H_2(g) \qquad \textbf{reduction half-reaction}$$
$$Mg(s) \rightarrow Mg^{2+} + 2e^- \qquad \textbf{oxidation half reaction}$$

An activity series based on your observations of the demonstrations would be:

| Increasing Ease | $Mg(s)$ | $\rightarrow$ | $Mg^{2+} + 2e^-$ |
| Of Oxidation | $Zn(s)$ | $\rightarrow$ | $Zn^{2+} + 2e^-$ |
| ↑ | $Cu(s)$ | $\rightarrow$ | $Cu^{2+} + 2e^-$ |

## Safety

Wear your safety glasses at all times.
Use dropper bottles for carefully controlled delivery of drops of the liquids.

## Materials:

| Dropper bottles of the following solutions: | Four pieces each of the following solid metals: |
|---|---|
| silver nitrate, $AgNO_3$<br>iron(II) sulfate, $FeSO_4$<br>zinc nitrate, $Zn(NO_3)_2$<br>copper(II) nitrate, $Cu(NO_3)_2$<br>magnesium nitrate, $Mg(NO_3)_2$ | zinc (Zn)<br>magnesium (Mg)<br>copper (Cu)<br>silver (Ag)<br>iron (Fe), instructor demo |

## Procedure:

1. Obtain samples of all of the metals listed on the data table except for iron. Placing them on a paper towel with their names written on the paper towel may be helpful for identification purposes.

2. Add one drop of each solution to each of the metals indicated in the data table.

3. Fill in the appropriate block of **Data Table 1** with a description of what you observe for each metal-metal ion combination. A description may include color

changes, formation of bubbles, dissolving of a solid, etc.  Be sure to look at the interior of the drop and at the metal surface.

4. Note that for each specific metal-metal ion combination there is a corresponding metal ion-metal combination.  For example:

$$Zn(s) + Cu^{2+}$$
$$and \quad Cu(s) + Zn^{2+}$$

If the reaction is spontaneous in one direction, it will not be spontaneous in the opposite direction.

**Cleaning Up:**
Clean up in a way that protects you and your environment.  Carefully clean and dry each piece of leftover metal and place it in the appropriate recycling container.  Clean the reaction surface by absorbing the contents onto a paper towel, rinse it with a damp paper towel, and dry it.  Dispose of the paper towels in the waste bin.  Wash your hands thoroughly with soap and water.

# DAY 6: BUILD YOUR OWN VOLTAIC CELLS - BATTERIES

**Overview:**
You will:
1. Learn the terminology associated with voltaic cells.
2. Build a number of small-scale batteries (voltaic cells) from metals and solutions of metals ions and measure the voltages they produce.
3. Construct an electrochemical activity series and compare it to the chemical activity series you constructed in the last class.
4. Learn how to calculate standard electrochemical potentials for chemical reactions given a table of standard potentials for half-reactions.

**Objectives**
**By the end of this class, you should be able to:**
- **Build and test simple voltaic cells.**
- **Describe the chemistry of voltaic cells by writing half-reactions.**
- **Construct an electrochemical series from experimental data.**
- **Define and use the terms cathode and anode.**
- **Understand the purpose of a salt bridge in a voltaic cell.**
- **Know the function of each component in a voltaic cell.**
- **Appreciate that a battery is a voltaic cell.**
- **Recognize that in a voltaic cell, the half-reactions are separated and that we are making the electrons travel through a wire.**
- **Properly place in order an electrochemical series given an activity series and vice versa.**
- **Predict the direction of a reaction given an activity or electrochemical series.**
- **Write a cell reaction given an activity or electrochemical series.**
- **Calculate the voltage of a cell given the reduction potentials of its constituent half-cells.**

**Purpose:**
In this lab you will build some small-scale batteries (voltaic cells) from metals and solutions of metal ions. A voltmeter will be used to measure and compare the voltages they produce. The information can be related to the redox chemistry involved and to the activity series you developed in the previous lab.

**Definitions:**
Voltaic cell: an electrochemical cell in which a spontaneous chemical reaction is used to produce electricity. Batteries involve voltaic cells.
Anode: the electrode at which oxidation takes place
Cathode: the electrode at which reduction takes place

## Introduction

Batteries (voltaic cells) are simple devices that harness the tendency of electrons to move as a result of activity differentials thus transforming chemical energy into electrical energy. The reactions involved in batteries are oxidation-reduction reactions. One reactant inside the battery is being reduced and gains electrons while another reactant is being oxidized and loses electrons to the substance being reduced. Unlike your last lab, in this case, the electron flow is controlled and forced to move through a circuit. The flow of electrons between the two half-reactions constitutes an electric current. The tendency for the electrons to flow is measured as a voltage. A voltaic cell is illustrated in Figure 1. The half-reactions take place in separate (half) cells so that the electron flow between the two half-reactions is forced to proceed through an external circuit. The circuit is completed using a salt bridge that contains ions not involved in either half-reaction. Electrical contact in the external circuit is made between the electrodes where the voltmeter is shown. In the example shown, electrons flow from the copper anode to the silver cathode in the external circuit, ions carry the current through the half-cell solutions and through the salt bridge, and thus the circuit is complete. To measure the voltage difference between the two half-cells, we use a voltmeter in the position shown. To use the electrochemical cell as a battery, we simply replace the voltmeter with the electrical device of your choice; for example, a light bulb, a small motor, a smoke detector, etc. (but we won't do this).

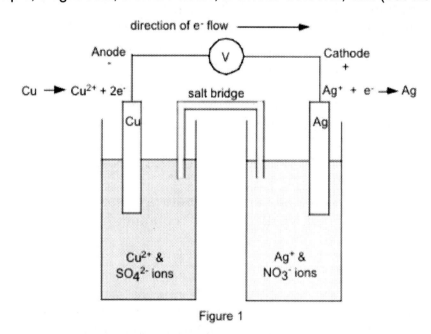

Figure 1

## Which metal-metal ion combinations can be used to build a voltaic cell?

In the activity series lab you observed that some metal ions gain electrons more readily than others, and you subsequently set up a table listing five assigned metal ions in order of reactivity. The table is reproduced below with $Pb^{2+}$ replacing $Fe^{2+}$ for clarity of results in today's experiment. As you have learned, any metal ion on the list will react only with a metal that is below it in the list. For example, silver ions ($Ag^+$) will react with all of the other metal in the list. Lead ions ($Pb^{2+}$) will react only with Zn and Mg. Magnesium ions ($Mg^{2+}$) will not react with any of the metals on the list.

$$Ag^{+} + 1e^{-} \rightarrow Ag(s)$$
$$Cu^{2+} + 2e^{-} \rightarrow Cu(s)$$
$$Pb^{2+} + 2e^{-} \rightarrow Pb(s)$$
$$Zn^{2+} + 2e^{-} \rightarrow Zn(s)$$
$$Mg^{2+} + 2e^{-} \rightarrow Mg(s)$$

⇑ increasing ease of reduction

increasing ease of oxidation ⇓

## Safety
- Wear your safety glasses at all times in the laboratory.
- Use dropper bottles only for carefully controlled delivery of liquids.

## Materials
Bottles of the following solutions:
    silver nitrate, $AgNO_3$
    magnesium nitrate, $Mg(NO_3)_2$
    zinc nitrate, $Zn(NO_3)_2$
    copper(II) nitrate, $Cu(NO_3)_2$
    lead(II) nitrate, $Pb(NO_3)_2$
    sodium nitrate, $NaNO_3$

Solids:
    Silver, Ag
    Copper, Cu
    Magnesium, Mg
    Lead, Pb
    Zinc, Zn

## Procedure
1. **Measure the voltages of the commercial cells** (batteries) provided. Reverse the leads and measure the voltage again. **Record all results in the appropriate spots on the data sheets.** Indicate both the value of the voltage and whether your voltage readings are positive or negative relative to the color of the voltmeter wires. The goal here is to teach you how to use the voltmeter.

2. **Build a copper/zinc voltaic cell** using electrodes, solutions and filter paper.
a. Cut a rectangular piece of filter paper about the size of the template shown below. Place the filter paper on a paper towel.

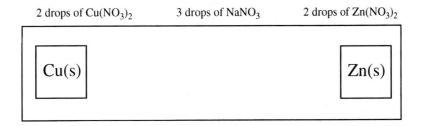

2 drops of $Cu(NO_3)_2$      3 drops of $NaNO_3$      2 drops of $Zn(NO_3)_2$

Cu(s)                      Zn(s)

b. Add drops of each solution so the center solution barely overlaps the other two solutions.
c. Place a piece of copper metal so that it is in the center of the $Cu^{2+}$ solution

and a piece of zinc metal so that it is in the center of the $Zn^{2+}$ solution.
d.  Measure the voltage of the cell you just made.  Reverse the voltmeter leads and measure the voltage again.  Record your results.

3.      **Simple construction of four voltaic cells** on one piece of filter paper.
a.  Cut a piece of filter paper as shown in the template below (you can make it bigger).

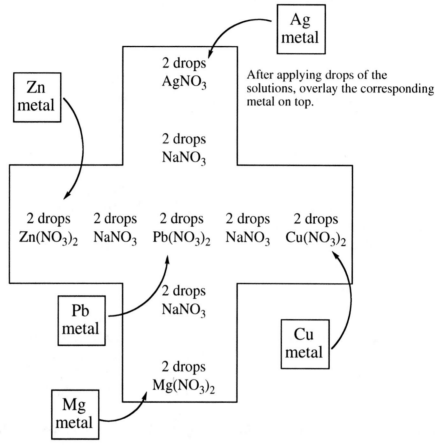

b.  Add a few drops of each solution as noted so that each "arm" is wet.  The $NaNO_3$ solution should just touch the other solutions.
c.  Position a piece of the indicated metal on each arm so that it touches its metal ion solution.
d.  Measure the voltages of each cell that has lead as one of the possible half-cells. To do this, keep the black wire in firm contact with the Pb and place the red wire in turn on each of the other metals.  Record the voltages for each metal pair.  In each case, note whether the metal being tested is acting as the anode or the cathode relative to lead.

4. Measure the voltage of the cell that has magnesium as the anode and silver as the cathode.

# DAY 7: Electrolysis

## Overview:
You will:
1. Learn about electrolysis.
2. Carry out the electrolysis of water.
3. Use the electrolysis of water to provide the fuel for a fuel cell.

## Objectives
**By the end of this class you should be able to**
- **Use a table of standard reduction potentials.**
- **Construct an electrolysis cell.**
- **Know the function of each component in an electrolysis cell.**
- **Identify and write half-cell reactions for the electrolysis products at the anode and cathode.**
- **State that in a voltaic cell, chemistry is used to create electricity, whereas in an electrolytic cell, electricity is used to do chemistry.**
- **Compare and contrast voltaic and electrolytic cells.**
- **Recognize that in an electrolytic cell, a non-spontaneous reaction is forced to occur.**
- **State that the volume of a gas is proportional to the number of molecules of gas.**
- **Explain why a salt must be added to distilled water in order to carry out the electrolysis of water.**
- **Identify the anode and cathode of an electrolytic cell.**
- **Discuss the energy transformations that occur in the hydrogen fuel cell we used in class and relate these to voltaic cells, electrolytic cells, and acid-base chemistry.**

## Purpose
In this lab you will observe a simple **electrolysis** cell and use it to electrolyze water solutions. Some information about the amount and type of the products formed can be directly related to the half-cell reactions. Acid-base indicators and visual observations will be used to check the product identity at each electrode.

## Definition:
Electrolysis cell: an electrochemical cell in which electricity is used to run an otherwise nonspontaneous chemical reaction.

## Introduction
A voltaic cell converts chemical energy to electrical energy and an electrolysis cell converts electrical energy to chemical energy. Or, more simply stated, in a voltaic cell chemical reactions are used to generate "oomph" and in an electrolysis cell "oomph" is used to generate chemical reactions. How this is done can be illustrated in their respective cell configurations. Note in the voltaic cell (Figure 1) that there is no battery in the circuit and that the two half-cell reactions are in separate containers. In the voltaic cell, the natural tendency of the two half-cells prevails. Reduction occurs in the half-cell that has the greater reduction potential. Oxidation occurs in the half-cell with the lower reduction potential, and electrons spontaneously flow from the anode to the cathode.

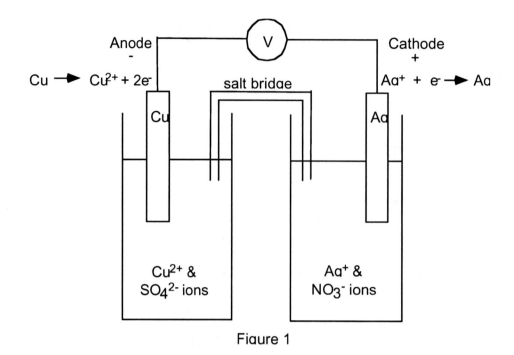

Figure 1

In an electrolysis cell, we force things to go in the other direction. We insert a battery into the cell with a voltage greater than that of our voltaic cell. This battery has enough "oomph" to overcome the natural tendency of the cell and force the electrons to go in the opposite direction they would have gone. Note that in the electrolysis cell (Figure 2) there is a battery and the two half-reactions occur in the same cell.

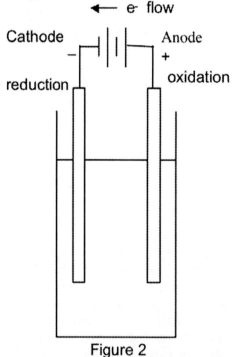

Figure 2

Oxidation still occurs at the anode and reduction still occurs at the cathode but the sign of the electrodes is switched. The cathode is positive in a voltaic cell and negative in an electrolysis cell.

The basis of the conductivity tester that you used in previous labs was the movement of positive cations and negative anions through a solution, and these ions were said to "carry the current". They not only "carried the current" but also were oxidized and reduced at the electrodes by electrons supplied by the battery. If you looked closely at the conductivity tester's leads, you may have seen some evidence of the reactions taking place. A gaseous product is the easiest to see. Electrolysis was taking place at the surface of the leads (electrodes).

In today's lab, we shall examine the electrolysis of water. Before we consider this, let us consider what would happen in a voltaic cell, a circuit that you are used to setting up. In an activity series written as reductions, you would find the following half-reactions (in order):

$$O_2(g) + 4H^+(aq) + 4e^- \rightarrow 2H_2O(l)$$
$$2H_2O(l) + 2e^- \rightarrow H_2(g) + 2OH^-(aq)$$

In the voltaic cell, we would expect that the one on top would proceed in the direction as written, forcing the one on the bottom to go in reverse:

$$O_2(g) + 4H^+(aq) + 4e^- \rightarrow 2H_2O(l)$$
$$H_2(g) + 2OH^-(aq) \rightarrow 2H_2O(l) + 2e^-$$

Of course, we would need to make sure that electrons gained equals the electrons lost to get the overall equation:

$$O_2(g) + 4H^+(aq) + 4e^- \rightarrow 2H_2O(l)$$
$$\underline{2H_2(g) + 4OH^-(aq) \rightarrow 4H_2O(l) + 4e^-}$$
$$O_2(g) + 2H_2(g) + 4H^+(aq) + 4OH^-(aq) \rightarrow 6H_2O(l)$$

As you learned in the acid/base labs, $H^+$ and $OH^-$ combine to form water (and release energy), so the final equation can be rewritten as follows:

$$O_2(g) + 2H_2(g) + 4H_2O(l) \rightarrow 6H_2O(l)$$

We now have water molecules on both sides of the equation. In a chemical equation, just like in an algebra equation, we can subtract something from both sides of the equation and maintain the equality. We will thus subtract 4 water molecules from both sides of the equation to give the following final very important equation:

$$O_2(g) + 2H_2(g) \rightarrow 2H_2O(l)$$

In the electrolysis cell we shall set up, we shall apply enough of a voltage to overcome the natural tendencies and force the reaction to go in reverse.

$$2H_2O(l) \rightarrow O_2(g) + 2H_2(g)$$

Looking back at our initial half-reactions, this corresponds to the half-reaction on the bottom in the reduction potentials list proceeding as written in our electrolysis cell, with the one on top being forced to go in reverse:

$$2H_2O(l) \rightarrow O_2(g) + 4H^+(aq) + 4e^-$$
$$2H_2O(l) + 2e^- \rightarrow H_2(g) + 2OH^-(aq)$$

## Safety

- Wear your safety glasses at all times.

**Materials**

| Solutions | Apparatus |
|---|---|
| Sodium Sulfate, Na$_2$SO$_4$ | Commercial electrolysis apparatus |
| Bromothymol Blue (BTB) indicator | |

**Procedure**
**Part I: Electrolysis of Water in a Petri Dish**
See Figure 2 in this lab and using a battery, electrical wires with clips, and paperclips, **set up an electrolysis cell for tap water**. Record your observations in Table 1. Now add a small amount of sodium sulfate to the water. Record your observations in Table 1.

**Part II: Electrolysis of Water Using a Larger Scale Electrolysis Apparatus**
1.      In a well plate, determine the color response of bromothymol blue (BTB) acid-base indicator to acid and to base. To do this, add one drop of the indicator solution to each of two wells. To one of the wells, add five drops of 0.1 M HCl. To the other well add five drops of 0.1 M NaOH. Record your results in Table 2.

2.      Your instructor will have set up an apparatus similar to the one below. Walk over to the apparatus.

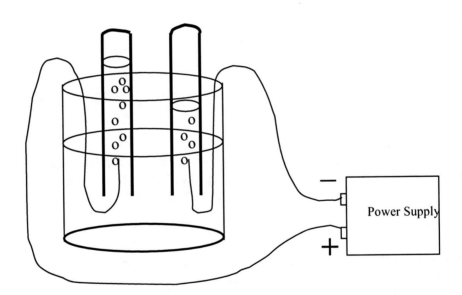

In this apparatus, the test tubes were originally filled with tap water to which BTB and sodium sulfate had been added. The apparatus was connected to the power supply to complete the circuit, and the power supply was plugged in to the wall outlet. Electrolysis should be occurring in the apparatus.

3.      Observe and record what is happening at each electrode. Be sure to that to record which electrode is the cathode (negative) and which is the anode (positive).

4.      Measure and record a) the height of the gas column in each tube and b) the color of the solution in each tube.

**Part III: Electrolysis Supplying a Fuel Cell**
**Your instructor will demonstrate and discuss the Solar Powered Fuel Cell based on the following procedure.**

1. Observe and record the volume of gas in the oxygen cylinder and in the hydrogen cylinder. With the gas outlet tubes closed on the fuel cell, turn on the lamp. Bubbling should begin. Allow electrolysis to occur until about 10 mL of hydrogen has been collected. Now read the volume of oxygen that has simultaneously been collected. With assistance, open the two gas outlets at the same time. Does the fan move? If not, allow the electrolysis to continue until the fan begins to move when the gas outlets are opened.

2. Record the volume of hydrogen and oxygen in each cylinder and calculate 1) the volume of each gas formed and 2) the ratio of the volume of hydrogen to the volume of oxygen.

# Day 8: Batteries, Rechargeable Batteries, and Wrap-Up

**Overview:**
You will
1. Learn about commercial batteries.
2. Learn about rechargeable batteries.
3. Determine the pH of household products using pH paper and red cabbage indicator.
4. Restore silver using household products.
5. Discuss various resources available for elementary school science teachers.

**Objectives:**
**By the end of this class, you should be able to**
- **Understand that energy can be stored and transferred in many ways**
- **Compare commercial batteries to the voltaic cells we have built.**
- **Understand that in a rechargeable battery, when we are drawing current, the battery is acting as a voltaic cell but that when we are recharging it, we are carrying out electrolysis.**
- **Predict the acidity and basicity of everyday products.**

**Some Useful Websites (list prepared 10/12/2009)**
General Resources for Science Teachers:

NASA for Educators 5-8 many resources: www.nasa.gov

Science News for Kids: www.sciencenewsforkids.org

Chemical Education Foundation: You be the Chemist (ybtc):
http://www.chemed.org/ybtc/home.aspx

Specific Resources Dealing with Today's Class:

Red Cabbage Juice Experiment:
http://www.cchem.berkeley.edu/demolab/demo_txt/CabbIndic.htm

Fuel Cells with the "Car Talk Guys", Nova school
http://www.pbs.org/wgbh/nova/sciencenow/3210/01.html

Other Resources Dealing with Fuel Cells:
http://www.nfcrc.uci.edu/2/default.aspx
http://www.fuelcells.org/
http://www.clean-air.org/

# APPENDIX
## Standard Reduction Potentials

| **Oxidizing Agent** | | | | | **Reducing Agent** | **Reduction Potential (V)** |
|---|---|---|---|---|---|---|
| $F_2$ | $+$ | $2e-$ | $\rightarrow$ | | $2F^-$ | 2.87 |
| $PbO_2 +$ | $H_2 +$ | $SO_4^{2-} + 2H^+ + 2e-$ | $\rightarrow$ | $PbSO_4$ | $+ 2H_2O$ | 1.69 |
| $Cl_2$ | $+$ | $2e-$ | $\rightarrow$ | | $2Cl^-$ | 1.36 |
| $O_2 +$ | $4H^+$ | $+ 4e-$ | $\rightarrow$ | | $2H_2O$ | 1.23 |
| $Br_2$ | $+$ | $2e-$ | $\rightarrow$ | | $2Br^-$ | 1.07 |
| $Hg^{+2}$ | $+$ | $2e-$ | $\rightarrow$ | | $Hg$ | 0.85 |
| $Ag^+$ | $+$ | $e-$ | $\rightarrow$ | | $Ag$ | 0.80 |
| $Fe^{+3}$ | $+$ | $e-$ | $\rightarrow$ | | $Fe^{+2}$ | 0.77 |
| $I_2$ | $+$ | $2e-$ | $\rightarrow$ | | $2I^-$ | 0.54 |
| $Cu^{+2}$ | $+$ | $2e-$ | $\rightarrow$ | | $Cu$ | 0.34 |
| $Sn^{+4}$ | $+$ | $2e-$ | $\rightarrow$ | | $Sn^{+2}$ | 0.15 |
| $2H^+$ | $+$ | $2e-$ | $\rightarrow$ | | $H_2$ | 0.00 |
| $Fe^{+3}$ | $+$ | $3e-$ | $\rightarrow$ | | $Fe$ | -0.04 |
| $Pb^{+2}$ | $+$ | $2e-$ | $\rightarrow$ | | $Pb$ | -0.13 |
| $Sn^{+2}$ | $+$ | $2e-$ | $\rightarrow$ | | $Sn$ | -0.14 |
| $PbSO_4 +$ | $2H^+ +$ | $2e-$ | $\rightarrow$ | $Pb +$ | $H_2SO_4$ | -0.36 |
| $Cd^{+2}$ | $+$ | $2e-$ | $\rightarrow$ | | $Cd$ | -0.40 |
| $Fe^{+2}$ | $+$ | $2e-$ | $\rightarrow$ | | $Fe$ | -0.44 |
| $Cr^{+3}$ | $+$ | $3e-$ | $\rightarrow$ | | $Cr$ | -0.74 |
| $Zn^{+2}$ | $+$ | $2e-$ | $\rightarrow$ | | $Zn$ | -0.76 |
| $2H_2O(l)$ | $+$ | $2e-$ | $\rightarrow$ | $H_2(g)$ | $+ 2OH^-$ | -0.83 |
| $Al^{+3}$ | $+$ | $3e-$ | $\rightarrow$ | | $Al$ | -1.66 |
| $Mg^{+2}$ | $+$ | $2e-$ | $\rightarrow$ | | $Mg$ | -2.38 |
| $Na^+$ | $+$ | $e-$ | $\rightarrow$ | | $Na$ | -2.71 |
| $Li^+$ | $+$ | $e-$ | $\rightarrow$ | | $Li$ | -3.04 |

# Photo Credits

PROLOGUE

*Page 2:* ©Holger Mette/iStockphoto. *Page 5:* M. Claye/Photo Researchers. *Page 7:* David A. Hardy/Photo Researchers. *Page 8:* Tom & Pat Leeson/Photo Researchers, Inc. *Page 9:* ©Xinhua/ZUMAPRESS. Com.

CHAPTER 1

*Page 12:* Christopher Robbins/Image Source. *Page 14 (top left):* FStop/Image Source. *Page 14 (top right):* ©Martin McCarthy/iStockphoto. *Page 14 (bottom right):* ©Héléne Vallée/iStockphoto. *Page 14 (bottom left):* ©Sawayasu Tsuji/iStockphoto Page 19:* Media Bakery. *Page 23:* MIR Bettmann/Corbis Images. *Page 28 (bottom left):* David Gould/The Image Bank/Getty Images. *Page 28 (bottom center):* Dennis O'Clair/Stone/Getty Images. *Page 28 (bottom right):* James Prince/Photo Researchers. *Page 29 (top left):* David R. Frazier/Photo Researchers. *Page 29 (top right):* Media Bakery. *Page 31 (top):* Andy Washnik. *Page 31 (bottom left):* Andy Washnik. *Page 31 (bottom right):* Andy Washnik. *Page 33 (top left):* Courtesy NASA. *Page 33 (right):* Professor P. Motta/Photo Researchers. *Page 34:* Media Bakery.

CHAPTER 2

*Page 52:* Courtesy NASA/JPL-Caltech. *Page 55 (center):* Ted Kinsman/Photo Researchers. *Page 55 (top center):* Sidney Moulds/Photo Researchers. *Page 55 (left)* Digital Vision/Punchstock. *Page 57:* MIR Jim Zuckerman/Corbis Images. *Page 58:* IBM Research/Peter Arnold Images/Photolibrary. *Page 65:* Simon Fraser/Photo Researchers, Inc. *Page 68:* Media Bakery. *Page 69:* Media Bakery. *Page 70:* Amanaimages/Image Source. *Page 71:* M. Claye/Jacana/Photo Researchers. *Page 73 (left):* Michael Watson. *Page 73 (right):* Andy Washnik. *Page 75:* Media Bakery.

CHAPTER 3

*Page 84:* ©Jonathan Smith/Lonely Planet Images/Age Fotostock America, Inc. *Page 87 (left):* Roberto DeGugliemo/Photo Researchers. *Page 87 (center):* Media Bakery. *Page 87 (right):* Vega/Taxi/Getty Images. *Page 88:* Comstock/SUPERSTOCK. *Page 89 (left):* Michael Watson. *Page 89 (center):* Richard Megna/Fundamental Photographs. *Page 89 (right):* Julian Calder/©Corbis Images. *Page 90:* © 2011 Theodore Gray periodictable.com. *Page 96 (top left):* Peter Lerman. *Page 96 (top bottom):* Andy Washnik. *Page 97 (top):* Andrew Lambert/Photo Researchers, Inc. *Page 97 (bottom)*

Media Bakery. *Page 101:* afotoshop/Shutterstock. *Page 102 (top):* Andy Washnik. *Page 102 (bottom):* Dann Coffey/The Image Bank/Getty Images. *Page 106:* Mark Burnett/Photo Researchers, Inc. *Page 106:* MIR Josie Lepe/San Jose Mercury News/NewsCom.

CHAPTER 4

*Page 116 (top):* Andy Washnik. *Page 118:* Richard T. Nowitz/Photo Researchers, Inc. *Page 119 (top):* Media Bakery. *Page 119 (bottom):* Media Bakery. *Page 120:* Michael Watson. *Page 122:* Charles D. Winters/Photo Researchers, Inc. *Page 131:* Photo by Vincent LaRussa/©John Wiley & Sons, Inc. *Page 132:* Andy Washnik. *Page 133:* Andy Washnik.

CHAPTER 05

*Page 146:* ©Adrian Sherratt/Alamy. *Page 148:* Media Bakery. *Page 151 (left):* ©Dan Chippendale/iStockphoto. *Page 151 (center):* Michael Dalton/Fundamental Photographs. *Page 151 (right):* Media Bakery. *Page 152:* Michael Watson. *Page 157:* Michael Watson. *Page 163:* Media Bakery. *Page 165:* Photo by Vincent LaRussa/John Wiley & Sons, Inc. *Page 167:* Paul Silverman/Fundamental Photographs.

CHAPTER 6

*Page 178:* © A Kosten/J Kosten/Age Fotostock America, Inc. *Page 181:* Courtesy NASA. *Page 186:* Richard Megna/Fundamental Photographs. *Page 187:* Charles D. Winters/Photo Researchers. *Page 188:* OAR/National Undersea Research Program (NURP); NOAA. *Page 190:* Charles D. Winters/Photo Researchers. *Page 192 (top):* Michael Watson. *Page 192 (center):* Michael Watson. *Page 192 (bottom):* Andy Washnik. *Page 196 (left):* Andy Washnik. *Page 196 (center):* Andy Washnik. *Page 196 (right):* Andy Washnik. *Page 197 (left):* Andy Washnik. *Page 197 (center):* Andy Washnik. *Page 197 (right):* Andy Washnik. *Page 199:* Charles D. Winters/Photo Researchers, Inc. *Page 200:* Charles D. Winters/Photo Researchers, Inc. *Page 201:* Andy Washnik.

CHAPTER 7

*Page 212:* Media Bakery. *Page 218:* ©John Cancalosi/Age Fotostock America, Inc. *Page 221:* Stone/Getty Images. *Page 222:* Kip Peticolas/Fundamental Photographs. *Page 225:* Tony Cenicola/The New York Times/Redux Pictures. *Page 229:* Media Bakery. *Page 231:* Friedrich Saurer/Photo Researchers, Inc.

## CHAPTER 17

*Page W-2:* Media Bakery. *Page W-7 (top):* Andy Washnik. *Page W-7 (center):* Andy Washnik. *Page W-7 (bottom):* Andy Washnik. *Page W-12:* ©Wave Royalty Free/Age Fotostock America, Inc. *Page W-14:* Jon Feingersh Photography Inc./Image Source. *Page W-16 (left):* Peter Lerman. *Page W-16 (center):* KENCKOphotography/Shutterstock.com. *Page W-16 (right):* Michael Ventura/Bruce Coleman, Inc./Photoshot. *Page W-15:* MIR Charels Peterson/The Image Bank/Getty Images. *Page W-21:* Andy Washnik. *Page W-24:* Richard Megna/Fundamental Photographs. *Page W-26:* Andy Washnik. *Page W-29:* MIR Ken Karp. *Page W-28:* Charles D. Winters/Photo Researchers. *Page W-30:* Cordelia Molloy/Photo Researchers, Inc.

## CHAPTER 18

*Page W-44:* Courtesy Jack Malone. *Page W-51:* Media Bakery. *Page W-54 (top):* Bjarte Rettedal/Image Source. *Page W-54 (bottom):* Amanaimages/Image Source. *Page W-67:* MIR Chris Butler/Photo Researchers.

## APPENDIX A

*Opener:* Image Source.